Course	College Algebra
Course Number	**MAT 1853**
	Palm Beach Atlantic University
	Mathematics

http://create.mheducation.com

ISBN-10: 1121455611 ISBN-13: 9781121455610

Contents

Credits

Functions, Graphs, and Models 1

Modeling with Linear and Quadratic Functions 137

Functions, Graphs, and Models

Functions, Graphs, and Models

THE function concept is one of the most important ideas in mathematics. To study math beyond the elementary level, you absolutely need to have a solid understanding of functions and their graphs. In this chapter, you'll learn the fundamentals of what functions are all about, and how to use them. In subsequent chapters, this will pay off as you study particular types of functions in depth. In the first section of this chapter, we discuss the techniques involved in using an electronic graphing device like a graphing calculator. In the remaining sections, we introduce the concept of functions and discuss general properties of functions and their graphs. Everything you learn in this chapter will increase your chance of success in this course, and in almost any other course you may take that involves mathematics.

CHAPTER 1

OUTLINE

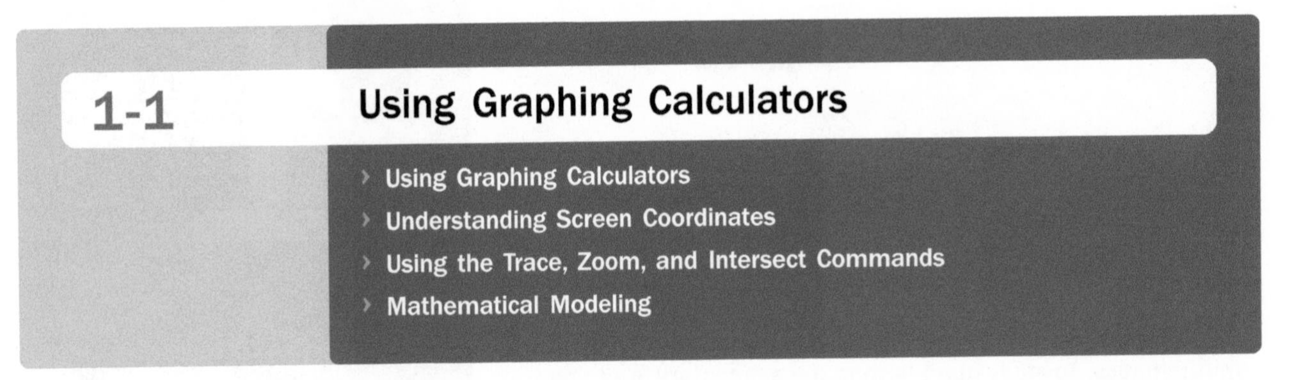

1-1 Using Graphing Calculators

- Using Graphing Calculators
- Understanding Screen Coordinates
- Using the Trace, Zoom, and Intersect Commands
- Mathematical Modeling

The use of technology to aid in drawing and analyzing graphs is revolutionizing mathematics education and is the primary motivation for this book. Your ability to interpret mathematical concepts and to discover patterns of behavior will be greatly increased as you become proficient with an electronic graphing device. In this section we introduce some of the basic features of electronic graphing devices. Additional features will be introduced as the need arises. If you have already used an electronic graphing device in a previous course, you can use this section to quickly review basic concepts. If you need to refresh your memory about a particular feature, consult the Technology Index at the end of this book to locate the textbook discussion of that particular feature.

Using Graphing Calculators

We will begin with the use of electronic graphing devices to graph equations. We will refer to any electronic device capable of displaying graphs as a **graphing utility.** The two most common graphing utilities are handheld graphing calculators and computers with appropriate software. It's essential that you have such a device handy as you proceed through this book.

Since many different brands and models exist, we will discuss graphing calculators only in general terms. Refer to your manual for specific details relative to your own graphing calculator.*

An image on the screen of a graphing calculator is made up of darkened rectangles called **pixels** (Fig. 1). The pixel rectangles are the same size, and don't change in size during any application. Graphing calculators use pixel-by-pixel plotting to produce graphs.

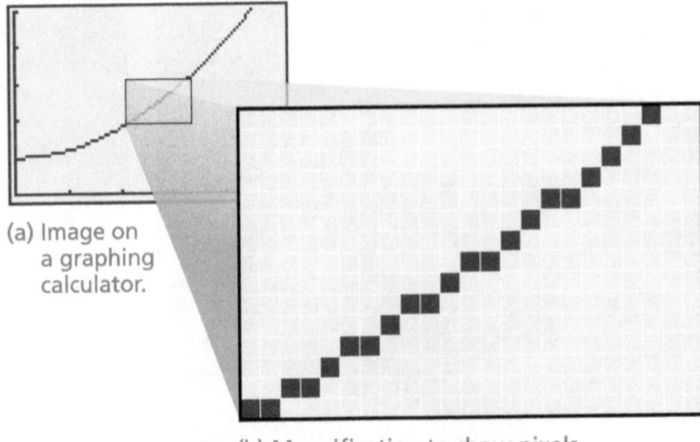

Figure 1 Pixel-by-pixel plotting on a graphing calculator.

*Manuals for most brands of graphing calculators are readily available on the Internet.

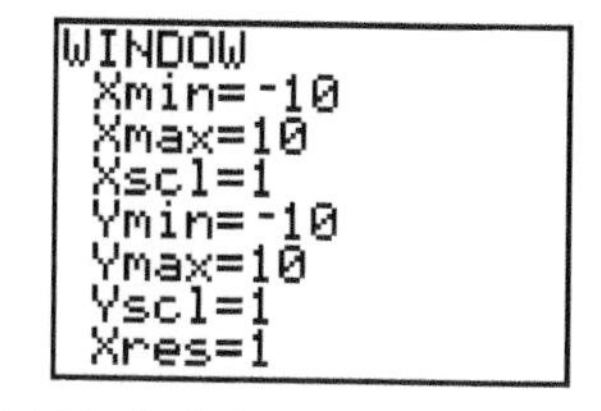

(a) Standard window variable values

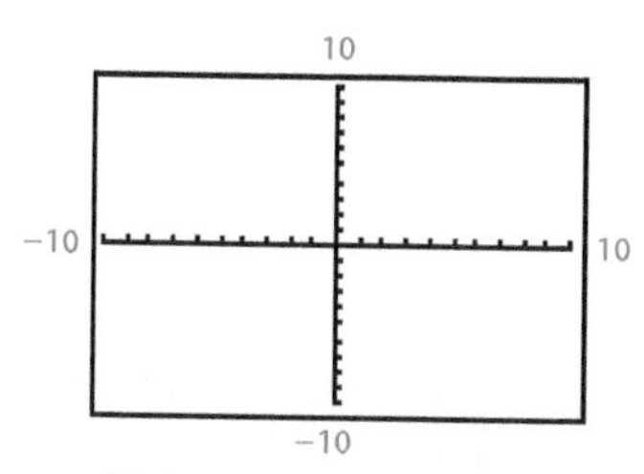

(b) Standard viewing window

› **Figure 2** A standard viewing window and its dimensions.

The accuracy of the graph depends on the resolution of the graphing calculator. Most graphing calculators have screen resolutions of between 50 and 75 pixels per inch, which results in fairly rough but very useful graphs. Some computer systems can print very high quality graphs with resolutions greater than 1,000 pixels per inch.

Most graphing calculator screens are rectangular. The graphing screen on a graphing calculator represents a portion of the plane in the rectangular coordinate system. But this representation is an approximation, because pixels are not really points, as is clearly shown in Figure 1. Points are geometric objects without dimensions (you can think of them as "infinitely small"), whereas a pixel has dimensions. The coordinates of a pixel are usually taken at the center of the pixel and represent all the infinitely many geometric points within the pixel. Fortunately, this does not cause much of a problem, as we will see.

The portion of a rectangular coordinate system displayed on the graphing screen is called a **viewing window** and is determined by assigning values to six **window variables:** the lower limit, upper limit, and scale for the x axis and the lower limit, upper limit, and scale for the y axis. Figure 2(a) illustrates the names and values of **standard window variables,** and Figure 2(b) shows the resulting **standard viewing window.**

The names **Xmin, Xmax, Xscl, Ymin, Ymax,** and **Yscl** will be used for the six window variables. Xscl and Yscl determine the distance between tick marks on the x and y axes, respectively. **Xres** is a seventh window variable on some graphing calculators that controls the screen resolution; we will always leave this variable set to the default value 1. The window variables may be displayed slightly differently by your graphing calculator. In this book, when a viewing window of a graphing calculator is pictured in a figure, the values of Xmin, Xmax, Ymin, and Ymax are indicated by labels to make the graph easier to read [see Fig. 2(b)]. These labels are always centered on the sides of the viewing window, regardless of the location of the axes.

REMARK: We think it's important that actual output from existing graphing calculators be used in this book. The majority of the graphing calculator images in this book are screen dumps from a Texas Instruments TI-84 graphing calculator. Occasionally we use screen dumps from a TI-86 graphing calculator, which has a wider screen. You may not always be able to produce an exact replica of a figure on your graphing calculator, but the differences will be relatively minor.

We now turn to the use of a graphing calculator to graph equations that can be written in the form

$$y = (\text{some expression in } x) \tag{1}$$

Graphing an equation of the type shown in equation (1) using a graphing calculator is a simple three-step process:

› **GRAPHING EQUATIONS USING A GRAPHING CALCULATOR**

Step 1. Enter the equation.

Step 2. Enter values for the window variables. (A good rule of thumb for choosing Xscl and Yscl, unless there are reasons to the contrary, is to choose each about one-tenth the width of the corresponding variable range.)

Step 3. Press the GRAPH command.

The following example illustrates this procedure for graphing the equation $y = x^2 - 4$. (See Example 1 of Appendix B, Section B-2 for a hand-drawn sketch of this equation.)

EXAMPLE 1

Graphing an Equation with a Graphing Calculator

Use a graphing calculator to graph $y = x^2 - 4$ for $-5 \le x \le 5$ and $-5 \le y \le 15$.

SOLUTION

Press the Y= key to display the equation editor and enter the equation [Fig. 3(a)]. Press WINDOW to display the window variables and enter the given values for these variables [Fig. 3(b)]. Press GRAPH to obtain the graph in Figure 3(c). (The form of the screens in Figure 3 may differ slightly, depending on the graphing calculator used.)

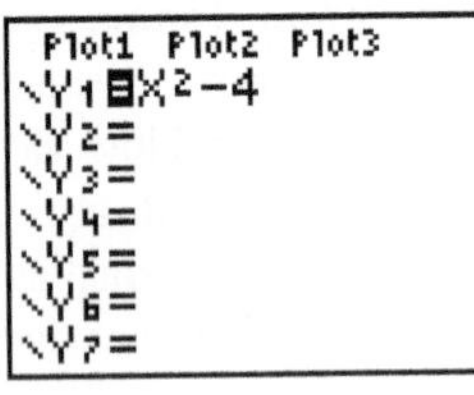

(a) Enter equation.

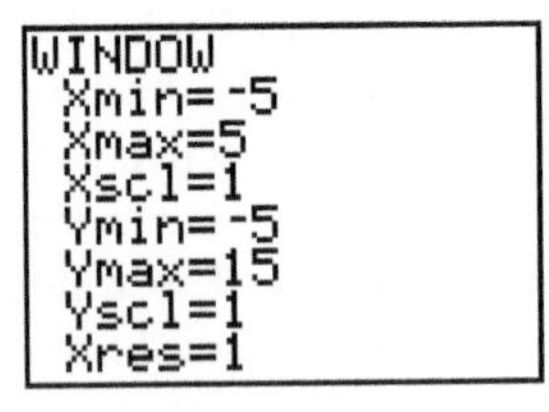

(b) Enter window variables.

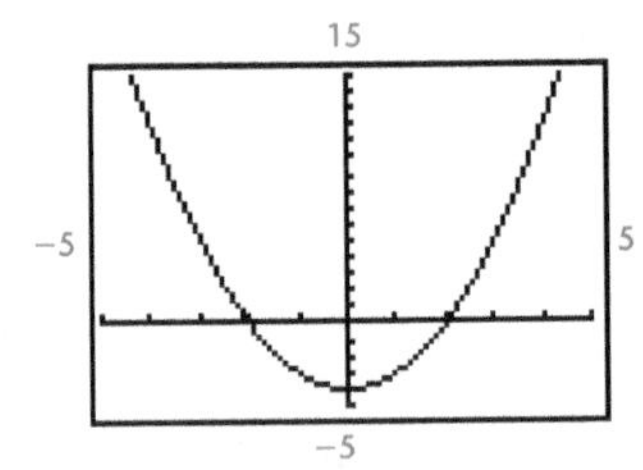

(c) Press the graph command.

› **Figure 3** Graphing is a three-step process.

MATCHED PROBLEM 1*

Use a graphing calculator to graph $y = 8 - x^2$ for $-5 \le x \le 5$ and $-10 \le y \le 10$.

REMARK: For Example 1, we displayed a screen shot for each step in the graphing procedure. Generally, we will show only the final results, as illustrated in Figure 3(c).

Often, it is helpful to think about an appropriate viewing window before starting to graph an equation. This can help save time, as well as increase your odds of seeing the whole graph.

*Answers to matched problems in a given section are found near the end of the section, before the exercise set.

EXAMPLE 2 Finding an Appropriate Viewing Window

Find an appropriate viewing window in which to graph the equation $y = \sqrt{x - 13}$ with a graphing calculator.

SOLUTIONS

Algebraic Solution

We begin by thinking about reasonable x values for this equation. Since y values are determined by an expression under a root, only x values that result in $x - 13$ being nonnegative will have an associated y value. So we write and solve the inequality

$$x - 13 \geq 0$$
$$x \geq 13$$

This tells us that there will be points on the graph only for x values 13 or greater.

Next, we make a table of values for selected x values to see what y values are appropriate. Note that we chose x values that make it easy to compute y.

x	13	14	17	22	29	38
y	0	1	2	3	4	5

To clearly display all of these points and leave some space around the edges, we choose $X_{\min} = 10$, $X_{\max} = 40$, $Y_{\min} = -1$, and $Y_{\max} = 10$.

Graphical Solution

We first enter the equation $y_1 = \sqrt{x - 13}$ in a graphing calculator (Fig. 4).

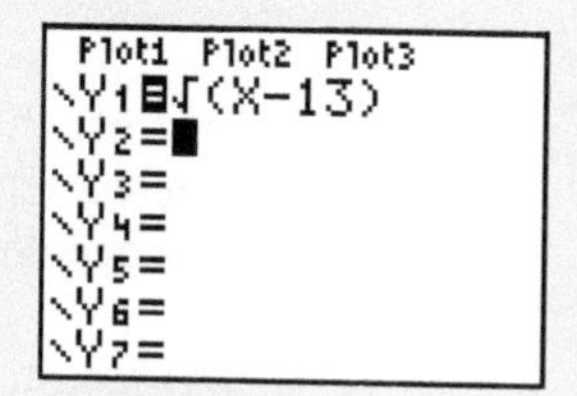

› Figure 4

We then make a table of values for selected x values after trying a variety of choices for x (Fig. 5).*

X	Y1
11	ERROR
12	ERROR
12.9	ERROR
13	0
20	2.6458
25	3.4641
35	4.6904

X=11

› Figure 5

We find that there are no points on the graph for x values less than 13, and there appear to be points for all x values greater than or equal to 13.

To clearly display all of these points and leave some space around the edges, we choose $X_{\min} = 10$, $X_{\max} = 40$, $Y_{\min} = -1$, and $Y_{\max} = 10$.

MATCHED PROBLEM 2

Find an appropriate viewing window in which to graph the equation $y = 2 + \sqrt{x + 15}$ with a graphing calculator.

*Many graphing calculators can construct a table of values like the one in Figure 5 using the TBLSET and TABLE commands.

The next example illustrates how a graphing calculator can be used as an aid to sketching the graph of an equation by hand. The example illustrates the use of algebraic, numeric, and graphic approaches; an understanding of all three approaches will be a big help in problem solving.

EXAMPLE 3 Using a Graphing Calculator as an Aid to Hand Graphing—Net Cash Flow

The net cash flow y in millions of dollars of a small high-tech company from 1998–2006 is given approximately by the equation

$$y = 0.4x^3 - 2x + 1 \qquad -4 \le x \le 4 \tag{2}$$

where x represents the number of years before or after 2002, when the board of directors appointed a new CEO.

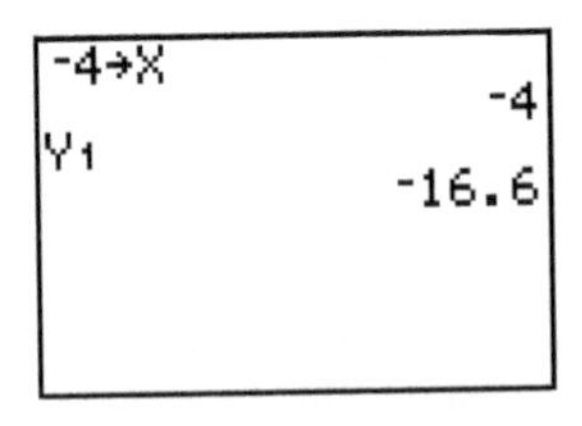

(a)

X	Y1
-4.0	-16.6
-3.0	-3.8
-2.0	1.8
-1.0	2.6
0.0	1.0
1.0	-.6
2.0	.2

Y1=.4X^3-2X+1

(b)

› **Figure 6**

(A) Construct a table of values for equation (2) for each year starting with 1998 and ending with 2006. Compute y to one decimal place.

(B) Obtain a graph of equation (2) in the viewing window of your graphing calculator. Plot the table values from part A by hand on graph paper, then join these points with a smooth curve using the graph in the viewing window as an aid.

SOLUTIONS

(A) After entering the given equation as y_1, we can find the value of y for a given value of x by storing the value of x in the variable X and simply displaying y_1, as shown in Figure 6(a). To speed up this process, we can compute an entire table of values directly, as shown in Figure 6(b). We organize these results in Table 1.

Recall that x represents years before or after 2002, and y represents cash flow in millions of dollars.

Table 1 Net Cash Flow

Year	1998	1999	2000	2001	2002	2003	2004	2005	2006
x	−4	−3	−2	−1	0	1	2	3	4
y (million $)	−16.6	−3.8	1.8	2.6	1	−0.6	0.2	5.8	18.6

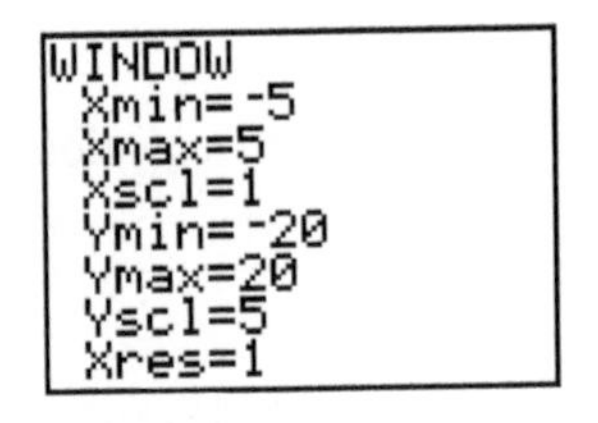

› **Figure 7**

(B) To create a graph of equation (2) in the viewing window of a graphing calculator, we select values for the viewing window variables that cover a little more than the values shown in Table 1, as shown in Figure 7. We add a grid to the viewing window to obtain the graphing calculator graph shown in Figure 8(a). (On many graphing calculators, this option is on the FORMAT screen.) The corresponding hand sketch is shown in Figure 8(b).

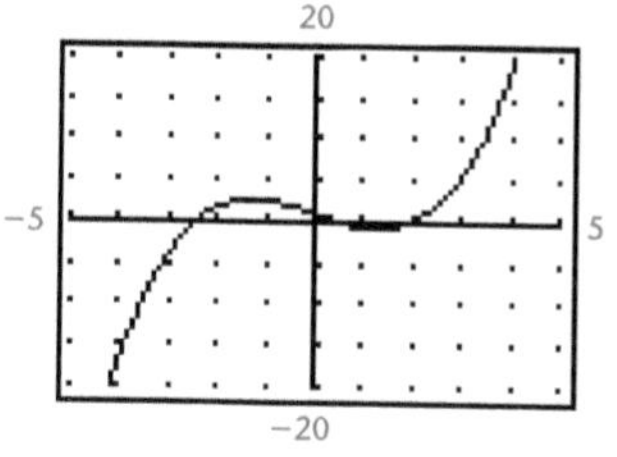

(a) Graphing calculator graph

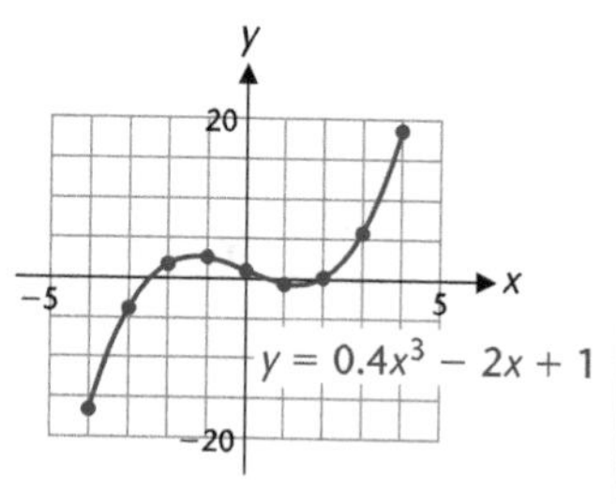

(b) Hand sketch

› **Figure 8** Net cash flow.

REMARKS:

1. In applied problems, it's a great idea to begin by writing down what each variable in the problem represents.
2. Table 1 is useful for analyzing this data since it gives us specific detail; the equation and graph are also useful because they give us a quick overview of cash flow. Each viewpoint has its specific value.

MATCHED PROBLEM 3

The company in Example 3 is in competition with another company whose net cash flow y in millions of dollars from 1998 to 2006 is given approximately by the equation

$$y = 1 + 1.9x - 0.2x^3 \qquad -4 \le x \le 4 \tag{3}$$

where x represents the number of years before or after 2002.

(A) Construct a table of values for equation (3) for each year starting with 1998 and ending with 2006. Compute y to one decimal place.

(B) Plot the points corresponding to the table by hand, then hand sketch the graph of the equation with the help of a graphing calculator.

››› EXPLORE-DISCUSS 1

The choice of the viewing window has a pronounced effect on the shape of a graph. Graph $y = -x^3 + 2x$ in each of the following viewing windows:

(A) $-1 \le x \le 1, -1 \le y \le 1$

(B) $-10 \le x \le 10, -10 \le y \le 10$

(C) $-100 \le x \le 100, -100 \le y \le 100$

Which window gives the best view of the graph of this equation, and why?

› Understanding Screen Coordinates

We now take a closer look at *screen coordinates* of pixels. Earlier we indicated that the coordinates of the center point of a pixel are usually used as the **screen coordinates of the pixel,** and these coordinates represent all points within the pixel. As you might expect, screen coordinates of pixels change as you change values of window variables.

To find screen coordinates of various pixels, move a *cursor* around the viewing window and observe the coordinates displayed on the screen. A **cursor** is a special symbol, such as a plus (+) or times (×) sign, that locates one pixel on the screen at a time. As the cursor is moved around the screen, it moves from pixel to pixel. To see this, set the window variables in your graphing calculator so that $-5 \le x \le 5$ and $-5 \le y \le 5$, and activate a grid for the screen. Move the cursor as close as you can to the point (2, 2) and observe what happens. Figure 9 shows the screen coordinates of the four pixels that are closest to (2, 2). The coordinates displayed on your screen may vary slightly from these, depending on the graphing calculator used.

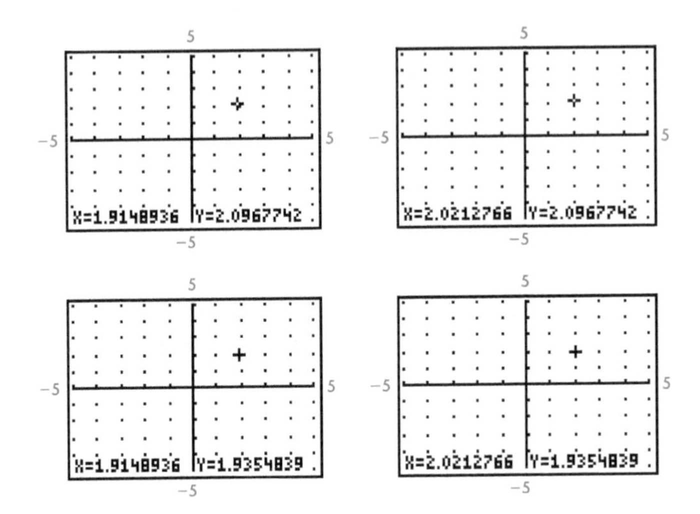

› **Figure 9** Screen coordinates of pixels near (2, 2).

Any of the four pixels in Figure 9 can be used to approximate the point (2, 2), but it turns out that it is not possible to find a pixel in this viewing window whose screen coordinates are exactly (2, 2). Try to repeat this exercise with different window variables, say, $-7 \le x \le 7$ and $-7 \le y \le 7$.

› Using the Trace, Zoom, and Intersect Commands

When analyzing the graph of an equation, it's often useful to find the coordinates of certain points on the graph. Using the **TRACE** command on a graphing calculator is one way to accomplish this. The trace feature places a cursor directly on the graph and only permits movement left and right along the graph. The coordinates displayed during the tracing movement are coordinates of points that satisfy the equation. In most cases, these coordinates are not the same as the pixel screen coordinates displayed using the unrestricted cursor movement that we discussed earlier. Instead, they are the *exact* coordinates of points on the graph.

››› EXPLORE-DISCUSS 2

Graph the equation $y = x$ in a standard viewing window.

(A) Without selecting the TRACE command, move the cursor to a point on the screen that appears to lie on the graph of $y = x$ and is as close to (5, 5) as possible. Record these coordinates. Do these coordinates satisfy the equation $y = x$?

(B) Now select the TRACE command and move the cursor along the graph of $y = x$ to a point that has the same x coordinate found in part A. Is the y coordinate of this point the same as you found in part A? Do the coordinates of the point using trace satisfy the equation $y = x$?

(C) Explain the difference in using trace along a curve and trying to use unrestricted movement of a cursor along a curve.

Most graphing calculators have a **ZOOM** command. In general, **zooming in** on a graph reduces the window variables and magnifies the portion of the graph visible in the viewing window [Fig. 10(a)]. **Zooming out** enlarges the window variables so that more of the graph is visible in the viewing window [Fig. 10(b)].

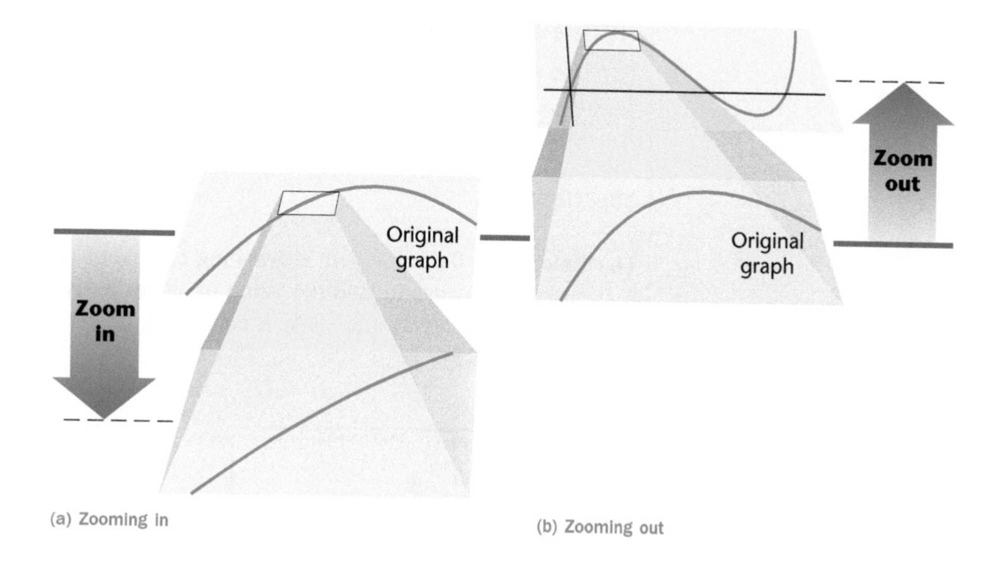

(a) Zooming in (b) Zooming out

› **Figure 10** The zoom operation.

››› EXPLORE-DISCUSS 3

Figure 11 shows the ZOOM menu on a TI-84.* We want to explore the effects of some of these options on the graph of $y = x$. Enter this equation in the equation editor and select ZStandard from the ZOOM menu. What are the window variables? In each of the following, position the cursor at the origin and select the indicated zoom option. Observe the changes in the window variables and examine the coordinates displayed by tracing along the curve.

(A) ZSquare **(B)** ZDecimal **(C)** ZInteger **(D)** ZoomFit

ZOOM MEMORY
1:ZBox
2:Zoom In
3:Zoom Out
4:ZDecimal
5:ZSquare
6:ZStandard
7:ZTrig
8:ZInteger
9:ZoomStat
0:ZoomFit

› **Figure 11** The ZOOM menu on a TI-84.

Another command found on most graphing calculators is **INTERSECT**† or **ISECT.** This command enables the user to find the point(s) where two curves intersect without using trace or zoom.

The use of trace, zoom, and intersect is best illustrated by examples.

*The ZOOM menu on other graphing calculators may look quite different from the one on the TI-84.
†On the TI-84, INTERSECT is found on the CALC (2nd-TRACE) menu.

EXAMPLE 4 Using Trace, Zoom, and Intersect

Let $y = 0.01x^3 + 1$.

(A) Use the TRACE command to find y when $x = 5$.

(B) Use the TRACE and ZOOM commands to find x when $y = 5$.

(C) Use the INTERSECT command to find x when $y = 5$.

Round answers to two decimal places.

SOLUTIONS

(A) Enter $y_1 = 0.01x^3 + 1$ in a graphing calculator (Fig. 12). In Example 3, we discussed two ways to find the value of y_1 for a given value of x. Now we want to discuss a third way, the TRACE command. Graph y_1 in the standard viewing window (Fig. 13).

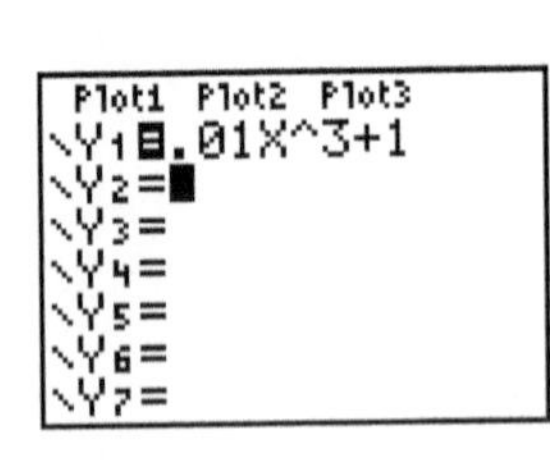

› Figure 12

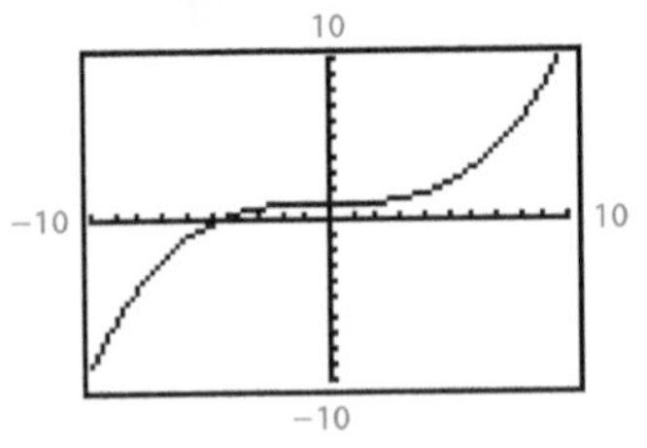

› Figure 13

Select the TRACE command and move the cursor as close to $x = 5$ as possible (Fig. 14). This shows that $y = 2.33$ when $x = 5.11$, not quite what we want. However, we can direct the trace command to use the exact value of $x = 5$ by simply entering 5 (Fig. 15) and pressing ENTER (Fig. 16).

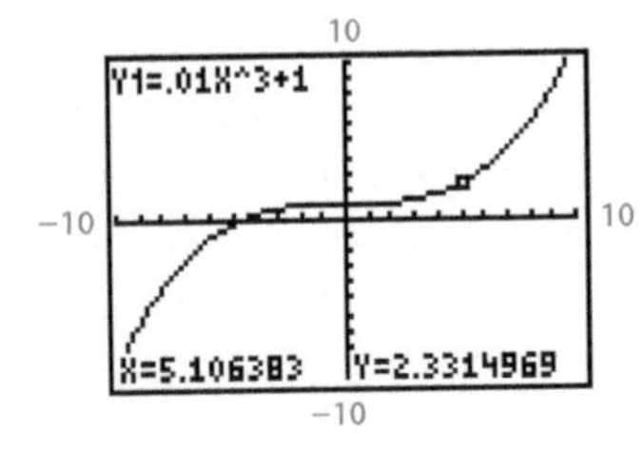

› Figure 14

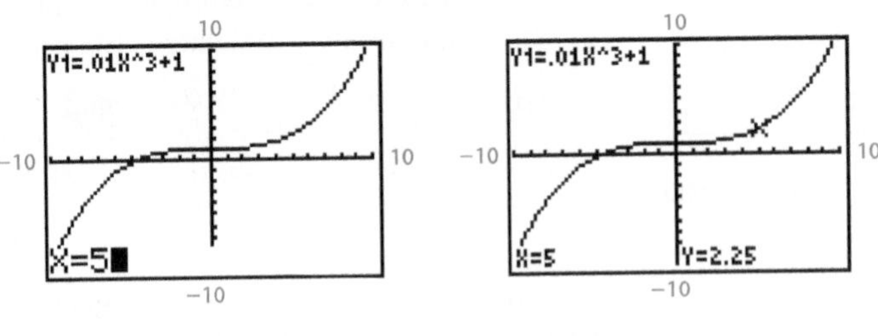

› Figure 15 › Figure 16

From Figure 16 we see that $y = 2.25$ when $x = 5$.

(B) Select the TRACE command and move the cursor as close to $y = 5$ as possible (Fig. 17). This shows that $x = 7.45$ when $y = 5.13$, again not exactly what we want. We cannot direct the TRACE command to use the exact value $y = 5$ since it only allows us to input x values. Instead we press the ZOOM command and select Zoom In to obtain more accuracy (Fig. 18). Then we select the TRACE command and move the cursor as close to $y = 5$ as possible (Fig. 19).

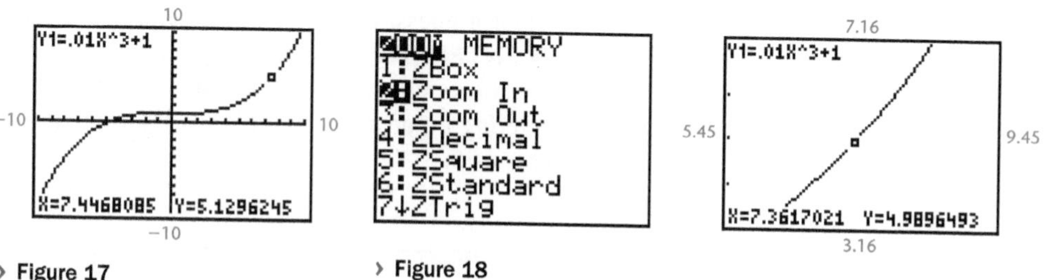

› Figure 17

› Figure 18

› Figure 19

Now we see that $x = 7.36$ when $y = 4.99$. This is an improvement, but we can do better. Repeating the Zoom In command and tracing along the curve (Fig. 20), we see that $x = 7.37$ when $y = 5.00$.

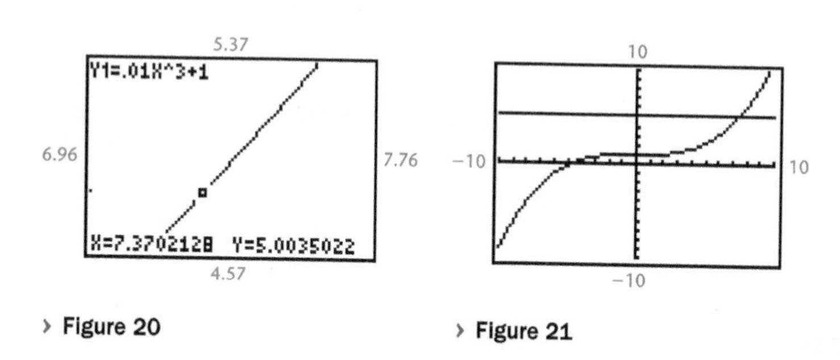

› Figure 20

› Figure 21

(C) Enter $y_2 = 5$ in the graphing calculator and graph y_1 and y_2 in the standard viewing window (Fig. 21). Now there are two curves displayed on the graph. The horizontal line is the graph of $y_2 = 5$, and the other curve is the familiar graph of y_1. The coordinates of the intersection point of the two curves must satisfy both equations. Clearly, the y coordinate of this intersection point is 5. The x coordinate is the value we are looking for. We can use the INTERSECT command to find the coordinates of the intersection point in Figure 21. When we select the INTERSECT command, we are asked to make three choices: the first curve, the second curve, and a guess. When the desired equation is displayed at the top of the screen, press ENTER to select it (Figs. 22 and 23). It doesn't matter which of the two graphs is designated as the first curve. (If there are more than two curves, use the up and down arrows to select the desired equation, then press ENTER.)

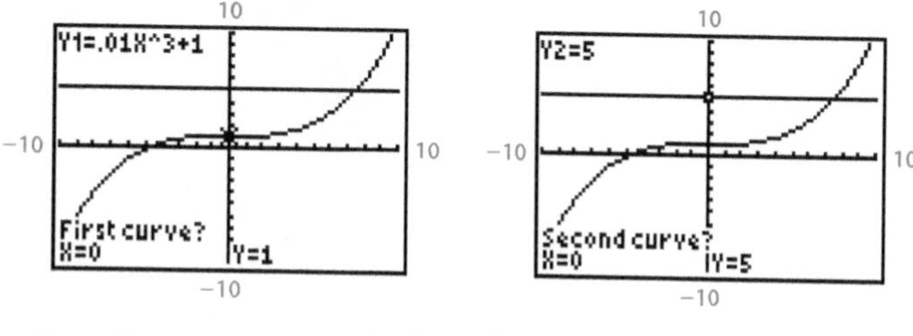

› Figure 22

› Figure 23

To enter a guess, move the cursor close to the intersection point (Fig. 24) and press ENTER (Fig. 25). On many models, you can enter an x value close to the intersection rather than moving the cursor. (We will see a more important use of entering a guess in Example 5.) Examining Figure 25, we see that $x = 7.37$ when $y = 5$.

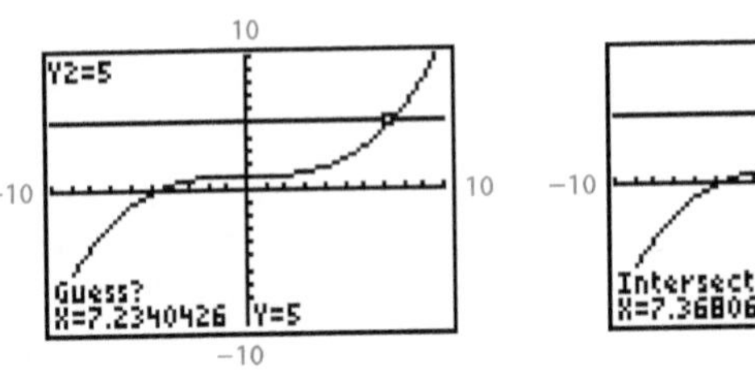

› **Figure 24**

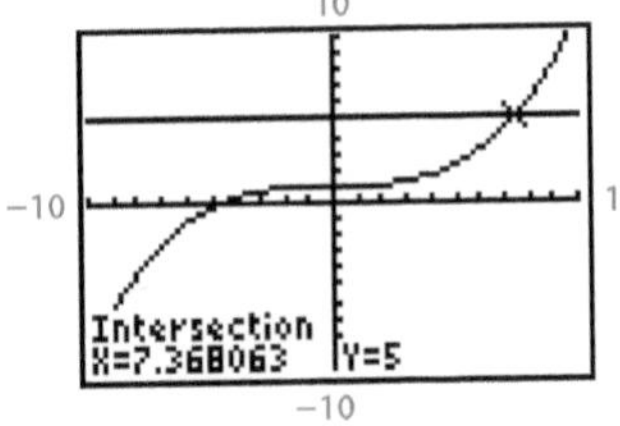

› **Figure 25**

MATCHED PROBLEM 4

Repeat Example 4 for $y = 1 - 0.02x^3$.

EXAMPLE 5 Solving an Equation with Multiple Solutions

Use a graphing calculator to solve the equation

$$x^3 + 20x^2 + 60x = 200$$

Round answers to two decimal places.

SOLUTION

We will solve this equation by graphing both sides in the same viewing window and finding the intersection points. First we enter $y_1 = x^3 + 20x^2 + 60x$ and $y_2 = 200$ in the graphing calculator (Fig. 26) and graph in the standard viewing window (Fig. 27).

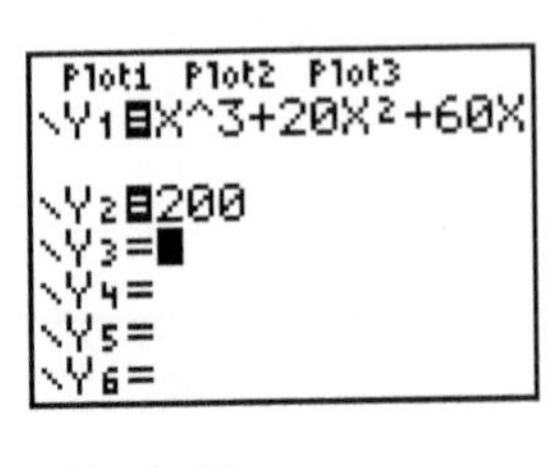

› **Figure 26**

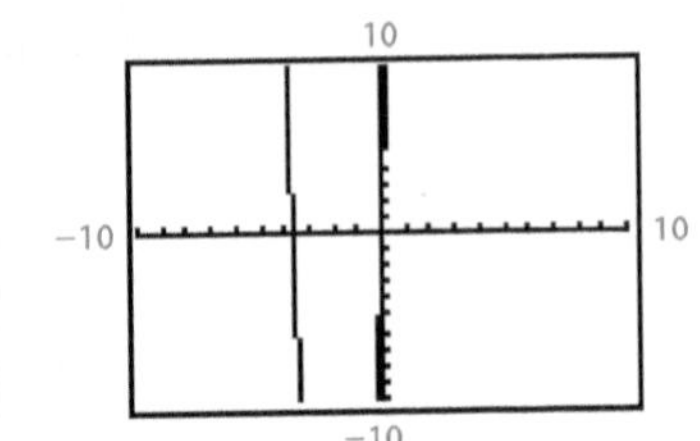

› **Figure 27**

A lot of students will always start with the standard viewing window, but in this case it is a poor choice. Because we are seeking the values of x that make the left side of the equation equal to 200, we need a value for Ymax that is larger than 200. Changing Ymax to 300 and Yscl to 30 produces a new graph (Fig. 28). The two curves intersect twice in this window. The x coordinates of these points are the solutions we are looking for. But first, could there be other solutions that are not visible in this window? To find out, we must investigate the behavior outside this window. A table is the most convenient way to do this (Figs. 29 and 30).

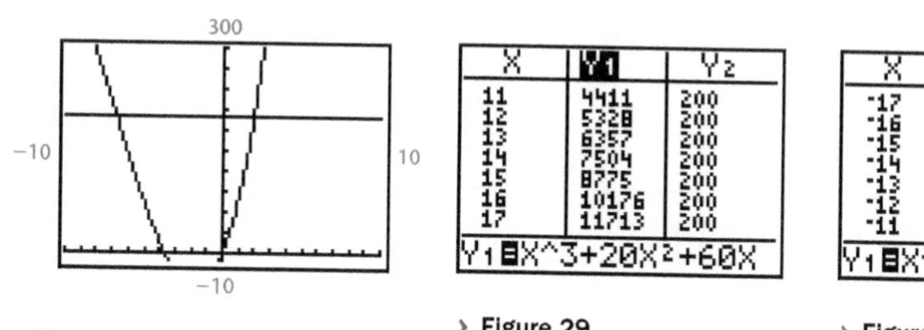

› Figure 28

› Figure 29

› Figure 30

Examining Figure 29, we see that the values of y_1 are getting very large. It's unlikely that there will be additional solutions to the equation $y_1 = 200$ for larger values of x. Examining Figure 30, we see that there are values of y_1 that are on both sides of 200, so there's a good chance that there will be additional solutions for more negative values of x. Based on the table values in Figure 30, we make the following changes in the window variables: Xmin $= -20$, Xscl $= 5$, Ymax $= 500$, Ymin $= -200$, Yscl $= 50$. This produces the graph in Figure 31. Examining the values of y_1 for values of x to the left of this window (Fig. 32), we conclude that there are no other intersection points.

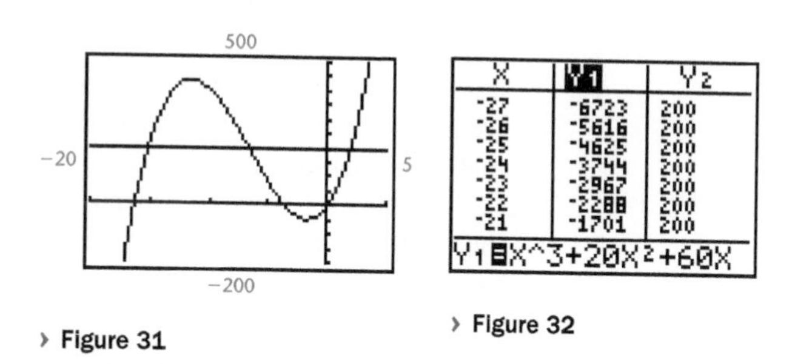

› Figure 31

› Figure 32

Now we use the INTERSECT command to find the x coordinates of the three intersection points in Figure 31. We select the two equations as before (Figs. 33 and 34). This time, the guess is very important. We have to specify which intersection point to find. To do this, we make a guess that is close to the desired point. We first select the leftmost intersection point by moving the cursor to that point (Fig. 35) and pressing ENTER.

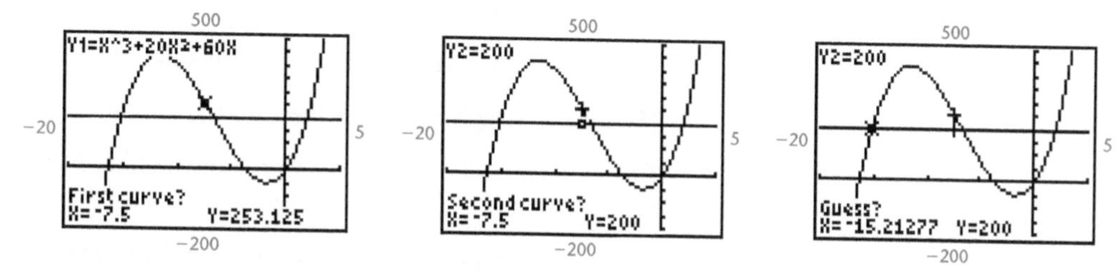

› Figure 33

› Figure 34

› Figure 35

The coordinates of the leftmost intersection point are displayed at the bottom of the screen (Fig. 36). To find the other two intersection points, we repeat the entire process. When we get to the screen that asks for a guess, we place the cursor near the point we are looking for and press ENTER (Figs. 37 and 38).

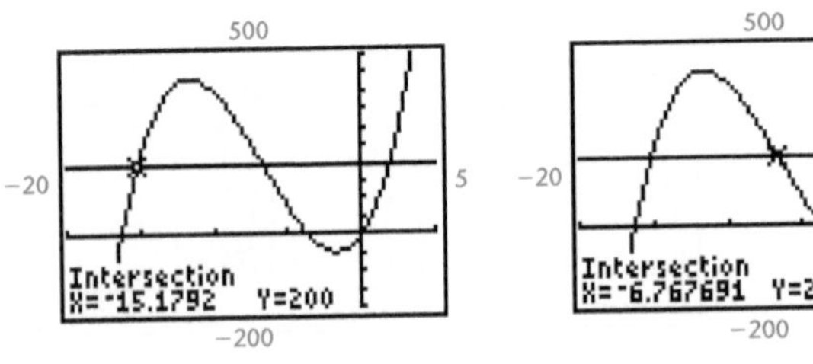

› Figure 36

› Figure 37

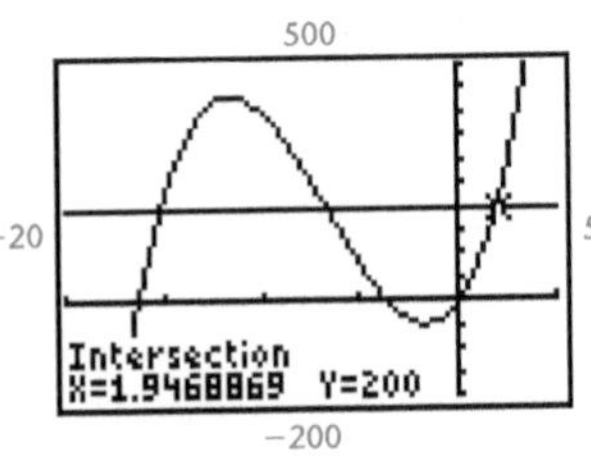

› Figure 38

Thus, we see that the solutions to $x^3 + 20x^2 + 60x = 200$ are $x = -15.18$, $x = -6.77$, and $x = 1.95$.

MATCHED PROBLEM 5

Solve $x^3 + 10x^2 - 100x = 100$. Round answers to two decimal places.

In the solution to Example 5, we had to rely on examining tables and our intuition to conclude that the two graphs intersected only three times. One of the major objectives of this course is to broaden our knowledge of graphs and equations so that we can be more definitive in our reasoning. For example, in Chapter 3 we will show that any equation like the one in Example 5 can have no more than three solutions.

Examples 1 through 5 dealt with a variety of methods for finding the value of y that corresponds to a given value of x and the value(s) of x that correspond to a given value of y. These methods are summarized in the following box.

› FINDING SOLUTIONS TO AN EQUATION

Assume the equation is entered in a graphing calculator as $y_1 =$ (expression with variable x).

To find solutions (x, y) given $x =$ some number a, use any of the following methods:

Method 1. Store a in X on the graphing calculator and display y_1 on the home screen.

Method 2. Set TBLSTART to a and display the table.

Method 3. Graph y_1, select the TRACE command, and enter a.

To find solutions (x, y) given $y =$ some number b, use either of the following methods:

Method 1. Graph y_1 and use TRACE and ZOOM.

Method 2. Graph y_1 and $y_2 = b$ and use INTERSECT.

Mathematical Modeling

Now that we are able to solve equations on a graphing calculator, there are many applications that we can investigate. The term **mathematical modeling** refers to the process of using an equation or equations to describe data from the real world. The next example develops a mathematical model for manufacturing a box to certain specifications.

EXAMPLE 6 Manufacturing

A packaging company plans to manufacture open boxes from 11- by 17-inch sheets of cardboard by cutting x- by x-inch squares out of the corners and folding up the sides, as shown in Figure 39.

(A) Write an equation for the volume y of the resulting box in terms of the length x of the sides of the squares that are cut out. Indicate appropriate restrictions on x.
(B) Graph the equation for appropriate values of x. Adjust the window variables for y to include the entire graph of interest.
(C) Find the smallest square that can be cut out to produce a box with a volume of 150 cubic inches.

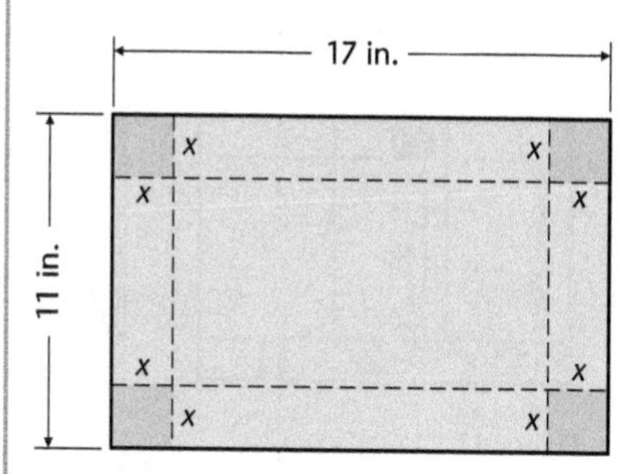

Figure 39 Template for boxes.

SOLUTIONS

(A) The dimensions of the box are expressed in terms of x in Figure 40(a), and the box is shown in Figure 40(b) with the sides folded up and dimensions added. From this figure we can write an equation of the volume in terms of x and establish restrictions on x.

Figure 40 Box with dimensions added.

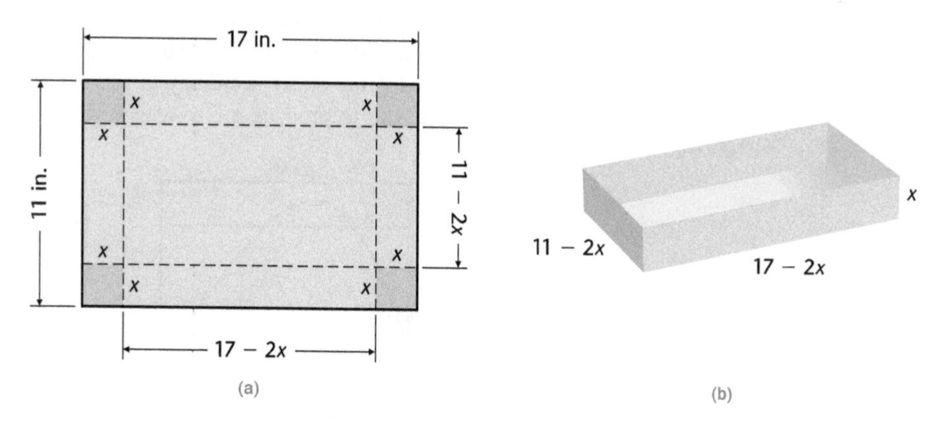

Note that the three dimensions of the box are x, $17 - 2x$, and $11 - 2x$. Of course, all of these dimensions have to be positive, so $x > 0$, $11 - 2x > 0$, and $17 - 2x > 0$. Now we solve the two latter inequalities:

$11 - 2x > 0$	$17 - 2x > 0$	Add $2x$ to each side.
$11 > 2x$	$17 > 2x$	Divide both sides by 2.
$5.5 > x$	$8.5 > x$	If $x < 5.5$, then it is also less than 8.5.

We find that x has to be greater than zero and less than 5.5. (Inequalities are reviewed in Appendix B, Section B-1.)

The volume of a rectangular box is the product of its three dimensions, so the volume of the box is given by

$$y = x(17 - 2x)(11 - 2x) \qquad 0 < x < 5.5 \tag{4}$$

(B) Entering this equation in a graphing calculator (it doesn't need to be multiplied out) and evaluating it for several integers between 0 and 5 (Fig. 41), it appears that a good choice for the window dimensions for y is $0 \le y \le 200$. This choice can easily be changed if there is too much space above the graph or if part of the graph we are interested in is out of the viewing window. Figure 42 shows the graph of equation (4) in the selected viewing window.

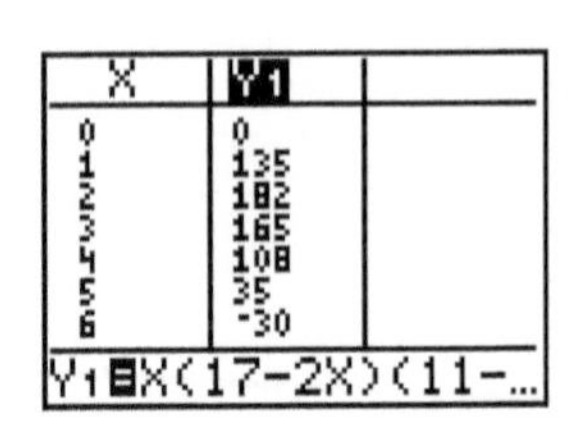

› Figure 41

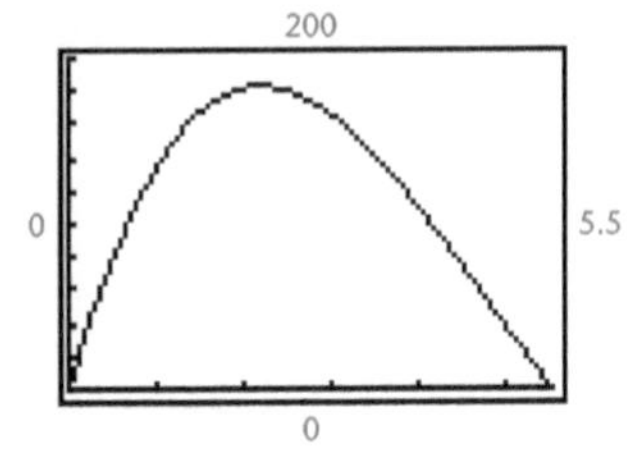

› Figure 42

(C) We want to find the smallest value of x for which $y = 150$. That is, we want to solve the equation

$$x(17 - 2x)(11 - 2x) = 150$$

We will solve this equation using the INTERSECT command. Entering $y_2 = 150$ in the graphing calculator and pressing GRAPH produces the two curves shown in Figure 43. The curves intersect twice. Because we were asked for the smallest value of x that satisfies the equation, we want the intersection point on the left (Fig. 44).

From Figure 44, we see that y is 150 when x is 1.19, so the smallest square that can be cut out to produce a box with a volume of 150 cubic inches is 1.19 inches.

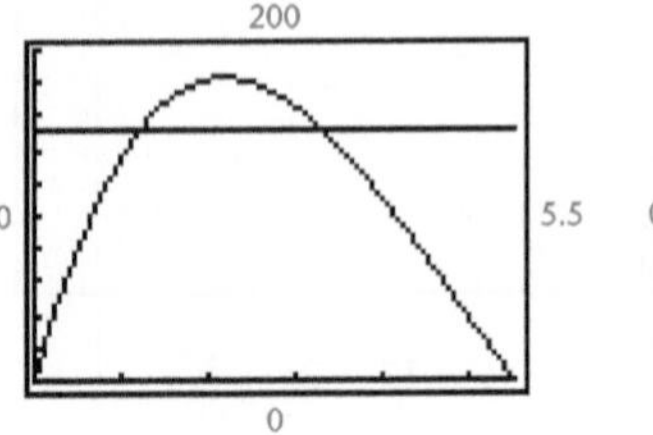

› Figure 43

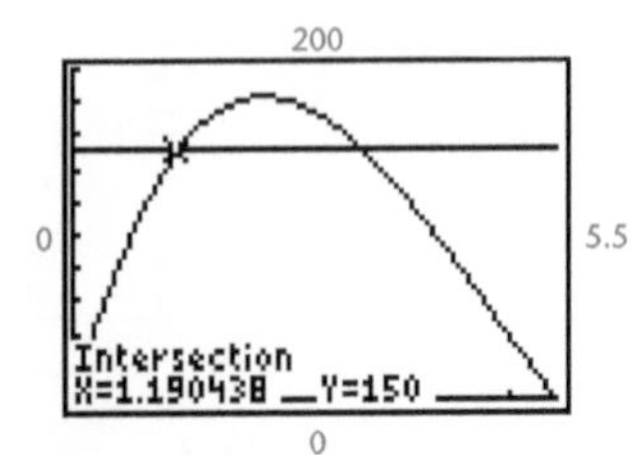

› Figure 44

››› CAUTION ›››

When providing an answer to application problems, it's almost always essential to attach appropriate units to your answer, in this case inches.

MATCHED PROBLEM 6

Refer to Example 6. Approximate to two decimal places the size of the largest square that can be cut out to produce a volume of 150 cubic inches.

ANSWERS TO MATCHED PROBLEMS

1.

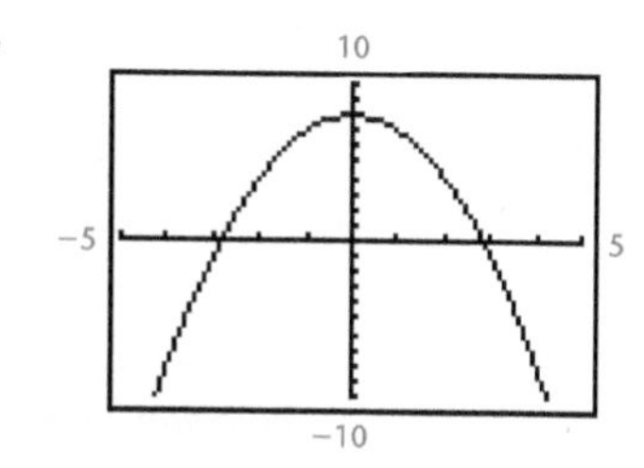

2. One possible choice is Xmin = −20, Xmax = 10, Ymin = −1, Ymax = 10

3.

Year	1998	1999	2000	2001	2002	2003	2004	2005	2006
x	−4	−3	−2	−1	0	1	2	3	4
y	6.2	0.7	−1.2	−0.7	1	2.7	3.2	1.3	−4.2

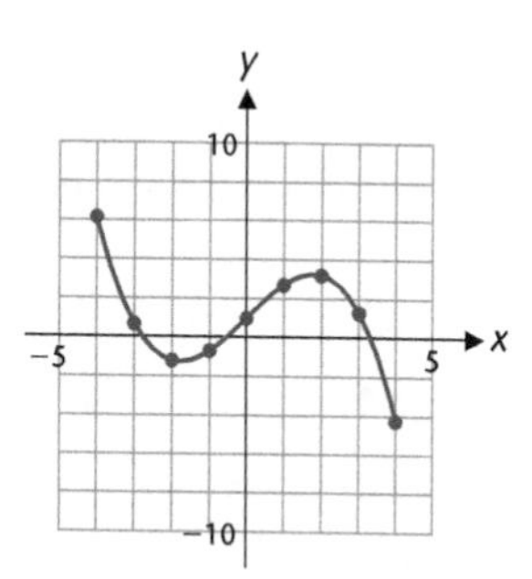

4. (A) −1.5 (B) −5.85 (C) −5.85

5. −15.90, −0.92, 6.82

6. 3.32 in.

1-1 Exercises

In Problems 1–6, determine if the indicated point lies in the viewing window defined by

$$\text{Xmin} = -7, \text{Xmax} = 9, \text{Ymin} = -4, \text{Ymax} = 11$$

1. $(0, 0)$ **2.** $(0, 10)$ **3.** $(10, 0)$

4. $(-3, -5)$ **5.** $(-5, -3)$ **6.** $(-8, 12)$

7. Consider the points in the following table:

x	3	6	−7	−4	0
y	−9	−4	14	0	2

(A) Find the smallest rectangle in a Cartesian coordinate system that will contain all the points in the table. State your answer in terms of the window variables Xmin, Xmax, Ymin, and Ymax.

(B) Enter the window variables you determined in part A and display the corresponding viewing window. Can you use the cursor to display the coordinates of the points in the table on the graphing calculator screen? Discuss the differences between the rectangle in the plane and the pixels displayed on the screen.

8. Repeat Problem 7 for the following table.

x	−4	0	−2	7	4
y	2	−4	0	−2	3

9. Explain the significance of Xmin, Xmax, and Xscl when using a graphing calculator.

10. Explain the significance of Ymin, Ymax, and Yscl when using a graphing calculator.

In Problems 11–16, graph each equation in a standard viewing window.

11. $y = -x$ **12.** $y = 0.5x$

13. $y = 9 - 0.4x^2$ **14.** $y = 0.3x^2 - 4$

15. $y = 2\sqrt{x + 5}$ **16.** $y = -2\sqrt{x + 5}$

In Problems 17–20, find an appropriate viewing window in which to graph the given equation with a graphing calculator.

17. $y = \sqrt{x + 18}$ **18.** $y = \sqrt{x - 17}$

19. $y = 13 - \sqrt{10 - 2x}$ **20.** $y = \sqrt{4x + 36} - 17$

For each equation in Problems 21–26, use the TABLE command on a graphing calculator to construct a table of values over the indicated interval, computing y values to the nearest tenth of a unit. Plot these points on graph paper, then with the aid of a graph on a graphing calculator, complete the hand sketch of the graph.

21. $y = 4 + 4x - x^2, -2 \le x \le 6$ (Use even integers for the table.)

22. $y = 2x^2 + 12x + 5, -7 \le x \le 1$ (Use odd integers for the table.)

23. $y = 2\sqrt{2x + 10}, -5 \le x \le 5$ (Use odd integers for the table.)

24. $y = \sqrt{8 - 2x}, -4 \le x \le 4$ (Use even integers for the table.)

25. $y = 0.5x(4 - x)(x + 2), -3 \le x \le 5$ (Use odd integers for the table.)

26. $y = 0.5x(x + 3.5)(2.8 - x), -4 \le x \le 4$ (Use even integers for the table.)

In Problems 27–30, graph the equation in a standard viewing window. Approximate to two decimal places the x coordinates of the points in this window that are on the graph of the equation and have the indicated y coordinates. First use TRACE and ZOOM, then INTERSECT.

27. $y = 4 - 3\sqrt[3]{x + 4}$
(A) $(x, 8)$ (B) $(x, -1)$

28. $y = 3 + 4\sqrt[3]{x - 4}$
(A) $(x, 8)$ (B) $(x, -6)$

29. $y = 3 + x + 0.1x^3$
(A) $(x, 4)$ (B) $(x, -7)$

30. $y = 2 - 0.5x - 0.1x^3$
(A) $(x, 7)$ (B) $(x, -5)$

The graphs of each pair of equations in Problems 31–40 intersect in exactly two points. Find a viewing window that clearly shows both points of intersection (there are many windows that will do this). Then use INTERSECT to find the coordinates of each intersection point to two decimal places.

31. $y = x^2 - 10x, y = 12 - 5x$

32. $y = x^2 + 15x, y = 15 + 10x$

33. $y = 15x - x^2, y = 10 - 4x$

34. $y = -x^2 - 20x, y = 10x + 15$

35. $y = 0.4x^2 - 5x + 10, y = 5 + 9x - 0.3x^2$

36. $y = 0.2x^2 + 7x - 15, y = 9 - 7x - 0.1x^2$

37. $y = \sqrt{9x + 20}, y = 0.2x + 10$

38. $y = 20 - \sqrt{5x + 5}, y = 14 - 0.1x$

39. $y = \sqrt{x + 10}, y = 0.1x^2 - 5x - 10$

40. $y = \sqrt{5 - x}, y = 0.1x^2 + 5x$

41. (A) Sketch the graph of $x^2 + y^2 = 9$ by hand and identify the curve.*
(B) Graph $y_1 = \sqrt{9 - x^2}$ and $y_2 = -\sqrt{9 - x^2}$ in the standard viewing window of a graphing calculator. How do these graphs compare to the graph you drew in part A?
(C) Apply each of the following ZOOM options to the graphs in part B and determine which options produce a curve that looks like the curve you drew in part A: ZDecimal, ZSquare, ZoomFit

42. (A) Sketch the graph of $x^2 + y^2 = 4$ by hand and identify the curve.
(B) Graph $y_1 = \sqrt{4 - x^2}$ and $y_2 = -\sqrt{4 - x^2}$ in the standard viewing window of a graphing calculator. How do these graphs compare to the graph you drew in part A?
(C) Apply each of the following ZOOM options to the graphs in part B and determine which options produce a curve that looks like the curve you drew in part A: ZDecimal, ZSquare, ZoomFit

In Problems 43–46, use the INTERSECT command on a graphing calculator to solve each equation for the indicated values of b. Round answers to two decimal places.

43. $0.1x^3 - x^2 - 5x + 100 = b$
(A) $b = 25$ (B) $b = 75$ (C) $b = 125$

44. $0.1x^3 + x^2 - 7x - 100 = b$
(A) $b = -125$ (B) $b = -75$ (C) $b = 75$

45. $0.01x^4 + 4x + 50 = b$
(A) $b = 25$ (B) $b = 75$

46. $0.01x^4 - 3x + 50 = b$
(A) $b = 25$ (B) $b = 75$

In Problems 47–50, use the INTERSECT command on a graphing calculator to solve each equation for the indicated values of b. Round answers to two decimal places.

47. $1{,}200x - x^3 = b$
(A) $b = 12{,}000$ (B) $b = 16{,}000$ (C) $b = 20{,}000$

48. $x^3 - 300x = b$
(A) $b = 1{,}000$ (B) $b = 2{,}000$ (C) $b = 3{,}000$

49. $x^4 + 4{,}000x = b$
(A) $b = 30{,}000$ (B) $b = -30{,}000$ (C) $b = -40{,}000$

50. $800x^2 - x^4 = b$
(A) $b = 100{,}000$ (B) $b = 160{,}000$ (C) $b = 200{,}000$

In Problems 51–56, use the INTERSECT command on a graphing calculator to solve each equation. Round answers to two decimal places. (Hint: See Exercises 31–40)

51. $0.2x^4 + x^3 = \frac{1}{2}x + 2$

52. $\sqrt{x + 9} + 3 = 9 + x - 5x^2$

53. $x^2 - 3x + 1 = \sqrt{2x - 7}$

54. $\sqrt[3]{x^2 + 2} = 2x^4 - 7x^2 + 11$

55. $0.05(x + 4)^3 + 4 = 17 - x$

56. $3x - 29 = 5\sqrt[3]{-5 - 2x}$

57. The point $(\sqrt{2}, 2)$ is on the graph of $y = x^2$. Use TRACE and ZOOM to approximate $\sqrt{2}$ to four decimal places. Compare your result with the direct calculator evaluation of $\sqrt{2}$.

58. The point $(\sqrt[3]{4}, 4)$ is on the graph of $y = x^3$. Use TRACE and ZOOM to approximate $\sqrt[3]{4}$ to four decimal places. Compare your result with the direct calculator evaluation of $\sqrt[3]{4}$.

59. In a few sentences, discuss the difference between the mathematical coordinates of a point and the screen coordinates of a pixel.

60. In a few sentences, discuss the difference between the coordinates displayed during unrestricted cursor movement and those displayed during the trace procedure.

APPLICATIONS

61. PROFIT The monthly profit in dollars for a small consulting firm can be modeled by the equation $y = -16.7x^3 - 400x^2 + 6{,}367x - 7{,}000$, where x is the number of new clients acquired during that month. For tax purposes, the owner asks the manager to try to make the December profit as close as possible to $11,000. How many new clients should the manager try bring in?

62. METEOROLOGY The average monthly high temperature in degrees Fahrenheit in Cincinnati for the first 10 months of the year can be modeled very accurately by the equation $y = -0.21x^3 + 2.24x^2 + 2.33x + 33.67$, where x is the month, with $x = 1$ corresponding to January. A wedding planner in Cincinnati is asked to set a date in a month where the high temperature is most likely to be close to 75 degrees. What month would be the best choice?

*Graphs of equations of this form are reviewed in Appendix B, Section B-3.

63. MANUFACTURING A rectangular open-top box is to be constructed out of an 8.5-inch by 11-inch sheet of thin cardboard by cutting x-inch squares out of each corner and bending the sides up, as in Figures 39 and 40 in Example 6. What size squares to two decimal places should be cut out to produce a box with a volume of 55 cubic inches? Give the dimensions to two decimal places of all possible boxes with the given volume.

64. MANUFACTURING A rectangular open-top box is to be constructed out of a 9-inch by 12-inch sheet of thin cardboard by cutting x-inch squares out of each corner and bending the sides up as shown in Figures 39 and 40 in Example 6. What size squares to two decimal places should be cut out to produce a box with a volume of 72 cubic inches? Give the dimensions to two decimal places of all possible boxes with the given volume.

65. MANUFACTURING A box with a lid is to be cut out of a 12-inch by 24-inch sheet of thin cardboard by cutting out six x-inch squares and folding as indicated in the figure. What are the dimensions to two decimal places of all possible boxes that will have a volume of 100 cubic inches?

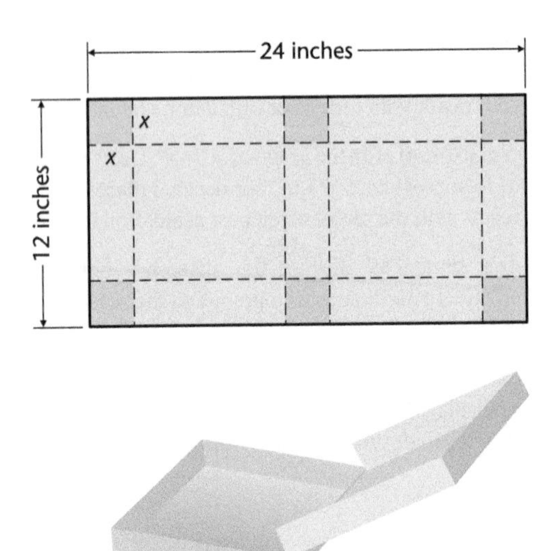

66. MANUFACTURING A box with a lid is to be cut out of a 10-inch by 20-inch sheet of thin cardboard by cutting out six x-inch squares and folding as indicated in the figure. What are the dimensions to two decimal places of all possible boxes that will have a volume of 75 cubic inches? (Refer to the figure for Problem 65.)

67. MANUFACTURING An oil tank in the shape of a right circular cylinder* has a volume of 40,000 cubic feet. If regulations for such tanks require that the radius plus the height must be 50 feet, find the radius and the height to two decimal places.

*Geometric formulas can be found in Appendix C.

68. MANUFACTURING A drinking container in the shape of a right circular cone* has a volume of 50 cubic inches. If the radius plus the height of the cone is 8 inches, find the radius and the height to two decimal places.

69. PRICE AND DEMAND A nationwide office supply company sells high-grade paper for laser printers. The price per case y (in dollars) and the weekly demand x for this paper are related approximately by the equation

$$y = 100 - 0.6\sqrt{x} \qquad 5{,}000 \le x \le 20{,}000$$

(A) Complete the following table. Approximate each value of x to the nearest hundred cases.

x			
y	20	25	30

(B) Does the demand increase or decrease if the price is increased from $25 to $30? By how much?
(C) Does the demand increase or decrease if the price is decreased from $25 to $20? By how much?

70. PRICE AND DEMAND Refer to the relationship between price and demand given in Problem 69.
(A) Complete the following table. Approximate each value of x to the nearest hundred cases.

x			
y	35	40	45

(B) Does the demand increase or decrease if the price is increased from $40 to $45? By how much?
(C) Does the demand increase or decrease if the price is decreased from $40 to $35? By how much?

71. PRICE AND REVENUE Refer to Problem 69. The revenue from the sale of x cases of paper at $\$y$ per case is given by the product $R = xy$.
(A) Use the results from Problem 69 to complete the following table of revenues.

y	20	25	30
R			

(B) Does the revenue increase or decrease if the price is increased from $25 to $30? By how much?
(C) Does the revenue increase or decrease if the price is decreased from $25 to $20? By how much?
(D) If the current price of paper is $25 per case and the company wants to increase revenue, should it raise the price $5, lower the price $5, or leave the price unchanged?

72. PRICE AND REVENUE Refer to Problem 70. The revenue from the sale of x cases of paper at $\$y$ per case is given by the product $R = xy$.
(A) Use the results from Problem 70 to complete the following table of revenues.

y	35	40	45
R			

(B) Does the revenue increase or decrease if the price is increased from $40 to $45? By how much?
(C) Does the revenue increase or decrease if the price is decreased from $40 to $35? By how much?
(D) If the current price of paper is $40 per case and the company wants to increase revenue, should it raise the price $5, lower the price $5, or leave the price unchanged?

1-2 Functions

The idea of correspondence plays a really important role in understanding the concept of functions, which is almost certainly the most important idea in this course. The good news is that you have already had years of experience with correspondences in everyday life. For example,

For every person, there is a corresponding age.
For every item in a store, there is a corresponding price.
For every season, there is a corresponding Super Bowl champion.
For every circle, there is a corresponding area.
For every number, there is a corresponding cube.

One of the most basic and important ways that math can be applied to other areas of study is the establishment of correspondences among various types of phenomena. In many cases, once a correspondence is known, it can be used to make important decisions and predictions. An engineer can use a formula to predict the weight capacity of a stadium grandstand. A political operative decides how many resources to allocate to a race given current polling results. A computer scientist can use formulas to compare the efficiency of algorithms for sorting data stored on a computer. An economist would like to be able to predict interest rates, given the rate of change of the money supply. And the list goes on and on . . . .

Defining Relations and Functions

What do all of the preceding examples have in common? Each of them describes the matching of elements in one set with elements in a second set. There is a special name for such a correspondence.

DEFINITION 1 Definition of Relation

A **relation** is a correspondence that matches up two sets of objects. The first set is called the **domain,** and the set of all corresponding elements is called the **range.**

REMARK: Some graphing calculators use the term *range* to refer to the window variables. In this book, *range* will always refer to the range of a relation.

Two examples of relations are provided below.

Table 1 Manufacturers of the Five Top Selling Cars in America, 1/1/06–8/31/06

Manufacturer	Model
Toyota	Camry
	Corolla
Honda	Accord
	Civic
Chevrolet	Impala

Source: Forbes.com

Table 2 Sales of the Five Top Selling Cars in America, 1/1/06–8/31/06

Model	U.S. Sales
Camry	302,636
Corolla	274,074
Accord	250,663
Civic	225,212
Impala	197,304

Table 1 specifies a relation with domain {Toyota, Honda, Chevrolet}, and range {Camry, Corolla, Accord, Civic, Impala}. Table 2 specifies a relation with domain {Camry, Corolla, Accord, Civic, Impala} and range {302,636, 274,074, 250,663, 225,212, 197,304}.

Notice that in Table 1, two of the domain elements (Toyota and Honda) correspond to more than one range element. But in Table 2, each domain element corresponds to a unique range element. We will give relations like the latter a special name.

> **DEFINITION 2 Definition of Function**
>
> A **function** is a relation in which every element in the domain corresponds to one and only one element in the range.

Note that Table 2 defines a function, while Table 1 does not; both Toyota and Honda (domain elements) correspond to more than one range element.

››› EXPLORE-DISCUSS 1

(A) Consider the set of students enrolled in a college and the set of faculty members of that college. Define a relation between the two sets by saying that a student corresponds to a faculty member if the student is currently enrolled in a course taught by that faculty member. Is this relation a function? Discuss.

(B) Write an example of a function based on a real-life situation, then write a similar example of a relation that is not a function.

We now turn to an alternative way to represent relations. Every relation can be specified using ordered pairs of elements, where the first component represents a domain element and the second component represents the corresponding range element. Using this approach, the relations specified in Tables 1 and 2 can be written as follows:

F = {(Toyota, Camry), (Toyota, Corolla), (Honda, Accord), (Honda, Civic), (Chevrolet, Impala)}

G = {(Camry, 302,636), (Corolla, 274,074), (Accord, 250,663), (Civic, 225,212), (Impala, 197,304)}

(If this notation reminds you of points on a graph, good for you! You already have a leg up on the next section.)

In relation G, notice that no two ordered pairs have the same first component and different second components. This tells us that relation G is a function. On the other hand, in relation F, the first two ordered pairs have the same first component and different second components. This means that relation F is not a function.

This ordered pair approach suggests an alternative (but equivalent) way of defining the concept of a function.

› DEFINITION 3 Set Form of the Definition of Function

A **function** is a set of ordered pairs with the property that no two ordered pairs have the same first component and different second components.

The set of all first components in a function is called the **domain** of the function, and the set of all second components is called the **range.**

EXAMPLE 1 Determining If Ordered Pairs Define a Function

State the domain and range of each relation, then determine whether the relation is a function.

(A) $S = \{(1, 4), (2, 3), (3, 2), (4, 3), (5, 4)\}$
(B) $T = \{(1, 4), (2, 3), (3, 2), (2, 4), (1,5)\}$

SOLUTIONS

(A) The domain and range are

Domain $= \{1, 2, 3, 4, 5\}$
Range $= \{2, 3, 4\}$

Because all of the ordered pairs in S have distinct first components, this relation is a function.

(B) The domain and range are

Domain $= \{1, 2, 3\}$
Range $= \{2, 3, 4, 5\}$

Because there are ordered pairs in relation T with the same first component and different second components [for example, $(1, 4)$ and $(1, 5)$], this relation is not a function.

MATCHED PROBLEM 1

State the domain and range of each relation, then determine whether the relation is a function.

(A) $S = \{(-2, 1), (-1, 2), (0, 0), (-1, 1), (-2, 2)\}$
(B) $T = \{(-2, 1), (-1, 2), (0, 0), (1, 2), (2, 1)\}$

REMARK: Notice that in Relation S of Example 1, the range values 3 and 4 each correspond to two different domain values. This does not violate the definition of function, since no domain value appears more than once in the list of ordered pairs.

Defining Functions by Equations

So far, we have described a particular function in various ways: (1) by a verbal description; (2) by a table; and (3) by a set of ordered pairs. We will see that if the domain and range are sets of numbers, we can also define a function by an equation, or by a graph.

If the domain of a function is a large or infinite set, it may be impractical or impossible to actually list all of the ordered pairs that belong to the function, or to display the function in a table. Such a function can often be defined by a verbal description of the "rule of correspondence" that clearly specifies the element of the range that corresponds to each element of the domain. For example, "to each real number corresponds its square." When the domain and range are sets of numbers, the algebraic and graphical analogs of the verbal description are the equation and graph, respectively. We will find it valuable to be able to view a particular function from multiple perspectives—algebraic (in terms of an equation), graphical (in terms of a graph), and numeric (in terms of a table or ordered pairs).

Both versions of our definition of function are very general. The objects in the domain and range can be pretty much anything, and there is no restriction on the number of elements in each.

In this text, we are primarily interested, however, in functions with real number domains and ranges. Unless otherwise indicated, **the domain and range of a function will be sets of real numbers.** For such a function we often use an equation in two variables to specify both the rule of correspondence and the set of ordered pairs.

Consider the equation

$$y = x^2 + 2x \qquad x \text{ any real number} \tag{1}$$

This equation assigns to each domain value x exactly one range value y. For example,

$$\text{If } x = 4, \quad \text{then} \quad y = (4)^2 + 2(4) = 24$$
$$\text{If } x = -\tfrac{1}{3}, \quad \text{then} \quad y = (-\tfrac{1}{3})^2 + 2(-\tfrac{1}{3}) = -\tfrac{5}{9}$$

Thus, we can view equation (1) as a function with rule of correspondence

$$y = x^2 + 2x \qquad x \text{ corresponds to } x^2 + 2x$$

or, equivalently, as a function with set of ordered pairs

$$\{(x, y) \mid y = x^2 + 2x, x \text{ a real number}\}$$

This is called set-builder notation and is read as "The set of all ordered pairs (x, y) such that $y = x^2 + 2x$, where x is a real number." The variable x is called an *independent variable,* indicating that values can be assigned "independently" to x from the domain. The variable y is called a *dependent variable,* indicating that the value of y "depends" on the value assigned to x and on the given equation. In general, any variable used as a placeholder for domain values is called an **independent variable;** any variable used as a placeholder for range values is called a **dependent variable.**

We often refer to a value of the independent variable as the input of the function, and the corresponding value of the dependent variable as the associated output. In this regard, a function can be thought of as a process that accepts an input from the domain and outputs an appropriate range element.

Next, we address the question of which equations can be used to define functions.

> **FUNCTIONS DEFINED BY EQUATIONS**
>
> In an equation in two variables, if to each value of the independent variable there corresponds exactly one value of the dependent variable, then the equation defines a function.
>
> If there is any value of the independent variable to which there corresponds more than one value of the dependent variable, then the equation does not define a function.

We have already decided that equation (1) defines a function. Now we will look at an example of an equation that does not define a function,

$$y^2 = x, \text{ where } x \text{ is any real number.} \qquad (2)$$

For $x = 9$, for example, there are two associated values of the dependent variable, $y = 3$ and $y = -3$. Thus, equation (2) does not define a function.

Notice that we have used the phrase "an equation defines a function" rather than "an equation is a function." This is a somewhat technical distinction, but it is employed consistently in mathematical literature and we will adhere to it in this text.

››› EXPLORE-DISCUSS 2

(A) Graph $y = x^2 - 4$ for $-5 \le x \le 5$ and $-5 \le y \le 5$ and trace along this graph. Discuss the relationship between the coordinates displayed while tracing and the function defined by this equation.

(B) The graph of the equation $x^2 + y^2 = 16$ is a circle. Because most graphing calculators will accept only equations that have been solved for y, we must graph both of the equations $y_1 = \sqrt{16 - x^2}$ and $y_2 = -\sqrt{16 - x^2}$ to produce a graph of the circle. Graph these equations for $-5 \le x \le 5$ and $-5 \le y \le 5$. Then try different values for Xmin and Xmax until the graph looks more like a circle. Use the TRACE command to find two points on this circle with the same x coordinate and different y coordinates.

(C) Is it possible to graph a single equation of the form $y =$ (expression in x) on your graphing calculator and obtain a graph that is not the graph of a function? Explain your answer.

REMARK: If we want the graph of a circle to actually appear to be circular, we must choose window variables so that a unit length on the x axis is the same number of pixels as a unit length on the y axis. Such a window is often referred to as a *squared viewing window*. Most graphing calculators have an option under the zoom menu that does this automatically.

One way to determine if an equation defines a function is to examine its graph. The graphs of the equations

$$y = x^2 - 4 \qquad \text{and} \qquad x^2 + y^2 = 16$$

are shown in Figure 1.

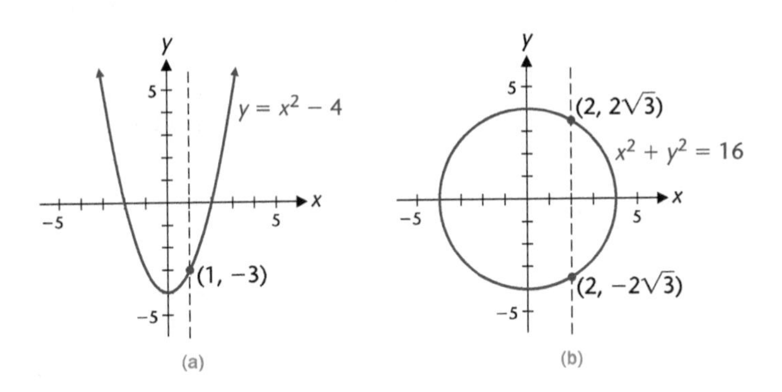

› **Figure 1** Graphs of equations and the vertical line test.

The graph in Figure 1(a) is a parabola and the graph in Figure 1(b) is a circle.* Each vertical line intersects the parabola in exactly one point. This shows that to each value of the independent variable x there corresponds exactly one value of the dependent variable y. For example, to the x value 1 there corresponds only the y value -3 [Fig. 1(a)]. Thus, the equation $y = x^2 - 4$ defines a function. On the other hand, there are vertical lines that intersect the circle in Figure 1(b) in two points. For example, the vertical line through $x = 2$ intersects the circle in the points $(2, 2\sqrt{3})$ and $(2, -2\sqrt{3})$ [Fig. 1(b)]. Thus, to the x value 2 there correspond two y values, $2\sqrt{3}$ and $-2\sqrt{3}$. Consequently, the equation $x^2 + y^2 = 16$ does not define a function. These observations are generalized in Theorem 1.

› THEOREM 1 Vertical Line Test for a Function

An equation defines a function if each vertical line in the rectangular coordinate system passes through at most one point on the graph of the equation.

If any vertical line passes through two or more points on the graph of an equation, then the equation does not define a function.

EXAMPLE 2 Determining If an Equation Defines a Function

Determine if each equation defines a function with independent variable x.

(A) $y = 2x^2 - 3$
(B) $2x - 1 = y^2$

*Parabolas and circles are discussed extensively later in the book.

SOLUTIONS

Algebraic Solutions

(A) For any real number x, the square of x is a unique number. When you multiply the square by 2 and then subtract 3, the result is still a unique number. Thus, for any input x, there is a unique output y, and the equation defines a function.

(B) For any real number x, as long as $2x - 1$ is positive, there will be two associated values of y whose square will equal $2x - 1$, one positive and one negative. Thus, the equation has more than one output for certain inputs, and does not define a function.

Graphical Solutions

(A) We enter the equation into a graphing calculator, then graph in a standard viewing window.

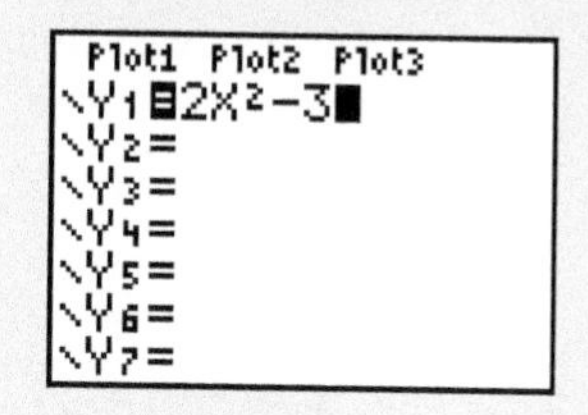

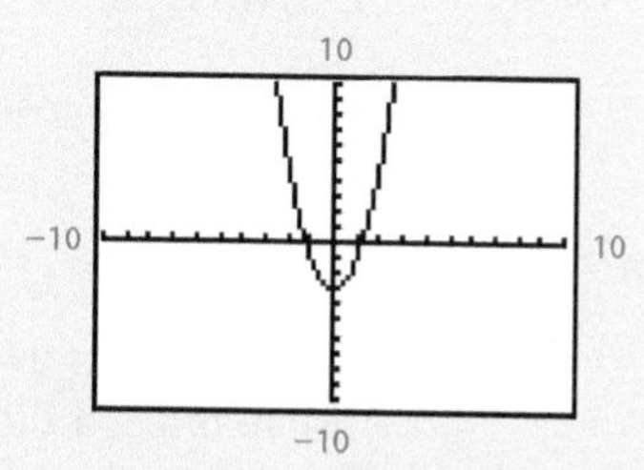

Any vertical line will pass through the graph only once, so the equation defines a function.

(B) To enter this equation in a graphing calculator, we must first solve for y:

$$2x - 1 = y^2$$

$$y = \sqrt{2x - 1} \quad \text{or} \quad y = -\sqrt{2x - 1}$$

We enter these two equations as Y_1 and Y_2 and graph in a standard viewing window.

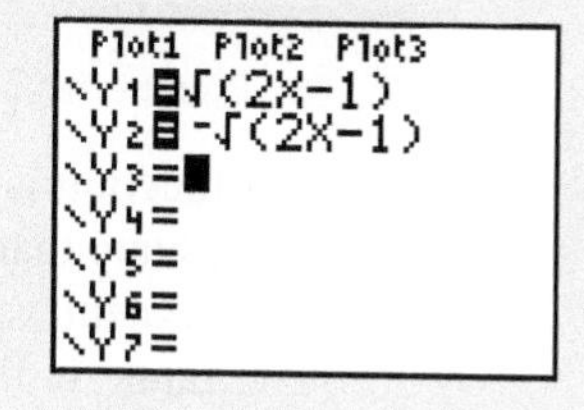

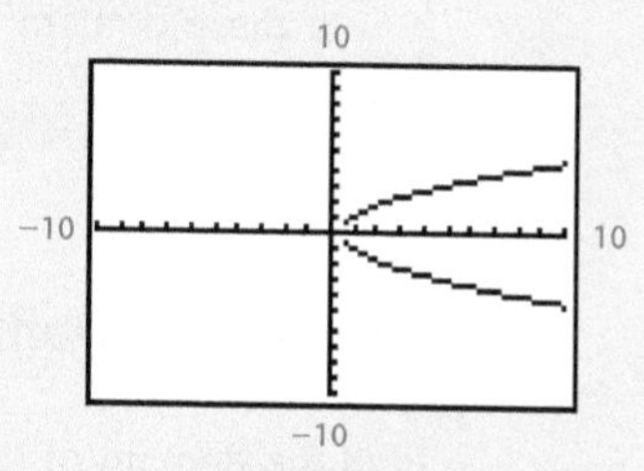

Almost any vertical line that intersects the graph at all will actually intersect it twice, so we conclude that the equation does not define a function.

MATCHED PROBLEM 2

Determine if each equation defines a function with independent variable x.

(A) $y^2 + 4 = 3x$
(B) $y = 7 - x^2$

Finding the Domain of a Function

Sometimes when a function is defined by an equation, a domain is specified, as in

$$y = 2x^2 + 5, \quad x > 0$$

The "$x > 0$" tells us that the domain is all positive real numbers.

More often, a function is defined by an equation with no domain specified. Refer to Figure 1 on page 27. Because the expression $x^2 - 4$ represents a real number for any real number input x, the function defined by the equation $y = x^2 - 4$ is defined for all real numbers. Thus, its domain is the set of all real numbers, often denoted by the letter R or the interval* $(-\infty, \infty)$. On the other hand, the expression $\sqrt{16 - x^2}$ represents a real number only if the expression under the root, $16 - x^2$, is nonnegative. This occurs only for x values from -4 to 4. Thus, the domain of the function $y = \sqrt{16 - x^2}$ is $\{x \mid -4 \le x \le 4\}$ or $[-4, 4]$. Unless a domain is specified, we will adhere to the following convention regarding domains and ranges for functions defined by equations.

AGREEMENT ON DOMAINS AND RANGES

If a function is defined by an equation and the domain is not indicated, then we assume that the domain is the set of all real number replacements of the independent variable that produce *real values* for the dependent variable. The range is the set of all values of the dependent variable corresponding to these domain values.

EXAMPLE 3

Finding the Domain of a Function

Find the domain of the function defined by the equation $y = 4 + \sqrt{x + 2}$, assuming x is the independent variable.

*See Appendix B, Section B-1, for a discussion of interval notation and inequalities.

SOLUTION

For $\sqrt{x + 2}$ to be real, $x + 2$ must be greater than or equal to 0. This occurs when x is greater than or equal to -2.

$$\text{Domain} = \{x \mid x \geq -2\} \quad \text{or} \quad [-2, \infty)$$

Note that in many cases we will dispense with set notation and simply write $x \geq -2$ instead of $\{x \mid x \geq -2\}$.

MATCHED PROBLEM 3

Find the domain of the function defined by the equation $y = 3 + \sqrt{-x}$, assuming x is the independent variable.

› Using Function Notation

We will use letters to name functions and to provide a very important and convenient notation for defining functions. For example, if f is the name of the function defined by the equation $y = 2x + 1$, we could use the formal representations

$$f{:}\, y = 2x + 1 \qquad \text{Rule of correspondence}$$

or

$$f{:}\{(x, y) \mid y = 2x + 1\} \qquad \text{Set of ordered pairs}$$

But instead, we will simply write

$$f(x) = 2x + 1 \qquad \text{Function notation}$$

The symbol $f(x)$ is read "f of x," "f at x," or "the value of f at x" and represents the number in the range of the function f (the output) that is paired with the domain value x (the input).

››› CAUTION ›››

The symbol "$f(x)$" should *never* be read as "f times x." The notation does not represent a product. It tells us that the function named f has independent variable x.

$f(x)$ is the value of the function f at x.

$2(x) = 2x$ is algebraic multiplication.

Using function notation, $f(3)$ is the output for the function f associated with the input 3.

We find this range value by replacing x with 3 wherever x occurs in the function definition

$$f(x) = 2x + 1$$

and evaluating the right side,

$$\begin{aligned} f(3) &= 2 \cdot 3 + 1 \\ &= 6 + 1 \\ &= 7 \end{aligned}$$

The statement $f(3) = 7$ indicates in a concise way that the function f assigns the range value 7 to the domain value 3 or, equivalently, that the ordered pair (3, 7) belongs to f.

The symbol $f: x \rightarrow f(x)$, read "f maps x into $f(x)$," is also used to denote the relationship between the domain value x and the range value $f(x)$ (Fig. 2).

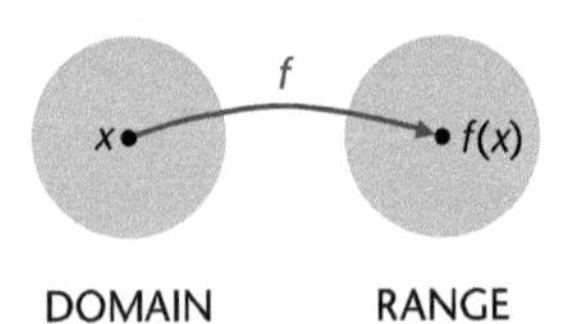

The function f "maps" the domain value x into the range value $f(x)$.

› **Figure 2** Function notation.

In many cases, when defining functions with equations, we will use the symbols y and $f(x)$ interchangeably. Whenever we write $y = f(x)$, we assume that x is an independent variable and that y and $f(x)$ both represent the dependent variable.

Letters other than f and x can be used to represent functions and independent variables. For example,

$$g(t) = t^2 - 3t + 7$$

defines g as a function of the independent variable t. To find $g(-2)$, we replace t by -2 wherever t occurs in

$$g(t) = t^2 - 3t + 7$$

and evaluate the right side:

$$\begin{aligned} g(-2) &= (-2)^2 - 3(-2) + 7 \\ &= 4 + 6 + 7 \\ &= 17 \end{aligned}$$

Thus, the function g assigns the range value 17 to the domain value -2; the ordered pair $(-2, 17)$ belongs to g.

It is important to understand and remember the definition of the symbol $f(x)$:

> **DEFINITION 4 The Symbol $f(x)$**

The symbol $\boldsymbol{f(x)}$, read "f of x," represents the real number in the range of the function f corresponding to the domain value x. The symbol $f(x)$ is also called the *value of the function f at x*. The ordered pair $(x, f(x))$ belongs to the function f. If x is a real number that is not in the domain of f, then f is *undefined* at x and $f(x)$ *does not exist.*

EXAMPLE 4 Evaluating Functions

For

$$f(x) = \frac{15}{x - 3} \qquad g(x) = 16 + 3x - x^2 \qquad h(x) = \frac{6}{\sqrt{x} - 1}$$

find:

(A) $f(6)$ (B) $g(-7)$ (C) $h(-2)$ (D) $f(0) + g(4) - h(16)$

SOLUTIONS

In each case, the independent variable is replaced with the given domain value.

(A) $f(6) \boxed{= \frac{15}{6 - 3}} = \frac{15}{3} = 5$*

(B) $g(-7) \boxed{= 16 + 3(-7) - (-7)^2} = 16 - 21 - 49 = -54$

(C) $h(-2) = \frac{6}{\sqrt{-2} - 1}$

But $\sqrt{-2}$ is not a real number. Because we have agreed to restrict the domain of a function to values of x that produce real values for the function, -2 is not in the domain of h and $h(-2)$ does not exist.

(D) $f(0) + g(4) - h(16)$

$$\boxed{= \frac{15}{0 - 3} + [16 + 3(4) - 4^2] - \frac{6}{\sqrt{16} - 1}}$$

$$= \frac{15}{-3} + 12 - \frac{6}{3}$$

$$= -5 + 12 - 2 = 5$$

*The dashed "think boxes" are used to enclose steps that may be performed mentally.

MATCHED PROBLEM 4

Use the functions in Example 4 to find

(A) $f(-2)$ (B) $g(6)$ (C) $h(-8)$ (D) $\frac{f(8)}{h(9)}$

EXAMPLE 5 Finding the Domain of a Function

Find the domain of $g(t) = 5 + 2t - 3t^2$.

SOLUTION

Because $5 + 2t - 3t^2$ represents a real number for all replacements of t by real numbers, the domain of g is R, the set of all real numbers. To express this domain in interval notation, we write

$$\text{Domain of } g = (-\infty, \infty)$$

MATCHED PROBLEM 5

Find the domain of $h(w) = 3w^2 + 2w - 9$.

The reasoning used in Example 5 can be applied to any polynomial: **The domain of any polynomial is *R*, the set of real numbers.** (We will study polynomials extensively in Chapter 3.)

EXAMPLE 6 Finding the Domain of a Function

Find the domain of $F(w) = \frac{5}{w^2 - 9}$.

SOLUTION

Because division by 0 is not defined, we must exclude all values of w that would make the denominator 0. Factoring the denominator, we can write

$$F(w) = \frac{5}{w^2 - 9} = \frac{5}{(w - 3)(w + 3)} \qquad a^2 - b^2 = (a - b)(a + b)$$

Thus, we see that $w = 3$ and $w = -3$ both make the denominator zero and must be excluded from the domain of F. That is,

$$\begin{aligned} \text{Domain of } F &= \{w \mid w \neq 3, w \neq -3\} && \text{Set notation} \\ &= (-\infty, -3) \cup (-3, 3) \cup (3, \infty) && \text{Interval notation} \end{aligned}$$

We often simplify this by writing

$$F(w) = \frac{5}{w^2 - 9} \qquad w \neq 3, w \neq -3$$

MATCHED PROBLEM 6

Find the domain of $G(w) = \dfrac{5}{w^2 - 1}$.

EXAMPLE 7 Finding the Domain of a Function

Find the domain of $s(x) = \sqrt{3 - x}$.

SOLUTIONS

Algebraic Solution

Because $\sqrt{3 - x}$ is not a real number when $3 - x$ is a negative real number, we must restrict the domain of s to the real numbers x for which $3 - x$ is nonnegative:

$$\begin{aligned} 3 - x &\geq 0 \\ 3 &\geq x \end{aligned}$$

Thus, we have

$$\begin{aligned} \text{Domain of } s &= \{x \mid x \leq 3\} \\ &= (-\infty, 3] \end{aligned}$$

or, more informally,

$$s(x) = \sqrt{3 - x} \qquad x \leq 3$$

Graphical Solution

Entering $y_1 = \sqrt{3 - x}$ in the equation editor and graphing in a standard viewing window produces Figure 3.

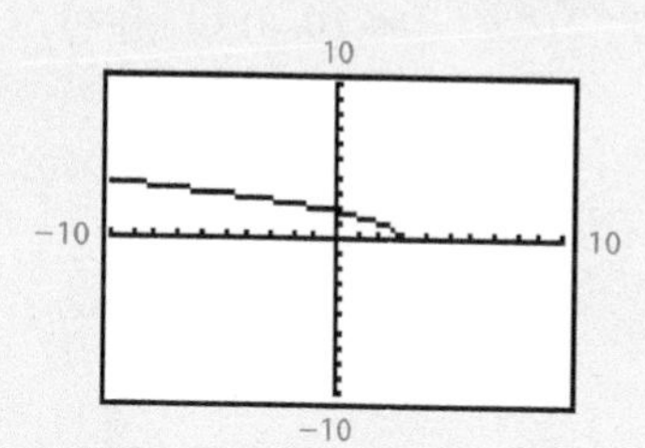

› Figure 3

Using a table (Fig. 4), we see that evaluating s at any number greater than 3 produces an error message, whereas evaluating s for large negative values produces no errors.

X	Y1
3	0
4	ERROR
3.5	ERROR
3.0001	ERROR
-1000	31.67
-10000	100.01
-1E6	1000

Y1=√(3−X)

› Figure 4

We conclude that the domain of s is $(-\infty, 3]$.

MATCHED PROBLEM 7

Find the domain of $r(t) = \sqrt{t - 5}$.

EXAMPLE 8 Finding the Domain of a Function

Find the domain of $f(x) = \dfrac{2}{2 - \sqrt{x}}$.

SOLUTIONS

Algebraic Solution

Because $\sqrt{x}$ is not a real number for negative real numbers x, x must be a nonnegative real number. Because division by 0 is not defined, we must exclude any values of x that make the denominator 0. To find x values that make the denominator zero, we solve

$$\begin{aligned} 2 - \sqrt{x} &= 0 \\ 2 &= \sqrt{x} \\ 4 &= x \end{aligned}$$

and conclude that the domain of f is all nonnegative real numbers except 4. This can be written as

$$\begin{aligned} \text{Domain of } f &= \{x \mid x \geq 0, x \neq 4\} \\ &= [0, 4) \cup (4, \infty) \end{aligned}$$

Graphical Solution

Figure 5 shows the graph of $y = 2/(2 - \sqrt{x})$ in a standard viewing window.

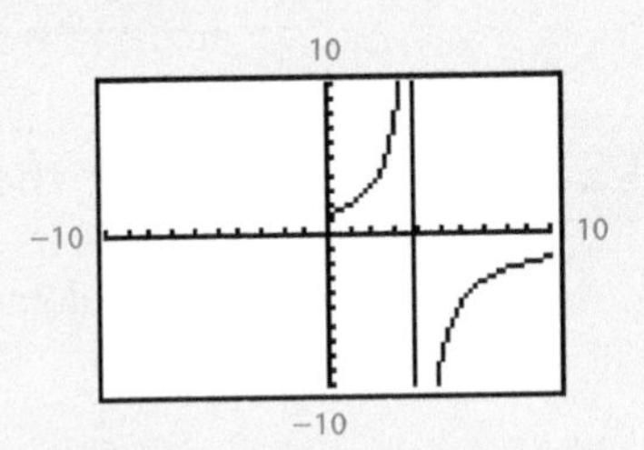

› Figure 5

The curve appears to start at $x = 0$, indicating that f is not defined for $x < 0$. Evaluating f at a small negative number confirms this (Fig. 6). The vertical line on the graph indicates some strange behavior at $x = 4$. Evaluating f at $x = 4$ (Fig. 6) shows that f is not defined at $x = 4$. Evaluating f at large positive numbers produces no errors.

X	Y1
-1E-4	ERROR
0	1
4	ERROR
100	-.25
1000	-.0675
100000	-.0064
1E7	-6E-4

Y1=2/(2−√(X))

› Figure 6

We conclude that

$$\begin{aligned} \text{Domain of } f &= \{x \mid x \geq 0, x \neq 4\} \\ &= [0, 4) \cup (4, \infty) \end{aligned}$$

MATCHED PROBLEM 8

Find the domain of $g(x) = \dfrac{1}{\sqrt{x} - 1}$.

Refer to Figure 5. What do you think caused the break in this graph? Explore-Discuss 3 will help you find out.

››› EXPLORE-DISCUSS 3

Graph $y = 2/(2 - \sqrt{x})$ in a standard viewing window (see Fig. 5).

(A) Press TRACE and move the cursor as close to $x = 4$ on the left side of 4 as possible. What is the y coordinate of this point?

(B) Now move the cursor as close to $x = 4$ on the right side of 4 as possible. What is the y coordinate of this point?

(C) Change Ymax to a value greater than the y coordinate in (A) and Ymin to a value less than the y coordinate in (B).

(D) Redraw the graph in the window from part (C) and discuss the result.

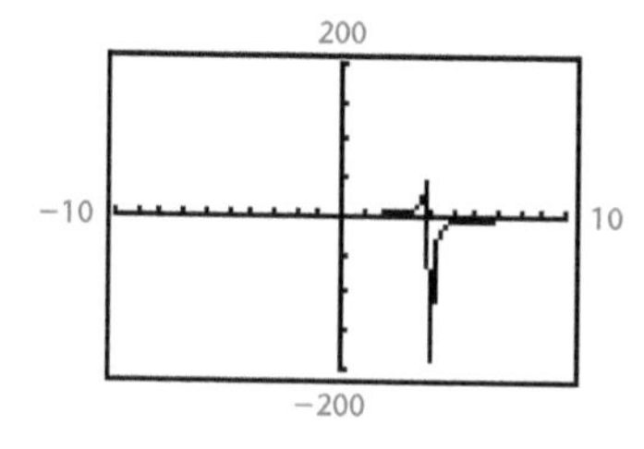

› **Figure 7**

Depending on the model of graphing calculator you have, your efforts in Explore-Discuss 3 may have produced a graph similar to Figure 7. The nearly vertical line is produced by connecting the last point on the left of $x = 4$ with the first point on the right of $x = 4$.

In addition to evaluating functions at specific numbers, it is important to be able to evaluate functions at expressions that involve one or more variables. For example, the **difference quotient**

$$\frac{f(x + h) - f(x)}{h} \qquad \text{for } x \text{ and } x + h \text{ in the domain of } f,\ h \neq 0$$

is studied extensively in a calculus course.

››› EXPLORE-DISCUSS 4

Let x and h be any real numbers.

(A) If $f(x) = 3x + 2$, which of the following is correct?

(i) $f(x + h) = 3x + 2 + h$

(ii) $f(x + h) = 3x + 3h + 2$

(iii) $f(x + h) = 3x + 3h + 4$

(B) If $f(x) = x^2$, which of the following is correct?

(i) $f(x + h) = x^2 + h^2$

(ii) $f(x + h) = x^2 + h$

(iii) $f(x + h) = x^2 + 2xh + h^2$

(C) If $f(x) = x^2 + 3x + 2$, write a verbal description of the operations that must be performed to evaluate $f(x + h)$.

EXAMPLE 9 Evaluating and Simplifying a Difference Quotient

For $f(x) = x^2 + 4x + 5$, find and simplify:*

(A) $f(2)$ (B) $f(2 + h)$ (C) $\dfrac{f(2 + h) - f(2)}{h}$

(D) $f(x + h)$ (E) $\dfrac{f(x + h) - f(x)}{h}$

SOLUTIONS

(A) $f(2) = 2^2 + 4(2) + 5 = 17$

(B) To find $f(2 + h)$, replace x with $2 + h$ everywhere it occurs in the equation that defines f, then simplify:

$$\begin{aligned} f(2 + h) &= (2 + h)^2 + 4(2 + h) + 5 \\ &= 4 + 4h + h^2 + 8 + 4h + 5 \\ &= h^2 + 8h + 17 \end{aligned}$$

(C) Using parts (A) and (B), we have

$$\frac{f(2 + h) - f(2)}{h} = \frac{\overbrace{(h^2 + 8h + 17)}^{f(2+h)} - \overbrace{(17)}^{f(2)}}{h}$$

$$= \frac{h^2 + 8h}{h} = \frac{h(h + 8)}{h} = h + 8$$

(D) To find $f(x + h)$, we replace x with $x + h$ everywhere it appears in the equation that defines f and simplify:

$$\begin{aligned} f(x + h) &= (x + h)^2 + 4(x + h) + 5 \\ &= x^2 + 2xh + h^2 + 4x + 4h + 5 \end{aligned}$$

(E) Using the result of part (D), we get

$$\frac{f(x + h) - f(x)}{h} = \frac{\overbrace{(x^2 + 2xh + h^2 + 4x + 4h + 5)}^{f(x+h)} - \overbrace{(x^2 + 4x + 5)}^{f(x)}}{h}$$

$$= \frac{x^2 + 2xh + h^2 + 4x + 4h + 5 - x^2 - 4x - 5}{h}$$

$$= \frac{2xh + h^2 + 4h}{h} = \frac{h(2x + h + 4)}{h} = 2x + h + 4$$

MATCHED PROBLEM 9

Repeat Example 9 for $f(x) = x^2 + 3x + 7$.

*The symbol [calculus icon] denotes problems that are related to calculus.

››› CAUTION ›››

1. If f is a function, then the symbol $f(x + h)$ represents the value of f at the number $x + h$ and must be evaluated by replacing the independent variable in the equation that defines f with the expression $x + h$, as we did in Example 9. Do not confuse this notation with the familiar algebraic notation for multiplication:

$$f(x + h) \neq fx + fh \qquad f(x + h) \text{ is function notation.}$$
$$4(x + h) = 4x + 4h \qquad 4(x + h) \text{ is algebraic multiplication notation.}$$

2. There is another common incorrect interpretation of the symbol $f(x + h)$. If f is an arbitrary function, then

$$f(x + h) \neq f(x) + f(h)$$

It is possible to find some particular functions for which $f(x + h) = f(x) + f(h)$ is a true statement, but in general these two expressions are not equal.

3. Finally, note that even though both may be read aloud as "f of x plus h," $f(x + h)$ is *not* the same as $f(x) + h$. (See Explore-Discuss 4.)

› Modeling and Data Analysis

The next example explores the relationship between the *algebraic* definition of a function, the *numeric* values of the function, and a *graphical* representation of the function. The interplay between the algebraic, numeric, and graphical aspects of a function is one of the central themes of this book. In this example, we also see how a function can be used to describe data from the real world, a process that we referred to in Section 1-1 as mathematical modeling.

EXAMPLE 10 Consumer Debt

Revolving-credit debt (in billions of dollars) in the United States over a 25-year period is given in Table 3. A financial analyst used statistical techniques to produce a mathematical model for this data:

$$f(x) = 0.7x^2 + 14.6x + 45.9$$

where $x = 0$ corresponds to 1980.

Table 3 Revolving-Credit Debt

Year	Total Debt (Billions)
1980	$58.5
1985	$128.9
1990	$234.8
1995	$443.2
2000	$663.8
2005	$848.3

Source: Federal Reserve System.

Compare the data and the model both numerically and graphically. Use the modeling function f to estimate the debt to the nearest tenth of a billion in 2006 and in 2010.

SOLUTION

Most graphing calculators have the ability to manipulate a list of numbers, such as the total debt in Table 3. The relevant commands are usually found by pressing STAT* (Fig. 8). Then select EDIT and enter the data. Enter the years as L1 and the debt as L2 (Fig. 9). Unlike the TABLE command, which computes a y value for each x value you enter, the EDIT command does not assume any correspondence between the numbers in two different lists. It is your responsibility to make sure that each pair on the same line in Figure 9 corresponds to a line in Table 3.

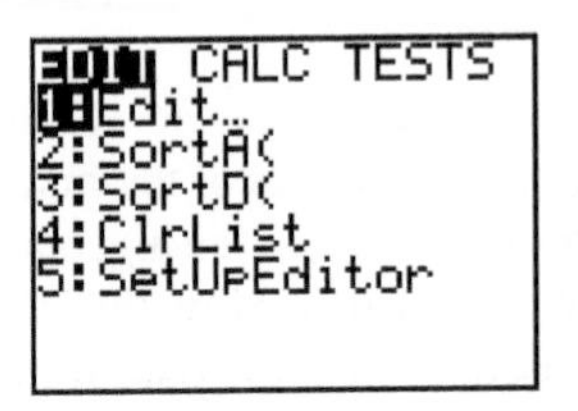

› Figure 8

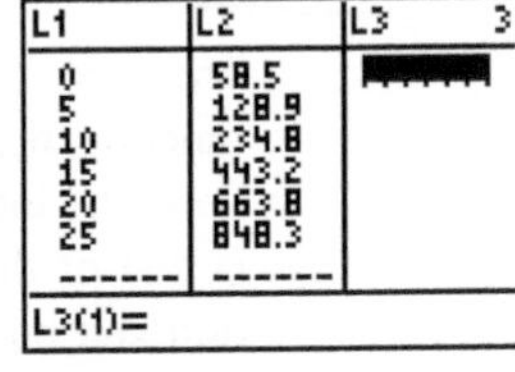

› Figure 9

A graph of a finite data set is called a **scatter plot.** To form a scatter plot for the data in Table 3, first press STAT PLOT (Fig. 10) and select Plot1 (Fig. 11). The Plot1 screen contains a number of options, some of which you select by placing the cursor over the option and pressing ENTER. First, select ON to activate the plot. Then select the type of plot you want. The darkened choice in Figure 11 produces a scatter plot. Next use the 2nd key to enter L1 for the Xlist and L2 for the Ylist. Finally, select the mark you want to use for the plot.

Before graphing the data, we must enter values for the window variables that will produce a window that contains the points in the scatter plot. Examining the data in Figure 9, we see that Xmin $= -5$, Xmax $= 30$, Xscl $= 5$, Ymin $= 0$, Ymax $= 1000$, and Yscl $= 100$ should provide a viewing window that contains all of these points.

*We used a TI-84 to produce the screen shots in this section. If you are using a different graphing calculator, consult your manual for the appropriate commands.

(We chose Xmin = −5 to clearly show the point at $x = 0$.) Pressing GRAPH displays the scatter plot (Fig. 12).

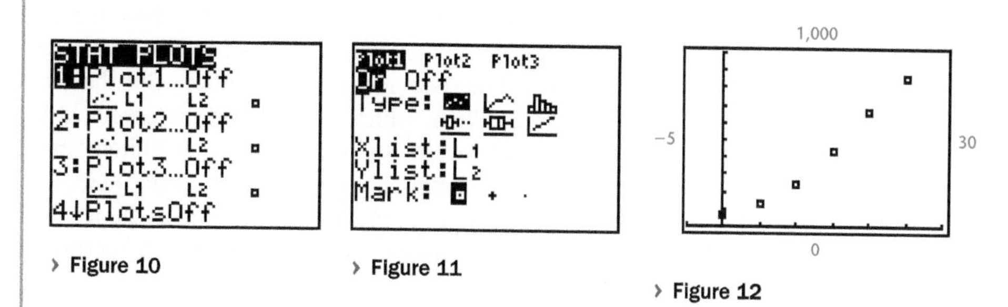

› Figure 10 › Figure 11 › Figure 12

Now we enter the modeling function in the equation editor (Fig. 13) and use the TABLE command to evaluate the function (Fig. 14). To compare the data and the function numerically, we enter the data from Figure 9 and the values from Figure 14 in Table 4. To compare them graphically, we press GRAPH to graph both the model and the scatter plot (Fig. 15).

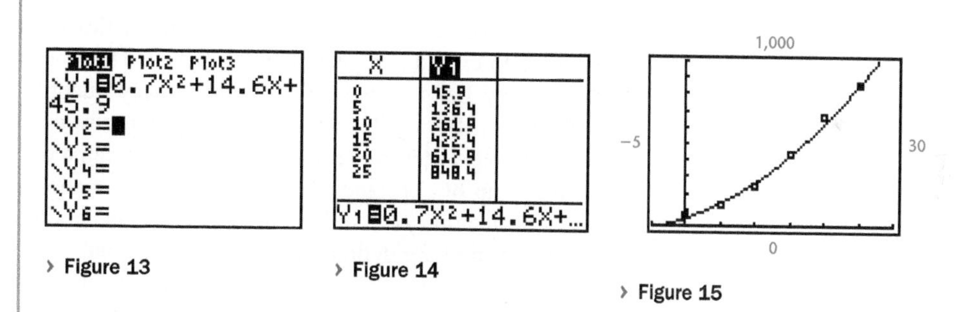

› Figure 13 › Figure 14 › Figure 15

Table 4

x	0	5	10	15	20	25
Debt	58.5	128.9	234.8	443.2	663.8	848.3
$f(x)$	45.9	136.4	261.9	422.4	617.9	848.4

To estimate the debt in 2006 and 2010, we evaluate $f(x)$ at 26 and 30.

$$f(26) = 898.7 \qquad f(30) = 1{,}113.9$$

So the revolving-credit debt should be \$898.7 billion in 2006 and \$1,113.9 billion (or \$1.1139 trillion) in 2010.

Table 5

Year	Total Debt (Billions)
1980	44.1
1985	74.0
1990	91.6
1995	131.9
2000	184.4
2005	228.6

MATCHED PROBLEM 10

Credit union debt (in billions of dollars) in the United States is given in Table 5. Repeat Example 10 using these data and the modeling function

$$y = 0.15x^2 + 3.6x + 45.9$$

REMARKS:

1. Modeling functions like the function f in Example 10 provide reasonable and useful representations of the given data, but they don't always correctly predict future behavior. For example, the model in Example 10 indicates that the revolving-credit debt for 2006 should be about \$898.7 billion. But the actual debt for 2006 turned out to be \$875.2 billion, which differs from the predicted value by more than \$23 billion. (As the old government saying goes, "A billion here and a billion there, and pretty soon you're talking about some real money!") Getting the most out of mathematical modeling requires both an understanding of the techniques used to develop the model and frequent reevaluation, modification, and interpretation of the results produced by the model.
2. The tricky part in mathematical modeling is usually finding a function that models a given set of data. We will discuss methods for doing this in Chapter 2. It turns out that this is fairly easy to do with a graphing calculator.

› A Brief History of the Function Concept

The history of the use of functions in mathematics illustrates the tendency of mathematicians to extend and generalize a concept. The word *function* appears to have been first used by Leibniz in 1694 to stand for any quantity associated with a curve. By 1718, Johann Bernoulli considered a function any expression made up of constants and a variable. Later in the same century, Euler came to regard a function as any equation made up of constants and variables. Euler made extensive use of the extremely important notation $f(x)$, although its origin is generally attributed to Clairaut (1734).

The form of the definition of function that had been used until well into the twentieth century (many texts still contain this definition) was formulated by Dirichlet (1805–1859). He stated that, if two variables x and y are so related that for each value of x there corresponds exactly one value of y, then y is said to be a (single-valued) function of x. He called x, the variable to which values are assigned at will, the independent variable, and y, the variable whose values depend on the values assigned to x, the dependent variable. He called the values assumed by x the domain of the function, and the corresponding values assumed by y the range of the function.

Now, because set concepts permeate almost all mathematics, we have the more general definition of function presented in this section in terms of sets of ordered pairs of elements.

ANSWERS TO MATCHED PROBLEMS

1. (A) Domain $= \{-2, -1, 0\}$, Range $= \{0, 1, 2\}$; S is not a function.
(B) Domain $= \{-2, -1, 0, 1, 2\}$, Range $= \{0, 1, 2\}$; T is a function.
2. (A) No (B) Yes **3.** $x \le 0$ **4.** (A) -3 (B) -2 (C) Does not exist (D) 1
5. All real numbers or $(-\infty, \infty)$
6. All real numbers except -1 and 1 or $(-\infty, -1) \cup (-1, 1) \cup (1, \infty)$
7. $t \ge 5$ or $[5, \infty)$ **8.** $x \ge 0, x \ne 1$ or $[0, 1) \cup (1, \infty)$
9. (A) 17 (B) $h^2 + 7h + 17$ (C) $h + 7$ (D) $x^2 + 2xh + h^2 + 3x + 3h + 7$
(E) $2x + h + 3$

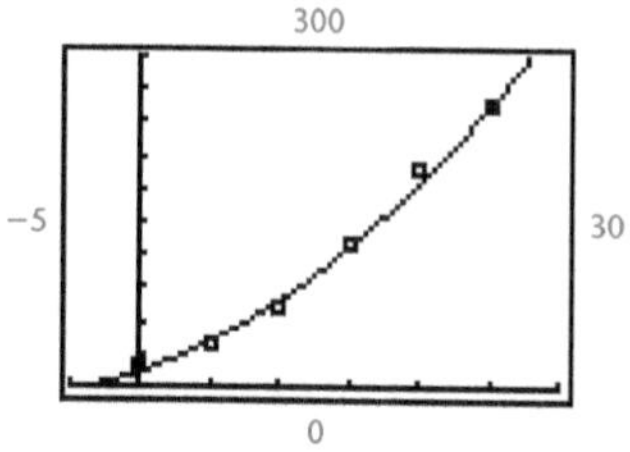

300

−5 30

0

10.

x	0	5	10	15	20	25
Debt	44.1	74.0	91.6	131.9	184.4	228.6
$f(x)$	45.9	67.7	97.2	134.2	178.7	230.8

The credit union debt should be \$242.1 billion in 2006, and \$290.4 billion in 2010.

1-2 Exercises

1. True or False: Every relation is a function. Explain your answer.

2. True or False: Every function is a relation. Explain your answer.

3. Explain the difference between $f(x + h)$ and $f(x) + h$.

4. Explain the difference between $f(x)$, where f represents a function, and $2(x)$.

Indicate whether each relation in Problems 5–10 defines a function, then write each as a set of ordered pairs.

5. Domain / Range

$-1 \to 3$
$0 \to 2$
$1 \to 1$

6. Domain / Range

$2 \to 1$
$4 \to 3$
$6 \to 5$

7. Domain / Range

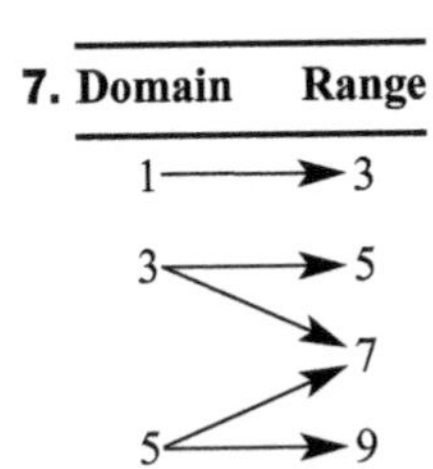

8. Domain / Range

$-1 \to 0$
$-1 \to 5$
$-2 \to 5$
$-3 \to 8$

9. Domain / Range

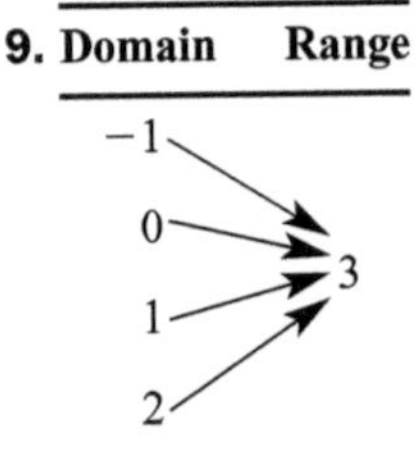

10. Domain / Range

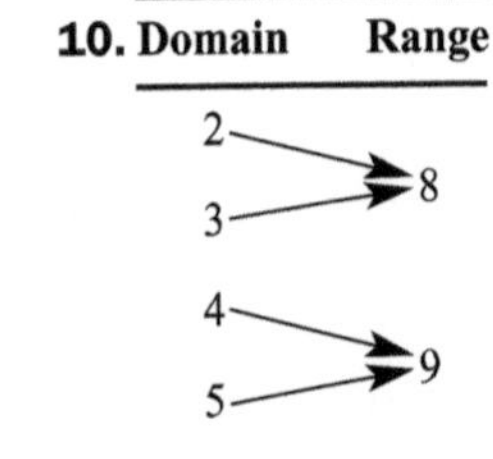

In Problems 11–16, write the domain and range of each relation, then indicate whether the relation defines a function.

11. $\{(2, 4), (3, 6), (4, 8), (5, 10)\}$

12. $\{(-1, 4), (0, 3), (1, 2), (2, 1)\}$

13. $\{(10, -10), (5, -5), (0, 0), (5, 5), (10, 10)\}$

14. $\{(-10, 10), (-5, 5), (0, 0), (5, 5), (10, 10)\}$

15. $\{(0, 1), (1, 1), (2, 1), (3, 2), (4, 2), (5, 2)\}$

16. $\{(1, 1), (2, 1), (3, 1), (1, 2), (2, 2), (3, 2)\}$

**Indicate whether each graph in Problems 17–22 is the graph of a function.*

17.

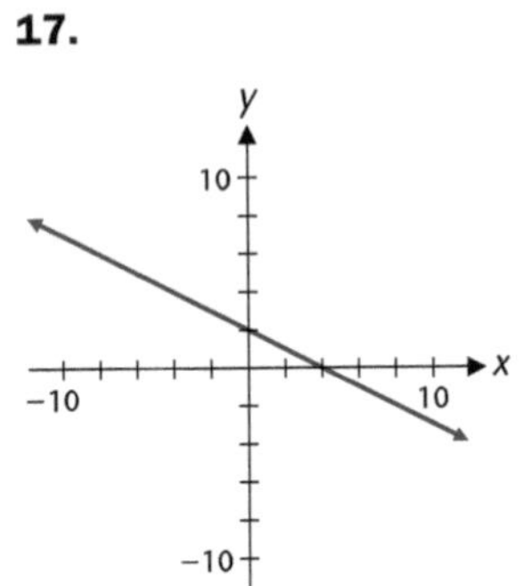

18.

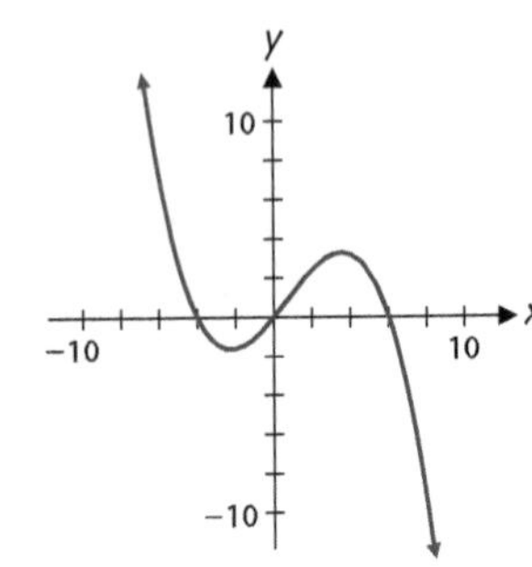

19.

y
10
x
−10
10
−10

20.

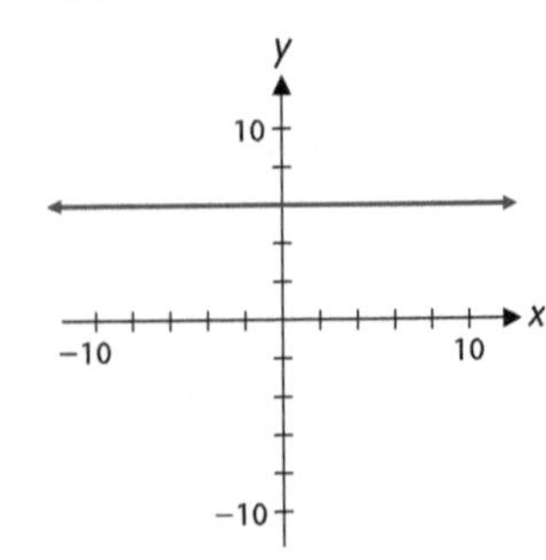

*The symbol denotes problems that require graphical interpretation.

21. **22.**

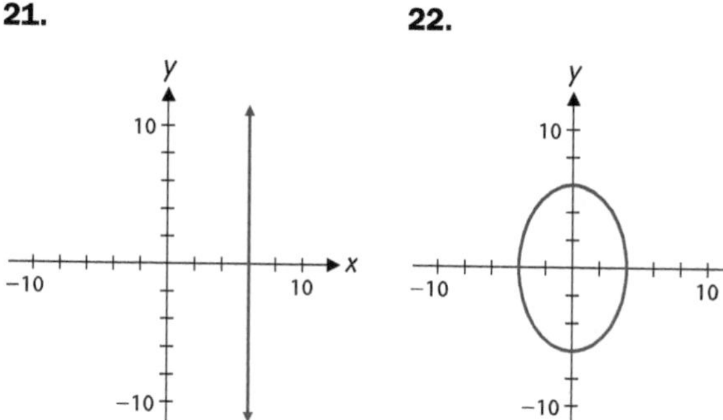

In Problems 23 and 24, which of the indicated correspondences define functions? Explain.

23. Let W be the set of residents of Wisconsin and let R and S be the set of members of the U.S. House of Representatives and the set of members of the U.S. Senate, respectively, elected by the residents of Wisconsin.

(A) A resident corresponds to the congressperson representing the resident's congressional district.

(B) A resident corresponds to the senators representing the resident's state.

24. Let P be the set of patients in a hospital and let D be the set of doctors and N the set of nurses, respectively, that are on the staff of the hospital.

(A) A patient corresponds to a doctor if that doctor admitted the patient to the hospital.

(B) A patient corresponds to a nurse if that nurse cares for the patient.

In Problems 25–28, determine if the indicated equation defines a function. Justify your answer.

25. $x + y = 4$ **26.** $x^2 + y = 4$

27. $x + y^2 = 4$ **28.** $x^2 + y^2 = 4$

Problems 29–40 refer to the functions

$f(x) = 3x - 5$ $g(t) = 4 - t$

$F(m) = 3m^2 + 2m - 4$ $G(u) = u - u^2$

Evaluate as indicated.

29. $f(-1)$ **30.** $g(6)$

31. $G(-2)$ **32.** $F(-3)$

33. $F(-1) + f(3)$ **34.** $G(2) - g(-3)$

35. $2F(-2) - G(-1)$ **36.** $3G(-2) + 2F(-1)$

37. $\dfrac{f(0) \cdot g(-2)}{F(-3)}$ **38.** $\dfrac{g(4) \cdot f(2)}{G(1)}$

39. $\dfrac{f(4) - f(2)}{2}$ **40.** $\dfrac{g(5) - g(3)}{2}$

In Problems 41–56, find the domain of the indicated function. Express answers informally using inequalities, then formally using interval notation.

41. $f(x) = 4 - 9x + 3x^2$ **42.** $g(x) = 1 + 7x - x^2$

43. $h(z) = \dfrac{2}{4 - z}$ **44.** $k(z) = \dfrac{z}{z - 3}$

45. $g(t) = \sqrt{t - 4}$ **46.** $h(t) = \sqrt{6 - t}$

47. $k(w) = \sqrt{7 + 3w}$ **48.** $j(w) = \sqrt{9 + 4w}$

49. $H(u) = \dfrac{u}{u^2 + 4}$ **50.** $G(u) = \dfrac{u}{u^2 - 4}$

51. $L(v) = \dfrac{v + 2}{v^2 - 16}$ **52.** $K(v) = \dfrac{v + 8}{v^2 + 16}$

53. $M(x) = \dfrac{\sqrt{x + 4}}{x - 1}$ **54.** $N(x) = \dfrac{\sqrt{x - 3}}{x + 2}$

55. $s(t) = \dfrac{1}{3 - \sqrt{t}}$ **56.** $r(t) = \dfrac{1}{\sqrt{t} - 4}$

In Problems 57–60, find a function f that makes all three equations true. [Hint: There may be more than one possible answer, but there is one obvious answer suggested by the pattern illustrated in the equations.]

57. $f(1) = 2(1) - 3$
$f(2) = 2(2) - 3$
$f(3) = 2(3) - 3$

58. $f(1) = 5(1)^2 - 6$
$f(2) = 5(2)^2 - 6$
$f(3) = 5(3)^2 - 6$

59. $f(1) = 4(1)^2 - 2(1) + 9$
$f(2) = 4(2)^2 - 2(2) + 9$
$f(3) = 4(3)^2 - 2(3) + 9$

60. $f(1) = -8 + 5(1) - 2(1)^2$
$f(2) = -8 + 5(2) - 2(2)^2$
$f(3) = -8 + 5(3) - 2(3)^2$

61. If $F(s) = 3s + 15$, find $\dfrac{F(2 + h) - F(2)}{h}$.

62. If $K(r) = 7 - 4r$, find $\dfrac{K(1 + h) - K(1)}{h}$.

63. If $g(x) = 2 - x^2$, find $\dfrac{g(3 + h) - g(3)}{h}$.

64. If $P(m) = 2m^2 + 3$, find $\dfrac{P(2 + h) - P(2)}{h}$.

65. If $L(w) = -2w^2 + 3w - 1$, find $\dfrac{L(-2 + h) - L(-2)}{h}$.

66. If $D(p) = -3p^2 - 4p + 9$, find $\dfrac{D(-1 + h) - D(-1)}{h}$.

The verbal statement "function f multiplies the square root of the domain element by 2 and then subtracts 5" and the algebraic statement $f(x) = 2\sqrt{x} - 5$ define the same function. In Problems 67–70, translate each verbal definition of the function into an algebraic definition.

67. Function g multiplies the domain element by 3 and then adds 1.

68. Function f multiplies the domain element by 7 and then adds the product of 5 and the cube of the domain element.

69. Function F divides the domain element by the sum of 8 and the square root of the domain element.

70. Function G takes the square root of the sum of 4 and the square of the domain element.

In Problems 71–74, translate each algebraic definition of the function into a verbal definition.

71. $f(x) = 2x - 3x^2$ **72.** $g(x) = 5x^3 - 8x$

73. $F(x) = \sqrt{x^4 + 9}$ **74.** $G(x) = \dfrac{x}{3x - 6}$

In Problems 75–78, use the given information to write a verbal description of the function f and then find the equation for f(x).

75. $f(x + h) = 2(x + h)^2 - 4(x + h) + 6$

76. $f(x + h) = -7(x + h)^2 + 8(x + h) + 5$

77. $f(x + h) = 4(x + h) - 3\sqrt{x + h} + 9$

78. $f(x + h) = 2\sqrt[3]{x + h} - 6(x + h) - 5$

In Problems 79–86, for each given function f find and simplify:

(A) $\dfrac{f(x + h) - f(x)}{h}$ (B) $\dfrac{f(x) - f(a)}{x - a}$

79. $f(x) = 3x - 4$ **80.** $f(x) = -2x + 5$

81. $f(x) = x^2 - 1$ **82.** $f(x) = x^2 + x - 1$

83. $f(x) = -3x^2 + 9x - 12$ **84.** $f(x) = -x^2 - 2x - 4$

85. $f(x) = x^3$ **86.** $f(x) = x^3 + x$

In Problems 87 and 88, the domain of the function f is all real numbers x except x = 1. Describe the behavior of f for x values very close to 1, but not equal to 1. Support your conclusions with information obtained by exploring the graph of f near x = 1, by examining the numerical values of f near x = 1, and by algebraically simplifying the expression used to define f.

87. $f(x) = \dfrac{x^2 - 1}{x - 1}$ **88.** $f(x) = \dfrac{x^3 - 1}{x - 1}$

APPLICATIONS

89. BOILING POINT OF WATER At sea level, water boils when it reaches a temperature of 212°F. At higher altitudes, the atmospheric pressure is lower and so is the temperature at which water boils. The boiling point $B(x)$ in degrees Fahrenheit at an altitude of x feet is given approximately by

$$B(x) = 212 - 0.0018x$$

(A) Complete the following table.

x	0	5,000	10,000	15,000	20,000	25,000	30,000
$B(x)$							

(B) Based on the information in the table, write a brief verbal description of the relationship between altitude and the boiling point of water.

90. AIR TEMPERATURE As dry air moves upward, it expands and cools. The air temperature $A(x)$ in degrees Celsius at an altitude of x kilometers is given approximately by

$$A(x) = 25 - 9x$$

(A) Complete the following table.

x	0	1	2	3	4	5
$A(x)$						

(B) Based on the information in the table, write a brief verbal description of the relationship between altitude and air temperature.

91. PHYSICS—RATE The distance in feet that an object falls in the absence of air resistance is given by $s(t) = 16t^2$, where t is time in seconds.

(A) Find $s(0)$, $s(1)$, $s(2)$, and $s(3)$.

(B) Find and simplify $\dfrac{s(2 + h) - s(2)}{h}$.

(C) Evaluate the expression in part B for $h = \pm 1, \pm 0.1, \pm 0.01, \pm 0.001$.

(D) What happens in part C as h gets closer and closer to 0? What do you think this tells us about the motion of the object? [*Hint:* Think about what each of the numerator and denominator represents.]

92. PHYSICS—RATE An automobile starts from rest and travels along a straight and level road. The distance in feet traveled by the automobile is given by $s(t) = 10t^2$, where t is time in seconds.
(A) Find $s(8)$, $s(9)$, $s(10)$, and $s(11)$.
(B) Find and simplify $\frac{s(11 + h) - s(11)}{h}$.
(C) Evaluate the expression in part B for $h = \pm1, \pm0.1, \pm0.01, \pm0.001$.
(D) What happens in part C as h gets closer and closer to 0? What do you think this tells us about the motion of the object? [*Hint:* Think about what each of the numerator and denominator represents.]

93. CAR RENTAL A car rental agency computes daily rental charges for compact cars with the function

$$D(x) = 20 + 0.25x$$

where $D(x)$ is the daily charge in dollars and x is the daily mileage. Translate this algebraic statement into a verbal statement that can be used to explain the daily charges to a customer.

94. INSTALLATION CHARGES A telephone store computes charges for phone installation with the function

$$S(x) = 15 + 0.7x$$

where $S(x)$ is the installation charge in dollars and x is the time in minutes spent performing the installation. Translate this algebraic statement into a verbal statement that can be used to explain the installation charges to a customer.

MODELING AND DATA ANALYSIS

Table 6 contains the average price of admission (in dollars) to a motion picture and the total box office gross (in millions of dollars) for all theaters in the United States.

Table 6 Selected Financial Data for the Motion Picture Industry

Year	1997	1999	2001	2003	2005
Average Price of Admission ($)	4.59	5.08	5.66	6.03	6.41
Box Office Gross ($ in millions)	6,360	7,450	8,410	9,490	8,990

95. DATA ANALYSIS A mathematical model for the average price of admission to a motion picture is

$$A(t) = 0.23t + 4.6$$

where t represents time in years and $t = 0$ corresponds to 1997.
(A) Compare the model and the data graphically and algebraically.
(B) Estimate (to the nearest cent) the average price of admission in 2006 and 2007.

96. REVENUE ANALYSIS A mathematical model for the total box office gross is given by

$$G(t) = -54.6t^2 + 802t + 6240$$

where t represents time in years and $t = 0$ corresponds to 1997.
(A) Compare the model and the data graphically and algebraically.
(B) Estimate (to three significant digits) the total box office gross in 2006 and 2007.

Merck & Co., Inc. is the world's largest pharmaceutical company. Problems 97–100 refer to the data in Table 7 taken from the company's 2005 annual report.

Table 7 Selected Financial Data for Merck & Co., Inc.

($ in Billions)	1997	1999	2001	2003	2005
Sales	14.0	17.3	21.2	22.5	22.0
R & D Expenses	1.7	2.1	2.5	3.2	3.8
Net Income	4.6	5.9	7.3	6.8	4.6

97. SALES ANALYSIS A mathematical model for Merck's sales is given by

$$S(t) = -0.18t^2 + 2.5t + 14$$

where t is time in years and $t = 0$ corresponds to 1997.
(A) Compare the model and the data graphically and numerically.
(B) Estimate (to two significant digits) Merck's sales in 2006 and in 2008.
(C) Write a brief verbal description of Merck's sales from 1997 to 2005.

98. INCOME ANALYSIS A mathematical model for Merck's net income is given by

$$I(t) = -0.16t^2 + 1.3t + 4.4$$

where t is time in years and $t = 0$ corresponds to 1997.
(A) Compare the model and the data graphically and numerically.
(B) Estimate (to two significant digits) Merck's net income in 2006 and in 2008.
(C) Write a brief verbal description of Merck's net income from 1997 to 2005.

99. RESEARCH AND DEVELOPMENT ANALYSIS A mathematical model for Merck's sales as a function of research and development (R & D) expenses is given by

$$S(r) = -3.54r^2 + 23.3r - 15.5$$

where r represents R & D expenditures.
(A) Compare the model and the data graphically and numerically.
(B) Estimate (to two significant digits) Merck's sales if the company spends \$1.2 billion on research and development and if the company spends \$4.2 billion.

100. RESEARCH AND DEVELOPMENT ANALYSIS A mathematical model for Merck's net income as a function of R & D expenses is given by

$$I(r) = -2.47r^2 + 13.7r - 11.6$$

where r represents R & D expenditures.
(A) Compare the model and the data graphically and numerically.
(B) Estimate (to two significant digits) Merck's net income if the company spends \$1.2 billion on research and development and if the company spends \$4.2 billion.

1-3 Functions: Graphs and Properties

One of the key goals of this course is to provide you with a set of mathematical tools that can be used to analyze graphs. In many cases, these graphs will arise naturally from real-world situations. In fact, studying functions by analyzing their graphs is one of the biggest reasons that a graphing calculator is useful. In this section, we will discuss some basic concepts that are commonly used to describe graphs of functions.

Basic Concepts

In the previous section, we saw that one way to describe a function is in terms of ordered pairs. Based on your earlier experience with graphing, this definition of function may have reminded you of points on a graph, which are also described with an ordered pair of numbers. This simple connection between graphs and functions is the basis for the study of graphs of functions.

Every function that has a real-number domain and range has a graph, which is simply a pictorial representation of the ordered pairs of real numbers that make up the function. When functions are graphed, domain values are usually associated with the horizontal axis and range values with the vertical axis. In this regard, the **graph of a function** f is the same as the graph of the equation $y = f(x)$, where x is the independent variable and the first coordinate, or **abscissa,** of a point on the graph of f. The variables y and $f(x)$ can both be used to represent the dependent variable, and either one is the second coordinate, or **ordinate,** of a point on the graph of f (Fig. 1).

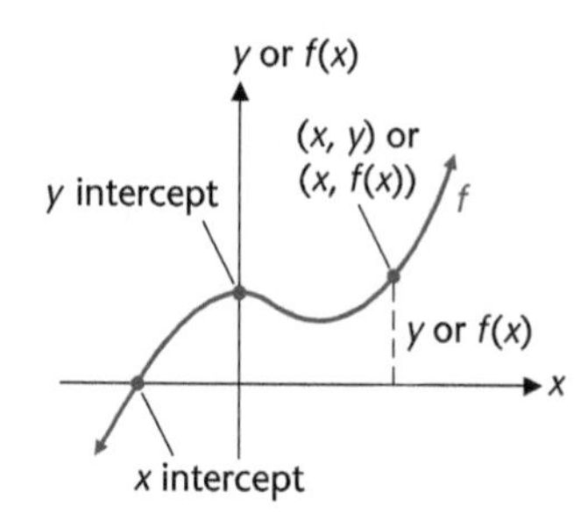

Figure 1 Graph of a function.

To reflect this typical usage of variables x and y, we often refer to the abscissa of a point as the ***x* coordinate,** and the ordinate as the ***y* coordinate.**

An x coordinate of a point where the graph of a function intersects the x axis is called an ***x* intercept** of the function.

Since the height of the graph, and consequently the value of the function, at such a point is zero, the x intercepts are often referred to as **real zeros** of the function. They are also solutions or **roots** of the equation $f(x) = 0$.

The y coordinate of a point where the graph of a function crosses the y axis is called the ***y* intercept** of the function. The y intercept is given by $f(0)$, provided 0 is in the domain of f. Note that a function can have more than one x intercept but can never have more than one y intercept—otherwise it would fail the vertical line test discussed in the last section and consequently fail to be a function.

In the first section of this chapter, we solved equations of the form $f(x) = c$ with a graphing calculator by graphing both sides of the equation and using the INTERSECT command. Most graphing calculators also have a **ZERO** or **ROOT** command that finds the x intercepts of a function directly from the graph of the function. Example 1 illustrates the use of this command.

EXAMPLE 1 Finding *x* and *y* Intercepts

Find the x and y intercepts (correct to three decimal places) of $f(x) = x^3 + x - 4$.

SOLUTION

The y intercept occurs at the point where $x = 0$, and from the graph of f in Figure 2, we see that it is $f(0) = -4$. We also see that there appears to be an x intercept between $x = 1$ and $x = 2$. We will use the ZERO command to find this intercept. First we are asked to select a **left bound** (Fig. 3). This is a value of x to the left of the x intercept. Next we are asked to find a **right bound** (Fig. 4). This is a value of x to the right of the x intercept. If a function has more than one x intercept, you should select the left and right bounds so that there is only one intercept between the bounds.

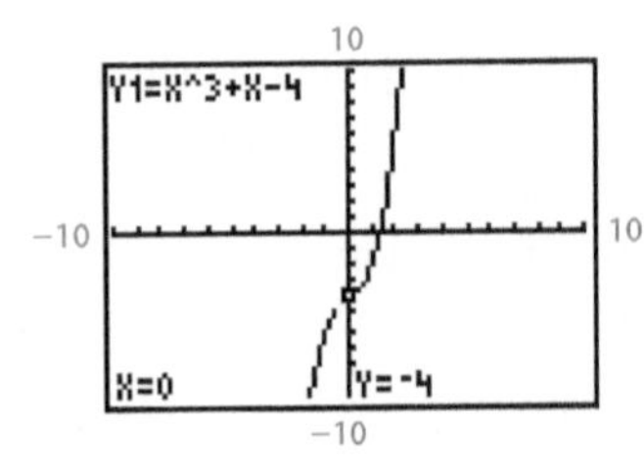

› Figure 2

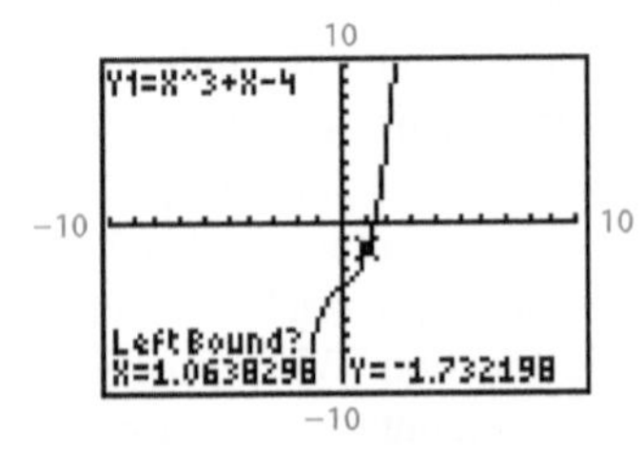

› Figure 3

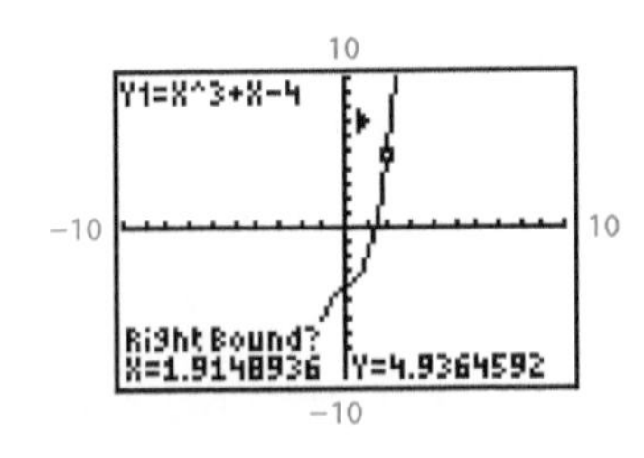

› Figure 4

Finally, we are asked to select a **guess.** The guess must be between the bounds and should be close to the intercept (Fig. 5). Figure 6 shows that the x intercept (to three decimal places) is 1.379.

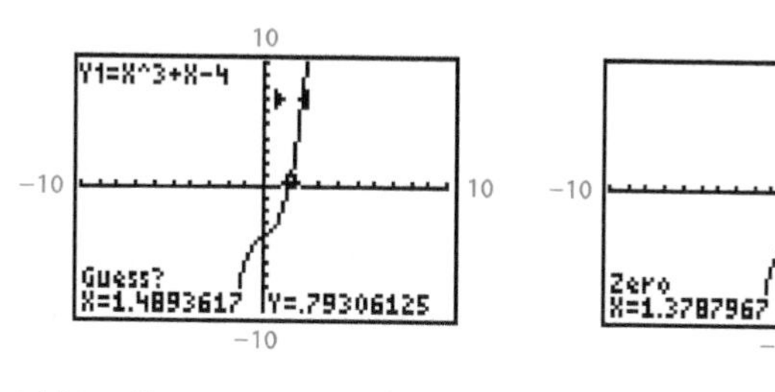

› Figure 5 › Figure 6

MATCHED PROBLEM 1

Find the x and y intercepts (correct to three decimal places) of $f(x) = x^3 + x + 5$.

››› EXPLORE-DISCUSS 1

Let $f(x) = x^2 - 2x - 5$.

(A) Use the ZERO command on a graphing calculator to find the x intercepts of f.

(B) Find all solutions to the equation $x^2 - 2x - 5 = 0$.

(C) Discuss the differences between the graph of f, the x intercepts, and the solutions to the equation $f(x) = 0$.

The domain of a function is the set of all the x coordinates of points on the graph of the function and the range is the set of all the y coordinates. It is very useful to view the domain and range as subsets of the coordinate axes as in Figure 7. Note the effective use of interval notation* in describing the domain and range of the functions in this figure. In Figure 7(a) a solid dot is used to indicate that a point is on the graph of the function and in Figure 7(b) an open dot to indicate that

*Interval notation is reviewed in Appendix B, Section B-1.

a point is not on the graph of the function. An open or solid dot at the end of a graph indicates that the graph terminates there, whereas an arrowhead indicates that the graph continues indefinitely beyond the portion shown with no significant changes of direction [see Fig. 7(b) and note that the arrowhead indicates that the domain extends infinitely far to the right, and the range extends infinitely far downward].

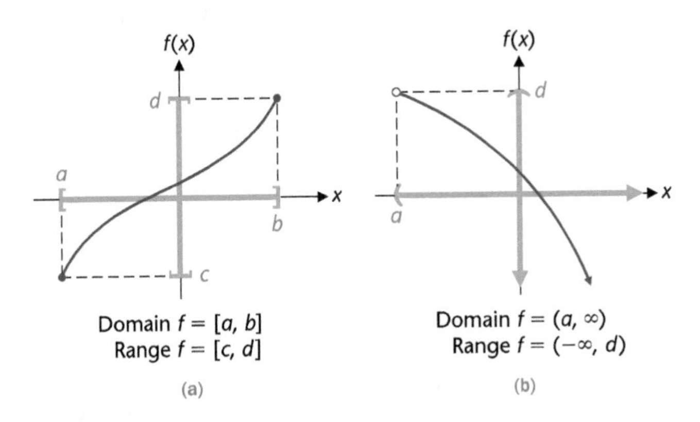

› **Figure 7** Domain and range.

EXAMPLE 2

Finding the Domain and Range from a Graph

(A) Find the domain and range of the function f whose graph is shown in Figure 8.

(B) Find $f(1)$, $f(3)$, and $f(5)$.

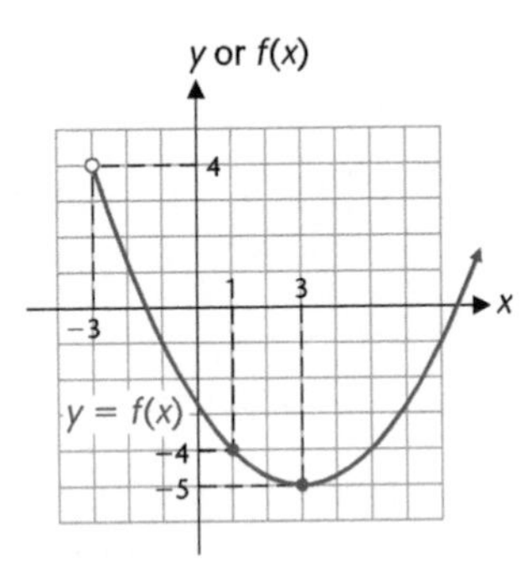

› **Figure 8**

SOLUTIONS

(A) The dot at the left end of the graph indicates that the graph terminates at that point, while the arrowhead on the right end indicates that the graph continues infinitely far to the right. So the x coordinates on the graph go from -3 to ∞. The open dot at $(-3, 4)$ indicates that -3 is not in the domain of f.

$$\text{Domain: } -3 < x < \infty \quad \text{or} \quad (-3, \infty)$$

The least y coordinate on the graph is -5, and there is no greatest y coordinate. (The arrowhead tells us that the graph continues infinitely far upward.) The closed dot at $(3, -5)$ indicates that -5 is in the range of f.

$$\text{Range: } -5 \leq y < \infty \quad \text{or} \quad [-5, \infty)$$

(B) The point on the graph with x coordinate 1 is $(1, -4)$, so $f(1) = -4$. Likewise, $(3, -5)$ and $(5, -4)$ are on the graph, so $f(3) = -5$ and $f(5) = -4$.

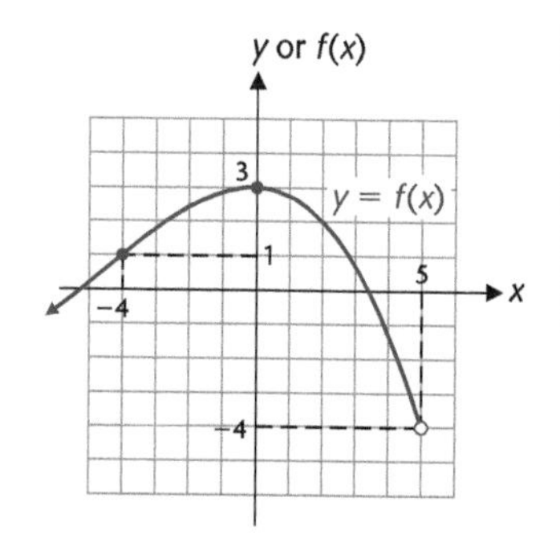

› Figure 9

MATCHED PROBLEM 2

(A) Find the domain and range of the function f given by the graph in Figure 9.

(B) Find $f(-4)$, $f(0)$, and $f(2)$.

››› CAUTION ›››

When using interval notation to describe domain and range, make sure that you always write the least number first! You should find the domain by working left to right along the x axis, and find the range by working bottom to top along the y axis.

› Identifying Increasing and Decreasing Functions

››› EXPLORE-DISCUSS 2

Graph each function in the standard viewing window, then write a verbal description of the behavior exhibited by the graph as x moves from left to right.

(A) $f(x) = 2 - x$ **(B)** $f(x) = x^3$

(C) $f(x) = 5$ **(D)** $f(x) = 9 - x^2$

We will now take a look at *increasing* and *decreasing* properties of functions. Informally, a function is increasing over an interval if its graph rises as the x coordinate increases (moves from left to right) over that interval. A function is decreasing over an interval if its graph falls as the x coordinate increases over that interval. A function is *constant* on an interval if its graph is horizontal over that interval (Fig. 10).

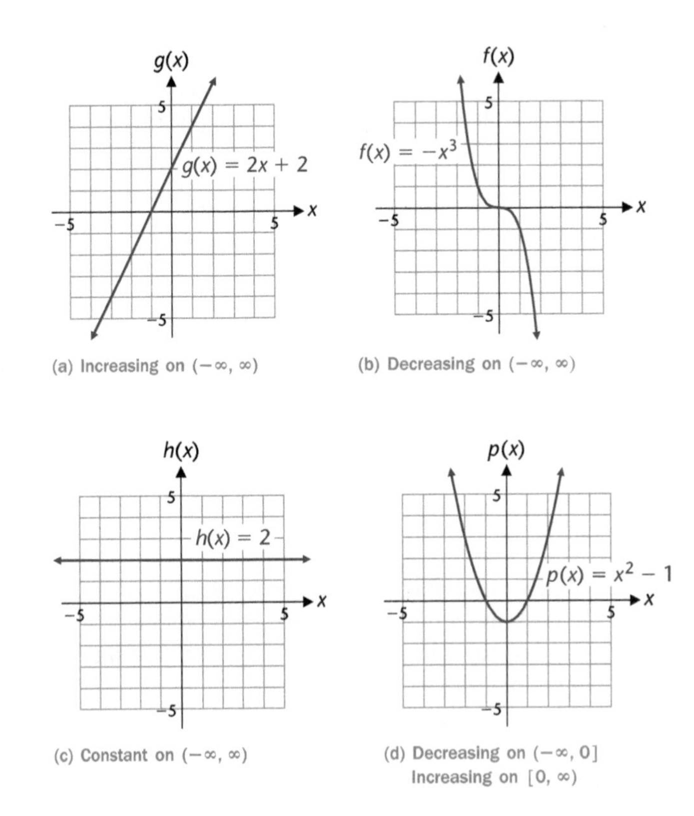

(a) Increasing on $(-\infty, \infty)$

(b) Decreasing on $(-\infty, \infty)$

(c) Constant on $(-\infty, \infty)$

(d) Decreasing on $(-\infty, 0]$
Increasing on $[0, \infty)$

Figure 10 Increasing, decreasing, and constant functions.

More formally, we define increasing, decreasing, and constant functions as follows:

DEFINITION 1 Increasing, Decreasing, and Constant Functions

Let I be an interval in the domain of function f. Then,

1. f is **increasing** on I and the graph of f is **rising** on I if $f(a) < f(b)$ whenever $a < b$ in I.
2. f is **decreasing** on I and the graph of f is **falling** on I if $f(a) > f(b)$ whenever $a < b$ in I.
3. f is **constant** on I and the graph of f is **horizontal** on I if $f(a) = f(b)$ whenever $a < b$ in I.

Refer to Figure 10(a) on page 51. As x moves from left to right, the values of g increase and the graph of g rises. In Figure 10(b), as x moves from left to right, the values of f decrease and the graph of f falls.

In Figure 10(c), the value of f doesn't change (remains constant), and the graph stays at the same height. In Figure 10(d), moving from left to right, the graph falls as x increases from $-\infty$ to 0, then rises from 0 to ∞.

EXAMPLE 3 Describing a Graph

The graph of

$$f(x) = x^3 - 12x + 4$$

is shown in Figure 11. Use the terms *increasing, decreasing, rising,* and *falling* to write a verbal description of this graph.

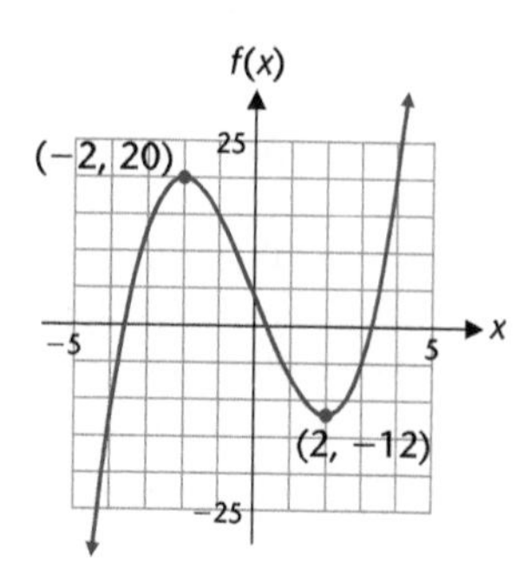

› **Figure 11** $f(x) = x^3 - 12x + 4$.

SOLUTION

The values of f increase and the graph of f rises as x increases from $-\infty$ to -2. The values of f decrease and the graph of f falls as x increases from -2 to 2. Finally, the values of f increase and the graph of f rises as x increases from 2 to ∞.

MATCHED PROBLEM 3

The graph of

$$f(x) = -x^3 - 3x^2 + 9x + 13$$

is shown in Figure 12. Use the terms *increasing, decreasing, rising,* and *falling* to write a verbal description of this graph.

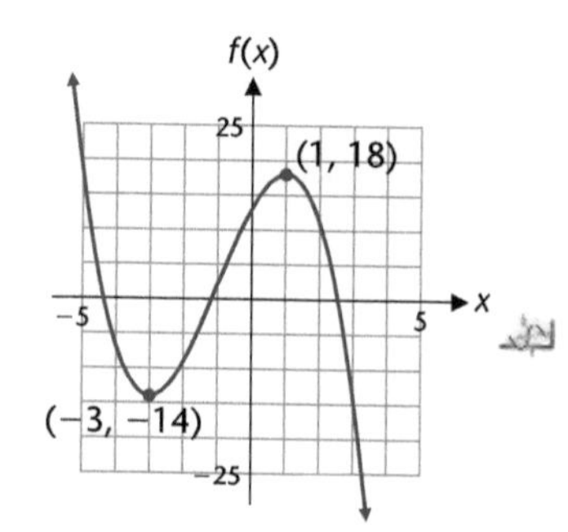

› **Figure 12**

››› CAUTION ›››

The arrow on the left edge of the graph in Figure 11 does not indicate that the graph is "moving" downward. It simply tells us that there are no significant changes in direction for x values less than -5. The graph is increasing on that portion.

› Finding Local Maxima and Minima

The graph of $f(x) = x^3 - 12x + 4$ from Example 3 (displayed in Figure 11) will help us to define some very important terms. Notice that at the point $(-2, 20)$, the function changes from increasing to decreasing. This means that the function value $f(-2) = 20$ is greater than any of the nearby values of the function. We will call such a point a *local maximum*. At the point $(2, -12)$, the function changes from decreasing to increasing. This means that the function value $f(2) = -12$ is less than any nearby values of the function. We will call such a point a *local minimum*.

Local maxima and minima* play a crucial role in the study of graphs of functions. For many graphs, they are the key points that determine the shape of the graph. We will also see that maxima and minima are very useful in application problems. When a function represents some quantity of interest (the profit made by a business, for example), finding the largest or smallest that quantity can get is usually very helpful.

The concepts of local maxima and minima are made more formal in the following definition:

› DEFINITION 2 Local Maxima and Local Minima

The function value $f(c)$ is called a **local maximum** if there is an interval (a, b) containing c such that

$$f(x) \leq f(c) \text{ for all } x \text{ in } (a, b)$$

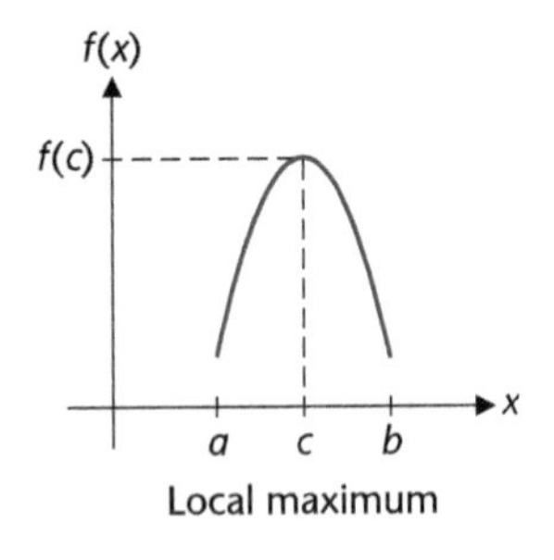

Local maximum

The function value $f(c)$ is called a **local minimum** if there is an interval (a, b) containing c such that

$$f(x) \geq f(c) \text{ for all } x \text{ in } (a, b)$$

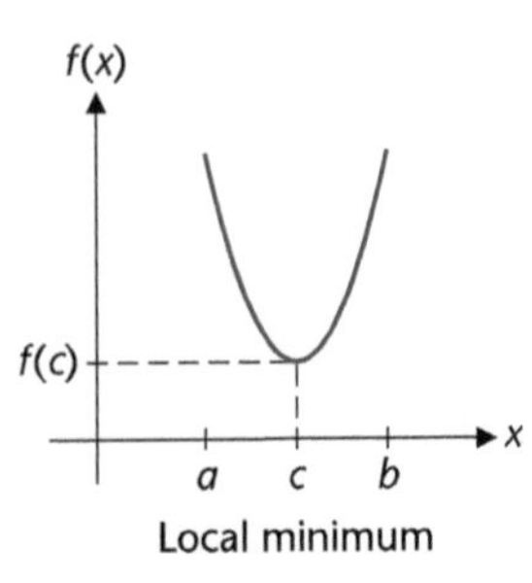

Local minimum

The function value $f(c)$ is called a **local extremum** if it is either a local maximum or a local minimum.

*Maxima and minima are the plural forms of maximum and minimum, respectively.

››› EXPLORE-DISCUSS 3

Plot the points $A = (0, 0)$, $B = (3, 4)$, $C = (7, 1)$, and $D = (10, 5)$ in a coordinate plane. Draw a curve that satisfies each of the following conditions.

(A) Passes through A and B and is always increasing.

(B) Passes through A, B, and C with a local maximum at $x = 3$.

(C) Passes through A, B, C, and D with a local maximum at $x = 3$ and a local minimum at $x = 7$.

What does this tell you about the connection between local extrema and increasing/decreasing properties of functions?

Since finding maximum or minimum values of functions is so important, most graphing calculators have commands that approximate local maxima and minima. Examples 4 and 5 illustrate the use of these commands.

EXAMPLE 4 Finding Local Extrema

Find the domain, any local extrema, and the range of

$$f(x) = x^2 - 40\sqrt{x}$$

Round answers to two decimal places.

SOLUTION

Because $\sqrt{x}$ represents a real number only if $x \geq 0$, the domain of f is $[0, \infty)$. First we must select a viewing window. Because the domain of f is $[0, \infty)$, we choose Xmin $= 0$. We will construct a table of values on a graphing calculator (Figs. 13 and 14) to help select the remaining window variables. From Figure 13 we see that Ymin should be less than -64.44. Figure 14 indicates that Xmax $= 15$ and Ymax greater than 70.081 should produce a reasonable view of the graph. Our choice for the window variables is shown in Figure 15.

X	Y1
0	0
1	-39
2	-52.57
3	-60.28
4	-64
5	-64.44
6	-61.98

Y1=-40√(X)+X²

› Figure 13

X	Y1
9	-39
10	-26.49
11	-11.66
12	5.4359
13	24.778
14	46.334
15	70.081

Y1=-40√(X)+X²

› Figure 14

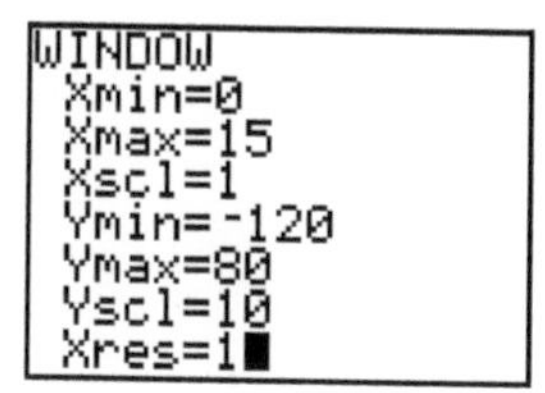

› Figure 15

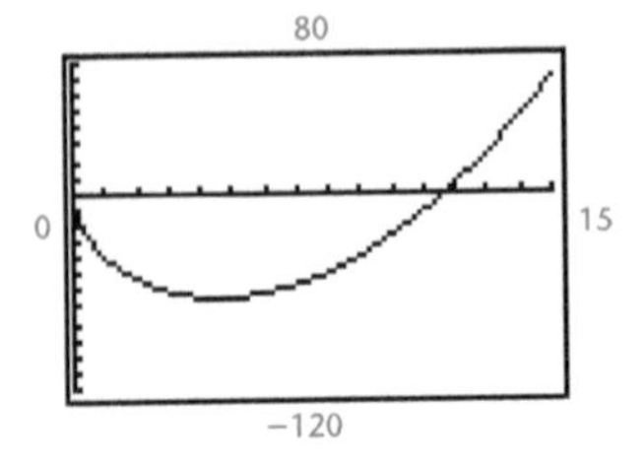

› Figure 16

The graph of f is shown in Figure 16. Notice that we adjusted Ymin to provide space at the bottom of the screen for the text that the graphing calculator will display.

Both the table in Figure 13 and the graph in Figure 16 indicate that f has a local minimum near $x = 5$. After selecting the **MINIMUM** command on our graphing calculator, we are asked to select a left bound (Fig. 17), a right bound (Fig. 18), and a guess (Fig. 19). Note the arrowheads that mark the right and left boundaries.

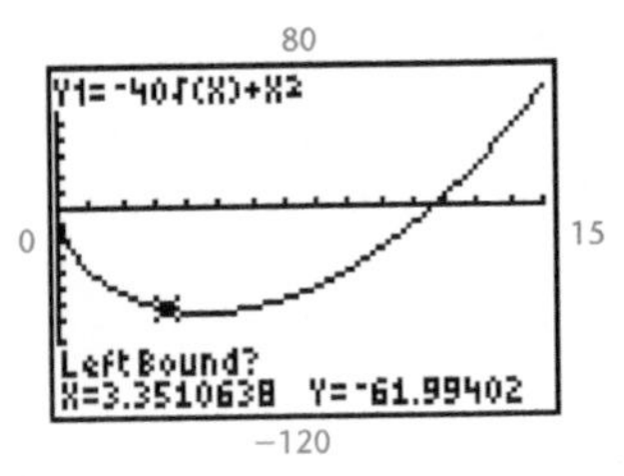

› Figure 17

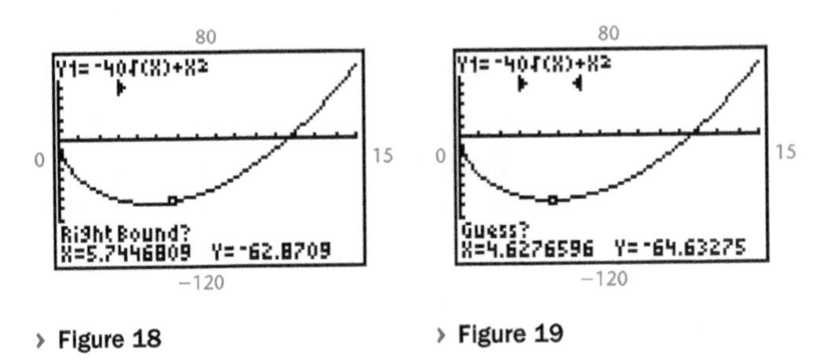

› Figure 18

› Figure 19

The final graph (Fig. 20) shows that, to two decimal places, f has a local minimum value of -64.63 at $x = 4.64$. The curve in Figure 20 suggests that as x increases to the right without bound, the values of $f(x)$ also increase without bound. The graph in Figure 21 and the table in Figure 22 support this suggestion. Thus, we conclude that there are no other local extrema and that the range of f is $[-64.63, \infty)$.

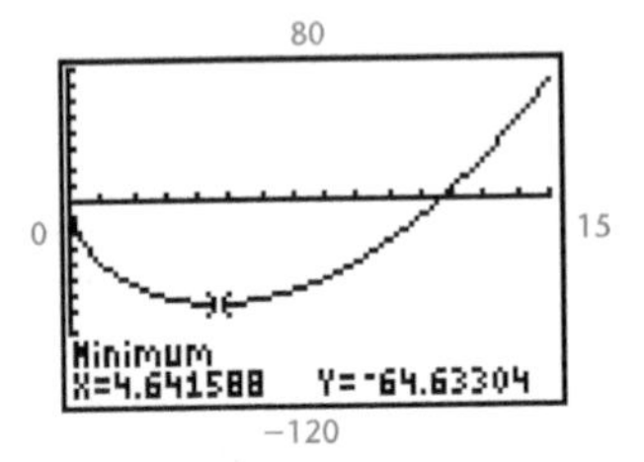

› Figure 20

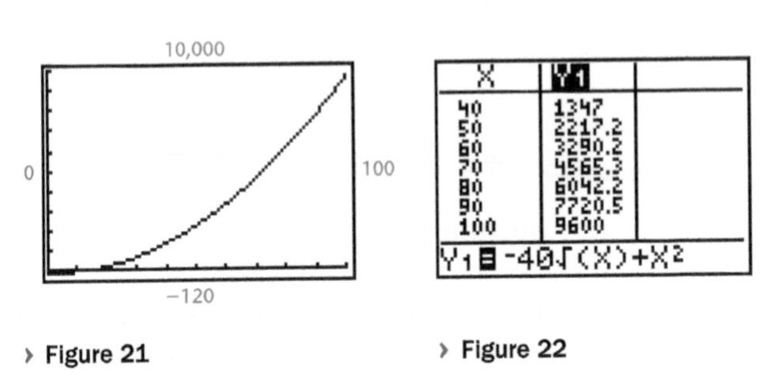

X	Y1
40	1347
50	2217.2
60	3290.2
70	4565.3
80	6042.2
90	7720.5
100	9600

Y1 = −40√(X)+X²

› Figure 21

› Figure 22

Summarizing our results, we have

$$\text{Domain of } f = [0, \infty)$$
$$\text{Range of } f = [-64.63, \infty)$$
$$\text{Local minimum: } f(4.64) = -64.63$$

MATCHED PROBLEM 4

Find the domain, any local extrema, and the range of

$$f(x) = x - 5\sqrt{x}$$

Round answers to two decimal places.

In Example 4, we used numerical and graphical evidence to conclude that f continues to increase as x increases to the right. It turns out that calculus techniques are required to be absolutely certain. Without calculus, we have to rely on intuitive arguments involving graphical and numerical techniques, as we did in Example 4. As we broaden our experience and become familiar with a larger variety of functions and their graphs, we'll be able to draw conclusions with a greater degree of certainty. This is one of the major objectives of this book.

› Mathematical Modeling

In Example 5, we use the MAXIMUM command to find the maximum value of a revenue function.

EXAMPLE 5 Maximizing Revenue

The revenue (in dollars) from the sale of x bicycle locks is given by

$$R(x) = 21x - 0.016x^2 \qquad 0 \le x \le 1{,}300$$

Find the number of locks that must be sold to maximize the revenue. What is the maximum revenue, to the nearest dollar?

SOLUTION

We begin by entering the revenue function as Y_1 and constructing a table of values for the revenue (Fig. 23). From the limits given in the problem, we select Xmin = 0 and Xmax = 1,300. The table in Figure 23 suggests that Ymax = 7,000 is a good choice and, as before, we select Ymin so the text displayed by the graphing calculator does not cover any important portions of the graph. We enter the window variables (Fig. 24) and use the MAXIMUM command (Fig. 25). (The MAXIMUM command works just like the MINIMUM command used in Example 4. The details of selecting the bounds and the initial guess are omitted.)

X	Y1
300	4860
400	5840
500	6500
600	6840
700	6860
800	6560
900	5940

Y1=21X−0.016X²

› Figure 23

WINDOW
Xmin=0
Xmax=1300
Xscl=100
Ymin=-3000
Ymax=7000
Yscl=1000
Xres=1

› Figure 24

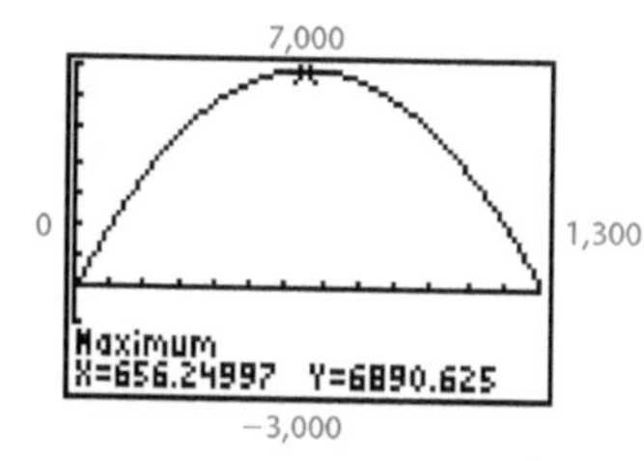

› Figure 25

X	Y1
656	6890.6
657	6890.6

Y1=21X−0.016X²

› Figure 26

The results in Figure 25 show that, to two decimal places, the maximum revenue is \$6,890.63 when $x = 656.25$ locks. But this cannot be the answer to the problem. It is not reasonable to sell one-fourth of a lock. Examining the values of R at $x = 656$ and $x = 657$ (Fig. 26), we conclude that the maximum revenue, to the nearest dollar, is \$6,891 when either 656 locks or 657 locks are sold.

MATCHED PROBLEM 5

The profit (in dollars) from the sale of x T-shirts is given by

$$P(x) = 17.5x - 0.016x^2 - 2{,}000 \qquad 0 \leq x \leq 1{,}300$$

Find the number of shirts that must be sold to maximize the profit. What is the maximum profit, to the nearest dollar?

Example 5 illustrates an important step in the mathematical modeling process. Solutions obtained from a model must be interpreted in terms of the original real-world problem. In the case of Example 5, the revenue function R is defined only for integer values of x, $x = 0, 1, 2, \ldots, 1{,}300$. However, for the purposes of mathematical analysis and as an aid in visualizing the behavior of the function R, we assume that the revenue function is defined for all x, $0 \leq x \leq 1{,}300$. After finding that the maximum value of the revenue function occurs at $x = 656.25$, we must remember to interpret this solution to mean either $x = 656$ or $x = 657$.

› Defining Functions Piecewise

You probably think of finding the absolute value of a number as a simple process: do nothing if the number is zero or greater, and throw away the negative sign if it's less than zero. In fact, we can think of absolute value as a function, and define it by a pair of formulas.

$$f(x) = |x| = \begin{cases} -x & \text{if } x < 0 \quad \text{For example, } |-4| = -(-4) = 4 \\ x & \text{if } x \geq 0 \quad \text{For example, } |3| = 3 \end{cases}$$

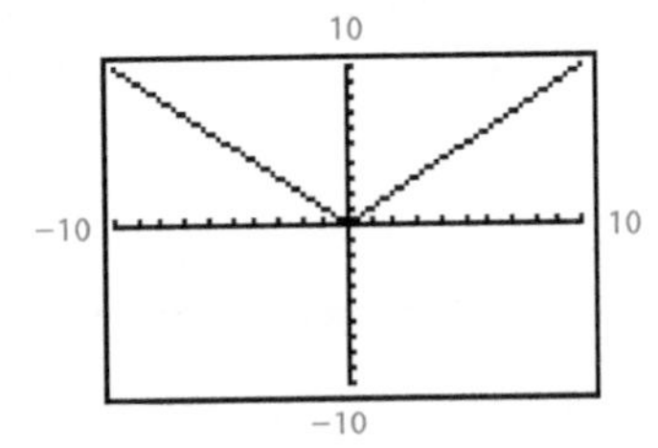

› **Figure 27** Graph of $f(x) = |x| = \text{abs}(x)$.

The output is the same as the input (x) for $x \geq 0$, and has the opposite sign as the input ($-x$) for $x < 0$.

The graph of $|x|$ is shown in Figure 27. Most graphing calculators use abs or ABS to denote this function, and the graph is produced directly using $y_1 = \text{abs}(x)$.

Obviously, the absolute value function is defined by different formulas for different parts of its domain. Functions whose definitions involve more than one formula are called **piecewise-defined functions.** Notice that the graph of the absolute value function has a **sharp corner** at (0, 0), a common characteristic of piecewise-defined functions. As Example 6 illustrates, piecewise-defined functions occur naturally in many applications.

EXAMPLE 6 **Rental Charges**

A car rental agency charges $0.25 per mile if the mileage does not exceed 100. If the total mileage exceeds 100, the agency charges $0.25 per mile for the first 100 miles and $0.15 per mile for any additional mileage.

(A) If x represents the number of miles a rented vehicle is driven, express the mileage charge $C(x)$ as a function of x.

(B) Complete the following table.

x	0	50	100	150	200
$C(x)$					

(C) Sketch the graph of $y = C(x)$ by hand, using a graphing calculator as an aid, and indicate the points in the table on the graph with solid dots.

SOLUTIONS

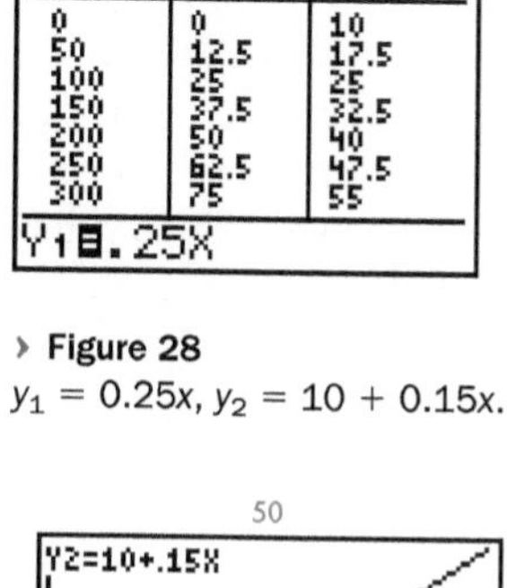

X	Y1	Y2
0	0	10
50	12.5	17.5
100	25	25
150	37.5	32.5
200	50	40
250	62.5	47.5
300	75	55

Y1=.25X

› **Figure 28**
$y_1 = 0.25x$, $y_2 = 10 + 0.15x$.

(A) If $0 \le x \le 100$, then

$$C(x) = 0.25x \quad \text{25 cents per mile up to a hundred}$$

If $x > 100$, then $x - 100$ represents the portion of the mileage over 100, and $0.15(x - 100)$ is the charge for this mileage. So if $x > 100$,

$$\begin{aligned} C(x) &= \underset{\text{Charge for the first 100 miles}}{0.25(100)} + \underset{\text{Charge for the additional mileage}}{0.15(x - 100)} \\ &= 25 + 0.15x - 15 \\ &= 10 + 0.15x \end{aligned}$$

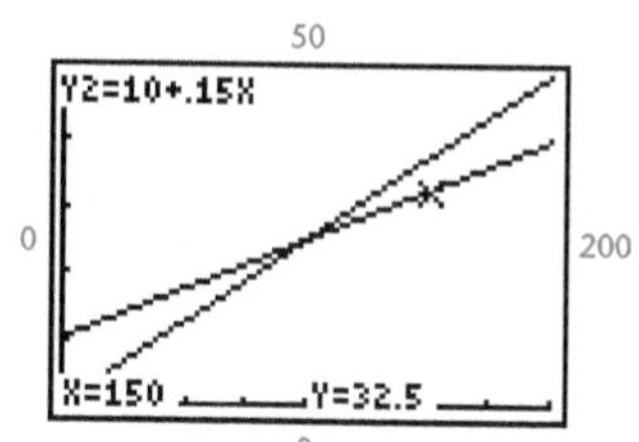

› **Figure 29**
$y_1 = 0.25x$, $y_2 = 10 + 0.15x$.

Thus, we see that C is a piecewise-defined function:

$$C(x) = \begin{cases} 0.25x & \text{if } 0 \le x \le 100 \\ 10 + 0.15x & \text{if } x > 100 \end{cases}$$

(B) Piecewise-defined functions are evaluated by first determining which formula applies and then using the appropriate formula to find the value of the function. To begin, we enter both formulas in a graphing calculator and use the TABLE command (Fig. 28). To complete the table, we use the values of $C(x)$ from the y_1 column if $0 \le x \le 100$, and from the y_2 column if $x > 100$. In essence, we are evaluating f using the top formula when $x \le 100$, and the bottom formula when $x > 100$.

x	0	50	100	150	200
$C(x)$	\$0	\$12.50	\$25	\$32.50	\$40

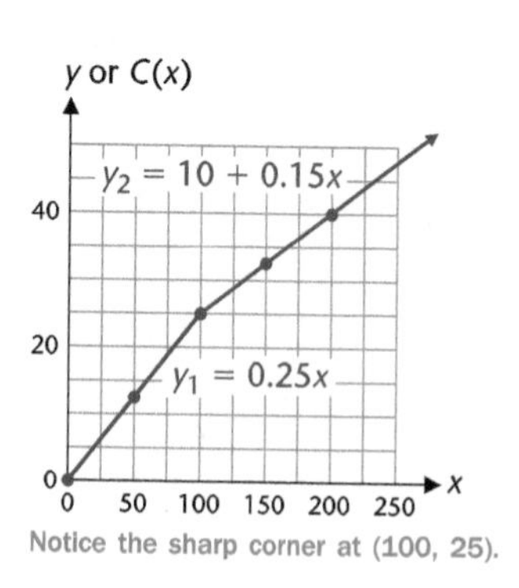

Notice the sharp corner at (100, 25).

› **Figure 30** Hand sketch of the graph of $y = C(x)$.

(C) Using a graph of both rules in the same viewing window as an aid (Fig. 29), we sketch the graph of $y = C(x)$ and add the points from the table to produce Figure 30.

MATCHED PROBLEM 6

Another car rental agency charges \$0.30 per mile when the total mileage does not exceed 75, and \$0.30 per mile for the first 75 miles plus \$0.20 per mile for the additional mileage when the total mileage exceeds 75.

(A) If x represents the number of miles a rented vehicle is driven, express the mileage charge $C(x)$ as a function of x.

(B) Complete the following table.

x	0	50	75	100	150
$C(x)$					

(C) Sketch the graph of $y = C(x)$ by hand, using a graphing calculator as an aid, and indicate the points in the table on the graph with solid dots.

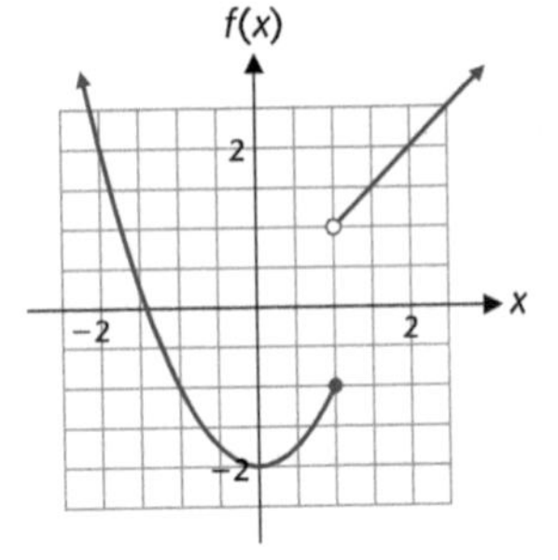

› **Figure 31** Graph of $f(x) = \begin{cases} x^2 - 2 & \text{for } x \le 1 \\ x & \text{for } x > 1 \end{cases}$

Refer to Figures 28 and 30 in the solution to Example 6. Notice that the two formulas in the definition of C produce the same value at $x = 100$ and that the graph of C contains no breaks. Informally, a graph (or portion of a graph) is said to be **continuous** if it contains no breaks or gaps and can be drawn without lifting a pen from the paper. A graph is **discontinuous** at any points where there is a break or a gap. For example, the graph of the function in Figure 31 is discontinuous at $x = 1$. The entire graph cannot be drawn without lifting a pen from the paper. (A formal presentation of continuity can be found in calculus texts.)

We conclude this section with a discussion of a particular piecewise-defined function that plays in important role in computer science. It is called the *greatest integer function.*

The greatest integer of a real number x, denoted by $[\![x]\!]$ is the largest integer that is less than or equal to x. That is, $[\![x]\!]$ is the integer n such that $n \le x < n + 1$ (Fig. 32).

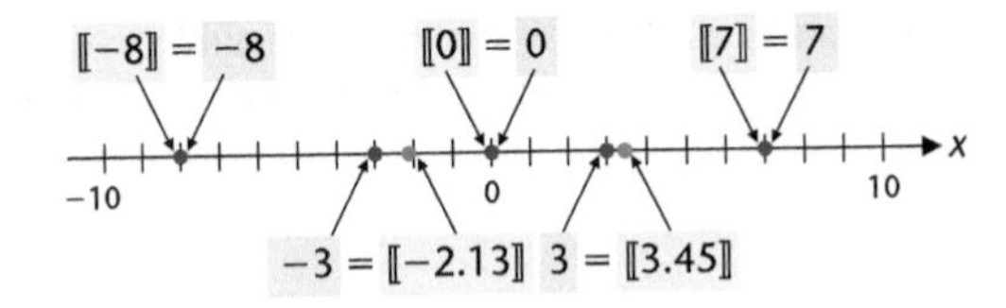

› **Figure 32**

The **greatest integer function** f is defined by the equation $f(x) = [\![x]\!]$. A piecewise definition of f for $-2 \le x < 3$ is shown on page 60 and a sketch of the graph of f for $-5 \le x \le 5$ is shown in Figure 33. Since the domain of f is all real numbers, the piecewise definition continues indefinitely in both directions, as does the stairstep pattern in the figure. Thus, the range of f is the set of all integers.

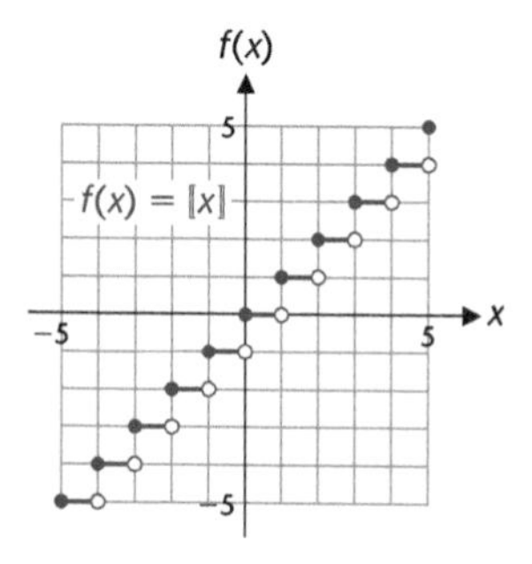

› **Figure 33** Greatest integer function.

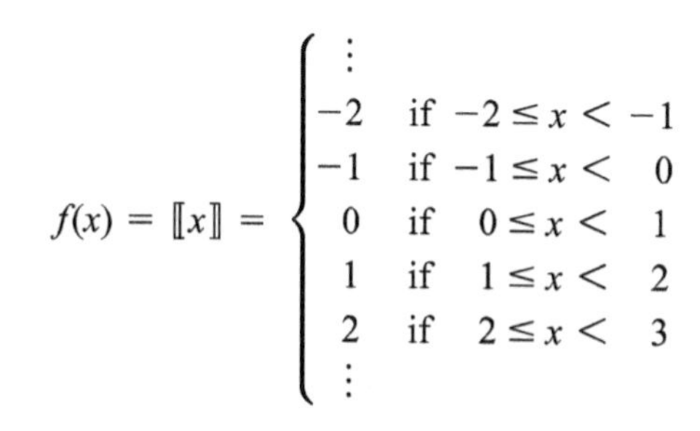

$$f(x) = [\![x]\!] = \begin{cases} \vdots \\ -2 & \text{if } -2 \le x < -1 \\ -1 & \text{if } -1 \le x < 0 \\ 0 & \text{if } 0 \le x < 1 \\ 1 & \text{if } 1 \le x < 2 \\ 2 & \text{if } 2 \le x < 3 \\ \vdots \end{cases}$$

Notice in Figure 33 that at each integer value of x there is a break in the graph, and between integer values of x there is no break. Thus, the greatest integer function is discontinuous at each integer n and continuous on each interval of the form $[n, n + 1)$.

Most graphing calculators will graph the greatest integer function, usually denoted by int, but these graphs require careful interpretation. Comparing the sketch of $y = [\![x]\!]$ in Figure 33 with the graph of $y = \text{int}(x)$ in Figure 34(a), we see that the graphing calculator has connected the endpoints of the horizontal line segments. This gives the appearance that the graph is continuous when it is not. To obtain a correct graph, consult the manual to determine how to change the graphing mode on your graphing calculator from **connected mode** to **dot mode** [Fig. 34(b)].

› **Figure 34** Greatest integer function on a graphing calculator.

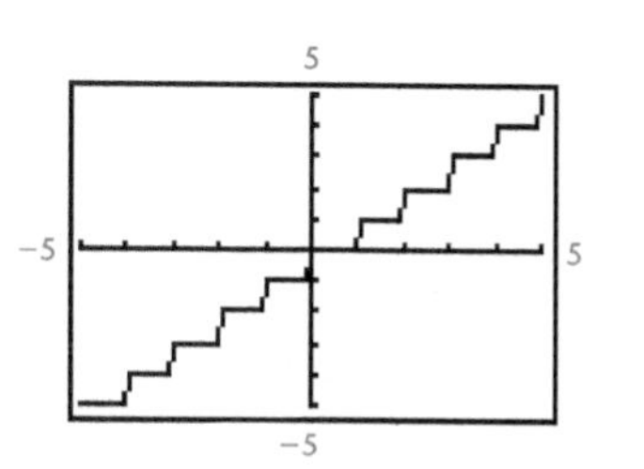

(a) Graph of $y = \text{int}(x)$ in the connected mode.

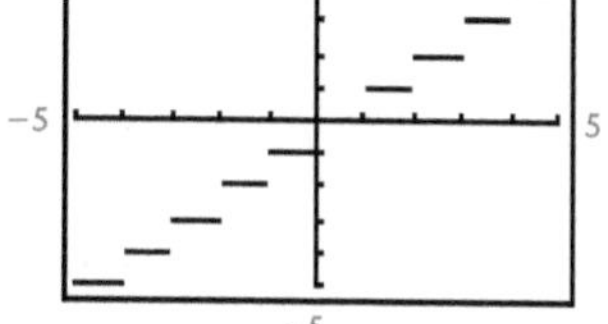

(b) Graph of $y = \text{int}(x)$ in the dot mode.

››› **CAUTION** ›››

When in connected mode, your graphing calculator will connect portions of a graph where a break should occur. To avoid misleading graphs, use the dot mode when graphing a function with discontinuities.

EXAMPLE 7 Computer Science

Let

$$f(x) = \frac{[\![10x + 0.5]\!]}{10}$$

Find

(A) $f(6)$ (B) $f(1.8)$ (C) $f(3.24)$ (D) $f(4.582)$ (E) $f(-2.68)$

What operation does this function perform?

SOLUTIONS

(A) $f(6) = \dfrac{[\![60.5]\!]}{10} = \dfrac{60}{10} = 6$

(B) $f(1.8) = \dfrac{[\![18.5]\!]}{10} = \dfrac{18}{10} = 1.8$

(C) $f(3.24) = \dfrac{[\![32.9]\!]}{10} = \dfrac{32}{10} = 3.2$

(D) $f(4.582) = \dfrac{[\![46.32]\!]}{10} = \dfrac{46}{10} = 4.6$

(E) $f(-2.68) = \dfrac{[\![-26.3]\!]}{10} = \dfrac{-27}{10} = -2.7$

x	$f[x]$
6	6
1.8	1.8
3.24	3.2
4.582	4.6
−2.68	−2.7

Comparing the values of x and $f(x)$ in the table, we conclude that this function rounds decimal fractions to the nearest tenth.

The greatest integer function is used in programming (in spreadsheet programs, for example) to round numbers to a specified accuracy.

MATCHED PROBLEM 7

Let $f(x) = [\![x + 0.5]\!]$. Find

(A) $f(6)$ (B) $f(1.8)$ (C) $f(3.24)$ (D) $f(-4.3)$ (E) $f(-2.69)$

What operation does this function perform?

ANSWERS MATCHED PROBLEMS

1. x intercept: -1.516; y intercept: 5
2. (A) Domain: $-4 < x < 5$ or $(-4, 5)$
Range: $-4 < y \le 3$ or $(-4, 3]$
(B) $f(-4) = 1; f(0) = 3; f(2) = 2$
3. The values of f decrease and the graph of f is falling on $(-\infty, -3)$ and $(1, \infty)$. The values of f increase and the graph of f is rising on $(-3, 1)$.
4. Domain: $[0, \infty)$; range: $[-6.25, \infty)$; local minimum: $f(6.25) = -6.25$
5. The maximum profit of $2,785 occurs when 547 shirts are sold.
6. (A) $C(x) = \begin{cases} 0.3x & \text{if } 0 \le x \le 75 \\ 7.5 + 0.2x & \text{if } x > 75 \end{cases}$

(B)

x	0	50	75	100	150
$C(x)$	$0	$15	$22.50	$27.50	$37.50

(C)

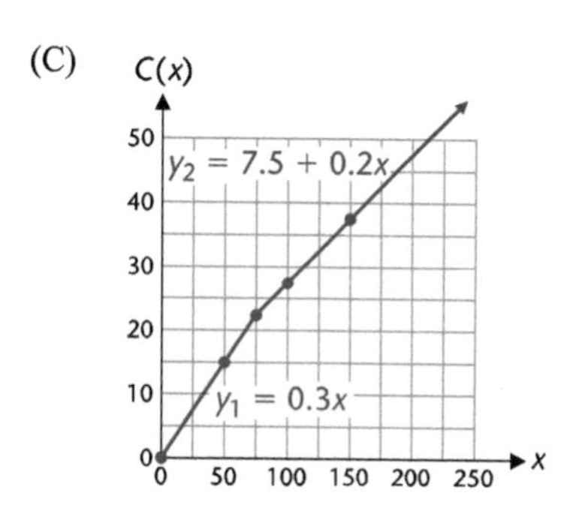

7. (A) 6 (B) 2 (C) 3 (D) -4 (E) -3; f rounds decimal fractions to the nearest integer.

1-3 Exercises

1. Describe in your own words what the graph of a function is.

2. Explain how to find the domain and range of a function from its graph.

3. How many y intercepts can a function have? What about x intercepts? Explain.

4. True or false: On any interval in its domain, every function is either increasing or decreasing. Explain.

5. Explain in your own words what it means to say that a function is increasing on an interval.

6. Explain in your own words what it means to say that a function is decreasing on an interval.

Problems 7–18 refer to functions f, g, h, k, p, and q given by the following graphs. (Assume the graphs continue as indicated beyond the parts shown.)

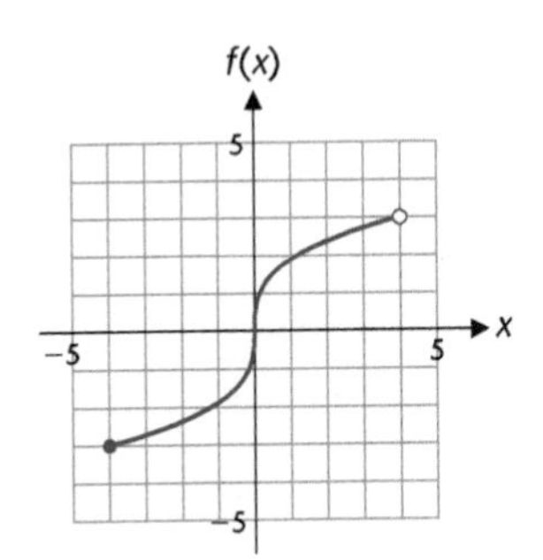

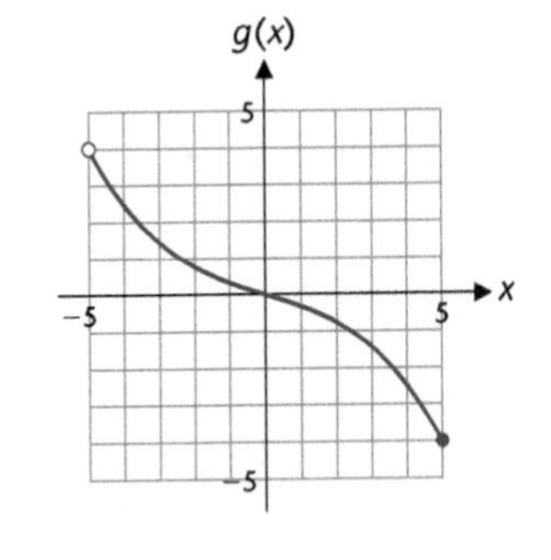

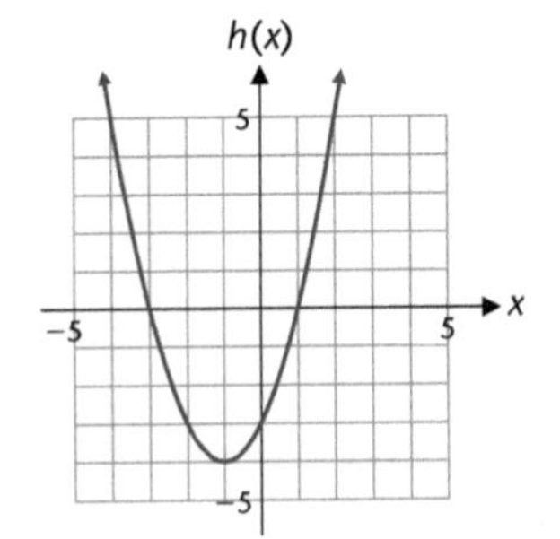

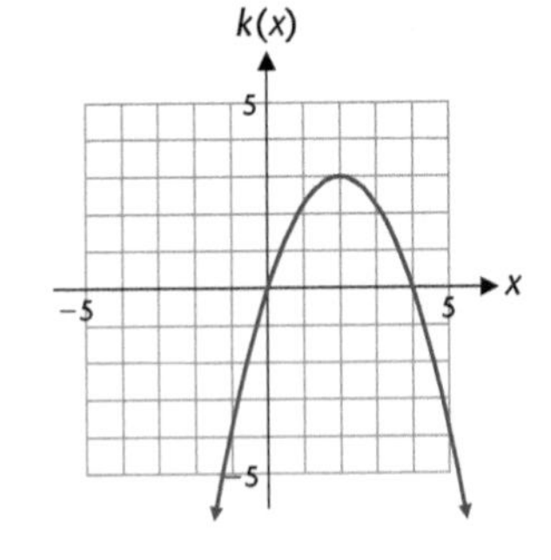

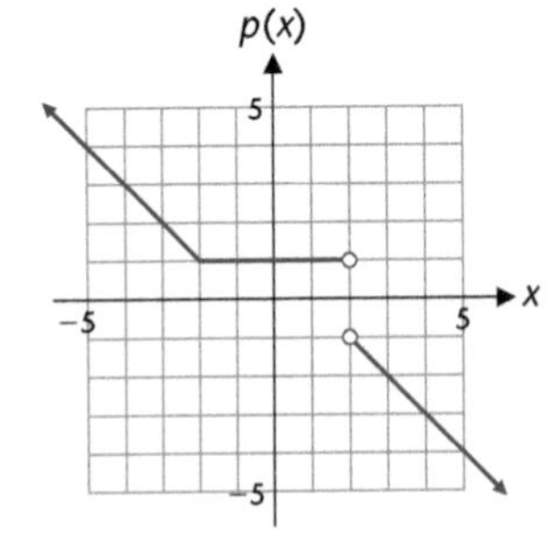

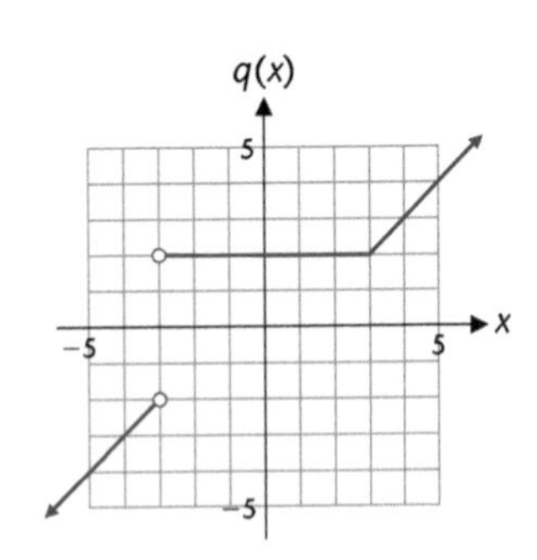

7. For the function f, find
(A) Domain
(B) Range
(C) x intercepts
(D) y intercept
(E) Intervals over which f is increasing
(F) Intervals over which f is decreasing

(G) Intervals over which f is constant
(H) Any points of discontinuity

8. Repeat Problem 7 for the function g.

9. Repeat Problem 7 for the function h.

10. Repeat Problem 7 for the function k.

11. Repeat Problem 7 for the function p.

12. Repeat Problem 7 for the function q.

13. Find $f(-4)$, $f(0)$, and $f(4)$.

14. Find $g(-5)$, $g(0)$, and $g(5)$.

15. Find $h(-3)$, $h(0)$, and $h(2)$.

16. Find $k(0)$, $k(2)$, and $k(4)$.

17. Find $p(-2)$, $p(2)$, and $p(5)$.

18. Find $q(-4)$, $q(-3)$, and $q(1)$.

In Problems 19–26, examine the graph of the function to determine the intervals over which the function is increasing, the intervals over which the function is decreasing, and the intervals over which the function is constant. Approximate the endpoints of the intervals to the nearest integer.

19. $f(x) = |x + 2| - 5$

20. $k(x) = |x - 2| - x$

21. $j(x) = 0.05x^3 + 0.25x^2 - 1.5x - 1.5$

22. $g(x) = -0.02x^3 - 0.14x^2 + 0.35x + 2.5$

23. $m(x) = |x - 3| - |x + 4|$

24. $q(x) = |x + 2| + |x - 4|$

25. $r(x) = |x + 4| - |x| + |x - 4|$

26. $s(x) = |x| - |x + 5| - |x - 3|$

In Problems 27–32, use a graphing calculator to find the x intercepts, y intercept, and any local extrema. Round answers to three decimal places.

27. $f(x) = x^2 - 5x - 9$

28. $g(x) = -x^2 + 7x + 14$

29. $h(x) = -x^3 + 4x + 25$

30. $k(x) = x^3 + 3x^2 - 15$

31. $m(x) = \sqrt{|x^2 - 12|}$

32. $n(x) = \sqrt{|x^3 - 12|}$

In Problems 33–38, sketch by hand the graph of a continuous function f over the interval [−5, 5] that is consistent with the given information.

33. The function f is increasing on $[-5, -2]$, constant on $[-2, 2]$, and decreasing on $[2, 5]$.

34. The function f is decreasing on $[-5, -2]$, constant on $[-2, 2]$, and increasing on $[2, 5]$.

35. The function f is decreasing on $[-5, -2]$, constant on $[-2, 2]$, and decreasing on $[2, 5]$.

36. The function f is increasing on $[-5, -2]$, constant on $[-2, 2]$, and increasing on $[2, 5]$.

37. The function f is decreasing on $[-5, -2]$, increasing on $[-2, 2]$, and decreasing on $[2, 5]$.

38. The function f is increasing on $[-5, -2]$, decreasing on $[-2, 2]$, and increasing on $[2, 5]$.

39. Review the informal description of the term increasing on page 51. Explain how the formal definition of increasing in Definition 1 really says the same thing.

40. Review the informal description of the term decreasing on page 51. Explain how the formal definition of decreasing in Definition 1 really says the same thing.

In Problems 41–46, sketch the graph of $y = f(x)$ and evaluate $f(-2)$, $f(-1)$, $f(1)$, and $f(2)$.

41. $f(x) = \begin{cases} x + 1 & \text{if } x \le 0 \\ -x + 1 & \text{if } x > 0 \end{cases}$

42. $f(x) = \begin{cases} x & \text{if } x < 1 \\ -x + 2 & \text{if } x \ge 1 \end{cases}$

43. $f(x) = \begin{cases} x + 2 & \text{if } x < -1 \\ x - 2 & \text{if } x \ge -1 \end{cases}$

44. $f(x) = \begin{cases} -x - 1 & \text{if } x \le 2 \\ -x + 5 & \text{if } x > 2 \end{cases}$

45. $f(x) = \begin{cases} x^2 + 1 & \text{if } x < 0 \\ -x^2 - 1 & \text{if } x > 0 \end{cases}$

46. $f(x) = \begin{cases} -x^2 - 2 & \text{if } x < 0 \\ x^2 + 2 & \text{if } x > 0 \end{cases}$

In Problems 47–54, use the graph of each function to find the domain, range, y intercept, and x intercepts. Round answers to two decimal places.

47. $m(x) = x^3 + 45x^2 - 30$

48. $f(x) = x^3 - 35x^2 + 25$

49. $n(x) = 200 + 200x^2 - x^4$

50. $g(x) = 200 - 40x^3 - x^4$

51. $h(x) = 8\sqrt{x} - x$

52. $s(x) = x - 18\sqrt{x}$

53. $k(x) = x^2 - 50\sqrt{x + 5}$

54. $t(x) = 30\sqrt{20 - x} - x^2$

In Problems 55–60, write a verbal description of the graph of the given function using the terms increasing, decreasing, rising, and falling, and indicate any local maximum and minimum values. Approximate the coordinates of any points used in your description to two decimal places.

55. $f(x) = x^3 - 12x^2 + 3x - 10$

56. $h(x) = x^3 + 15x^2 + 5x + 15$

57. $m(x) = 24|x| - x^2$

58. $n(x) = 15\sqrt{|x|} - x$

59. $g(x) = |x^2 - 5x - 300|$

60. $k(x) = |x^2 - 4x - 480|$

In Problems 61–66, write a verbal description of the graph of the given function using increasing and decreasing terminology, and indicating any local maximum and minimum values. Approximate the coordinates of any points used in your description to two decimal places.

61. $f(x) = x^2 + 4.3x - 32$

62. $g(x) = -x^2 + 6.9x + 25$

63. $h(x) = x^3 - x^2 - 74x + 60$

64. $k(x) = -x^3 + x^2 + 82x - 25$

65. $p(x) = |x^2 - x - 18|$

66. $q(x) = |x^2 - 2x - 30|$

In Problems 67–72, sketch the graph of a function f by hand that is continuous on the interval [−5, 5], except as noted, and is consistent with the given information.

67. The function f is increasing on $[-5, 0)$, discontinuous at $x = 0$, increasing on $(0, 5]$, $f(-2) = 0$, and $f(2) = 0$.

68. The function f is decreasing on $[-5, 0)$, discontinuous at $x = 0$, decreasing on $(0, 5]$, $f(-3) = 0$, and $f(3) = 0$.

69. The function f is discontinuous at $x = 0, f(-3) = -2$ is a local maximum, and $f(2) = 3$ is a local minimum.

70. The function f is discontinuous at $x = 0, f(-3) = 2$ is a local minimum, and $f(2) = -3$ is a local maximum.

71. The function f is discontinuous at $x = -2$ and $x = 2$, $f(-3) = -2$ and $f(3) = -2$ are local maxima, and $f(0) = 0$ is a local minimum.

72. The function f is discontinuous at $x = -2$ and $x = 2$, $f(-3) = 2$ and $f(3) = 2$ are local minima, and $f(0) = 0$ is a local maximum.

In Problems 73–78, graph $y = f(x)$ in a standard viewing window. Assuming that the graph continues as indicated beyond the part shown in this viewing window, find the domain, range, and any points of discontinuity. (Use the dot mode on your graphing calculator.)

73. $f(x) = \dfrac{|5x - 10|}{x - 2}$

74. $f(x) = \dfrac{4x + 12}{|x + 3|}$

75. $f(x) = x + \dfrac{|4x - 4|}{x - 1}$

76. $f(x) = x + \dfrac{|2x + 2|}{x + 1}$

77. $f(x) = |x| - \dfrac{|9 - 3x|}{x - 3}$

78. $f(x) = |x| + \dfrac{|2x + 4|}{x + 2}$

In Problems 79–84, write a piecewise definition of f and sketch the graph of f, by hand using a graphing calculator as an aid. Include sufficient intervals to clearly illustrate both the definition and the graph. Find the domain, range, and any points of discontinuity.

79. $f(x) = [\![x/2]\!]$

80. $f(x) = [\![x/3]\!]$

81. $f(x) = [\![3x]\!]$

82. $f(x) = [\![2x]\!]$

83. $f(x) = x - [\![x]\!]$

84. $f(x) = [\![x]\!] - x$

85. The function f is continuous and increasing on the interval $[1, 9]$ with $f(1) = -5$ and $f(9) = 4$.
(A) Sketch a graph of f that is consistent with the given information.
(B) How many times does your graph cross the x axis? Could the graph cross more times? Fewer times? Support your conclusions with additional sketches and/or verbal arguments.

86. Repeat Problem 85 if the function does not have to be continuous.

87. The function f is continuous on the interval $[-5, 5]$ with $f(-5) = -4, f(1) = 3$, and $f(5) = -2$.
(A) Sketch a graph of f that is consistent with the given information.
(B) How many times does your graph cross the x axis? Could the graph cross more times? Fewer times? Support your conclusions with additional sketches and/or verbal arguments.

88. Repeat Problem 87 if f is continuous on $[-8, 8]$ with $f(-8) = -6, f(-4) = 3, f(3) = -2$, and $f(8) = 5$.

89. The function f is continuous on $[0, 10]$, $f(5) = -5$ is a local minimum, and f has no other local extrema on this interval.
(A) Sketch a graph of f that is consistent with the given information.
(B) How many times does your graph cross the x axis? Could the graph cross more times? Fewer times? Support your conclusions with additional sketches and/or verbal arguments.

90. Repeat Problem 89 if $f(5) = 1$ and all other information is unchanged.

APPLICATIONS

91. REVENUE The revenue (in dollars) from the sale of x car seats for infants is given by

$$R(x) = 60x - 0.035x^2 \qquad 0 \le x \le 1{,}700$$

Find the number of car seats that must be sold to maximize the revenue. What is the maximum revenue (to the nearest dollar)?

92. PROFIT The profit (in dollars) from the sale of x car seats for infants is given by

$$P(x) = 38x - 0.035x^2 - 4{,}000 \qquad 0 \le x \le 1{,}700$$

Find the number of car seats that must be sold to maximize the profit. What is the maximum profit (to the nearest dollar)?

93. MANUFACTURING A box is to be made out of a piece of cardboard that measures 18 by 24 inches. Squares, x inches on a side, will be cut from each corner and then the ends and sides will be folded up (see the figure).

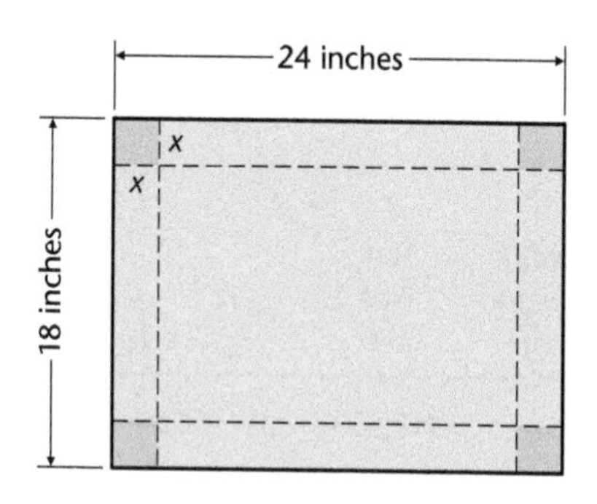

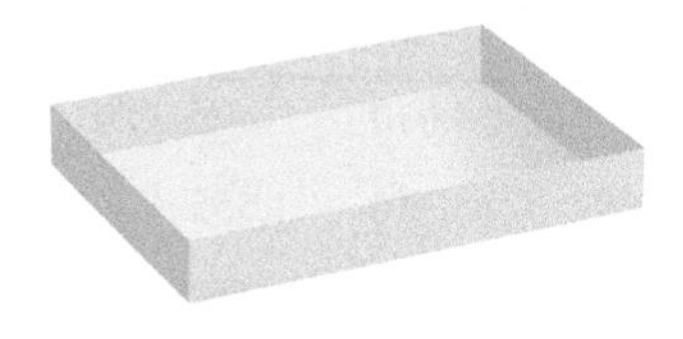

Find the size of the cutout squares that will make the maximum volume. What is the maximum volume? Round answers to two decimal places.

94. MANUFACTURING A box with a hinged lid is to be made out of a piece of cardboard that measures 20 by 40 inches. Six squares, x inches on a side, will be cut from each corner and the middle of the sides, and then the ends and sides will be folded up to form the box and its lid (see the figure).

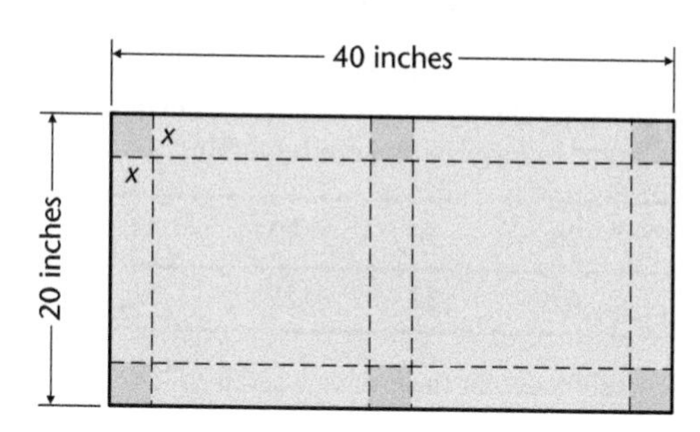

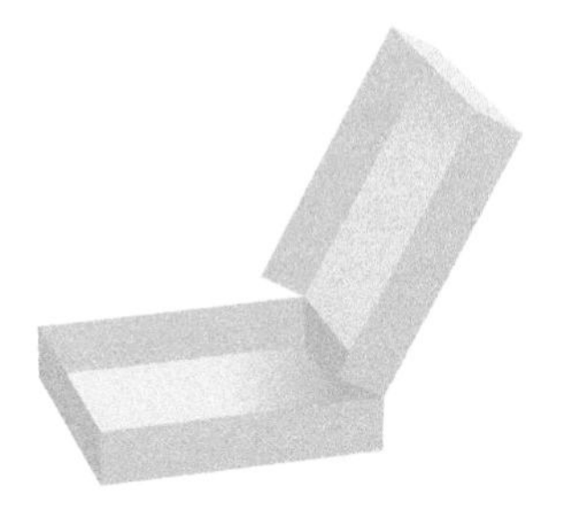

Find the size of the cutout squares that will make the maximum volume. What is the maximum volume? Round answers to two decimal places.

95. CONSTRUCTION A freshwater pipe is to be run from a source on the edge of a lake to a small resort community on an island 8 miles offshore, as indicated in the figure. It costs \$10,000 per mile to lay the pipe on land and \$16,000 per mile to lay the pipe in the lake. The total cost $C(x)$ in thousands of dollars of laying the pipe is given by

$$C(x) = 10(20 - x) + 16\sqrt{x^2 + 64} \qquad 0 \le x \le 20$$

Find the length (to two decimal places) of the land portion of the pipe that will make the production costs minimum. Find the minimum cost to the nearest thousand dollars.

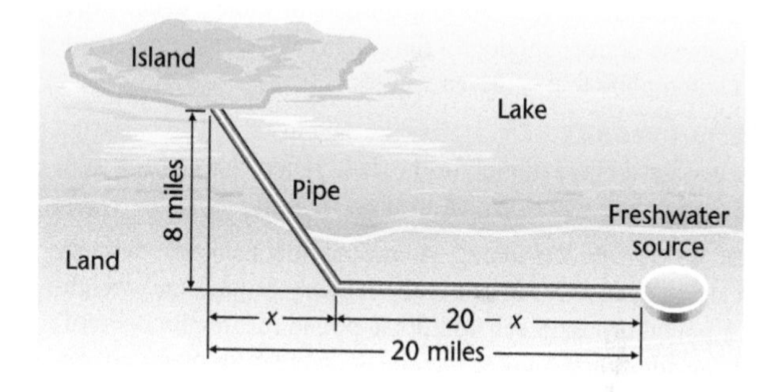

96. TRANSPORTATION The construction company laying the freshwater pipe in Problem 95 uses an amphibious vehicle to travel down the beach and then out to the island. The vehicle travels at 30 miles per hour on land and 7.5 miles per hour in water. The total time $T(x)$ in minutes for a trip from the freshwater source to the island is given by

$$T(x) = 2(20 - x) + 8\sqrt{x^2 + 64} \qquad 0 \le x \le 20$$

Find (to two decimal places) the length of the land portion of the trip that will make the time minimum. Find the minimum time to the nearest minute.

97. COMPUTER SCIENCE Let $f(x) = 10[\![0.5 + x/10]\!]$. Evaluate f at 4, −4, 6, −6, 24, 25, 247, −243, −245, and −246. What operation does this function perform?

98. COMPUTER SCIENCE Let $f(x) = 100[\![0.5 + x/100]\!]$. Evaluate f at 40, −40, 60, −60, 740, 750, 7,551, −601, −649, and −651. What operation does this function perform?

99. COMPUTER SCIENCE Use the greatest integer function to define a function f that rounds real numbers to the nearest hundredth.

100. COMPUTER SCIENCE Use the greatest integer function to define a function f that rounds real numbers to the nearest thousandth.

MODELING AND DATA ANALYSIS

Table 1 contains daily automobile rental rates from a New Jersey firm.

Table 1

Vehicle Type	Daily Charge	Included Miles	Mileage Charge*
Compact	\$32.00	100/Day	\$0.16/mile
Midsize	\$41.00	200/Day	\$0.18/mile

*Mileage charge does not apply to included miles.
Source: www.gogelauto.com

101. AUTOMOBILE RENTAL Use the data in Table 1 to construct a piecewise-defined model for the daily rental charge for a compact automobile that is driven x miles.

102. AUTOMOBILE RENTAL Use the data in Table 1 to construct a piecewise-defined model for the daily rental charge for a midsize automobile that is driven x miles.

103. DELIVERY CHARGES A nationwide package delivery service charges \$15 for overnight delivery of packages weighing 1 pound or less. Each additional pound (or fraction thereof) costs an additional \$3. Let $C(x)$ be the charge for overnight delivery of a package weighing x pounds.
(A) Write a piecewise definition of C for $0 < x \le 6$ and sketch the graph of C by hand.
(B) Can the function f defined by $f(x) = 15 + 3[\![x]\!]$ be used to compute the delivery charges for all x, $0 < x \le 6$? Justify your answer.

104. TELEPHONE CHARGES Calls to 900 numbers are charged to the caller. A 900 number hot line for tips and hints for video games charges \$4 for the first minute of the call and \$2 for each additional minute (or fraction thereof). Let $C(x)$ be the charge for a call lasting x minutes.
(A) Write a piecewise definition of C for $0 < x \le 6$ and sketch the graph of C by hand.
(B) Can the function f defined by $f(x) = 4 + 2[\![x]\!]$ be used to compute the charges for all x, $0 < x \le 6$? Justify your answer.

105. SALES COMMISSIONS An appliance salesperson receives a base salary of \$200 a week and a commission of 4% on all sales over \$3,000 during the week. In addition, if the weekly sales are \$8,000 or more, the salesperson receives a \$100 bonus. If x represents weekly sales (in dollars), express the weekly earnings $E(x)$ as a function of x, and sketch its graph. Identify any points of discontinuity. Find $E(5{,}750)$ and $E(9{,}200)$.

106. SERVICE CHARGES On weekends and holidays, an emergency plumbing repair service charges \$2.00 per minute for the first 30 minutes of a service call and \$1.00 per minute for each additional minute. If x represents the duration of a service call in minutes, express the total service charge $S(x)$ as a function of x, and sketch its graph. Identify any points of discontinuity. Find $S(25)$ and $S(45)$.

Table 2 contains income tax rates for Minnesota in a recent year.

Table 2

Status	Taxable Income Over	But Not Over	Tax Is	Of the Amount Over
Single	\$0	\$19,890	5.35%	\$0
	19,890	65,330	\$1,064 + 7.05%	19,890
	65,330	. . .	4,268 + 7.85%	65,330
Married	0	29,070	5.35%	0
	29,070	115,510	1,555 + 7.05%	29,070
	115,510	. . .	7,649 + 7.85%	115,510

107. STATE INCOME TAX Use the schedule in Table 2 to construct a piecewise-defined model for the taxes due for a single taxpayer with a taxable income of x dollars. Find the tax on the following incomes: \$10,000, \$30,000, \$100,000.

108. STATE INCOME TAX Use the schedule in Table 2 to construct a piecewise-defined model for the taxes due for a married taxpayer with a taxable income of x dollars. Find the tax on the following incomes: \$20,000, \$60,000, \$200,000.

109. TIRE MILEAGE An automobile tire manufacturer collected the data in the table relating tire pressure x, in pounds per square inch (lb/in.^{2}), and mileage in thousands of miles.

x	28	30	32	34	36
Mileage	45	52	55	51	47

A mathematical model for these data is given by

$$f(x) = -0.518x^2 + 33.3x - 481$$

(A) Compare the model and the data graphically and numerically.
(B) Find (to two decimal places) the mileage for a tire pressure of 31 lb/in.^{2} and for 35 lb/in.^{2}.
(C) Write a brief description of the relationship between tire pressure and mileage, using the terms *increasing, decreasing, local maximum,* and *local minimum* where appropriate.

110. STOCK PRICES The table lists the closing price of stock in Carnival Cruise Lines on the first trading day of each year from 2003 to 2007.

Year	03	04	05	06	07
Price	26.05	39.82	57.31	54.57	50.95

A mathematical model for Carnival's stock price is given by

$$f(x) = -3.93x^2 + 22.2x + 24.9$$

where $x = 0$ corresponds to 2003.

(A) Compare the model and the data graphically and numerically.

(B) What does the model predict the stock price will be at the beginning of 2008 and 2009? Round to the nearest cent.

(C) Write a brief verbal description of Carnival's stock price from 2003 to 2007, using *increasing, decreasing, local maximum,* and *local minimum* where appropriate.

1-4 Functions: Graphs and Transformations

We have seen that the graph of a function can provide valuable insight into the information provided by that function. But there is a seemingly endless variety of functions out there, and it seems like an insurmountable task to learn about so many different graphs. In this section, we will see that relationships between the formulas for certain functions lead to relationships between their graphs as well. For example, the functions

$$g(x) = x^2 + 2 \qquad h(x) = (x + 2)^2 \qquad k(x) = 2x^2$$

can be expressed in terms of the function $f(x) = x^2$ as follows:

$$g(x) = f(x) + 2 \qquad h(x) = f(x + 2) \qquad k(x) = 2f(x)$$

We will see that the graphs of functions g, h, and k are closely related to the graph of function f.

Once we understand these relationships, knowing the graph of a very simple function like $f(x) = x^2$ will enable us to learn about the graphs of many related functions.

› A Library of Elementary Graphs

As you progress through this book, you will encounter a number of basic functions that you will want to add to your library of elementary functions. Figure 1 on the next page shows six basic functions that you will encounter frequently. You should know the definition, domain, and range of each of these functions, and be able to recognize their graphs. To help you become familiar with these graphs, it would be a good idea to graph each basic function in Figure 1 on your graphing calculator.

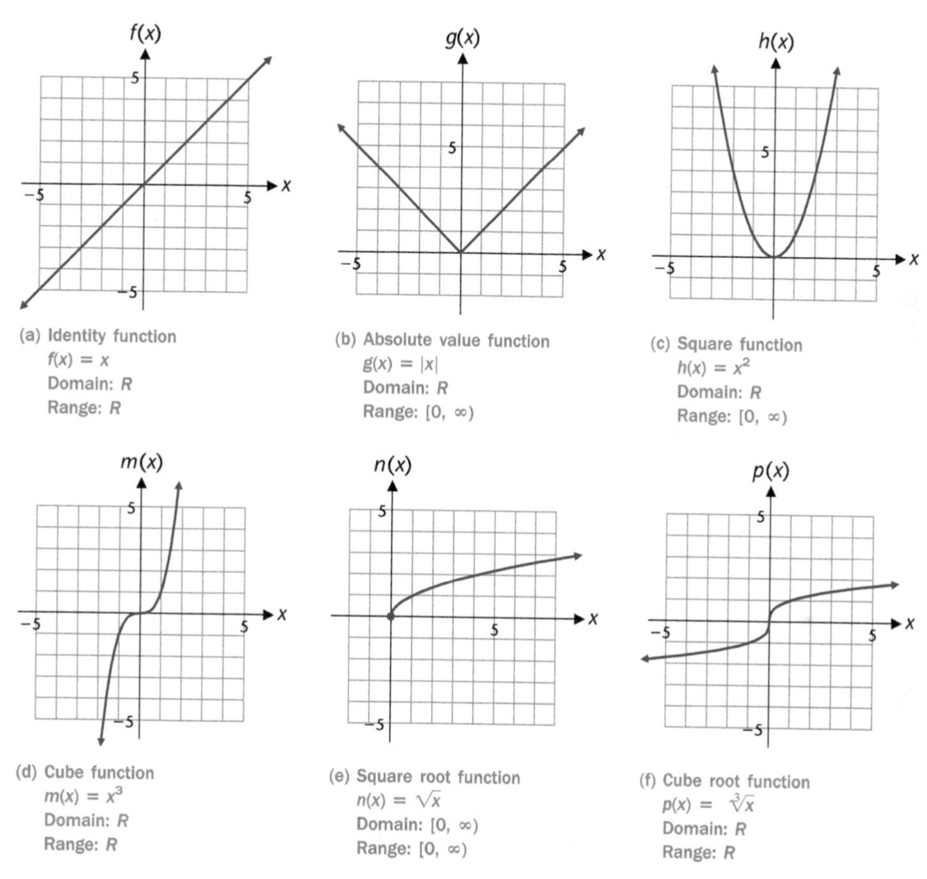

› **Figure 1** Some basic functions and their graphs.
[*Note*: Letters used to designate these functions may vary from context to context; *R* represents the set of all real numbers.]

Most graphing calculators allow you to define a number of functions, usually denoted by $y_1, y_2, y_3, \ldots$. You can graph all of these functions simultaneously, or you can select certain functions for graphing and suppress the graphs of the others. Consult your manual to determine how many functions can be stored in your graphing calculator at one time and how to select particular functions for graphing. Many of our investigations in this section will involve graphing two or more functions at the same time.

› Shifting Graphs Horizontally and Vertically

If a new function is formed by performing an operation on a given function, then the graph of the new function is called a **transformation** of the graph of the original function. For example, if we add a constant k to $f(x)$, then the graph of $y = f(x)$ is transformed into the graph of $y = f(x) + k$.

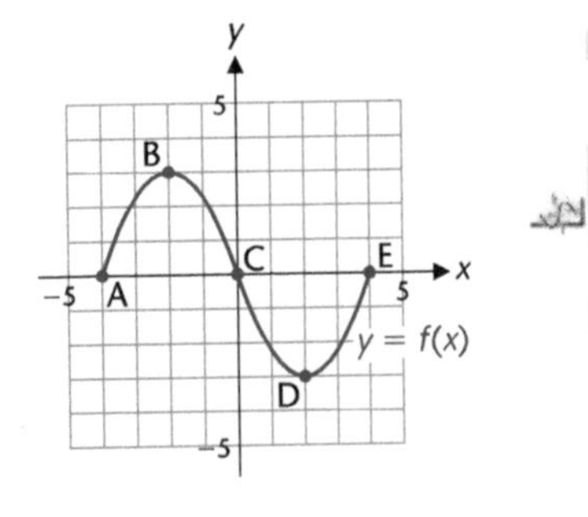

› **Figure 2**

Table 1

	x	$f(x)$
A	−4	0
B	−2	3
C	0	0
D	2	−3
E	4	0

››› EXPLORE-DISCUSS 1

The following activities refer to the graph of f shown in Figure 2 and the corresponding points on the graph shown in Table 1.

(A) Use the points in Table 1 to construct a similar table and then sketch a graph for each of the following functions: $y = f(x) + 2$, $y = f(x) - 3$. Describe the relationship between the graph of $y = f(x)$ and the graph of $y = f(x) + k$ for any real number k.

(B) Use the points in Table 1 to construct a similar table and then sketch a graph for each of the following functions: $y = f(x + 2)$, $y = f(x - 3)$. [*Hint:* Choose values of x so that $x + 2$ or $x - 3$ is in Table 1.] Describe the relationship between the graph of $y = f(x)$ and the graph of $y = f(x + h)$ for any real number h.

(C) Make a conjecture as to the relationship between the graph of $y = f(x)$ and the graph of $y = f(x + h) + k$ for any real numbers h and k. Then check your conjecture by constructing a table and sketching the graph for $y = f(x + 2) - 3$ and $y = f(x - 3) + 2$.

EXAMPLE 1 Vertical and Horizontal Shifts

(A) How are the graphs of $y = x^2 + 2$ and $y = x^2 - 3$ related to the graph of $y = x^2$? Confirm your answer by graphing all three functions simultaneously in the same viewing window.

(B) How are the graphs of $y = (x + 2)^2$ and $y = (x - 3)^2$ related to the graph of $y = x^2$? Confirm your answer by graphing all three functions simultaneously in the same viewing window.

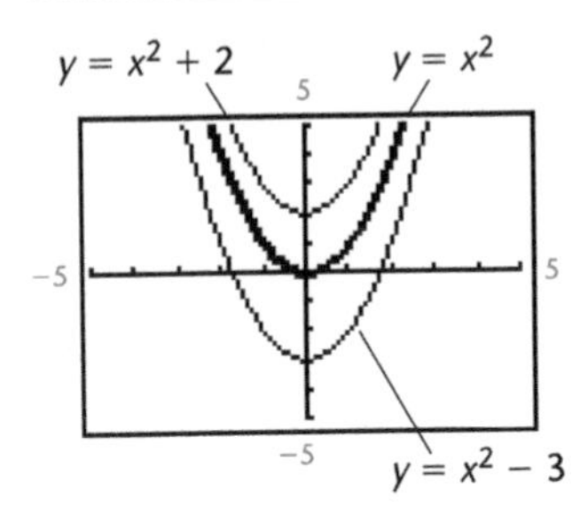

› **Figure 3** Vertical shifts.

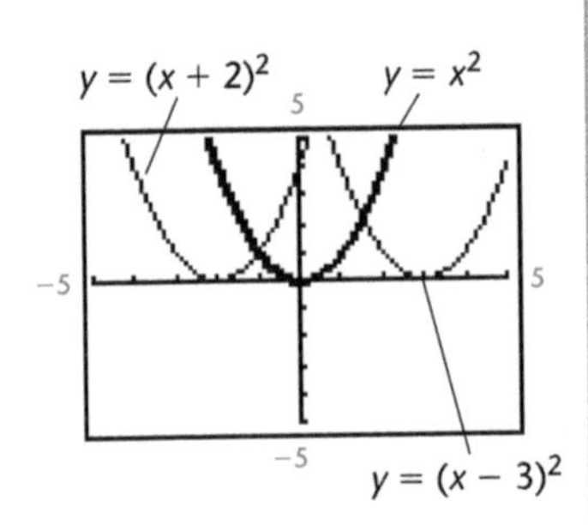

› **Figure 4** Horizontal shifts.

SOLUTIONS

(A) Note that the output of $y = x^2 + 2$ is always exactly two more than the output of $y = x^2$. Consequently, the graph of $y = x^2 + 2$ is the same as the graph of $y = x^2$ shifted upward two units, and the graph of $y = x^2 - 3$ is the same as the graph of $y = x^2$ shifted downward three units. Figure 3 confirms these conclusions. (It appears that the graph of $y = f(x) + k$ is the graph of $y = f(x)$ shifted up if k is positive and down if k is negative.)

(B) Note that the output of $y = (x + 2)^2$ is zero for $x = -2$, while the output of $y = x^2$ is zero for $x = 0$. This suggests that the graph of $y = (x + 2)^2$ is the same as the graph of $y = x^2$ shifted to the left two units, and the graph of $y = (x - 3)^2$ is the same as the graph of $y = x^2$ shifted to the right three units. Figure 4 confirms these conclusions. It appears that the graph of $y = f(x + h)$ is the graph of $y = f(x)$ shifted right if h is negative and left if h is positive.

MATCHED PROBLEM 1

(A) How are the graphs of $y = \sqrt{x} + 3$ and $y = \sqrt{x} - 1$ related to the graph of $y = \sqrt{x}$? Confirm your answer by graphing all three functions simultaneously in the same viewing window.

(B) How are the graphs of $y = \sqrt{x + 3}$ and $y = \sqrt{x - 1}$ related to the graph of $y = \sqrt{x}$? Confirm your answer by graphing all three functions simultaneously in the same viewing window.

Comparing the graph of $y = f(x) + k$ with the graph of $y = f(x)$, we see that the graph of $y = f(x) + k$ can be obtained from the graph of $y = f(x)$ by **vertically translating** (shifting) the graph of the latter upward k units if k is positive and downward $|k|$ units if k is negative. Comparing the graph of $y = f(x + h)$ with the graph of $y = f(x)$, we see that the graph of $y = f(x + h)$ can be obtained from the graph of $y = f(x)$ by **horizontally translating** (shifting) the graph of the latter h units to the left if h is positive and $|h|$ units to the right if h is negative.

››› CAUTION ›››

It may seem intuitive that a positive value of h for $y = f(x + h)$ should shift the graph of f to the right, but in fact it shifts it left. Likewise, a negative value of h shifts the graph to the right, the opposite of the more obvious guess.

EXAMPLE 2 Vertical and Horizontal Translations [Shifts]

The graphs in Figure 5 are either horizontal or vertical shifts of the graph of $f(x) = |x|$. Write appropriate equations for functions G, H, M, and N in terms of f.

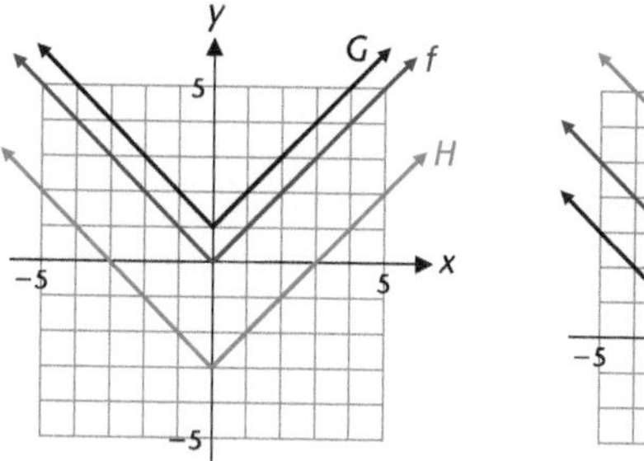

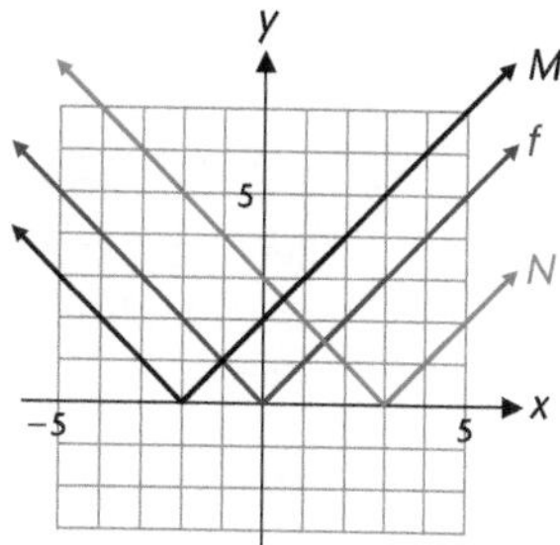

› **Figure 5** Vertical and horizontal shifts.

SOLUTION

The graphs of functions H and G are 3 units lower and 1 unit higher, respectively, than the graph of f, so H and G are vertical shifts given by

$$H(x) = |x| - 3 \qquad G(x) = |x| + 1$$

The graphs of functions M and N are 2 units to the left and 3 units to the right, respectively, of the graph of f, so M and N are horizontal shifts given by

$$M(x) = |x + 2| \qquad N(x) = |x - 3|$$

MATCHED PROBLEM 2

The graphs in Figure 6 are either horizontal or vertical shifts of the graph of $f(x) = x^3$. Write appropriate equations for functions H, G, M, and N in terms of f.

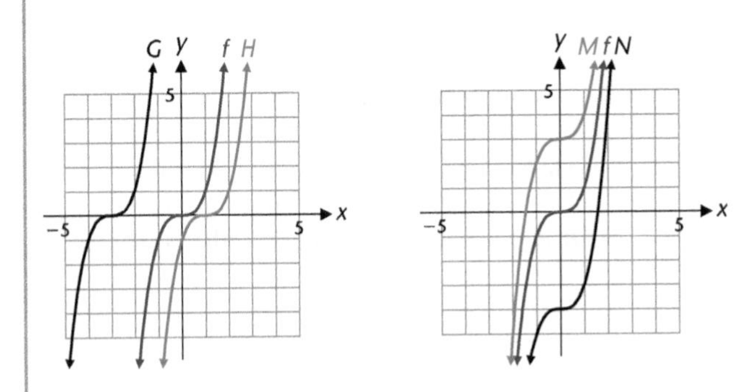

› **Figure 6** Vertical and horizontal shifts.

› Stretching and Shrinking Graphs

We will now investigate how the graph of $y = f(x)$ is related to the graph of $y = Af(x)$ and to the graph of $y = f(Ax)$ for different positive real numbers A.

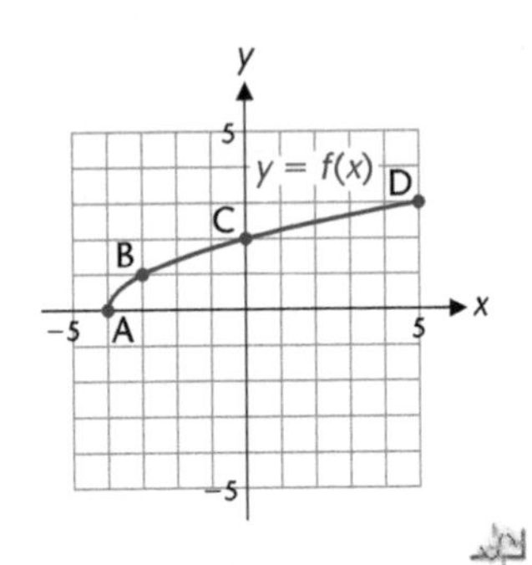

› **Figure 7**

Table 2

	x	$f(x)$
A	−4	0
B	−3	1
C	0	2
D	5	3

››› EXPLORE-DISCUSS 2

The following activities refer to the graph of f shown in Figure 7 and the corresponding points on the graph shown in Table 2.

(A) Construct a similar table and then sketch a graph for each of the following functions: $y = 2f(x), y = \frac{1}{2}f(x)$. Describe the relationship between the graph of $y = f(x)$ and the graph of $y = Af(x)$ for A any positive real number.

(B) Construct a similar table and then sketch a graph for each of the following functions: $y = f(2x), y = f(\frac{1}{2}x)$. [*Hint:* Select the x values for your table so that the multiples of x are in Table 2.] Describe the relationship between the graph of $y = f(x)$ and the graph of $y = f(Ax)$ for A any positive real number.

Comparing the graph of $y = Af(x)$ in Explore-Discuss 2 with the graph of $y = f(x)$, we see that the graph of $y = Af(x)$ can be obtained from the graph of $y = f(x)$ by multiplying each y coordinate of the latter by A. If $A > 1$, multiplying by A makes the y coordinates bigger; we say that this **vertically stretches** the graph of f. If $0 < A < 1$, multiplying by A makes the y coordinates smaller; this **vertically shrinks** the graph of f. Note that in each case, points on the x axis remain fixed, while all other points are "pulled away" from, or "pushed toward" the x axis.

Likewise, comparing the graph of $y = f(Ax)$ with the graph of $y = f(x)$, we see that the graph of $y = f(Ax)$ can be obtained from the graph of $y = f(x)$ by multiplying each x coordinate of the latter by $\frac{1}{A}$. This **horizontally stretches** the graph of $y = f(x)$ if $0 < A < 1$ and **horizontally shrinks** the graph of $y = f(x)$ if $A > 1$.

››› CAUTION ›››

As with horizontal shifts, horizontally stretching and shrinking work opposite the way you might expect. When $A > 1$, $f(Ax)$ is shrunk toward the y axis, and when $0 < A < 1$, $f(Ax)$ is stretched away from the y axis.

EXAMPLE 3 Stretches and Shrinks

(A) How are the graphs of $y = 2\sqrt[3]{x}$ and $y = 0.5\sqrt[3]{x}$ related to the graph of $y = \sqrt[3]{x}$? Confirm your answer by graphing all three functions simultaneously in the same viewing window.

(B) How are the graphs of $y = \sqrt[3]{2x}$ and $y = \sqrt[3]{0.5x}$ related to the graph of $y = \sqrt[3]{x}$? Confirm your answer by graphing all three functions simultaneously in the same viewing window.

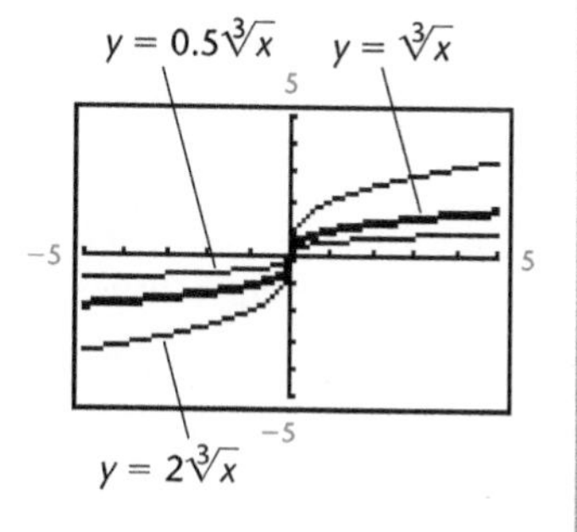

› **Figure 8** Vertical stretching and shrinking.

SOLUTIONS

(A) The graph of $y = 2\sqrt[3]{x}$ can be obtained from the graph of $y = \sqrt[3]{x}$ by multiplying each y value by 2. This stretches the graph vertically by a factor of 2. The graph of $y = 0.5\sqrt[3]{x}$ can be obtained from the graph of $y = \sqrt[3]{x}$ by multiplying each y value by 0.5. This shrinks the graph vertically by a factor of 0.5 (Fig. 8).

(B) The graph of $y = \sqrt[3]{2x}$ can be obtained from the graph of $y = \sqrt[3]{x}$ by multiplying each x value by $\frac{1}{2}$. This shrinks the graph horizontally by a factor of $\frac{1}{2}$. The graph of $y = \sqrt[3]{0.5x}$ can be obtained from the graph of $y = \sqrt[3]{x}$ by multiplying each x value by 2. This stretches the graph horizontally by a factor of 2 (Fig. 9).

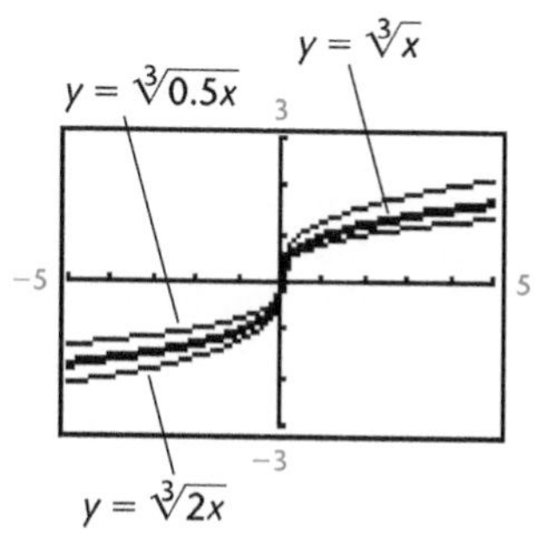

› **Figure 9** Horizontal stretching and shrinking.

MATCHED PROBLEM 3

(A) How are the graphs of $y = 2x^3$ and $y = 0.5x^3$ related to the graph of $y = x^3$? Confirm your answer by graphing all three functions simultaneously in the same viewing window.

(B) How are the graphs of $y = (2x)^3$ and $y = (0.5x)^3$ related to the graph of $y = x^3$? Confirm your answer by graphing all three functions simultaneously in the same viewing window.

› Reflecting Graphs in the x and y Axes

Next, we will investigate how the graphs of $y = -f(x)$ and $y = f(-x)$ are related to the graph of $y = f(x)$.

››› EXPLORE-DISCUSS 3

The following activities refer to the graph of f shown in Figure 10 and the corresponding points on the graph shown in Table 3.

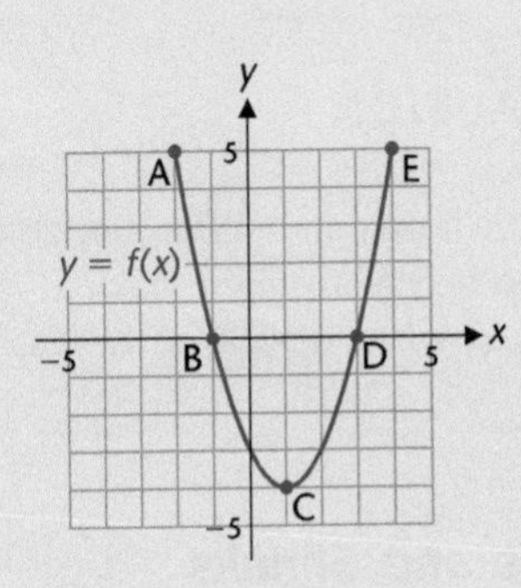

› **Figure 10**

Table 3

	x	$f(x)$
A	-2	5
B	-1	0
C	1	-4
D	3	0
E	4	5

(A) Construct a similar table and then sketch a graph for $y = -f(x)$. Describe the relationship between the graph of $y = f(x)$ and the graph of $y = -f(x)$.

(B) Construct a similar table and then sketch a graph for $y = f(-x)$. [*Hint:* Choose x values so that $-x$ is in Table 3.] Describe the relationship between the graph of $y = f(x)$ and the graph of $y = f(-x)$.

(C) Construct a similar table and then sketch a graph for $y = -f(-x)$. [*Hint:* Choose x values so that $-x$ is in Table 3.] Describe the relationship between the graph of $y = f(x)$ and the graph of $y = -f(-x)$.

The graph of $y = -f(x)$ can be obtained from the graph of $y = f(x)$ by changing the sign of each y coordinate. This has the effect of moving every point on the graph to the opposite side of the x axis. We call this a **reflection in the x axis.** In other words, the graph of $y = -f(x)$ is a mirror image of the graph of $y = f(x)$ on the opposite side of the x axis.

Similarly, the graph of $y = f(-x)$ can be obtained from the graph of $y = f(x)$ by changing the sign of every x coordinate. This has the effect of moving every point on the graph to the opposite side of the y axis, which we call a **reflection in the y axis.**

Finally, the graph of $y = -f(-x)$ can be obtained from the graph of $y = f(x)$ by changing the sign of each x coordinate *and* each y coordinate. This is called a **reflection in the origin,** and is equivalent to reflecting first in one axis, then in the other. Figure 11 illustrates these reflections for $f(x) = \sqrt{x}$.

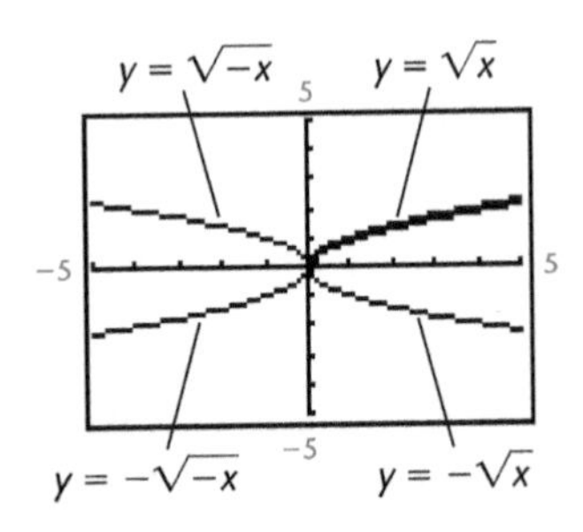

› **Figure 11** Reflections of the graph of $y = \sqrt{x}$.

The transformations we've studied so far are summarized in a box for easy reference.

› Figure 12 Graph transformations.

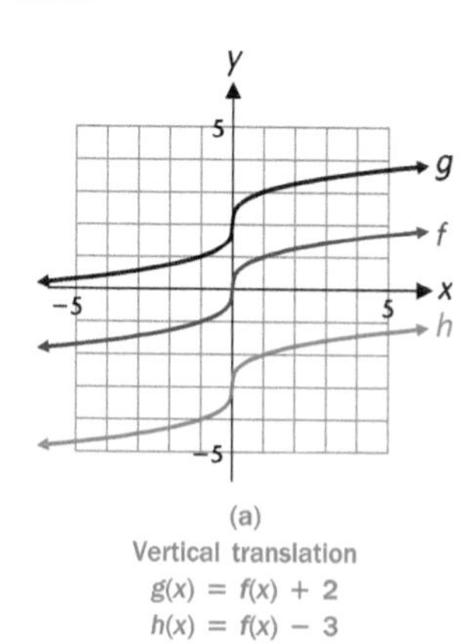

(a)
Vertical translation
$g(x) = f(x) + 2$
$h(x) = f(x) - 3$

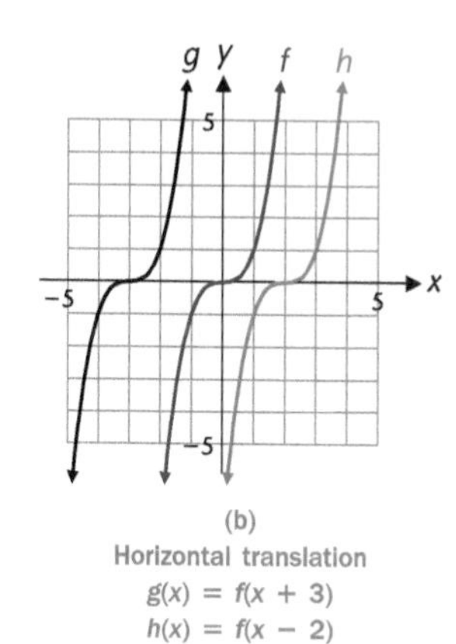

(b)
Horizontal translation
$g(x) = f(x + 3)$
$h(x) = f(x - 2)$

SUMMARY OF GRAPH TRANSFORMATIONS

Vertical Translation [Fig. 12(a)]:

$y = f(x) + k$ $\begin{cases} k > 0 & \text{Shift graph of } y = f(x) \text{ up } k \text{ units} \\ k < 0 & \text{Shift graph of } y = f(x) \text{ down } |k| \text{ units} \end{cases}$

Horizontal Translation [Fig. 12(b)]:

$y = f(x + h)$ $\begin{cases} h > 0 & \text{Shift graph of } y = f(x) \text{ left } h \text{ units} \\ h < 0 & \text{Shift graph of } y = f(x) \text{ right } |h| \text{ units} \end{cases}$

Vertical Stretch and Shrink [Fig. 12(c)]:

$y = Af(x)$ $\begin{cases} A > 1 & \text{Vertically stretch the graph of } y = f(x) \text{ by multiplying each } y \text{ value by } A \\ 0 < A < 1 & \text{Vertically shrink the graph of } y = f(x) \text{ by multiplying each } y \text{ value by } A \end{cases}$

Horizontal Stretch and Shrink [Fig. 12(d)]:

$y = f(Ax)$ $\begin{cases} A > 1 & \text{Horizontally shrink the graph of } y = f(x) \text{ by multiplying each } x \text{ value by } \frac{1}{A} \\ 0 < A < 1 & \text{Horizontally stretch the graph of } y = f(x) \text{ by multiplying each } x \text{ value by } \frac{1}{A} \end{cases}$

Reflection [Fig. 12(e)]:

$y = -f(x)$ Reflect the graph of $y = f(x)$ in the x axis
$y = f(-x)$ Reflect the graph of $y = f(x)$ in the y axis
$y = -f(-x)$ Reflect the graph of $y = f(x)$ in the origin

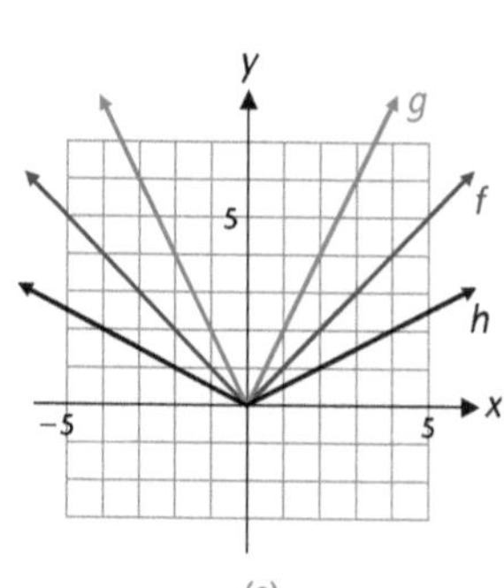

(c)
Vertical stretch and shrink
$g(x) = 2f(x)$
$h(x) = 0.5f(x)$

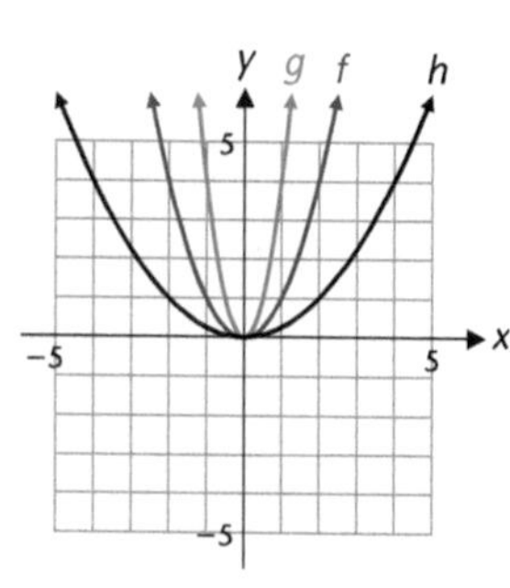

(d)
Horizontal stretch and shrink
$g(x) = f(2x)$
$h(x) = f(0.5x)$

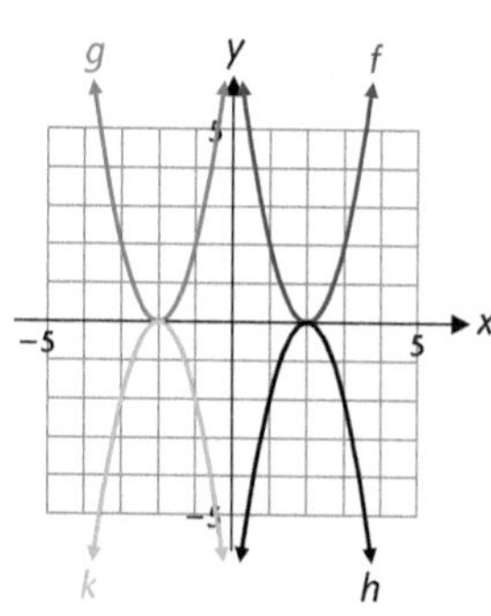

(e)
Reflection
$g(x) = f(-x)$
$h(x) = -f(x)$
$k(x) = -f(-x)$

››› EXPLORE-DISCUSS 4

(A) Use a graphing calculator to explore the graph of $y = A(x + h)^2 + k$ for various values of the constants A, h, and k. Discuss how the graph of $y = A(x + h)^2 + k$ is related to the graph of $y = x^2$.

(B) The graph of $y = A(x + h)^2 + k$ has both shifts and a stretch or shrink. Based on the graphs you explored in part A, which come first, shifts or a stretch/shrink? Can you think of an algebraic reason why this should be the case?

EXAMPLE 4 Combining Graph Transformations

The graph of $y = g(x)$ in Figure 13 is a transformation of the graph of $y = x^2$. Find an equation for the function g.

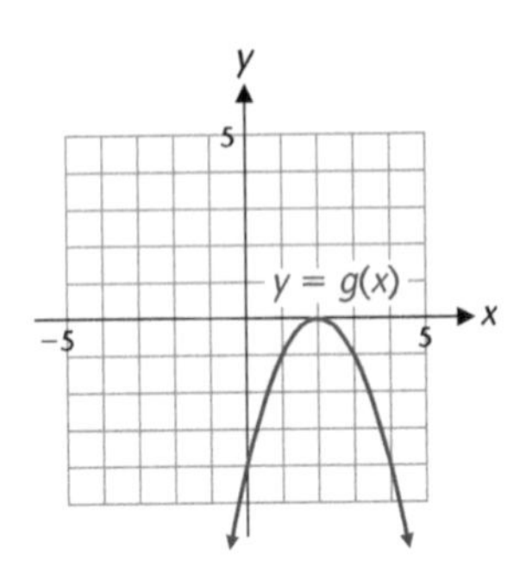

› **Figure 13**

SOLUTION

To transform the graph of $y = x^2$ [Fig. 14(a)] into the graph of $y = g(x)$, we first reflect the graph of $y = x^2$ in the x axis [Fig. 14(b)], then shift it to the right two units [Fig. 14(c)]. Thus, an equation for the function g is

$$g(x) = -(x - 2)^2$$

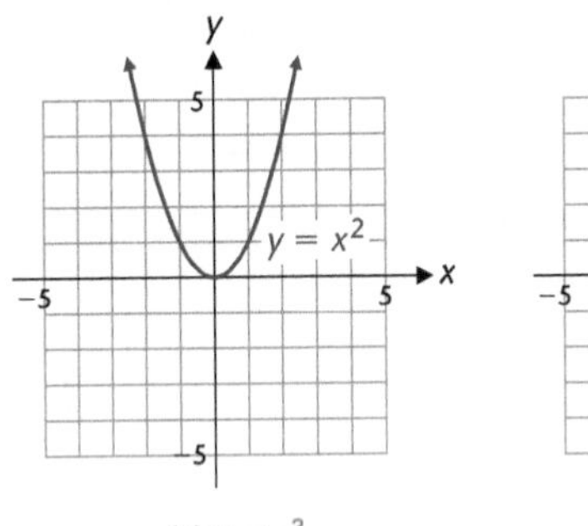

(a) $y = x^2$

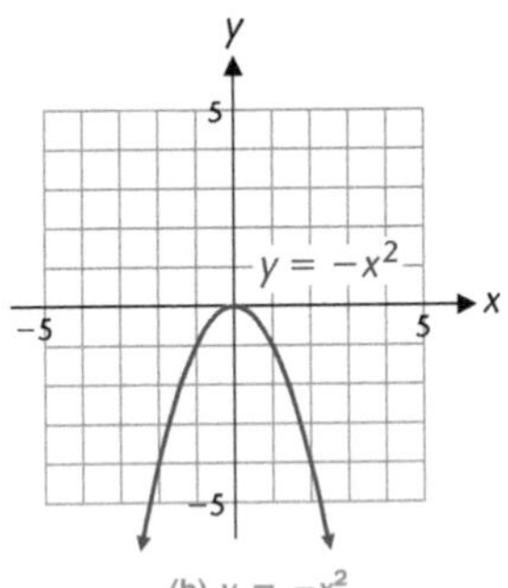

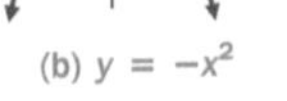
(b) $y = -x^2$

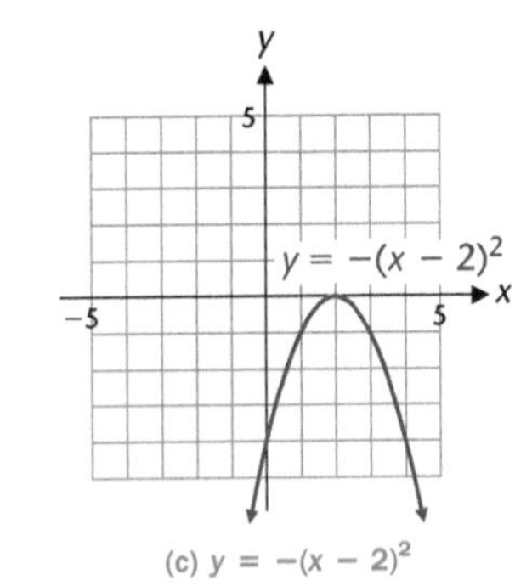

(c) $y = -(x - 2)^2$

› **Figure 14**

MATCHED PROBLEM 4

The graph of $y = h(x)$ in Figure 15 is a transformation of the graph of $y = x^3$. Find an equation for the function h.

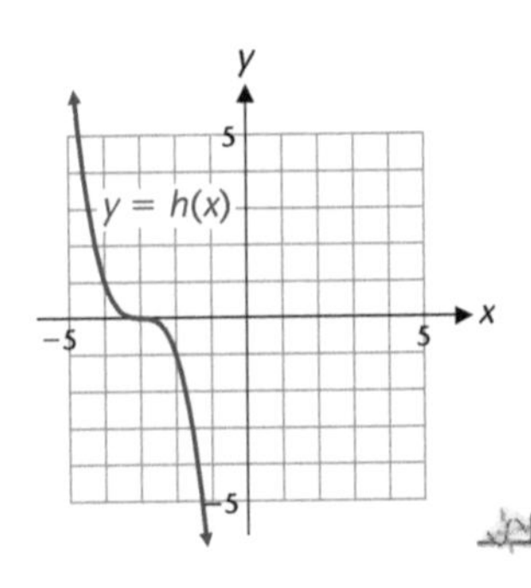

› **Figure 15**

Even and Odd Functions

Certain transformations leave the graphs of some functions unchanged. Review the graphs of $y = x^2$ and $y = x^3$ at the beginning of this section. Reflecting the graph of $y = x^2$ in the y axis does not change the graph. Functions with this property are called *even functions.* Similarly, reflecting the graph of $y = x^3$ in the x axis and then in the y axis does not change the graph. Functions with this property are called *odd functions.* More formally, we have the following definitions.

> **EVEN AND ODD FUNCTIONS**
>
> If $f(x) = f(-x)$ for all x in the domain of f, then f is an **even function.**
>
> If $f(-x) = -f(x)$ for all x in the domain of f, then f is an **odd function.**

The graph of an even function is said to be **symmetric with respect to the y axis** and the graph of an odd function is said to be **symmetric with respect to the origin** (Fig. 16).

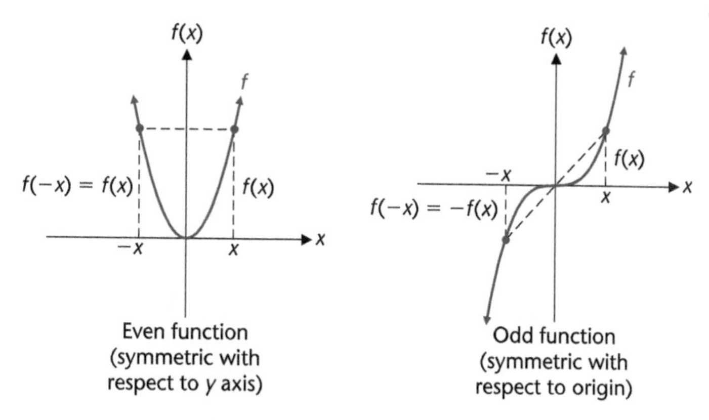

Figure 16 Even and odd functions.

Look again at the graphs of the basic functions in Figure 1. These graphs show that the square and absolute value functions are even functions, and the identity, cube, and cube root functions are odd functions. Notice in Figure 1(e) that the square root function is not symmetric with respect to the y axis or the origin. Thus, the square root function is neither even nor odd.

EXAMPLE 5 Testing for Even and Odd Functions

Determine whether the functions f, g, and h are even, odd, or neither.

(A) $f(x) = x^4 + 1$ (B) $g(x) = x^3 + 1$ (C) $h(x) = x^5 + x$

SOLUTIONS

(A) Algebraic Solution
We substitute $(-x)$ for x, then simplify.

$$\begin{aligned} f(x) &= x^4 + 1 \\ f(-x) &= (-x)^4 + 1 \\ &= [(-1)x]^4 + 1 \\ &= (-1)^4x^4 + 1 \\ &= x^4 + 1 \end{aligned}$$

The result is identical to $f(x)$, so f is even.

(B) Algebraic Solution

$$\begin{aligned} g(x) &= x^3 + 1 \\ g(-x) &= (-x)^3 + 1 \\ &= [(-1)x]^3 + 1 \\ &= (-1)^3x^3 + 1 \\ &= -x^3 + 1 \\ -g(x) &= -(x^3 + 1) \\ &= -x^3 - 1 \end{aligned}$$

Because $g(-x) \neq g(x)$ and $g(-x) \neq -g(x)$, g is neither even nor odd.

(C) Algebraic Solution

$$\begin{aligned} h(x) &= x^5 + x \\ h(-x) &= (-x)^5 + (-x) \\ &= -x^5 - x \\ &= -(x^5 + x) \end{aligned}$$

This is the negative of h, so h is odd.

(A) Graphical Solution
Enter $y_1 = x^4 + 1$ and $y_2 = y_1(-x)$ (Fig. 17), draw the graph (Fig. 18), and use the TRACE command or a table to see that the graphs are identical. Therefore f is even.

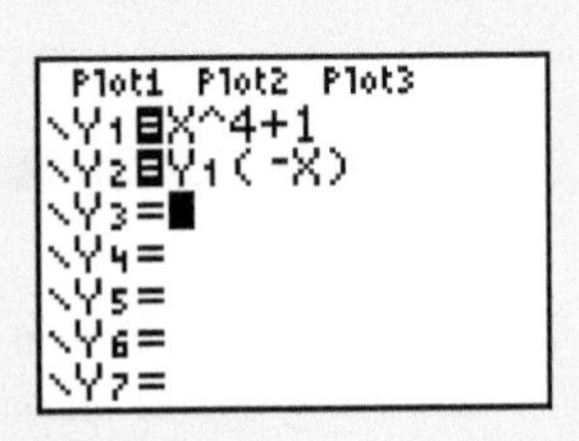

› Figure 17

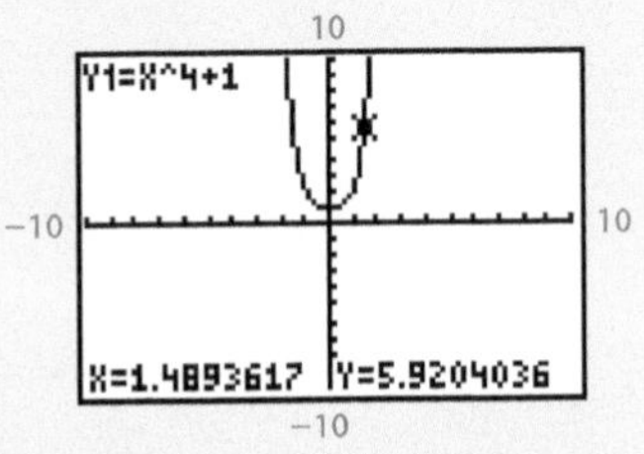

› Figure 18

(B) Graphical Solution
Enter $y_1 = x^3 + 1$, $y_2 = y_1(-x)$, and $y_3 = -y_1(x)$ (Fig. 19), graph (Fig. 20), and observe that no two of these functions are identical. Therefore, g is neither even nor odd.

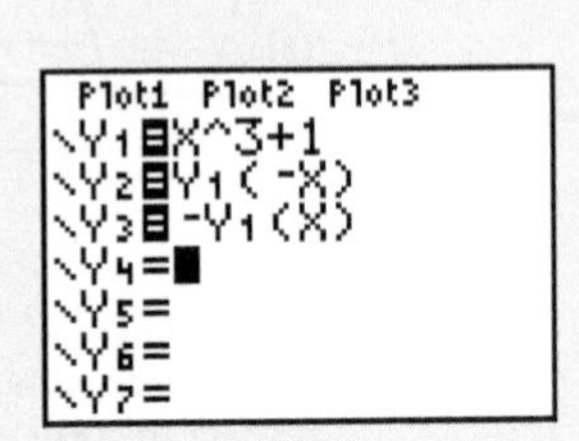

› Figure 19

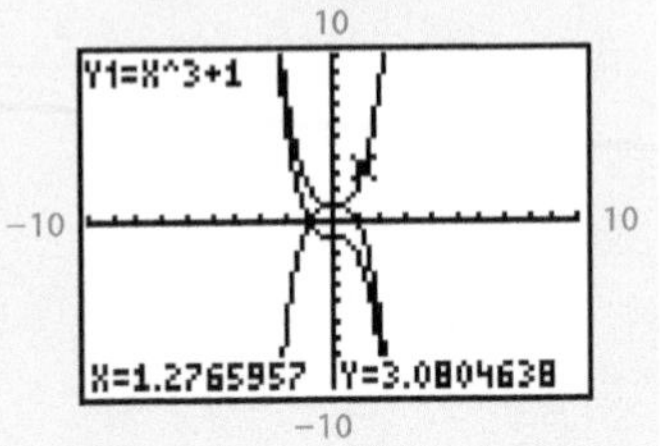

› Figure 20

(C) Graphical Solution
Enter $y_1 = x^5 + x$, $y_2 = y_1(-x)$, and $y_3 = -y_1(x)$ (Fig. 21), graph (Fig. 22), and use the TRACE command or a table to show that y_2 and y_3 are identical. Therefore, h is an odd function.

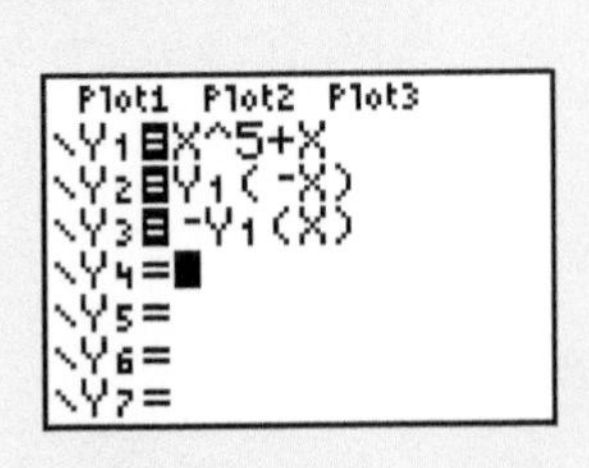

› Figure 21

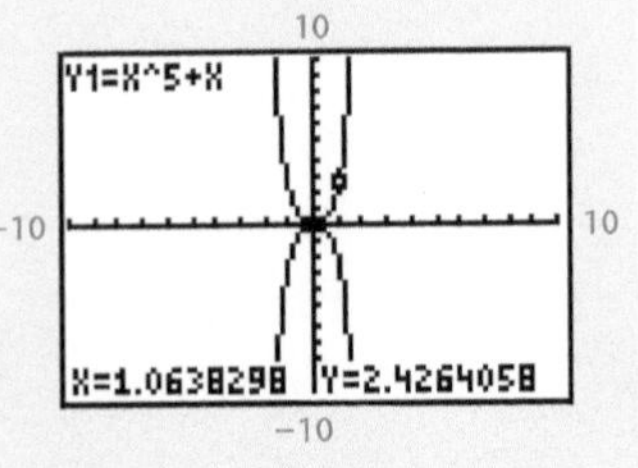

› Figure 22

MATCHED PROBLEM 5

Determine whether the functions F, G, and H are even, odd, or neither:

(A) $F(x) = x^3 - 2x$ (B) $G(x) = x^2 + 1$ (C) $H(x) = 2x + 4$

In the solution of Example 5, notice that we used the fact that

$$(-x)^n = \begin{cases} x^n & \text{if } n \text{ is an even integer} \\ -x^n & \text{if } n \text{ is an odd integer} \end{cases}$$

It is this property that explains the use of the terms *even* and *odd* when describing symmetry properties of the graphs of functions. In addition to being an aid to graphing, certain problems and developments in calculus and more advanced mathematics are simplified if we can recognize when a function is even or odd.

ANSWERS TO MATCHED PROBLEMS

1. (A) The graph of $y = \sqrt{x} + 3$ is the same as the graph of $y = \sqrt{x}$ shifted upward three units, and the graph of $y = \sqrt{x} - 1$ is the same as the graph of $y = \sqrt{x}$ shifted downward one unit. The figure confirms these conclusions.

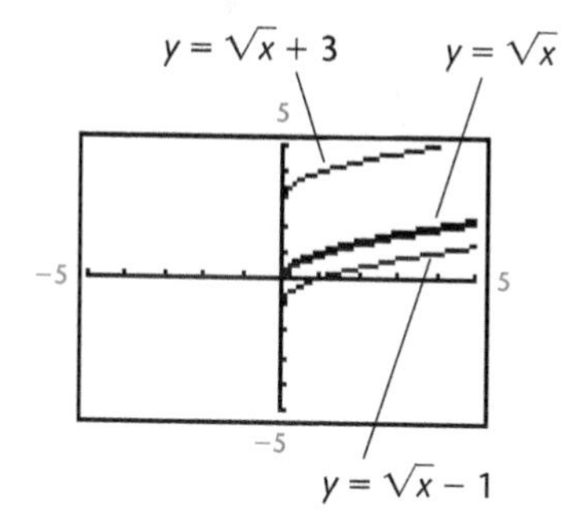

(B) The graph of $y = \sqrt{x + 3}$ is the same as the graph of $y = \sqrt{x}$ shifted to the left three units, and the graph of $y = \sqrt{x - 1}$ is the same as the graph of $y = \sqrt{x}$ shifted to the right one unit. The figure confirms these conclusions.

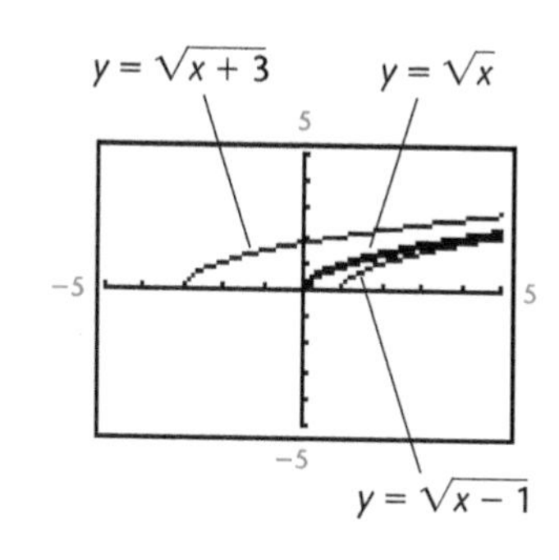

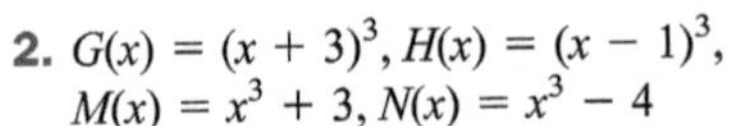

2. $G(x) = (x + 3)^3$, $H(x) = (x - 1)^3$,
$M(x) = x^3 + 3$, $N(x) = x^3 - 4$

3. (A) The graph of $y = 2x^3$ is a vertical stretch of the graph of $y = x^3$ by a factor of 2, and the graph of $y = 0.5x^3$ is a vertical shrink of the graph of $y = x^3$ by a factor of 1/2. The figure confirms these conclusions.

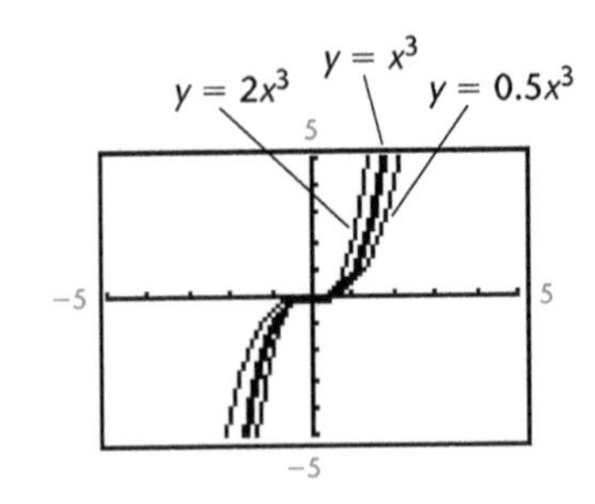

(B) The graph of $y = (2x)^3$ is a horizontal shrink of the graph of $y = x^3$ by a factor of 1/2, and the graph of $y = (0.5x)^3$ is a horizontal stretch of the graph of $y = x^3$ by a factor of 2. The figure confirms these conclusions.

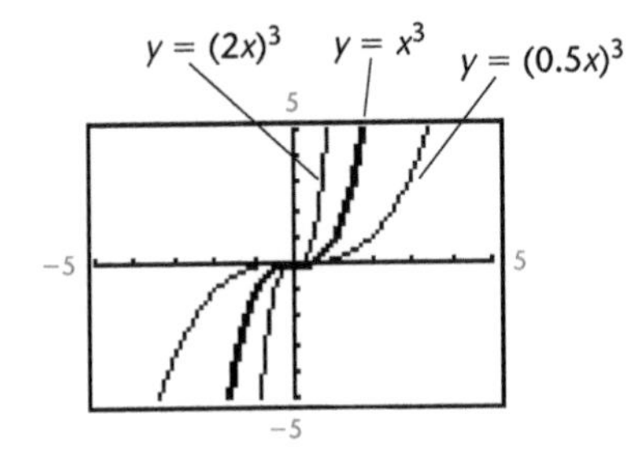

4. The graph of function h is a reflection in the x axis and a horizontal translation of three units to the left of the graph of $y = x^3$. An equation for h is $h(x) = -(x + 3)^3$.

5. (A) Odd (B) Even (C) Neither

1-4 Exercises

1. Explain why the graph of $y = f(x) + k$ is the same as the graph of $y = f(x)$ moved upward k units when k is positive.

2. Explain why the graph of $y = Af(x)$ is a vertical stretch of the graph of $y = f(x)$ if $A > 1$.

3. Is every function either even or odd? Explain.

4. Explain how the informal description of even and odd functions in terms of reflections on page 76 really says the same thing as the formal definition in the box on that page.

Problems 5–20 refer to the functions f and g given by the graphs below (the domain of each function is [−2, 2]). Use the graph of f or g, as required, to graph each given function.

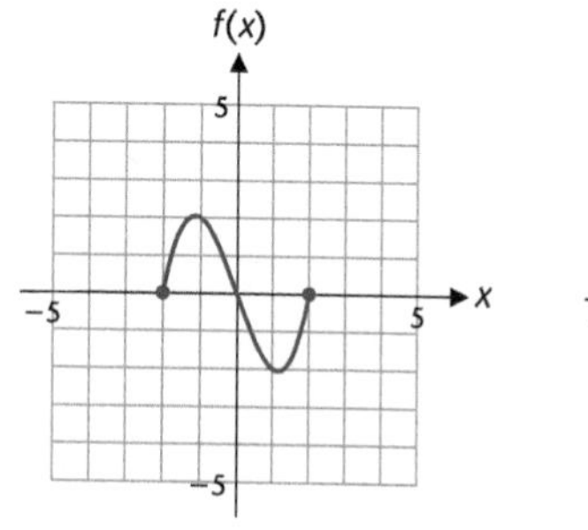

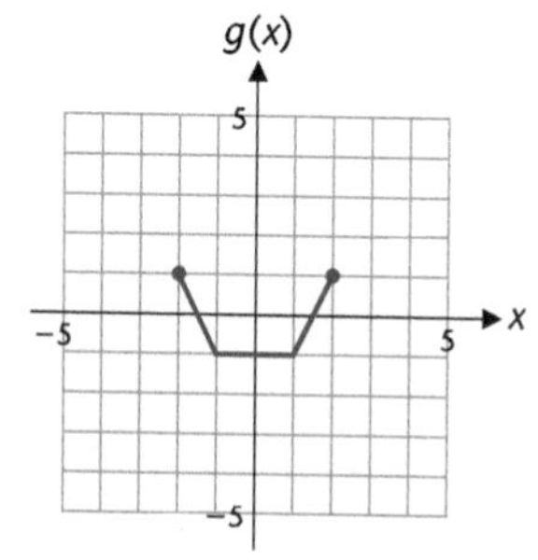

5. $f(x) + 2$

6. $g(x) - 1$

7. $g(x) + 2$

8. $f(x) - 1$

9. $f(x - 2)$

10. $g(x - 1)$

11. $g(x + 2)$

12. $f(x - 1)$

13. $-f(x)$

14. $-g(x)$

15. $2g(x)$

16. $\frac{1}{2}f(x)$

17. $g(2x)$

18. $f(\frac{1}{2}x)$

19. $f(-x)$

20. $-g(-x)$

Indicate whether each function in Problems 21–30 is even, odd, or neither.

21. $g(x) = x^3 + x$

22. $f(x) = x^5 - x$

23. $m(x) = x^4 + 3x^2$

24. $h(x) = x^4 - x^2$

25. $F(x) = x^5 + 1$

26. $f(x) = x^5 - 3$

27. $G(x) = x^4 + 2$

28. $P(x) = x^4 - 4$

29. $q(x) = x^2 + x - 3$

30. $n(x) = 2x - 3$

Each graph in Problems 31–38 is the result of applying a transformation to the graph of one of the six basic functions in Figure 1. Identify the basic function, describe the transformation verbally, and find an equation for the given graph. Check by graphing the equation on a graphing calculator.

31.

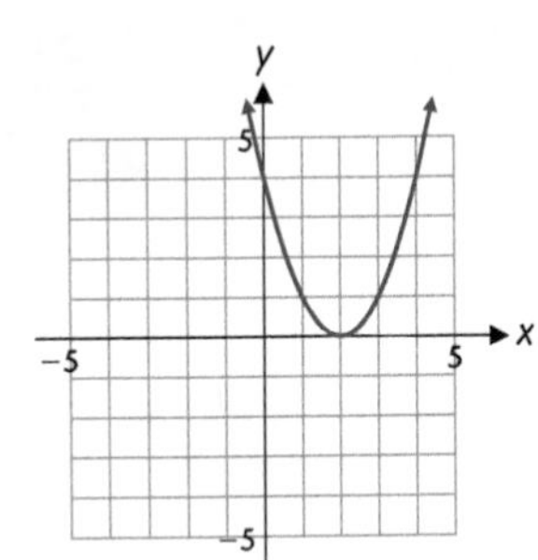

32.

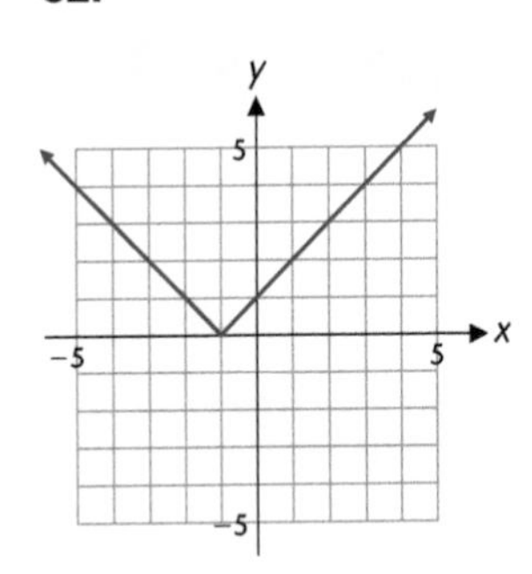

33.

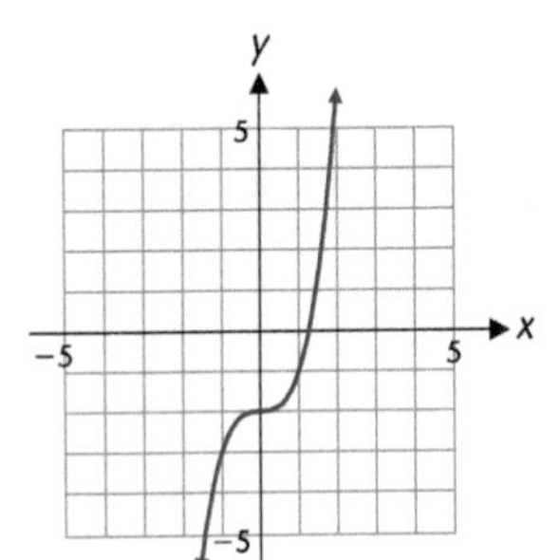

34.

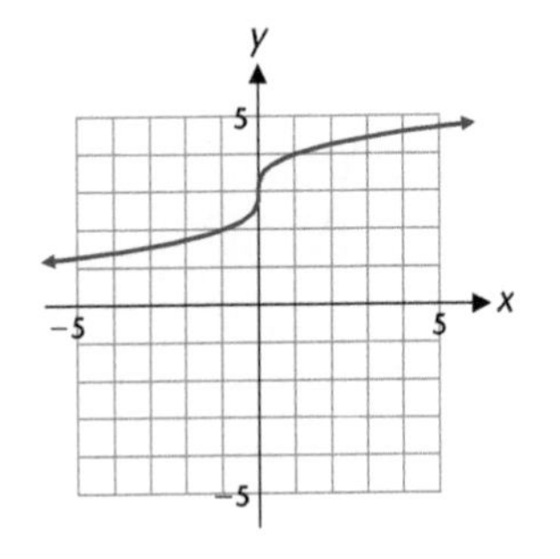

35.

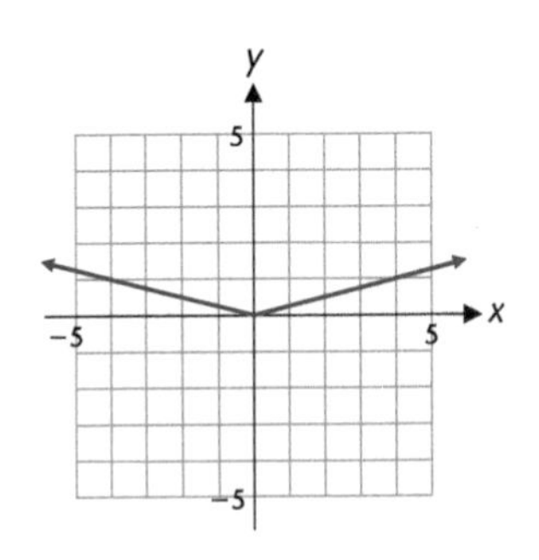

36.

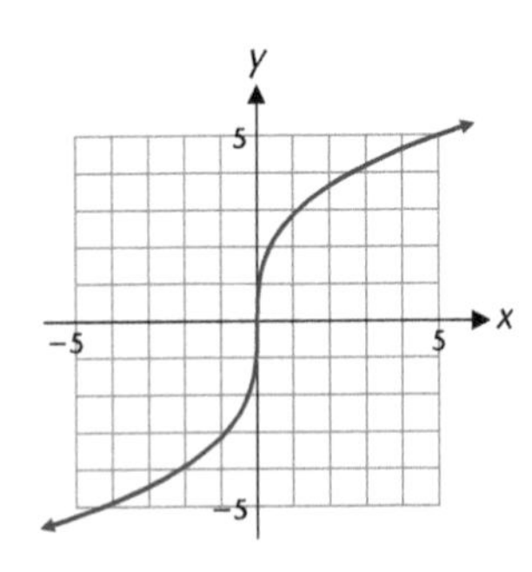

37.

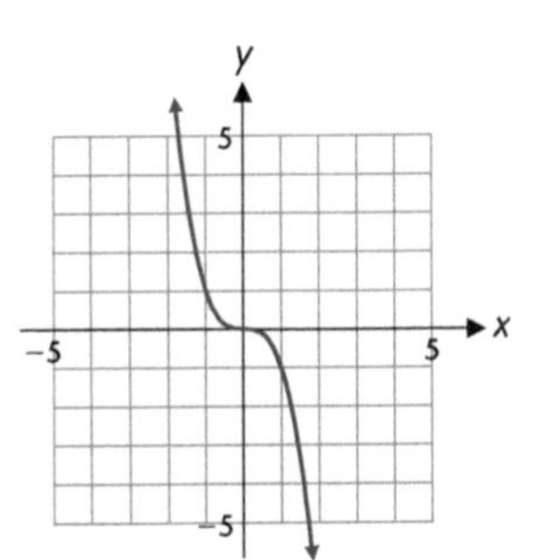

38.

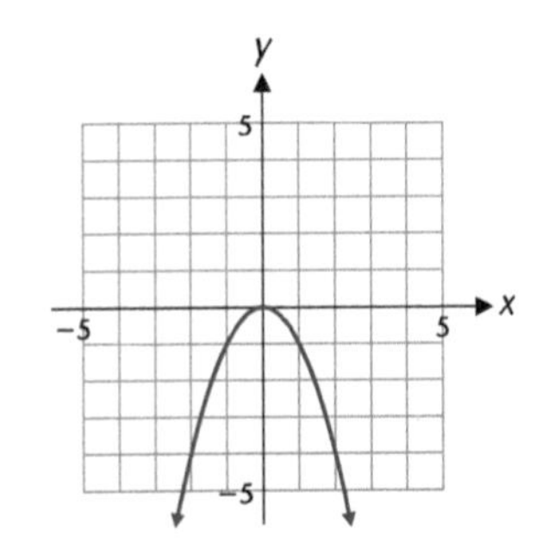

In Problems 39–46, the graph of the function g is formed by applying the indicated sequence of transformations to the given function f. Find an equation for the function g. Check your work by graphing f and g in a standard viewing window.

39. The graph of $f(x) = \sqrt[3]{x}$ is shifted four units to the left and five units down.

40. The graph of $f(x) = x^3$ is shifted five units to the right and four units up.

41. The graph of $f(x) = \sqrt{x}$ is shifted six units up, reflected in the x axis, and vertically shrunk by a factor of 0.5.

42. The graph of $f(x) = \sqrt{x}$ is shifted two units down, reflected in the x axis, and vertically stretched by a factor of 4.

43. The graph of $f(x) = x^2$ is reflected in the x axis, vertically stretched by a factor of 2, shifted four units to the left, and shifted two units down.

44. The graph of $f(x) = |x|$ is reflected in the x axis, vertically shrunk by a factor of 0.5, shifted three units to the right, and shifted four units up.

45. The graph of $f(x) = \sqrt{x}$ is horizontally stretched by a factor of 0.5, reflected in the y axis, and shifted two units to the left.

46. The graph of $f(x) = \sqrt[3]{x}$ is horizontally shrunk by a factor of 2, shifted three units up, and reflected in the y axis.

In Problems 47–54, indicate how the graph of each function is related to the graph of one of the six basic functions in Figure 1, then graph the function.

47. $f(x) = (x + 7)^2 + 9$

48. $g(x) = (x - 4)^2 - 6$

49. $h(x) = -|x - 8|$

50. $k(x) = -|x + 5|$

51. $p(x) = 3 - \sqrt{x}$

52. $q(x) = -2 + \sqrt{x + 3}$

53. $r(x) = -4x^2$

54. $s(x) = -0.5|x|$

Each graph in Problems 55–62 is the result of applying a sequence of transformations to the graph of one of the six basic functions in Figure 1. Find an equation for the given graph. Check by graphing the equation on a graphing calculator.

55.

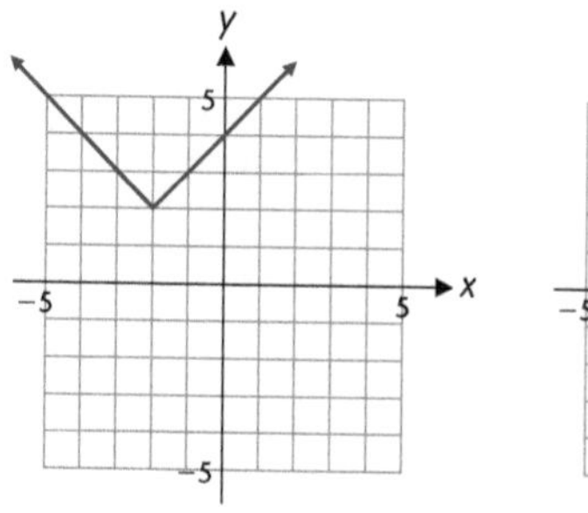

56.

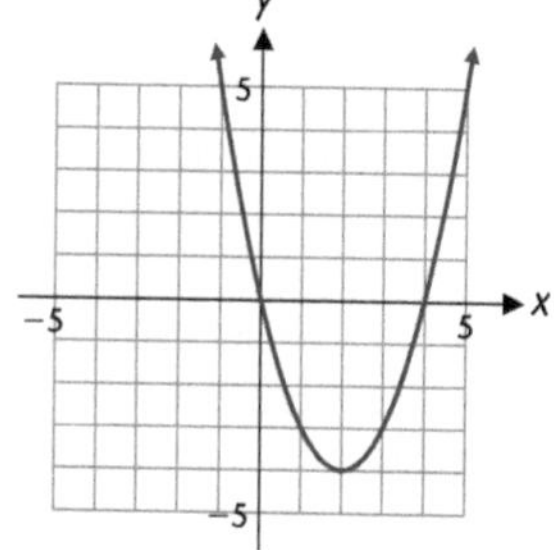

57.

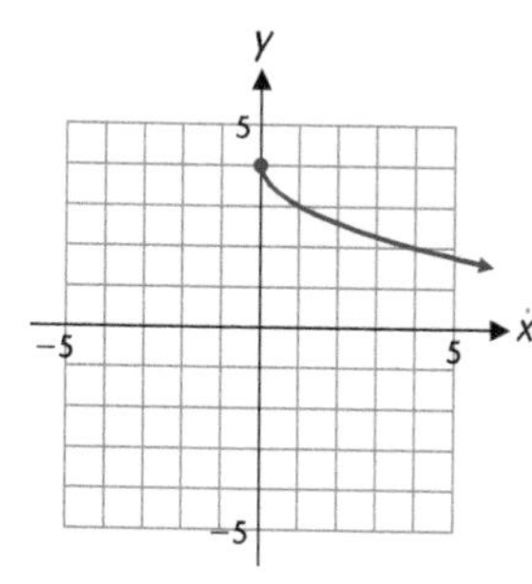

58.

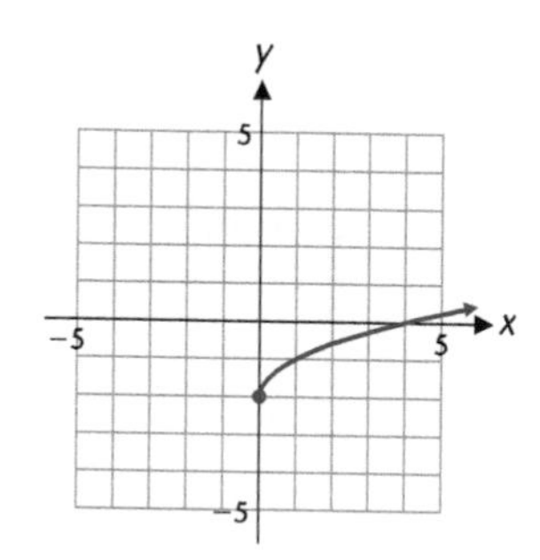

59.

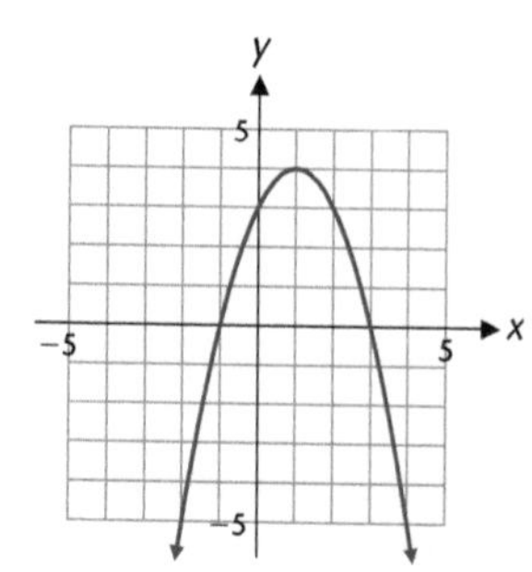

60.

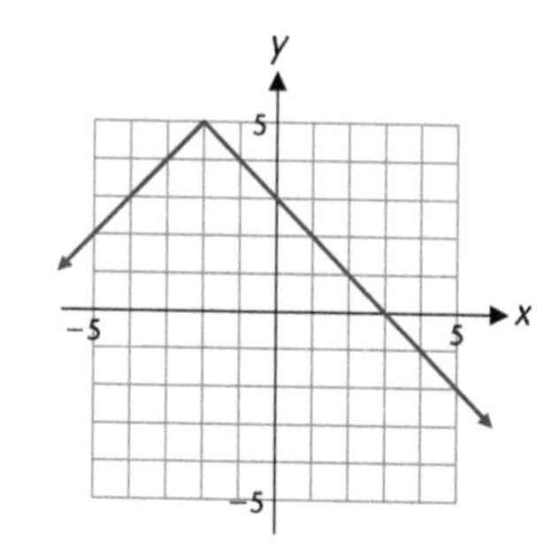

61.

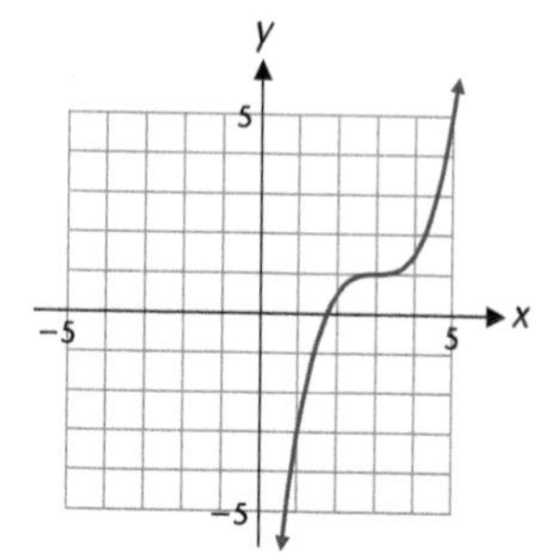

62.

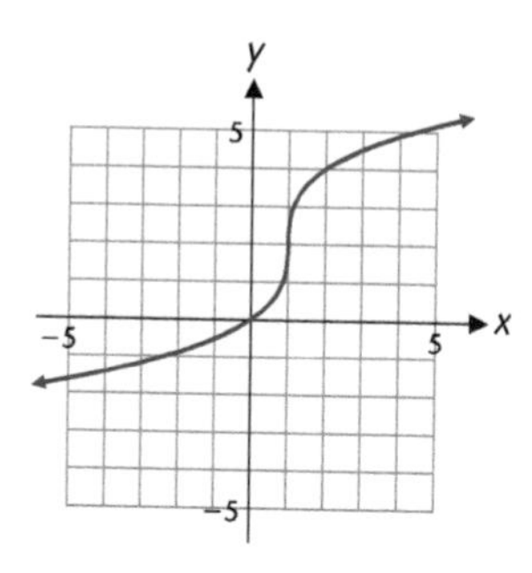

63. Consider the graphs of $f(x) = \sqrt[3]{8x}$ and $g(x) = 2\sqrt[3]{x}$.

(A) Describe each as a stretch or shrink of $y = \sqrt[3]{x}$.

(B) Graph both functions in the same viewing window on a graphing calculator. What do you notice?

(C) Rewrite the formula for f algebraically to show that f and g are in fact the same function. (This shows that for some functions, a horizontal stretch or shrink can also be interpreted as a vertical stretch or shrink.)

64. Consider the graphs of $f(x) = (3x)^3$ and $g(x) = 27x^3$.

(A) Describe each as a stretch or shrink of $y = x^3$.

(B) Graph both functions in the same viewing window on a graphing calculator. What do you notice?

(C) Rewrite the formula for f algebraically to show that f and g are in fact the same function. (This shows that for some functions, a horizontal stretch or shrink can also be interpreted as a vertical stretch or shrink.)

65. (A) Starting with the graph of $y = x^2$, apply the following transformations.

(i) Shift downward 5 units, then reflect in the x axis.

(ii) Reflect in the x axis, then shift downward 5 units.

What do your results indicate about the significance of order when combining transformations?

(B) Write a formula for the function corresponding to each of the above transformations. Discuss the results of part A in terms of order of operations.

66. (A) Starting with the graph of $y = |x|$, apply the following transformations.

(i) Stretch vertically by a factor of 2, then shift upward 4 units.

(ii) Shift upward 4 units, then stretch vertically by a factor of 2.

What do your results indicate about the significance of order when combining transformations?

(B) Write a formula for the function corresponding to each of the above transformations. Discuss the results of part A in terms of order of operations.

Changing the order in a sequence of transformations may change the final result. Investigate each pair of transformations in Problems 67–72 to determine if reversing their order can produce a different result. Support your conclusions with specific examples and/or mathematical arguments.

67. Vertical shift, horizontal shift

68. Vertical shift, reflection in y axis

69. Vertical shift, reflection in x axis

70. Vertical shift, stretch

71. Horizontal shift, reflection in x axis

72. Horizontal shift, shrink

Problems 73–76 refer to two functions f and g with domain $[-5, 5]$ and partial graphs as shown below.

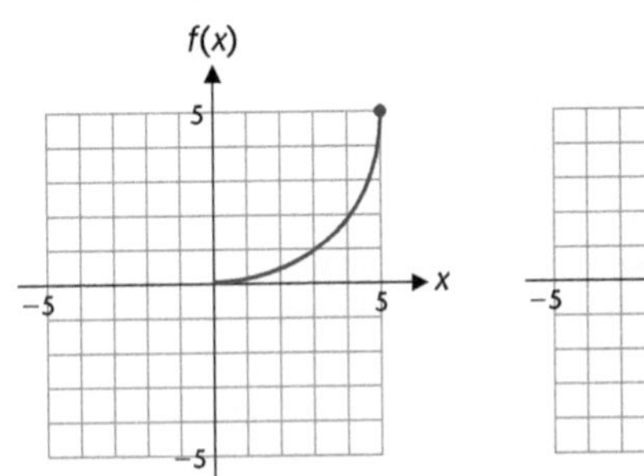

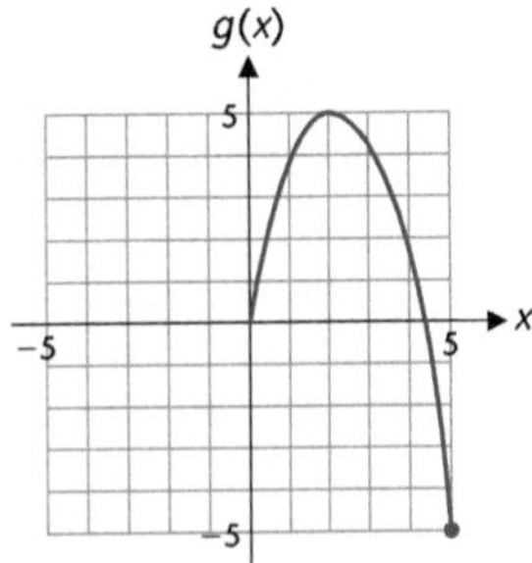

73. Complete the graph of f over the interval $[-5, 0]$, given that f is an even function.

74. Complete the graph of f over the interval $[-5, 0]$, given that f is an odd function.

75. Complete the graph of g over the interval $[-5, 0]$, given that g is an odd function.

76. Complete the graph of g over the interval $[-5, 0]$, given that g is an even function.

77. Let f be any function with the property that $-x$ is in the domain of f whenever x is in the domain of f, and let E and O be the functions defined by

$$E(x) = \tfrac{1}{2}[f(x) + f(-x)]$$

and

$$O(x) = \tfrac{1}{2}[f(x) - f(-x)]$$

(A) Show that E is always even.
(B) Show that O is always odd.
(C) Show that $f(x) = E(x) + O(x)$. What is your conclusion?

78. Let f be any function with the property that $-x$ is in the domain of f whenever x is in the domain of f, and let $g(x) = xf(x)$.
(A) If f is even, is g even, odd, or neither?
(B) If f is odd, is g even, odd, or neither?

In Problems 79–82, graph $f(x)$, $|f(x)|$, and $-|f(x)|$ in a standard viewing window. For purposes of comparison, it will be helpful to graph each function separately and make a hand sketch.

79. $f(x) = 0.2x^2 - 5$

80. $f(x) = 4 - 0.25x^2$

81. $f(x) = 4 - 0.1(x + 2)^3$

82. $f(x) = 0.25(x - 1)^3 - 1$

83. Describe the relationship between the graphs of $f(x)$ and $|f(x)|$ in Problems 79–82.

84. Describe the relationship between the graphs of $f(x)$ and $-|f(x)|$ in Problems 79–82.

APPLICATIONS

85. PRODUCTION COSTS Total production costs for a product can be broken down into fixed costs, which do not depend on the number of units produced, and variable costs, which do depend on the number of units produced. Thus, the total cost of producing x units of the product can be expressed in the form

$$C(x) = K + f(x)$$

where K is a constant that represents the fixed costs and $f(x)$ is a function that represents the variable costs. Use the graph of the variable-cost function $f(x)$ shown in the figure to graph the total cost function if the fixed costs are \$30,000.

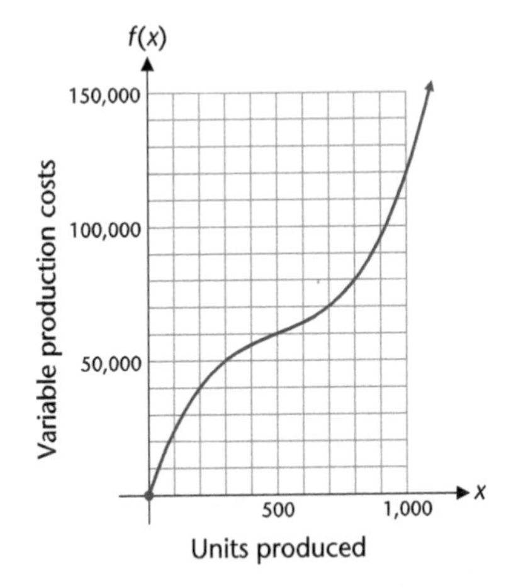

86. COST FUNCTIONS Refer to the variable-cost function $f(x)$ in Problem 85. Suppose construction of a new production facility results in a 25% decrease in the variable cost at all levels of output. If F is the new variable-cost function, use the graph of f to graph $y = F(x)$, then graph the total cost function for fixed costs of \$30,000.

87. TIMBER HARVESTING To determine when a forest should be harvested, forest managers often use formulas to estimate the number of board feet a tree will produce. A board foot equals

1 square foot of wood, 1 inch thick. Suppose that the number of board feet y yielded by a tree can be estimated by

$$y = f(x) = C + 0.004(x - 10)^3$$

where x is the diameter of the tree in inches measured at a height of 4 feet above the ground and C is a constant that depends on the species being harvested. Graph $y = f(x)$ for $C = 10, 15,$ and 20 simultaneously in the viewing window with Xmin = 10, Xmax = 25, Ymin = 10, and Ymax = 35. Write a brief verbal description of this collection of functions.

88. SAFETY RESEARCH If a person driving a vehicle slams on the brakes and skids to a stop, the speed v in miles per hour at the time the brakes are applied is given approximately by

$$v = f(x) = C\sqrt{x}$$

where x is the length of the skid marks and C is a constant that depends on the road conditions and the weight of the vehicle. The table lists values of C for a midsize automobile and various road conditions. Graph $v = f(x)$ for the values of C in the table simultaneously in the viewing window with Xmin = 0, Xmax = 100, Ymin = 0, and Ymax = 60. Write a brief verbal description of this collection of functions.

Road Condition	C
Wet (concrete)	3.5
Wet (asphalt)	4
Dry (concrete)	5
Dry (asphalt)	5.5

89. FAMILY OF CURVES In calculus, solutions to certain types of problems often involve an unspecified constant. For example, consider the equation

$$y = \frac{1}{C}x^2 - C$$

where C is a positive constant. The collection of graphs of this equation for all permissible values of C is called a **family of curves.** Graph the members of this family corresponding to $C = 2, 3, 4,$ and 5 simultaneously in a standard viewing window. Write a brief verbal description of this family of functions.

90. FAMILY OF CURVES A family of curves is defined by the equation

$$y = 2C - \frac{5}{C}x^2$$

where C is a positive constant. Graph the members of this family corresponding to $C = 1, 2, 3,$ and 4 simultaneously in a standard viewing window. Write a brief verbal description of this family of functions.

91. FLUID FLOW A cubic tank is 4 feet on a side and is initially full of water. Water flows out an opening in the bottom of the tank at a rate proportional to the square root of the depth (see the figure). Using advanced concepts from mathematics and physics, it can be shown that the volume of the water in the tank t minutes after the water begins to flow is given by

$$V(t) = \frac{64}{C^2}(C - t)^2 \qquad 0 \le t \le C$$

where C is a constant that depends on the size of the opening. Sketch by hand the graphs of $y = V(t)$ for $C = 1, 2, 4,$ and 8. Write a brief verbal description of this collection of functions. Based on the graphs, do larger values of C correspond to a larger or smaller opening?

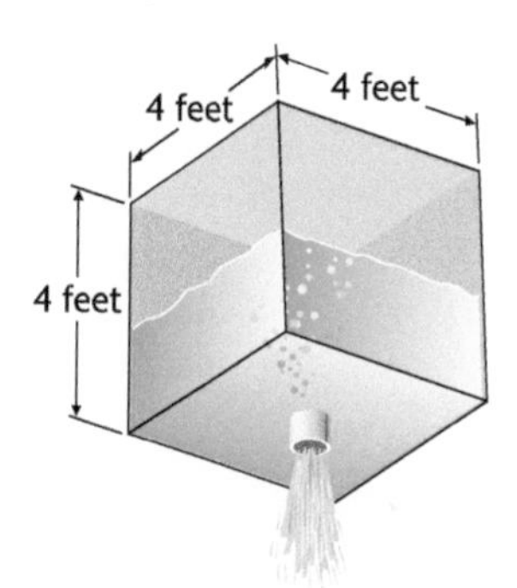

92. EVAPORATION A water trough with triangular ends is 9 feet long, 4 feet wide, and 2 feet deep (see the figure). Initially, the trough is full of water, but due to evaporation, the volume of the water in the trough decreases at a rate proportional to the square root of the volume. Using advanced concepts from mathematics and physics, it can be shown that the volume after t hours is given by

$$V(t) = \frac{1}{C^2}(t + 6C)^2 \quad 0 \le t \le 6|C|$$

where C is a constant. Sketch by hand the graphs of $y = V(t)$ for $C = -4, -5,$ and -6. Write a brief verbal description of this collection of functions. Based on the graphs, do values of C with a larger absolute value correspond to faster or slower evaporation?

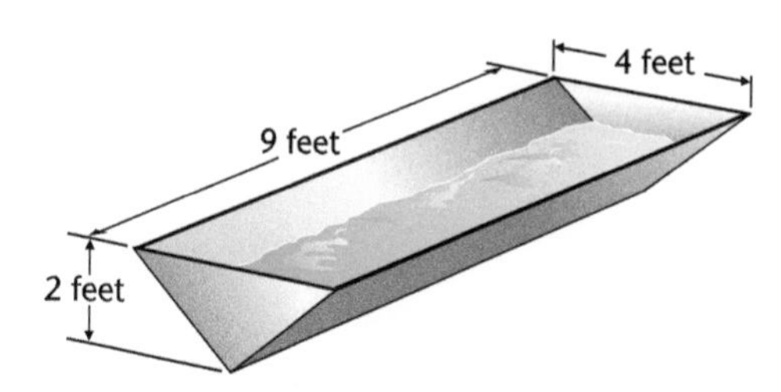

1-5 Operations on Functions; Composition

- Performing Operations on Functions
- Composing Functions
- Mathematical Modeling

Perhaps the most basic thing you've done in math classes is operations on numbers: things like addition, subtraction, multiplication, and division. In this section, we will explore the concept of operations on functions. In many cases, combining functions will enable us to model more complex and useful situations.

If two functions f and g are both defined at some real number x, then $f(x)$ and $g(x)$ are both real numbers, so it makes sense to perform the four basic arithmetic operations with $f(x)$ and $g(x)$. Furthermore, if $g(x)$ is a number in the domain of f, then it is also possible to evaluate f at $g(x)$. We will see that operations on the outputs of the functions can be used to define operations on the functions themselves.

Performing Operations on Functions

The functions f and g given by

$$f(x) = 2x + 3 \text{ and } g(x) = x^2 - 4$$

are both defined for all real numbers. Note that $f(3) = 9$ and $g(3) = 5$, so it would seem reasonable to assign the value $9 + 5$, or 14, to a new function $(f + g)(x)$. Based on this idea, for any real x we can perform the operation

$$f(x) + g(x) = (2x + 3) + (x^2 - 4) = x^2 + 2x - 1$$

Similarly, we can define other operations on functions:

$$f(x) - g(x) = (2x + 3) - (x^2 - 4) = -x^2 + 2x + 7$$
$$f(x)g(x) = (2x + 3)(x^2 - 4) = 2x^3 + 3x^2 - 8x - 12$$

For $x \neq \pm 2$ (to avoid zero in the denominator) we can also form the quotient

$$\frac{f(x)}{g(x)} = \frac{2x + 3}{x^2 - 4} \qquad x \neq \pm 2$$

Notice that the result of each operation is a new function. Thus, we have

$$(f + g)(x) = f(x) + g(x) = x^2 + 2x - 1 \qquad \text{Sum}$$
$$(f - g)(x) = f(x) - g(x) = -x^2 + 2x + 7 \qquad \text{Difference}$$
$$(fg)(x) = f(x)g(x) = 2x^3 + 3x^2 - 8x - 12 \qquad \text{Product}$$
$$\left(\frac{f}{g}\right)(x) = \frac{f(x)}{g(x)} = \frac{2x + 3}{x^2 - 4} \qquad x \neq \pm 2 \qquad \text{Quotient}$$

The sum, difference, and product functions are defined for all values of x, as were the original functions f and g, but the domain of the quotient function must be restricted to exclude those values where $g(x) = 0$.

› DEFINITION 1 Operations on Functions

The **sum, difference, product,** and **quotient** of the functions f and g are the functions defined by

$$(f + g)(x) = f(x) + g(x) \qquad \text{Sum function}$$

$$(f - g)(x) = f(x) - g(x) \qquad \text{Difference function}$$

$$(fg)(x) = f(x)g(x) \qquad \text{Product function}$$

$$\left(\frac{f}{g}\right)(x) = \frac{f(x)}{g(x)} \qquad g(x) \neq 0 \qquad \text{Quotient function}$$

The **domain** of each function consists of all elements in the domains of *both* f and g, with the exception that the values of x where $g(x) = 0$ must be excluded from the domain of the quotient function.

››› EXPLORE-DISCUSS 1

The following activities refer to the graphs of f and g shown in Figure 1 and the corresponding points on the graph shown in Table 1.

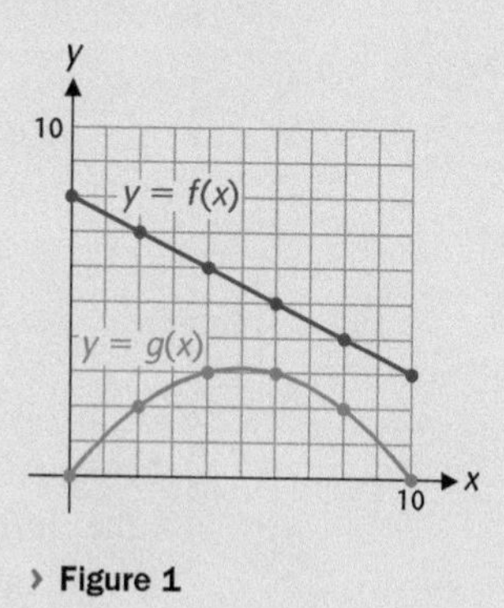

› **Figure 1**

Table 1

x	$f(x)$	$g(x)$
0	8	0
2	7	2
4	6	3
6	5	3
8	4	2
10	3	0

For each of the following functions, construct a table of values, sketch a graph, and state the domain and range.

(A) $(f + g)(x)$ **(B)** $(f - g)(x)$ **(C)** $(fg)(x)$ **(D)** $\left(\frac{f}{g}\right)(x)$

EXAMPLE 1 Finding the Sum of Two Functions

Let $f(x) = \sqrt{4 - x}$ and $g(x) = \sqrt{3 + x}$. Find $f + g$ and find its domain.

SOLUTIONS

Algebraic Solution

$$\begin{aligned}(f + g)(x) &= f(x) + g(x)\\ &= \sqrt{4 - x} + \sqrt{3 + x}\end{aligned}$$

The domains of f and g are

Domain of f: $x \leq 4$ or $(-\infty, 4]$
Domain of g: $x \geq -3$ or $[-3, \infty)$

Any x value that makes either of f or g undefined will make $f + g$ undefined as well, so only x values in the domains of *both* f and g are in the domain of $f + g$. In other words, the domain of $f + g$ is the intersection* of the first two sets in Figure 2:

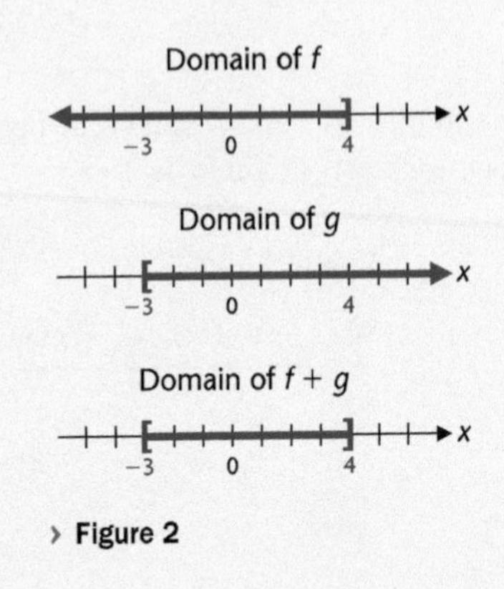

› **Figure 2**

The domain of $f + g$ is $[-3, 4]$.

Graphical Solution

We begin by entering $y_1 = \sqrt{4 - x}$, $y_2 = \sqrt{3 + x}$ in the equation editor of a graphing calculator. Note that $(f + g)(x) = \sqrt{4 - x} + \sqrt{3 + x}$. For convenience, we can enter this as $y_3 = y_1 + y_2$. The graph 5 of all three functions are shown in a standard viewing window in Figure 3. To get a better look at y_3, we turn off the graphs of y_1 and y_2, and change the viewing window (Fig. 4).

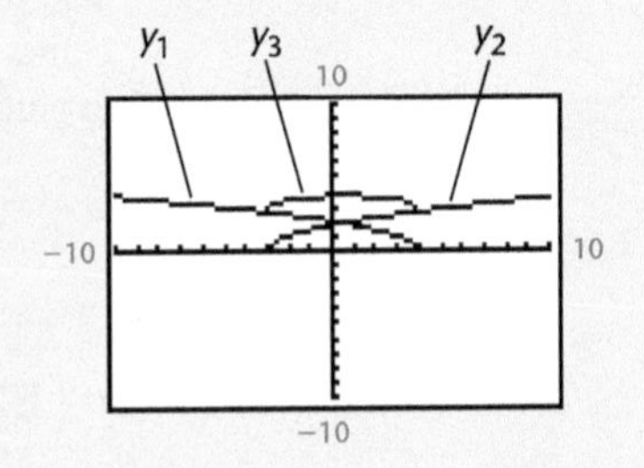

› **Figure 3** Graphs of y_1, y_2, and y_3.

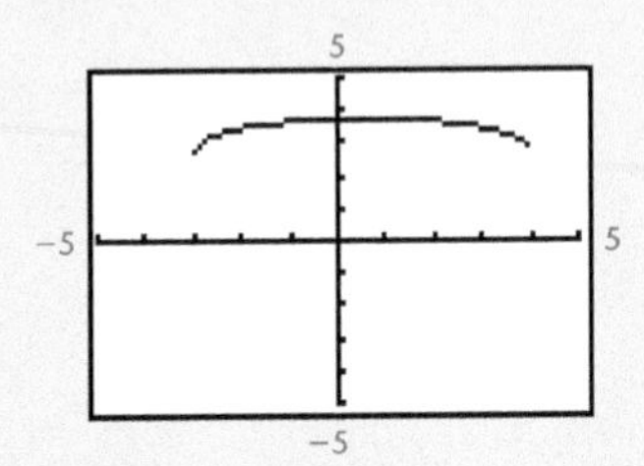

› **Figure 4** Graph of y_3.

Next we press TRACE and enter -3 (Fig. 5). Pressing the left arrow suggests that y_3 is not defined for $x < -3$ (Note the lack of y value in Fig. 6).

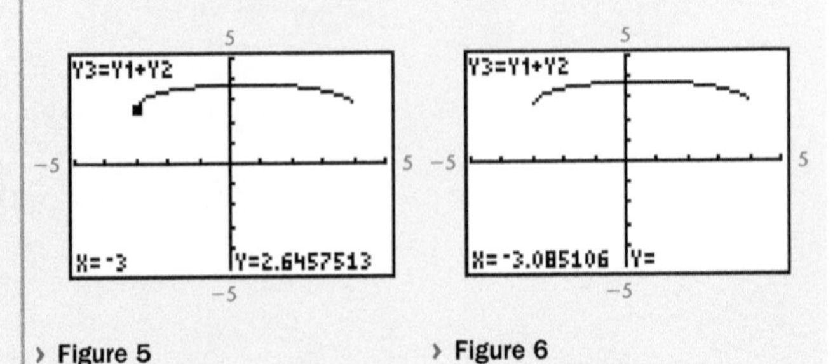

› **Figure 5** › **Figure 6**

*Intersection of intervals is discussed in Appendix B, Section B-1.

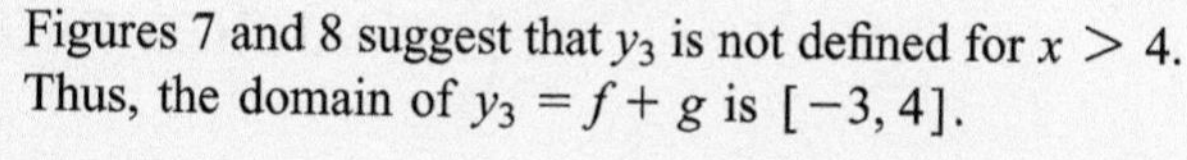

Figures 7 and 8 suggest that y_3 is not defined for $x > 4$. Thus, the domain of $y_3 = f + g$ is $[-3, 4]$.

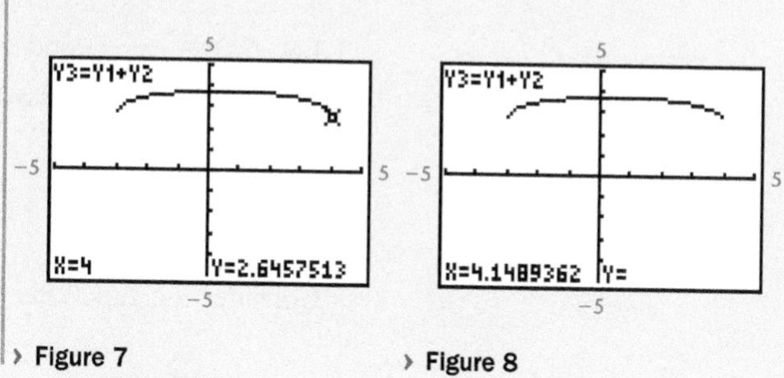

› Figure 7 › Figure 8

MATCHED PROBLEM 1

Let $f(x) = \sqrt{x}$ and $g(x) = \sqrt{10 - x}$. Find $f - g$ and find its domain.

EXAMPLE 2 Finding the Quotient of Two Functions

Let $f(x) = \dfrac{x}{x - 1}$ and $g(x) = \dfrac{x - 4}{x + 3}$. Find the function $\dfrac{f}{g}$ and find its domain.

SOLUTION

Because division by 0 must be excluded, the domain of f is all x except $x = 1$ and the domain of g is all x except $x = -3$. Now we find f/g.*

$$\left(\frac{f}{g}\right)(x) = \frac{f(x)}{g(x)} = \frac{\dfrac{x}{x - 1}}{\dfrac{x - 4}{x + 3}}$$ To divide by a fraction, multiply by the reciprocal.

$$= \frac{x}{x - 1} \cdot \frac{x + 3}{x - 4}$$ Multiply numerators and denominators.

$$= \frac{x(x + 3)}{(x - 1)(x - 4)} \qquad (1)$$

The fraction in equation (1) indicates that 1 and 4 must be excluded from the domain of f/g to avoid division by 0. But, equation (1) does not indicate that -3 must be excluded also. Although the fraction in equation (1) is defined at $x = -3$, -3 was excluded from the domain of g, so it must be excluded from the domain of f/g also.

The domain of f/g is all real numbers x except -3, 1, and 4 or $\{x \mid x \neq -3, 1, 4\}$.

*Operations on fractions are discussed in Appendix A, Section A-1.

MATCHED PROBLEM 2

Let $f(x) = \dfrac{1}{x + 2}$ and $g(x) = \dfrac{x - 5}{x}$. Find the function $\dfrac{f}{g}$ and find its domain.

Composing Functions

Consider the functions f and g given by

$$f(x) = \sqrt{x} \quad \text{and} \quad g(x) = 4 - 2x$$

Note that $g(0) = 4 - 2(0) = 4$ and $f(4) = \sqrt{4} = 2$. So if we apply these two functions *consecutively*, we get

$$f(g(0)) = f(4) = 2$$

In a diagram, this would look like

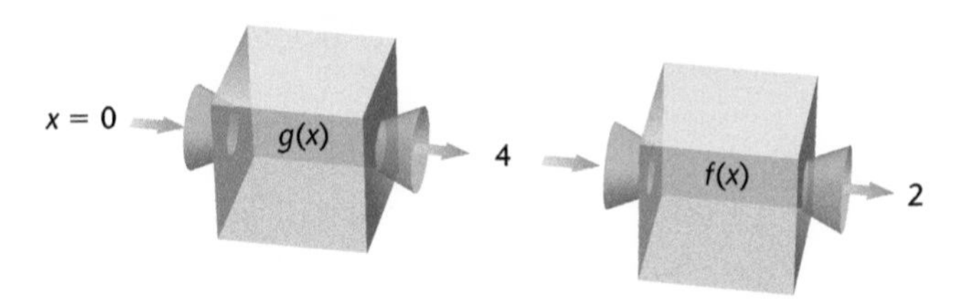

When two functions are applied consecutively, we call the result the **composition** of functions. We will use the symbol $f \circ g$ to represent the composition of f and g, which we formally define now.

DEFINITION 2 Composition of Functions

The composition of a function f with another function g is denoted by $f \circ g$ (read "f composed with g") and is defined by

$$(f \circ g)(x) = f(g(x))$$

EXAMPLE 3 Computing Composition From a Table

Table 2

x	$f(x)$	$g(x)$
−5	−8	11
−3	−6	2
0	−1	−6
2	5	−3
5	12	0

Functions f and g are defined by Table 2. Find $(f \circ g)(2)$, $(f \circ g)(5)$, and $(f \circ g)(-3)$.

SOLUTION

We will use the formula provided by Definition 2.

$$(f \circ g)(2) = f(g(2)) = f(-3) = -6$$
$$(f \circ g)(5) = f(g(5)) = f(0) = -1$$
$$(f \circ g)(-3) = f(g(-3)) = f(2) = 5$$

MATCHED PROBLEM 3

Table 3

x	$h(x)$	$k(x)$
−8	12	0
−4	18	22
0	40	−4
10	52	−8
20	70	−30

Functions h and k are defined by Table 3. Find $(h \circ k)(10)$, $(h \circ k)(-8)$, and $(h \circ k)(0)$.

››› CAUTION ›››

When computing $f \circ g$, it's important to keep in mind that the first function that appears in the notation (f, in this case) is actually the second function that is applied. For this reason, some people read $f \circ g$ as "f following g."

››› EXPLORE-DISCUSS 2

For $f(x) = \sqrt{x}$ and $g(x) = 4 - 2x$, complete Table 4.

Table 4

x	$g(x)$	$h(x) = f(g(x))$
0	$g(0) = 4$	$h(0) = f(g(0)) = f(4) = 2$
1		
2		
3		
4		

```
Plot1 Plot2 Plot3
\Y1=4-2X
\Y2=√(Y1)
\Y3=
\Y4=
\Y5=
\Y6=
\Y7=
```

› Figure 9

Now enter g and h in the equation editor of a graphing calculator as shown in Figure 9 and check your table. The domain of f is $\{x \mid x \geq 0\}$ and the domain of g is the set of all real numbers. What is the domain of h? Support your conclusion both algebraically and graphically.

So far, we have looked at composition on a point-by-point basis. Using algebra, we can find a formula for the composition of two functions.

EXAMPLE 4 Finding the Composition of Two Functions

Find $(f \circ g)(x)$ for $f(x) = x^2 - x$ and $g(x) = 3 + 2x$.

SOLUTION

We again use the formula in Definition 2.

$$\begin{aligned}(f \circ g)(x) &= f(g(x)) \\ &= f(3 + 2x) \\ &= (3 + 2x)^2 - (3 + 2x) \\ &= 9 + 12x + 4x^2 - 3 - 2x \\ &= 4x^2 + 10x + 6\end{aligned}$$

MATCHED PROBLEM 4

Find $(h \circ k)(x)$ for $h(x) = 11 + x^2$ and $k(x) = 4x - 1$.

››› EXPLORE-DISCUSS 3

(A) For $f(x) = x - 10$ and $g(x) = 3 + 7x$, find $(f \circ g)(x)$ and $(g \circ f)(x)$. Based on this result, what do you think is the relationship between $f \circ g$ and $g \circ f$ in general?

(B) Repeat for $f(x) = 2x + 1$ and $g(x) = \frac{x - 1}{2}$. Does this change your thoughts on the relationship between $f \circ g$ and $g \circ f$?

Explore-Discuss 3 tells us that order is important in composition. Sometimes $f \circ g$ and $g \circ f$ are equal, but more often they are not.

Finding the domain of a composition of functions can sometimes be a bit tricky. Based on the definition $(f \circ g)(x) = f(g(x))$, we can see that for an x value to be in the domain of $f \circ g$, two things must occur. First, x must be in the domain of g so that $g(x)$ is defined. Second, $g(x)$ must be in the domain of f, so that $f(g(x))$ is defined.

EXAMPLE 5

Finding the Composition of Two Functions

Find $(f \circ g)(x)$ and $(g \circ f)(x)$ and their domains for $f(x) = x^{10}$ and $g(x) = 3x^4 - 1$.

SOLUTION

$$(f \circ g)(x) = f(g(x)) = f(3x^4 - 1) = (3x^4 - 1)^{10}$$
$$(g \circ f)(x) = g(f(x)) = g(x^{10}) = 3(x^{10})^4 - 1 = 3x^{40} - 1$$

Note that the functions f and g are both defined for all real numbers. If x is any real number, then x is in the domain of g, so $g(x)$ is a real number. This then tells us that $g(x)$ is in the domain of f, which means that $f(g(x))$ is a real number. In other words, every real number is in the domain of $f \circ g$. Using similar reasoning, we can conclude that the domain of $g \circ f$ is also the set of all real numbers.

MATCHED PROBLEM 5

Find $(f \circ g)(x)$ and $(g \circ f)(x)$ and their domains for $f(x) = \sqrt[3]{x}$ and $g(x) = 7x + 5$.

The line of reasoning used in Example 5 can be used to deduce the following fact:

If two functions are both defined for all real numbers, then so is their composition.

››› EXPLORE-DISCUSS 4

Verify that if $f(x) = 1/(1 - 2x)$ and $g(x) = 1/x$, then $(f \circ g)(x) = x/(x - 2)$. Because division by 0 is not defined, $f \circ g$ is not defined at $x = 2$. Are there any other values of x where $f \circ g$ is not defined? Explain.

If either function in a composition is not defined for some real numbers, then, as Example 6 illustrates, the domain of the composition may not be what you first think it should be.

EXAMPLE 6

Finding the Composition of Two Functions

Find $(f \circ g)(x)$ for $f(x) = \sqrt{4 - x^2}$ and $g(x) = \sqrt{3 - x}$. Find the domain algebraically and check graphically.

SOLUTION

We begin by stating the domains of f and g, which is a good idea in any composition problem:

$$\text{Domain } f\text{: } -2 \le x \le 2 \quad \text{or} \quad [-2, 2]$$
$$\text{Domain } g\text{: } x \le 3 \quad \text{or} \quad (-\infty, 3]$$

Next we find the composition:

$$\begin{aligned}(f \circ g)(x) &= f(g(x)) \\ &= f(\sqrt{3 - x}) && \text{Substitute } \sqrt{3-x} \text{ for } g(x). \\ &= \sqrt{4 - (\sqrt{3 - x})^2} && \text{Square } (\sqrt{t})^2 = t \text{ as long as } t \ge 0. \\ &= \sqrt{4 - (3 - x)} && \text{Subtract.} \\ &= \sqrt{1 + x}\end{aligned}$$

Although $\sqrt{1 + x}$ is defined for all $x \ge -1$, we must restrict the domain of $f \circ g$ to those values that also are in the domain of g. Thus,

$$\text{Domain } f \circ g\text{: } x \ge -1 \text{ and } x \le 3 \quad \text{or} \quad [-1, 3]$$

To check this, enter $y_1 = \sqrt{3 - x}$ and $y_2 = \sqrt{4 - y_1^2}$. This defines y_2 as the composition $f \circ g$. Graph y_2 and use TRACE or a table to verify that $[-1, 3]$ is the domain of $f \circ g$ (Figs. 10–12).

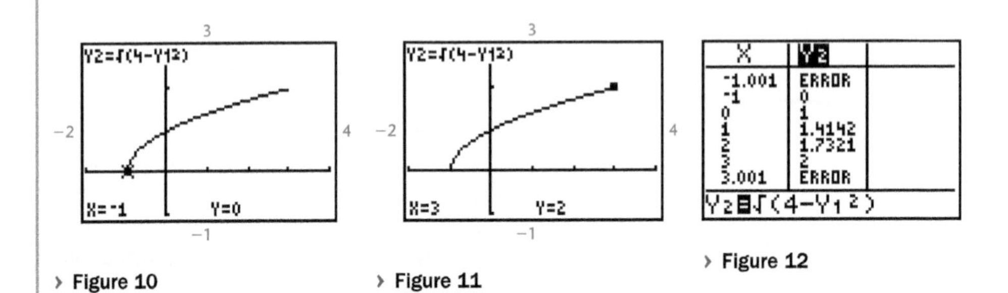

› Figure 10

› Figure 11

› Figure 12

MATCHED PROBLEM 6

Find $f \circ g$ for $f(x) = \sqrt{9 - x^2}$ and $g(x) = \sqrt{x - 1}$. Find the domain of $f \circ g$ algebraically and check graphically.

››› CAUTION ›››

The domain of $f \circ g$ cannot always be determined simply by examining the final form of $(f \circ g)(x)$. Any numbers that are excluded from the domain of g must also be excluded from the domain of $f \circ g$.

››› EXPLORE-DISCUSS 5

Here is another way to enter the composition of two functions in a graphing calculator. Refer to Example 6. Enter $y_1 = \sqrt{3 - x}$, $y_2 = \sqrt{4 - x^2}$, and $y_3 = y_2(y_1)$ in the equation editor of your graphing calculator and graph y_3. Does this graph agree with the graph we found in Example 6? Does your graphing calculator seem to handle this composition correctly? (Not all do!)

In calculus, it is not only important to be able to find the composition of two functions, but also to recognize when a given function is the composition of simpler functions.

EXAMPLE 7 Recognizing Composition Forms

Express h as a composition of two simpler functions for

$$h(x) = \sqrt{1 + 3x^4}$$

SOLUTION

If we were to evaluate this function for some x value, say, $x = 1$, we would do so in two stages. First, we would find the value of $1 + 3(1)^4$, which is 4. Then we would apply the square root to get 2. This shows that h can be thought of as two consecutive functions: First, $g(x) = 1 + 3x^4$, then $f(x) = \sqrt{x}$. So $h(x) = f(g(x))$, and we have written h as $f \circ g$.

MATCHED PROBLEM 7

Express h as the composition of two simpler functions for $h(x) = (4x^3 - 7)^4$.

The answers to Example 7 and Matched Problem 7 are not unique. For example, if $f(x) = \sqrt{1 + 3x}$ and $g(x) = x^4$, then

$$f(g(x)) = \sqrt{1 + 3g(x)} = \sqrt{1 + 3x^4} = h(x)$$

› Mathematical Modeling

The operations discussed in this section can be applied in many different situations. The next example shows how they are used to construct a model in economics.

EXAMPLE 8 Modeling Profit

The research department for an electronics firm estimates that the weekly demand for a certain brand of headphones is given by

$$x = f(p) = 20{,}000 - 1{,}000p \qquad 0 \le p \le 20 \qquad \text{Demand function}$$

This function describes the number x of pairs of headphones retailers are likely to buy per week at p dollars per pair. The research department also has determined that the total cost (in dollars) of producing x pairs per week is given by

$$C(x) = 25{,}000 + 3x \qquad \text{Cost function}$$

and the total weekly revenue (in dollars) obtained from the sale of these headphones is given by

$$R(x) = 20x - 0.001x^2 \qquad \text{Revenue function}$$

Express the firm's weekly profit as a function of the price p and find the price that produces the largest profit.

SOLUTION

The basic economic principle we are using is that profit is revenue minus cost. Thus, the profit function P is the difference of the revenue function R and the cost function C.

$$\begin{aligned} P(x) &= (R - C)(x) \\ &= R(x) - C(x) \\ &= (20x - 0.001x^2) - (25{,}000 + 3x) \\ &= 17x - 0.001x^2 - 25{,}000 \end{aligned}$$

This is a function of the demand x. We were asked to find the profit P as a function of the price p; we can accomplish this using composition, because $x = f(p)$.

$$\begin{aligned} (P \circ f)(p) &= P(f(p)) \\ &= P(20{,}000 - 1{,}000p) \\ &= 17(20{,}000 - 1{,}000p) - 0.001(20{,}000 - 1{,}000p)^2 - 25{,}000 \\ &= 340{,}000 - 17{,}000p - 400{,}000 + 40{,}000p - 1{,}000p^2 - 25{,}000 \\ &= -85{,}000 + 23{,}000p - 1{,}000p^2 \end{aligned}$$

Technically, $P \circ f$ and P are different functions, because the first has independent variable p and the second has independent variable x. However, because both functions represent the same quantity (the profit), it is customary to use the same symbol to name each function. Thus,

$$P(p) = -85{,}000 + 23{,}000p - 1{,}000p^2$$

expresses the weekly profit P as a function of price p. To find the price that produces the largest profit, we examine the graph of P. To do this, we will enter the function into our graphing calculator, using y_1 and x in place of P and p. Define

$$y_1 = -85{,}000 + 23{,}000x - 1{,}000x^2 \qquad 0 \le x \le 20$$

The limits for x were given in the statement of the problem. Examining a table (Fig. 13) suggests that reasonable limits on y_1 are $-100{,}000 \le y_1 \le 50{,}000$. Graphing y_1 and using the MAXIMUM command (Fig. 14) shows that the largest profit occurs when the price of a pair of headphones is \$11.50.

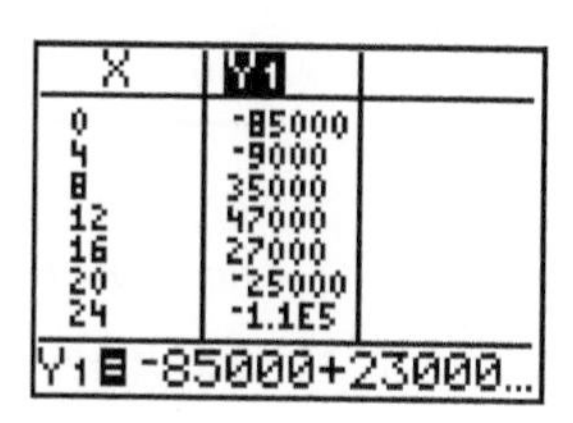

› **Figure 13**

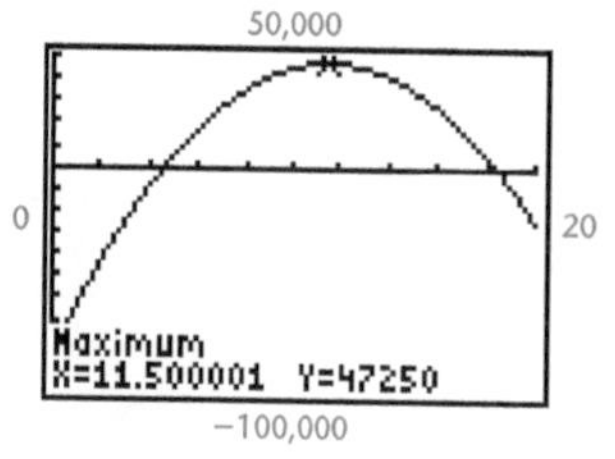

› **Figure 14**

MATCHED PROBLEM 8

Repeat Example 8 for the functions

$$x = f(p) = 10{,}000 - 1{,}000p \qquad 0 \le p \le 10$$
$$C(x) = 10{,}000 + 2x \qquad R(x) = 10x - 0.001x^2$$

ANSWERS TO MATCHED PROBLEMS

1. $(f - g)(x) = \sqrt{x} - \sqrt{10 - x}$; domain: $[0, 10]$

2. $\left(\dfrac{f}{g}\right)(x) = \dfrac{x}{(x + 2)(x - 5)}$; domain: all real numbers x except -2, 0, and 5

3. $(h \circ k)(10) = 12$; $(h \circ k)(-8) = 40$; $(h \circ k)(0) = 18$

4. $(h \circ k)(x) = 16x^2 - 8x + 12$

5. $(f \circ g)(x) = \sqrt[3]{7x + 5}$, domain: $(-\infty, \infty)$
$(g \circ f)(x) = 7\sqrt[3]{x} + 5$, domain: $(-\infty, \infty)$

6. $(f \circ g)(x) = \sqrt{10 - x}$; domain: $x \ge 1$ and $x \le 10$ or $[1, 10]$

7. $h(x) = (f \circ g)(x)$ where $f(x) = x^4$ and $g(x) = 4x^3 - 7$

8. $P(p) = -30{,}000 + 12{,}000p - 1{,}000p^2$
The largest profit occurs when the price is \$6.

1-5 Exercises

1. Explain how to find the sum of two functions.

2. Explain how to find the product of two functions.

3. Is the domain of f/g always the intersection of the domains of f and g? Explain.

4. Is the domain of fg always the intersection of the domains of f and g? Explain.

5. Is composition of functions a commutative* process? Explain.

6. Which of addition, subtraction, multiplication, and division of functions is commutative*? Explain.

Problems 7–18 refer to functions f and g whose graphs are shown below.

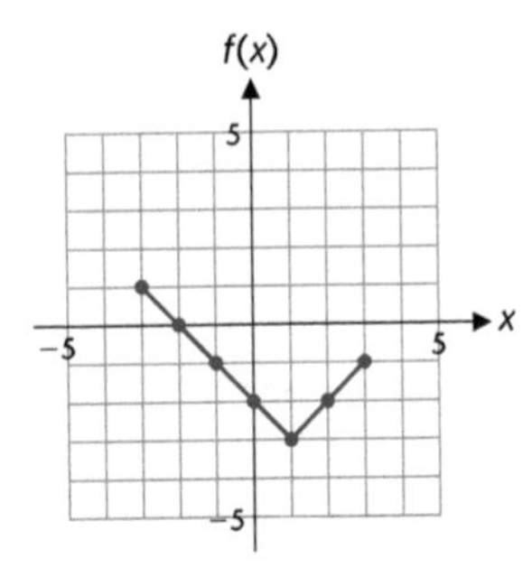

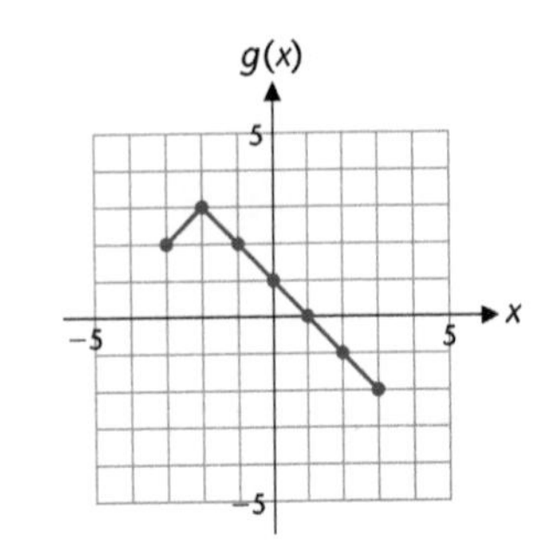

In Problems 7–10 use the graphs of f and g to construct a table of values and sketch the graph of the indicated function.

7. $(f + g)(x)$ **8.** $(g - f)(x)$

9. $(fg)(x)$ **10.** $(f - g)(x)$

In Problems 11–18, use the graphs of f and g to find each of the following:

11. $(f \circ g)(-1)$ **12.** $(f \circ g)(2)$

13. $(g \circ f)(-2)$ **14.** $(g \circ f)(3)$

15. $f(g(1))$ **16.** $f(g(0))$

17. $g(f(2))$ **18.** $g(f(-3))$

19. Functions f and g are defined by Table 5. Find $(f \circ g)(-7)$, $(f \circ g)(0)$, and $(f \circ g)(4)$.

20. Functions h and k are defined by Table 6. Find $(h \circ k)(-15)$, $(h \circ k)(-10)$, and $(h \circ k)(15)$.

Table 5

x	$f(x)$	$g(x)$
−7	5	4
−2	9	10
0	0	−2
4	3	6
6	−10	−3

Table 6

x	$h(x)$	$k(x)$
−20	−100	30
−15	−200	5
−10	−300	15
5	−150	8
15	−90	−10

In Problems 21–26, for the indicated functions f and g, find the functions $f + g$, $f - g$, fg, and f/g, and find their domains.

21. $f(x) = 4x$; $g(x) = x + 1$

22. $f(x) = 3x$; $g(x) = x - 2$

23. $f(x) = 2x^2$; $g(x) = x^2 + 1$

24. $f(x) = 3x$; $g(x) = x^2 + 4$

25. $f(x) = 3x + 5$; $g(x) = x^2 - 1$

26. $f(x) = 2x - 7$; $g(x) = 9 - x^2$

In Problems 27–32, for the indicated functions f and g, find the functions $f \circ g$, and $g \circ f$, and find their domains.

27. $f(x) = x^3$; $g(x) = x^2 - x + 1$

28. $f(x) = x^2$; $g(x) = x^3 + 2x + 4$

29. $f(x) = |x + 1|$; $g(x) = 2x + 3$

30. $f(x) = |x - 4|$; $g(x) = 3x + 2$

31. $f(x) = x^{1/3}$; $g(x) = 2x^3 + 4$

32. $f(x) = x^{2/3}$; $g(x) = 8 - x^3$

In Problems 33–36, find $f \circ g$ and $g \circ f$. Graph f, g, $f \circ g$, and $g \circ f$ in a squared viewing window and describe any apparent symmetry between these graphs.

33. $f(x) = \frac{1}{2}x + 1$; $g(x) = 2x - 2$

34. $f(x) = 3x + 2$; $g(x) = \frac{1}{3}x - \frac{2}{3}$

*You can find the definition of commutative in Appendix A, Section A-1.

35. $f(x) = -\frac{2}{3}x - \frac{5}{3}$; $g(x) = -\frac{3}{2}x - \frac{5}{2}$

36. $f(x) = -2x + 3$; $g(x) = -\frac{1}{2}x + \frac{3}{2}$

In Problems 37–42, for the indicated functions f and g, find the functions $f + g$, $f - g$, fg, and f/g, and find their domains.

37. $f(x) = \sqrt{2 - x}$; $g(x) = \sqrt{x + 3}$

38. $f(x) = \sqrt{x + 4}$; $g(x) = \sqrt{3 - x}$

39. $f(x) = \sqrt{x} + 2$; $g(x) = \sqrt{x} - 4$

40. $f(x) = 1 - \sqrt{x}$; $g(x) = 2 - \sqrt{x}$

41. $f(x) = \sqrt{x^2 + x - 6}$; $g(x) = \sqrt{7 + 6x - x^2}$

42. $f(x) = \sqrt{8 + 2x - x^2}$; $g(x) = \sqrt{x^2 - 7x + 10}$

In Problems 43–48, for the indicated functions f and g, find the functions $f \circ g$ and $g \circ f$, and find their domains.

43. $f(x) = \sqrt{x}$; $g(x) = x - 4$

44. $f(x) = \sqrt{x}$; $g(x) = 2x + 5$

45. $f(x) = x + 2$; $g(x) = \frac{1}{x}$

46. $f(x) = x - 3$; $g(x) = \frac{1}{x^2}$

47. $f(x) = |x|$; $g(x) = \frac{1}{x - 1}$

48. $f(x) = |x - 1|$; $g(x) = \frac{1}{x}$

Use the graphs of functions f and g shown below to match each function in Problems 49–52 with one of graphs (a)–(d).

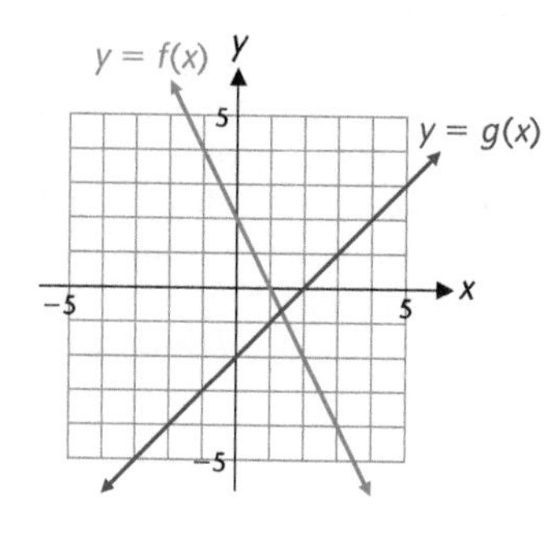

49. $(f + g)(x)$

50. $(f - g)(x)$

51. $(g - f)(x)$

52. $(fg)(x)$

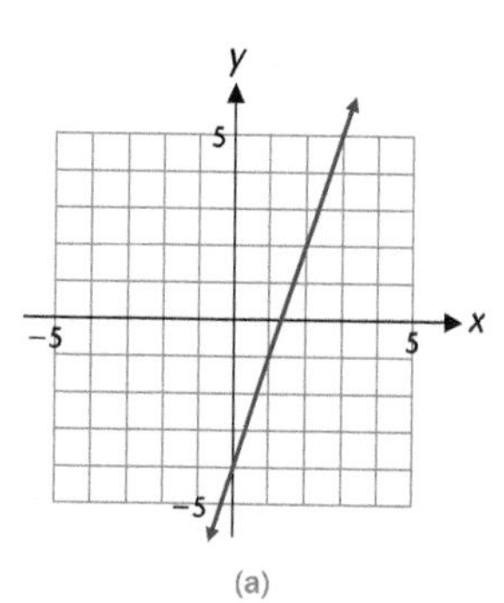

(a)

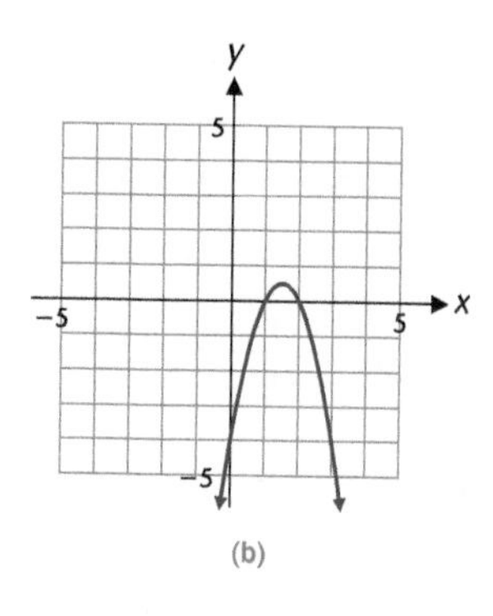

(b)

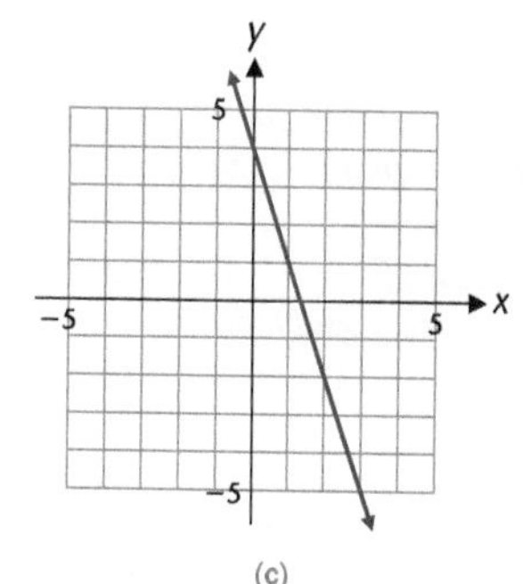

(c)

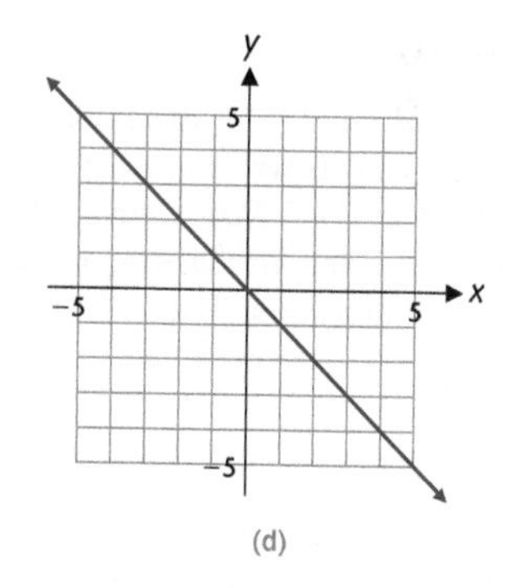

(d)

In Problems 53–60, express h as a composition of two simpler functions f and g.

53. $h(x) = (2x - 7)^4$

54. $h(x) = (3 - 5x)^7$

55. $h(x) = \sqrt{4 + 2x}$

56. $h(x) = \sqrt{3x - 11}$

57. $h(x) = 3x^7 - 5$

58. $h(x) = 5x^6 + 3$

59. $h(x) = \frac{4}{\sqrt{x}} + 3$

60. $h(x) = -\frac{2}{\sqrt{x}} + 1$

61. Is there a function g that satisfies $f \circ g = g \circ f = f$ for all functions f? If so, what is it?

62. Is there a function g that satisfies $fg = gf = f$ for all functions f? If so, what is it?

In Problems 63–66, for the indicated functions f and g, find the functions $f + g$, $f - g$, fg, and f/g, and find their domains.

63. $f(x) = x + \frac{1}{x}$; $g(x) = x - \frac{1}{x}$

64. $f(x) = x - 1$; $g(x) = x - \frac{6}{x - 1}$

65. $f(x) = 1 - \frac{x}{|x|}$; $g(x) = 1 + \frac{x}{|x|}$

66. $f(x) = x + |x|$; $g(x) = x - |x|$

In Problems 67–72, for the indicated functions f and g, find the functions $f \circ g$ and $g \circ f$, and find their domains.

67. $f(x) = \sqrt{4 - x}$; $g(x) = x^2$

68. $f(x) = \sqrt{x - 1}$; $g(x) = x^2$

69. $f(x) = \frac{x + 5}{x}$; $g(x) = \frac{x}{x - 2}$

70. $f(x) = \frac{x}{x - 1}$; $g(x) = \frac{2x - 4}{x}$

71. $f(x) = \sqrt{25 - x^2}$; $g(x) = \sqrt{9 + x^2}$

72. $f(x) = \sqrt{x^2 - 9}$; $g(x) = \sqrt{x^2 + 25}$

In Problems 73–78, enter the given expression for $(f \circ g)(x)$ exactly as it is written and graph on a graphing calculator for $-10 \le x \le 10$. Then simplify the expression, enter the result, and graph in a new viewing window, again for $-10 \le x \le 10$. Find the domain of $f \circ g$. Which is the correct graph of $f \circ g$?

73. $f(x) = \sqrt{5 - x^2}$; $g(x) = \sqrt{3 - x}$;
$(f \circ g)(x) = \sqrt{5 - (\sqrt{3 - x})^2}$

74. $f(x) = \sqrt{6 - x^2}$; $g(x) = \sqrt{x - 1}$;
$(f \circ g)(x) = \sqrt{6 - (\sqrt{x - 1})^2}$

75. $f(x) = \sqrt{x^2 + 5}$; $g(x) = \sqrt{x^2 - 4}$;
$(f \circ g)(x) = \sqrt{(\sqrt{x^2 - 4})^2 + 5}$

76. $f(x) = \sqrt{x^2 + 5}$; $g(x) = \sqrt{4 - x^2}$;
$(f \circ g)(x) = \sqrt{(\sqrt{4 - x^2})^2 + 5}$

77. $f(x) = \sqrt{x^2 + 7}$; $g(x) = \sqrt{9 - x^2}$;
$(f \circ g)(x) = \sqrt{(\sqrt{9 - x^2})^2 + 7}$

78. $f(x) = \sqrt{x^2 + 7}$; $g(x) = \sqrt{x^2 - 9}$;
$(f \circ g)(x) = \sqrt{(\sqrt{x^2 - 9})^2 + 7}$

APPLICATIONS

79. MARKET RESEARCH The demand x and the price p (in dollars) for a certain product are related by

$$x = f(p) = 4{,}000 - 200p \qquad 0 \le p \le 20$$

The revenue (in dollars) from the sale of x units is given by

$$R(x) = 20x - \frac{1}{200}x^2$$

and the cost (in dollars) of producing x units is given by

$$C(x) = 2x + 8{,}000$$

Express the profit as a function of the price p and find the price that produces the largest profit.

80. MARKET RESEARCH The demand x and the price p (in dollars) for a certain product are related by

$$x = f(p) = 5{,}000 - 100p \qquad 0 \le p \le 50$$

The revenue (in dollars) from the sale of x units and the cost (in dollars) of producing x units are given, respectively, by

$$R(x) = 50x - \frac{1}{100}x^2 \quad \text{and} \quad C(x) = 20x + 40{,}000$$

Express the profit as a function of the price p and find the price that produces the largest profit.

81. ENVIRONMENTAL SCIENCE An oil tanker aground on a reef is leaking oil that forms a circular oil slick about 0.1 foot thick (see the figure). The radius of the slick (in feet) t minutes after the leak first occurred is given by

$$r(t) = 0.4t^{1/3}$$

Express the volume of the oil slick as a function of t.

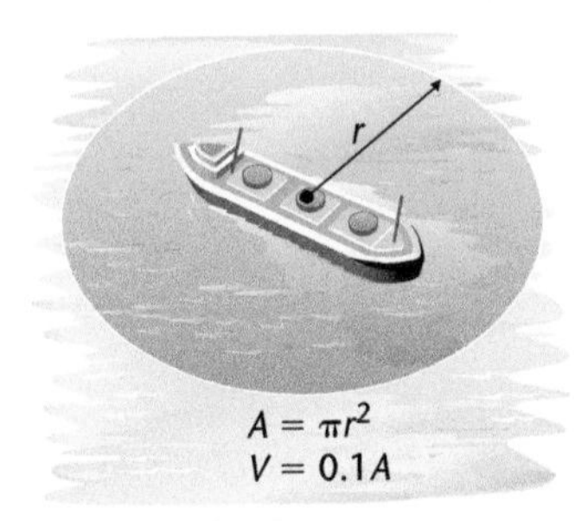

82. METEOROLOGY A weather balloon is rising vertically. An observer is standing on the ground 100 meters from the point where the weather balloon was released.
(A) Express the distance d between the balloon and the observer as a function of the balloon's distance h above the ground.
(B) If the balloon's distance above the ground after t seconds is given by $h = 5t$, express the distance d between the balloon and the observer as a function of t.

83. FLUID FLOW A conical paper cup with diameter 4 inches and height 4 inches is initially full of water. A small hole is made in the bottom of the cup and the water begins to flow out of the cup. Let h and r be the height and radius, respectively, of the water in the cup t minutes after the water begins to flow.

4 inches

4 inches

$V = \frac{1}{3}\pi r^2 h$

(A) Express r as a function of h.
(B) Express the volume V as a function of h.
(C) If the height of the water after t minutes is given by

$$h(t) = 0.5\sqrt{t}$$

express V as a function of t.

84. EVAPORATION A water trough with triangular ends is 6 feet long, 4 feet wide, and 2 feet deep. Initially, the trough is full of water, but due to evaporation, the volume of the water is decreasing. Let h and w be the height and width, respectively, of the water in the tank t hours after it began to evaporate.

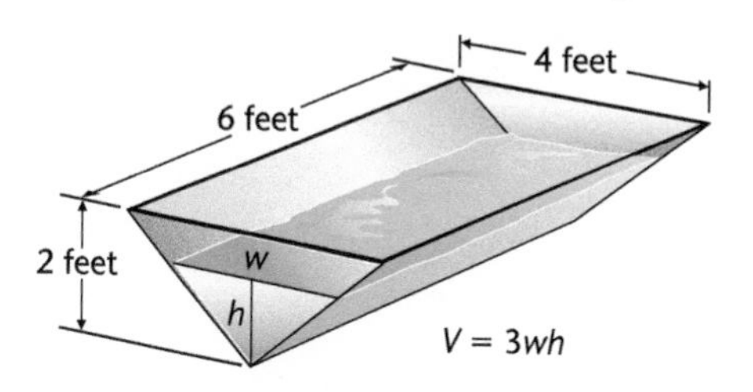

(A) Express w as a function of h.
(B) Express V as a function of h.
(C) If the height of the water after t hours is given by

$$h(t) = 2 - 0.2\sqrt{t}$$

express V as a function of t.

1-6 Inverse Functions

We have seen that many important mathematical relationships can be expressed in terms of functions. For example,

$C = \pi d$	The circumference of a circle is a function of the diameter d.
$V = s^3$	The volume of a cube is a function of length s of the edges.
$d = 1{,}000 - 100p$	The demand for a product is a function of the price p.
$F = \frac{9}{5}C + 32$	Temperature measured in °F is a function of temperature in °C.

In many cases, we are interested in *reversing* the correspondence determined by a function. For our examples,

$$d = \frac{C}{\pi}$$ The diameter of a circle is a function of the circumference C.

$$s = \sqrt[3]{V}$$ The length of the edge of a cube is a function of the volume V.

$$p = 10 - \frac{1}{100}d$$ The price of a product is a function of the demand d.

$$C = \frac{5}{9}(F - 32)$$ Temperature measured in °C is a function of temperature in °F.

As these examples illustrate, reversing the correspondence between two quantities often produces a new function. This new function is called the *inverse* of the original function. Later in this text we will see that many important functions are actually defined as the inverses of other functions.

In this section, we develop techniques for determining whether the inverse of a function exists, some general properties of inverse functions, and methods for finding the rule of correspondence that defines the inverse function. A review of function basics in the second section of this chapter would be very helpful at this point.

One-to-One Functions

Recall the set form of the definition of function:

> **A function is a set of ordered pairs with the property that no two ordered pairs have the same first component and different second components.**

However, it is possible that two ordered pairs in a function could have the same second component and different first components. If this does not happen, then we call the function a *one-to-one function.*

In other words, a function is one-to-one if there are no duplicates among the second components. It turns out that one-to-one functions are the only functions that have inverse functions.

DEFINITION 1 One-to-One Function

A function is **one-to-one** if no two ordered pairs in the function have the same second component and different first components.

››› EXPLORE-DISCUSS 1

Given the following sets of ordered pairs:

$$f = \{(0, 1), (0, 2), (1, 1), (1, 2)\}$$
$$g = \{(0, 1), (1, 1), (2, 2), (3, 2)\}$$
$$h = \{(0, 1), (1, 2), (2, 3), (3, 0)\}$$

(A) Which of these sets represent functions?

(B) Which of the functions are one-to-one functions?

(C) For each set that is a function, form a new set by reversing each ordered pair in the set. Which of these new sets represent functions?

(D) What do these results tell you about the result of reversing the ordered pairs for functions that are one-to-one, and for functions that are not one-to-one?

EXAMPLE 1

Determining Whether a Function Is One-to-One

Determine whether f is a one-to-one function for

(A) $f(x) = x^2$ (B) $f(x) = 2x - 1$

SOLUTIONS

(A) To show that a function is *not* one-to-one, all we have to do is find two different ordered pairs in the function with the same second component and different first components. Because

$$f(2) = 2^2 = 4 \quad \text{and} \quad f(-2) = (-2)^2 = 4$$

the ordered pairs (2, 4) and (−2, 4) both belong to f, and f is not one-to-one. Note that there's nothing special about 2 and −2 here: Any real number and its negative can be used in the same way.

(B) To show that a function *is* one-to-one, we have to show that no two ordered pairs have the same second component and different first components. To do this, we'll show that if any two ordered pairs $(a, f(a))$ and $(b, f(b))$ in f have the same second components, then the first components must also be the same. That is, we show that $f(a) = f(b)$ implies $a = b$. We proceed as follows:

$$f(a) = f(b) \quad \text{Assume second components are equal. Evaluate } f(a) \text{ and } f(b).$$
$$2a - 1 = 2b - 1$$
$$2a = 2b \quad \text{Simplify.}$$
$$a = b \quad \text{Conclusion: } f \text{ is one-to-one.}$$

By Definition 1, f is a one-to-one function.

MATCHED PROBLEM 1

Determine whether f is a one-to-one function for

(A) $f(x) = 4 - x^2$ (B) $f(x) = 4 - 2x$

The methods used in the solution of Example 1 can be stated as a theorem.

› THEOREM 1 One-to-One Functions

1. If $f(a) = f(b)$ for at least one pair of domain values a and b, $a \neq b$, then f is not one-to-one.
2. If the assumption $f(a) = f(b)$ always implies that the domain values a and b are equal, then f is one-to-one.

Applying Theorem 1 is not always easy—try testing $f(x) = x^3 + 2x + 3$, for example. (Good luck!) However, the graph of a function can help us develop a simple procedure for determining if a function is one-to-one. If any horizontal line intersects the graph in more than one point [as shown in Fig. 1(a)], then there is a second component (height) that corresponds to two different first components (x values). This shows that the function is not one-to-one.

On the other hand, if every horizontal line intersects the graph in just one point or not at all [as shown in Fig. 1(b)], the function is one-to-one. These observations form the basis of the *horizontal line test.*

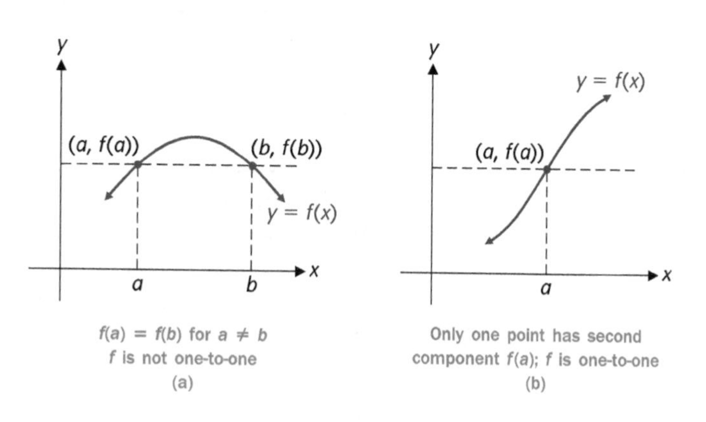

› **Figure 1** Intersections of graphs and horizontal lines.

› THEOREM 2 Horizontal Line Test

A function is one-to-one if and only if every horizontal line intersects the graph of the function in at most one point.

EXAMPLE 2 Using the Horizontal Line Test

Use the horizontal line test to determine if each function is one-to-one.

(A) $f(x) = -0.1x^2 + 1.4x + 10.1$ (B) $g(x) = 0.2x^3 + x$

SOLUTIONS

(A) We first use a graphing calculator to graph $f(x)$ in a standard viewing window (Fig. 2). It appears to pass the horizontal line test. But when we zoom out (Fig. 3) we see that there are many heights where a horizontal line will intersect the graph twice, so $f(x)$ is not one-to-one.

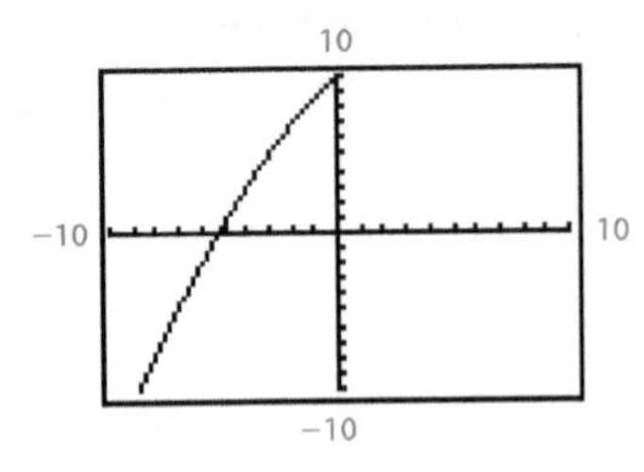

› Figure 2

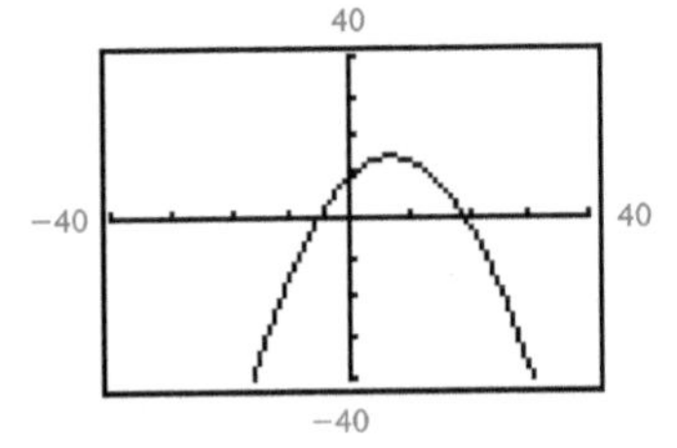

› Figure 3

(B) In a standard viewing window (Fig. 4), $g(x)$ appears to be one-to-one. We again zoom out (Fig. 5) and see that there don't appear to be any changes of direction in the graph. No horizontal line intersects the graph more than once, so $g(x)$ is one-to-one.

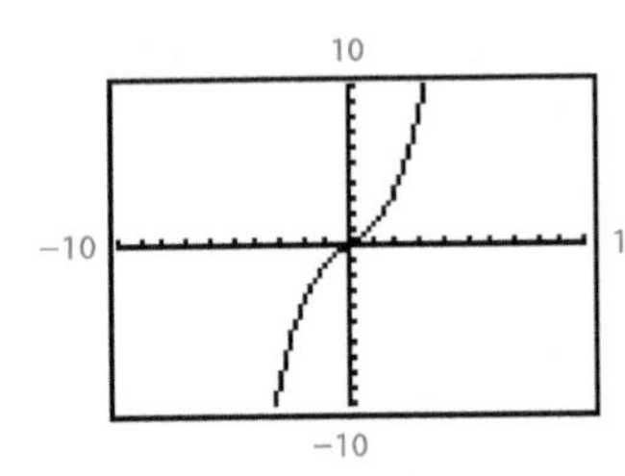

› Figure 4

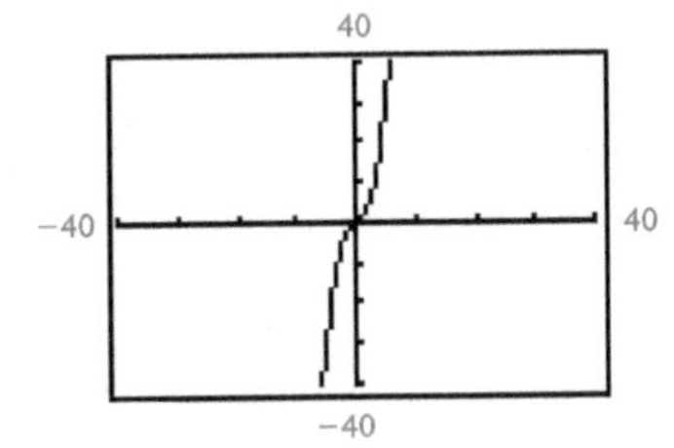

› Figure 5

MATCHED PROBLEM 2

Use the horizontal line test to determine if each function is one-to-one.

(A) $f(x) = \frac{11 - 3x}{5}$ (B) $g(x) = x^2 + 20x + 80$

››› CAUTION ›››

When using the horizontal line test to determine if a function is one-to-one, you have to be very careful about viewing windows. Make sure that you explore the graph enough to be reasonably certain that you're not missing some important features that are off the screen.

Example 2 suggests that a function fails to be one-to-one exactly when its graph changes direction somewhere. We'll see shortly that this is not true, but it *is* true that a function that is either increasing or decreasing throughout its domain will always pass the horizontal line test [Figs. 6(a) and 6(b)]. Thus, we have the following theorem.

› **Figure 6** Increasing, decreasing, and one-to-one functions.

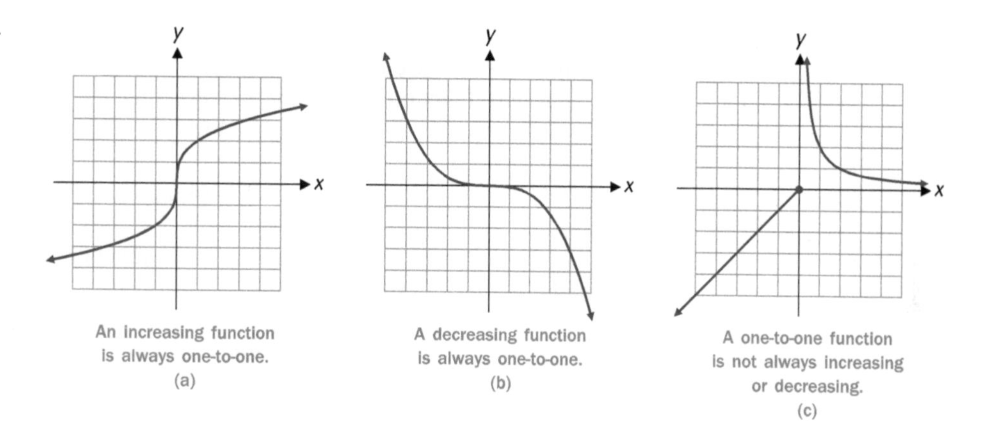

› **THEOREM 3 Increasing and Decreasing Functions**

If a function f is increasing throughout its domain or decreasing throughout its domain, then f is a one-to-one function.

The opposite of Theorem 3 is false. Consider the function whose graph is in Figure 6(c). This function is increasing on $(-\infty, 0]$ and decreasing on $(0, \infty)$, but the graph still passes the horizontal line test. So there are one-to-one functions that are neither increasing nor decreasing functions.

› Finding the Inverse of a Function

Now we want to see how we can form a new function by reversing the correspondence determined by a given function. Let g be the function defined as follows:

$$g = \{(-3, 9), (0, 0), (3, 9)\}$$ g is not one-to-one.

Notice that g is not one-to-one because the domain elements -3 and 3 both correspond to the range element 9. We can reverse the correspondence determined by function g simply by reversing the components in each ordered pair in g, producing the following set:

$$G = \{(9, -3), (0, 0), (9, 3)\}$$ G is not a function.

But the result is not a function because the domain element 9 corresponds to two different range elements, -3 and 3. On the other hand, if we reverse the ordered pairs in the function

$$f = \{(1, 2), (2, 4), (3, 9)\}$$ f is one-to-one.

we obtain

$$F = \{(2, 1), (4, 2), (9, 3)\}$$ F is a function.

This time f is a one-to-one function, and the set F turns out to be a function also. This new function F, formed by reversing all the ordered pairs in f, is called the *inverse* of f and is usually denoted by f^{-1}. In this case,

$$f^{-1} = \{(2, 1) (4, 2), (9, 3)\}$$ The inverse of f

Notice that f^{-1} is also a one-to-one function and that the following relationships hold:

$$\text{Domain of } f^{-1} = \{2, 4, 9\} = \text{Range of } f$$
$$\text{Range of } f^{-1} = \{1, 2, 3\} = \text{Domain of } f$$

Reversing all the ordered pairs in a one-to-one function forms a new one-to-one function and reverses the domain and range in the process. But reversing the ordered pairs from a function that is not one-to-one results in a new relation that is not a function. We are now ready to present a formal definition of the inverse of a function.

› DEFINITION 2 Inverse of a Function

If f is a one-to-one function, then the **inverse** of f, denoted f^{-1}, is the function formed by reversing all the ordered pairs in f. That is,

$$f^{-1} = \{(y, x) \mid (x, y) \text{ is in } f\}$$

If f is not one-to-one, then ***f does not have an inverse function*** and f^{-1} ***does not exist.***

››› CAUTION ›››

Do not confuse inverse notation and reciprocal notation:

$$2^{-1} = \frac{1}{2}$$ Reciprocal notation for numbers

$$(f(x))^{-1} = \frac{1}{f(x)}$$ Reciprocal notation for functions

$$f^{-1}(x) \neq \frac{1}{f(x)}$$ Inverse notation is not reciprocal notation.

Make sure that you read the symbol f^{-1} as "the inverse of f" or "f inverse," but *never* "f to the negative one power."

EXAMPLE 3 Finding the Inverse of a Function

Find the inverse if it exists.

(A) $f = \{(-3, 10), (-1, 8), (2, 5), (5, 8)\}$
(B) $g = \{(10, 15), (15, 20), (20, 25), (25, 30)\}$

SOLUTIONS

(A) Note that f has a second component, 8, that appears twice. So f is not one-to-one, and f^{-1} does not exist.

(B) Function g is one-to-one, so g^{-1} exists. We find it by reversing all of the ordered pairs.

$$g^{-1} = \{(15, 10), (20, 15), (25, 20), (30, 25)\}$$

MATCHED PROBLEM 3

Find the inverse of each function, if it exists.

(A) $F = \{(3/2, -5), (5/2, -7), (7/2, -9), (9/2, -11)\}$
(B) $G = \{(-10, 3), (10, -3), (-20, 3), (20, -3)\}$

The following properties of inverse functions follow directly from the definition.

› THEOREM 4 Properties of Inverse Functions

For a given function f, if f^{-1} exists, then

1. f^{-1} is a one-to-one function.
2. The domain of f^{-1} is the range of f.
3. The range of f^{-1} is the domain of f.

››› EXPLORE-DISCUSS 2

(A) For the function $f = \{(3, 5), (7, 11), (11, 17)\}$, find f^{-1}.

(B) What do you think would be the result of composing f with f^{-1}? Justify your answer using Definition 2.

(C) Check your conjecture from part B by finding both $f \circ f^{-1}$ and $f^{-1} \circ f$. Were you correct?

Explore-Discuss 2 brings up an important point: if you apply a function to any number in its domain, then apply the inverse of that function to the result, you'll get right back where you started. This leads to the following theorem.

› THEOREM 5 Inverse Functions and Composition

If f^{-1} exists, then

1. $f(f^{-1}(x)) = x$ for all x in the domain of f^{-1}.
2. $f^{-1}(f(x)) = x$ for all x in the domain of f.

If f and g are one-to-one functions satisfying

$$f(g(x)) = x \text{ for all } x \text{ in the domain of } g \text{ and}$$
$$g(f(x)) = x \text{ for all } x \text{ in the domain of } f$$

then f and g are inverses of one another.

We can use Theorem 5 to see if two functions defined by equations are inverses.

EXAMPLE 4 Deciding If Two Functions Are Inverses

Use Theorem 5 to decide if these two functions are inverses.

$$f(x) = 3x - 7 \qquad g(x) = \frac{x + 7}{3}$$

SOLUTION

The domain of both functions is all real numbers. For any x,

$$\begin{aligned} f(g(x)) &= f\left(\frac{x+7}{3}\right) && \text{Substitute into } f(x). \\ &= 3\left(\frac{x+7}{3}\right) - 7 && \text{Multiply.} \\ &= x + 7 - 7 && \text{Add.} \\ &= x \\ g(f(x)) &= g(3x - 7) && \text{Substitute into } g(x). \\ &= \frac{3x - 7 + 7}{3} && \text{Add.} \\ &= \frac{3x}{3} && \text{Simplify.} \\ &= x \end{aligned}$$

By Theorem 5, f and g are inverses.

MATCHED PROBLEM 4

Use Theorem 5 to decide if these two functions are inverses.

$$f(x) = \frac{2}{5}(11 - x) \qquad g(x) = -\frac{5}{2}x + 11$$

There is one obvious question that remains: when a function is defined by an equation, how can we find the inverse? Given a function $y = f(x)$, the first coordinates of points on the graph are represented by x, and the second coordinates are represented by y. Finding the inverse by reversing the order of the coordinates would then correspond to switching the variables x and y. This leads us to the following procedure, which can be applied whenever it is possible to solve $y = f(x)$ for x in terms of y.

Finding the Inverse of a Function f

Step 1. Find the domain of f and verify that f is one-to-one. If f is not one-to-one, then stop, because f^{-1} does not exist.

Step 2. If the function is written with function notation, like $f(x)$, replace the function symbol with the letter y. Then interchange x and y.

Step 3. Solve the resulting equation for y. The result is $f^{-1}(x)$.

Step 4. Find the domain of f^{-1}. Remember, the domain of f^{-1} must be the same as the range of f.

You can check your work using Theorem 5.

EXAMPLE 5

Finding the Inverse of a Function

Find f^{-1} for $f(x) = \sqrt{x-1}$.

SOLUTION

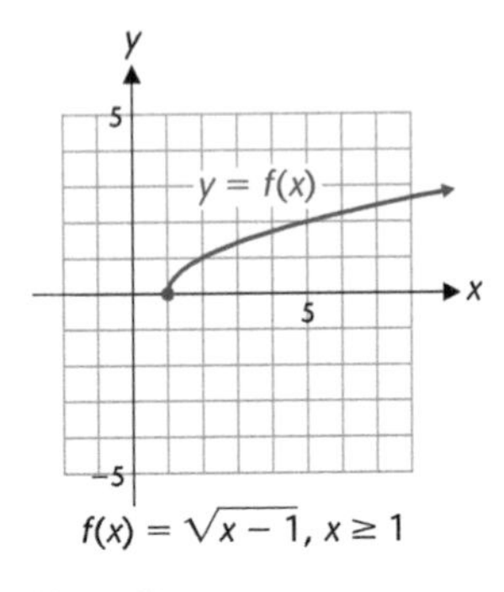

$f(x) = \sqrt{x-1}, x \geq 1$

› Figure 7

Step 1. Find the domain of f and verify that f is one-to-one. The domain of f is $[1, \infty)$. The graph of f in Figure 7 shows that f is one-to-one, so f^{-1} exists.

Step 2. Replace $f(x)$ with y, then interchange x and y.

$$y = \sqrt{x-1} \quad \text{Interchange } x \text{ and } y.$$
$$x = \sqrt{y-1}$$

Step 3. Solve the equation for y.

$$x = \sqrt{y-1} \quad \text{Square both sides.}$$
$$x^2 = y - 1 \quad \text{Add 1 to each side.}$$
$$x^2 + 1 = y$$

The inverse is $f^{-1}(x) = x^2 + 1$.

Step 4. Find the domain of f^{-1}.

The equation we found for f^{-1} is defined for all x, but the domain should be the range of f. From Figure 7, we see that the range of f is $[0, \infty)$ so that is the domain of f^{-1}. Therefore,

$$f^{-1}(x) = x^2 + 1 \qquad x \geq 0$$

CHECK

Find the composition of f with the alleged inverse (in both orders!).
For x in $[1, \infty)$, the domain of f, we have

$$\begin{aligned} f^{-1}(f(x)) &= f^{-1}(\sqrt{x-1}) && \text{Substitute } \sqrt{x-1} \text{ into } f^{-1}. \\ &= (\sqrt{x-1})^2 + 1 && \text{Square } \sqrt{x-1}. \\ &= x - 1 + 1 && \text{Add.} \\ &\stackrel{\checkmark}{=} x \end{aligned}$$

For x in $[0, \infty)$, the domain of f^{-1}, we have

$$\begin{aligned} f(f^{-1}(x)) &= f(x^2 + 1) && \text{Substitute } x^2 + 1 \text{ into } f. \\ &= \sqrt{(x^2 + 1) - 1} && \text{Add.} \\ &= \sqrt{x^2} && \sqrt{x^2} = |x| \text{ for any real number } x. \\ &= |x| && |x| = x \text{ for } x \geq 0. \\ &\stackrel{\checkmark}{=} x \end{aligned}$$

MATCHED PROBLEM 5

Find f^{-1} for $f(x) = \sqrt{x + 2}$.

The technique of finding an inverse by interchanging x and y leads to the following property of inverses that comes in very handy later in the course.

THEOREM 6 A Property of Inverses

If f^{-1} exists, then $x = f^{-1}(y)$ if and only if $y = f(x)$.

EXPLORE-DISCUSS 3

Most basic arithmetic operations can be reversed by performing a second operation: subtraction reverses addition, division reverses multiplication, squaring reverses taking the square root, and so on. Viewing a function as a sequence of reversible operations gives insight into the inverse function concept. For example, the function $f(x) = 2x - 1$ can be described verbally as a function that multiplies each domain element by 2 and then subtracts 1. Reversing this sequence describes a function g that adds 1 to each domain element and then divides by 2, or $g(x) = (x + 1)/2$, which is the inverse of the function f. For each of the following functions, write a verbal description of the function, reverse your description, and write the resulting algebraic equation. Verify that the result is the inverse of the original function.

(A) $f(x) = 3x + 5$ **(B)** $f(x) = \sqrt{x - 1}$ **(C)** $f(x) = \dfrac{1}{x + 1}$

Explore-Discuss 3 emphasizes that the inverse of a function is another function that performs the opposite steps in the opposite order as the original function. This helps us to understand the concept of inverses, but it also provides an alternative method for finding the inverse of some functions. We will explore this in the exercises.

› Mathematical Modeling

Example 6 shows how an inverse function is used in constructing a revenue model. See Example 8 in the last section.

EXAMPLE 6

Modeling Revenue

The research department for an electronics firm estimates that the weekly demand for a certain brand of headphones is given by

$$x = f(p) = 20{,}000 - 1{,}000p \qquad 0 \le p \le 20 \qquad \text{Demand function}$$

where x is the number of pairs of headphones retailers are likely to buy per week at p dollars per pair. Express the revenue as a function of the demand x.

SOLUTION

If x pairs of headphones are sold at p dollars each, the total revenue is

$$\begin{aligned} \text{Revenue} &= (\text{Number of pairs of headphones})(\text{price of each pair}) \\ &= xp \end{aligned}$$

To express the revenue as a function of the demand x, we must express the price in terms of x. That is, we must find the inverse of the demand function.

$$\begin{aligned} x &= 20{,}000 - 1{,}000p && \text{Subtract 20,000 from each side.} \\ x - 20{,}000 &= -1{,}000p && \text{Divide both sides by } -1{,}000. \\ \frac{x - 20{,}000}{-1{,}000} &= p && \text{Distribute.} \\ -0.001x + 20 &= p \end{aligned}$$

The inverse of the demand function is

$$p = f^{-1}(x) = 20 - 0.001x$$

and the revenue is given by

$$\begin{aligned} R &= xp \\ R(x) &= x(20 - 0.001x) \\ &= 20x - 0.001x^2 \end{aligned}$$

MATCHED PROBLEM 6

Repeat Example 6 for the demand function

$$x = f(p) = 10{,}000 - 1{,}000p \qquad 0 \leq p \leq 10$$

The demand function in Example 6 was defined with independent variable p and dependent variable x. When we found the inverse function, we did not rewrite it with independent variable p. Because p represents price and x represents number of pairs of headphones, to interchange these variables would be confusing. In most applications, the variables have specific meaning and should not be interchanged as part of the inverse process.

Example 6 illustrates an important application of inverse functions. We were given a function with input price and output demand, but we needed one with input demand and output price. This is exactly what inverse functions are all about!

Graphing Inverse Functions

EXPLORE-DISCUSS 4

The following activities refer to the graph of f in Figure 8 and Tables 1 and 2.

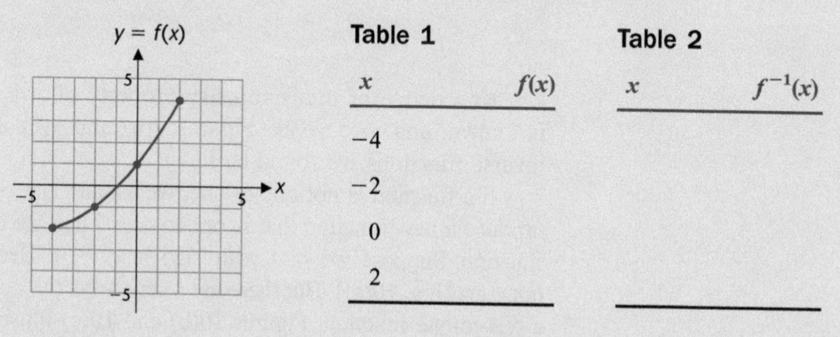

Figure 8

Table 1

x	$f(x)$
−4	
−2	
0	
2	

Table 2

x	$f^{-1}(x)$

(A) Complete the second column in Table 1.

(B) Reverse the ordered pairs in Table 1 and list the results in Table 2.

(C) Add the points in Table 2 to Figure 8 (or a copy of the figure) and sketch the graph of f^{-1}.

(D) Discuss any symmetry you observe between the graphs of f and f^{-1}.

There is an important relationship between the graph of any function and its inverse that is based on the following observation: In a rectangular coordinate system, switching the order of the coordinates moves a point to the opposite side of the line $y = x$. Specifically, any point P is moved to the point Q such that $y = x$ is the perpendicular bisector of segment PQ [Fig. 9(a)]. In other words, the points (a, b) and (b, a) are symmetric with respect to the line $y = x$. Theorem 7 is an immediate consequence of this observation.

› **Figure 9** Symmetry with respect to the line $y = x$.

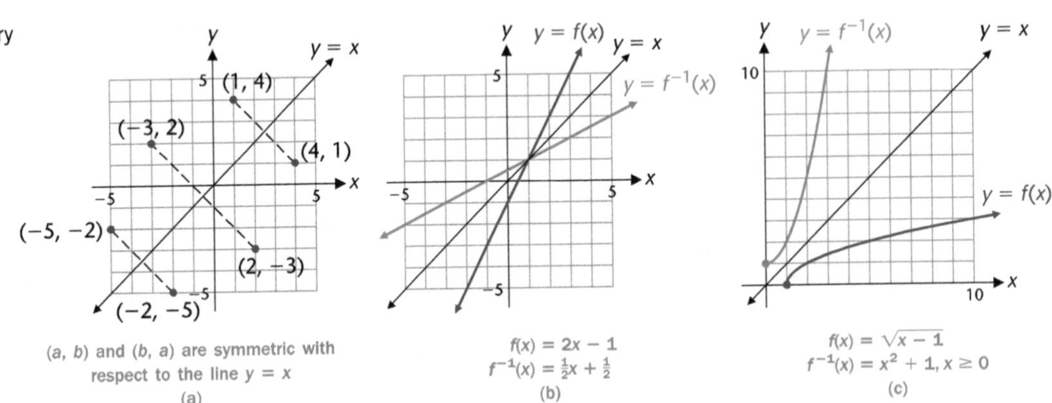

(a, b) and (b, a) are symmetric with respect to the line y = x
(a)

$f(x) = 2x - 1$
$f^{-1}(x) = \frac{1}{2}x + \frac{1}{2}$
(b)

$f(x) = \sqrt{x - 1}$
$f^{-1}(x) = x^2 + 1, x \geq 0$
(c)

> **THEOREM 7 Symmetry Property for the Graphs of f and f^{-1}**
>
> The graphs of $y = f(x)$ and $y = f^{-1}(x)$ are symmetric with respect to the line $y = x$.

Knowledge of this symmetry property allows us to graph f^{-1} if the graph of f is known, and vice versa. Figures 9(b) and 9(c) illustrate this property for the two inverse functions we found earlier.

If a function is not one-to-one, we usually can restrict the domain of the function to produce a new function that is one-to-one. Then we can find an inverse for the restricted function. Suppose we start with $f(x) = x^2 - 4$. Because f is not one-to-one, f^{-1} does not exist [Fig. 10(a)]. But there are many ways the domain of f can be restricted to obtain a one-to-one function. Figures 10(b) and 10(c) illustrate two such restrictions.

In essence, we are "forcing" the function to be one-to-one by throwing out a portion of the graph that would make it fail the horizontal line test.

› **Figure 10** Restricting the domain of a function.

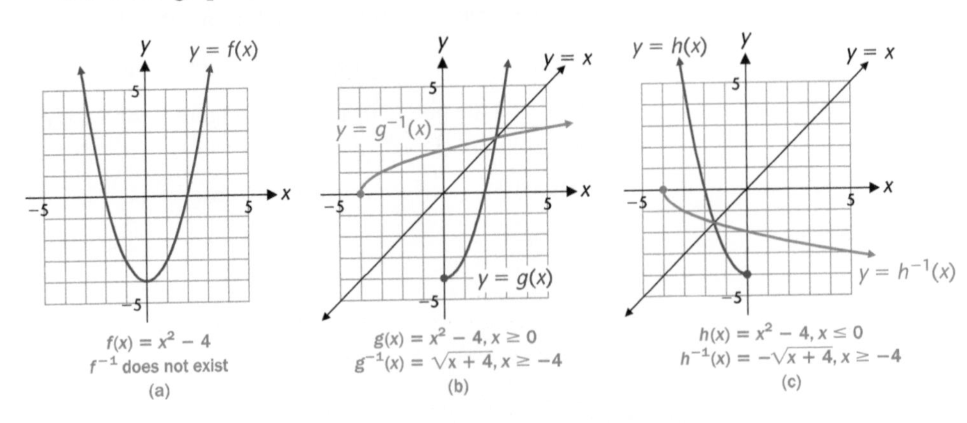

$f(x) = x^2 - 4$
f^{-1} does not exist
(a)

$g(x) = x^2 - 4, x \geq 0$
$g^{-1}(x) = \sqrt{x + 4}, x \geq -4$
(b)

$h(x) = x^2 - 4, x \leq 0$
$h^{-1}(x) = -\sqrt{x + 4}, x \geq -4$
(c)

Recall from Theorem 3 that increasing and decreasing functions are always one-to-one. This provides the basis for a convenient method of restricting the domain of a function:

If the domain of a function f is restricted to an interval on the x axis over which f is increasing (or decreasing), then the new function determined by this restriction is one-to-one and has an inverse.

We used this method to form the one-to-one functions g and h in Figure 10.

EXAMPLE 7 Finding the Inverse of a Function

Find the inverse of $f(x) = 5 - x^2$, $x \leq 0$. Graph f, f^{-1}, and $y = x$ in a squared viewing window on a graphing calculator. Then sketch the graph by hand, adding appropriate labels.

SOLUTION

Step 1. Find the domain of f and verify that f is one-to-one. We are given a domain of $(-\infty, 0]$. Note the syntax we used in Figure 11(a). Dividing $5 - x^2$ by the expression $(x \leq 0)$* restricts the graph to the domain we were given [Fig. 11(b)]. This graph shows that f is one-to-one.

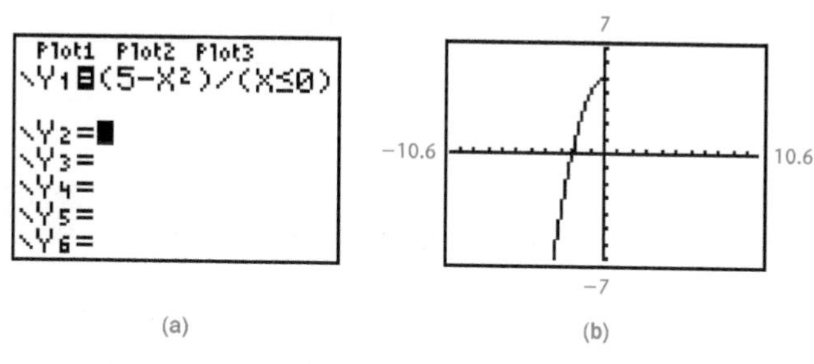

› Figure 11

Step 2. Replace $f(x)$ with y, then interchange x and y.

$$y = 5 - x^2$$
$$x = 5 - y^2$$

Step 3. Solve the equation for y.

$$x = 5 - y^2 \qquad \text{Add } y^2 \text{ to each side.}$$
$$y^2 + x = 5 \qquad \text{Subtract } x \text{ from each side.}$$
$$y^2 = 5 - x \qquad \text{Apply the square root to each side.}$$
$$y = \pm\sqrt{5 - x}$$

*The graphing calculator assigns this expression a value of 1 for $x \leq 0$, and a value of 0 for $x > 0$. This makes y_1 undefined for positive x values.

The restricted domain of f tells us which solution to use. Because $x \le 0$ for f, we must have $y \le 0$ for f^{-1}. We should choose the negative square root. The inverse is

$$f^{-1}(x) = -\sqrt{5 - x}$$

Step 4. Find the domain of f^{-1}. The equation $f^{-1}(x) = -\sqrt{5 - x}$ is defined only for $x \le 5$. From the graph in Figure 11(b), the range of f is also $(-\infty, 5]$, so

$$f^{-1}(x) = -\sqrt{5 - x} \qquad x \le 5$$

The check is left for the reader.

The graphs of f, f^{-1}, and $y = x$ on a graphing calculator are shown in Figure 12 and a hand sketch is shown in Figure 13. Note that we plotted several points on the graph of f and their reflections on the graph of f^{-1} to aid in preparing the hand sketch.

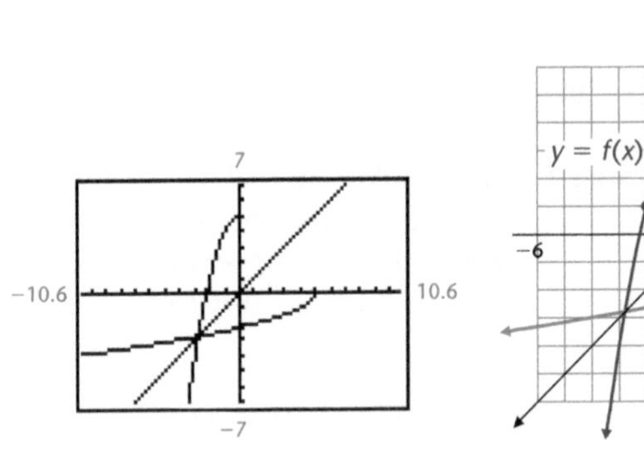

› Figure 12

› Figure 13

MATCHED PROBLEM 7

Find the inverse of $f(x) = 5 - x^2, x \ge 0$. Graph f, f^{-1}, and $y = x$ in the same coordinate system.

ANSWERS TO MATCHED PROBLEMS

1. (A) Not one-to-one (B) One-to-one **2.** (A) One-to-one (B) Not one-to-one
3. (A) $F^{-1} = \{(-5, 3/2), (-7, 5/2), (-9, 7/2), (-11, 9/2)\}$ (B) G^{-1} does not exist.
4. f and g are inverses. **5.** $f^{-1}(x) = x^2 - 2, x \ge 0$ **6.** $R(x) = 10x - 0.001x^2$
7. $f^{-1}(x) = \sqrt{5 - x}, x \le 5$

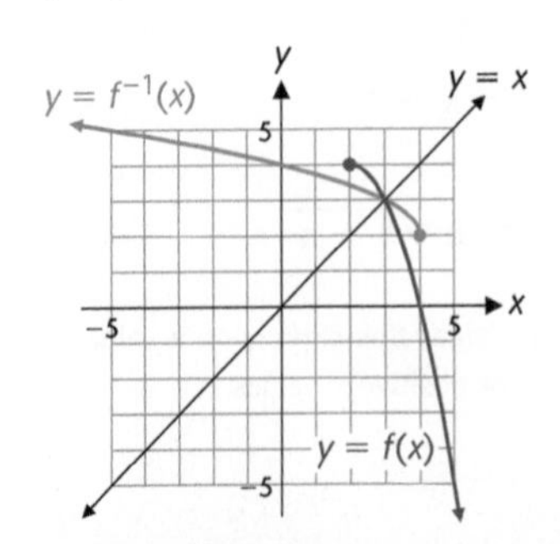

1-6 Exercises

For each set of ordered pairs in Problems 1–6, determine if the set is a function, a one-to-one function, or neither. Reverse all the ordered pairs in each set and determine if this new set is a function, a one-to-one function, or neither.

1. $\{(1, 2), (2, 1), (3, 4), (4, 3)\}$

2. $\{(-1, 0), (0, 1), (1, -1), (2, 1)\}$

3. $\{(5, 4), (4, 3), (3, 3), (2, 4)\}$

4. $\{(5, 4), (4, 3), (3, 2), (2, 1)\}$

5. $\{(1, 2), (1, 4), (-3, 2), (-3, 4)\}$

6. $\{(0, 5), (-4, 5), (-4, 2), (0, 2)\}$

Which of the functions in Problems 7–18 are one-to-one?

7.

Domain	Range
−2 →	−4
−1 →	−2
0 →	0
1 →	1
2 →	5

8.

Domain	Range
−2 →	−3
−1 →	−3
0 →	7
1 →	9
2 →	9

9.

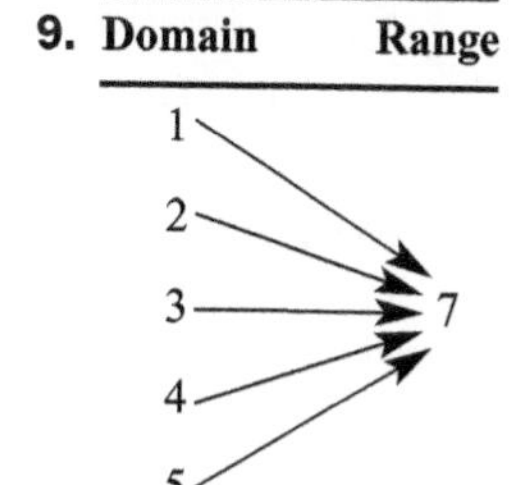

10.

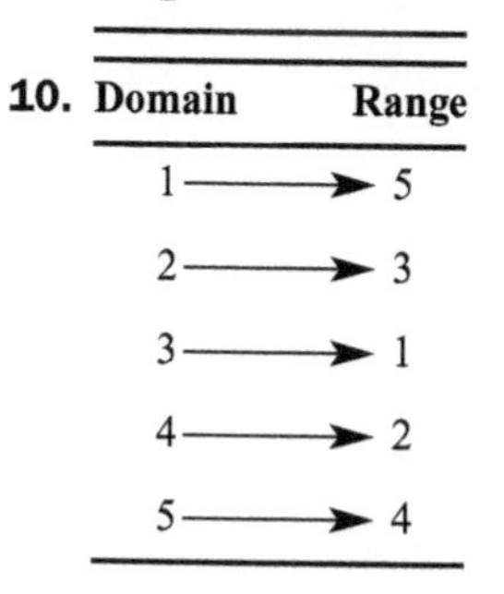

11.

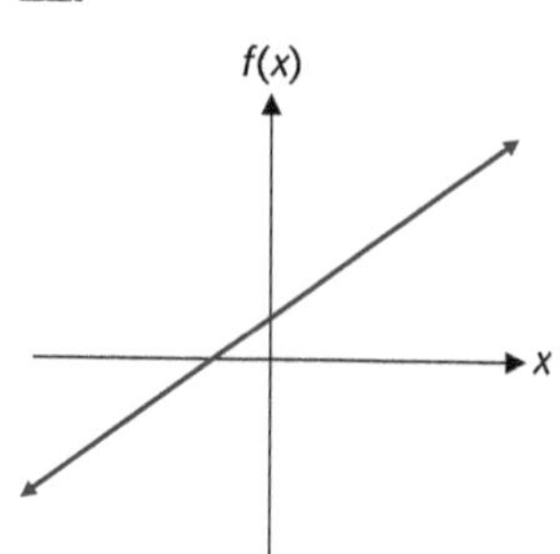

12.

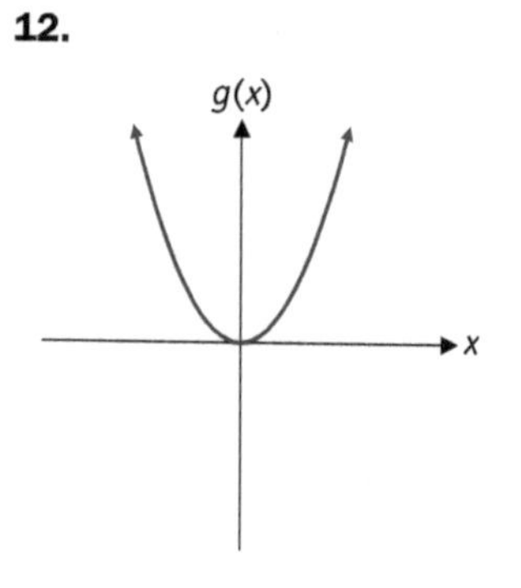

13.

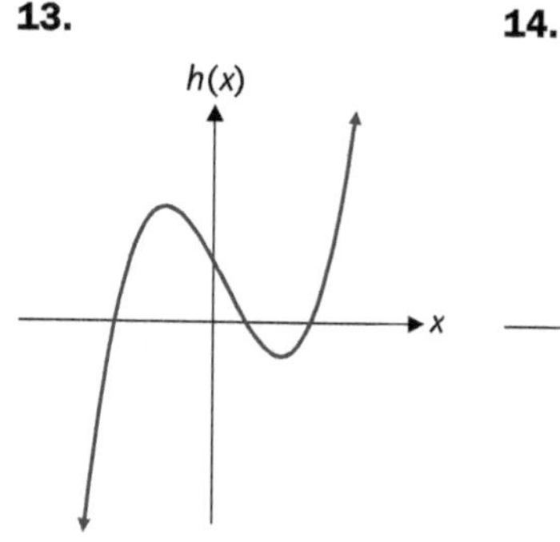

14.

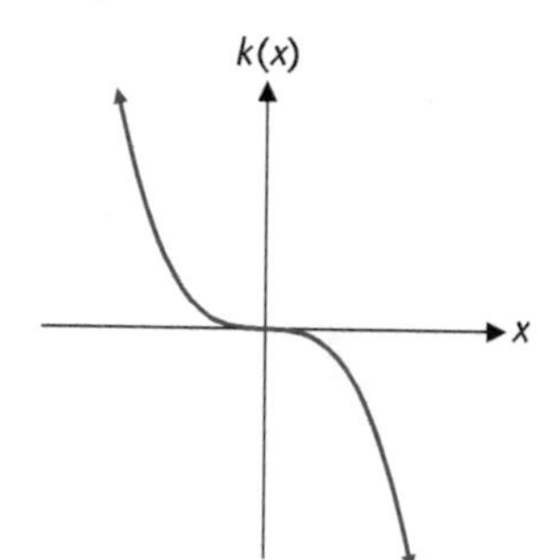

15.

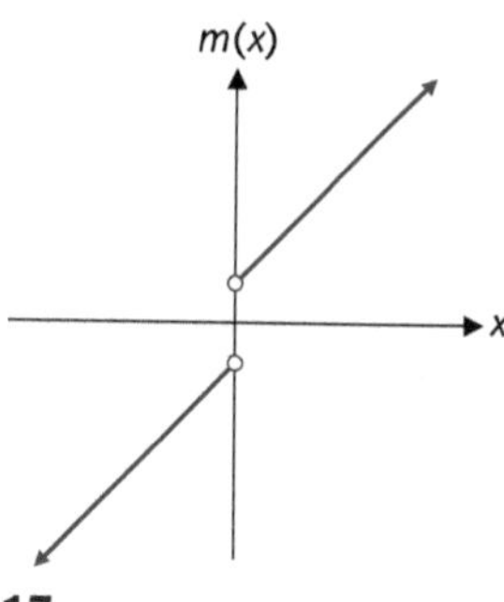

16.

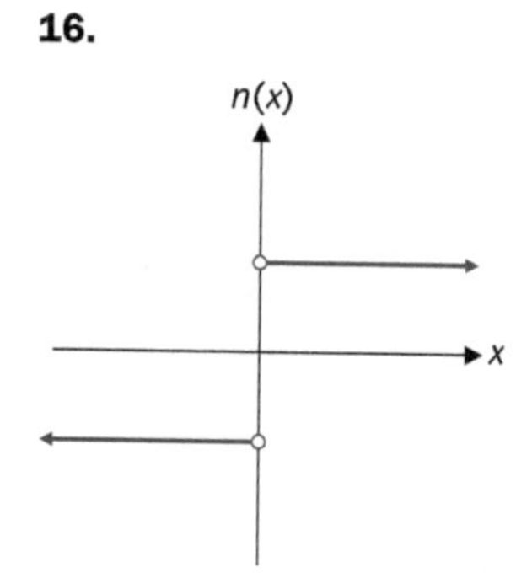

17.

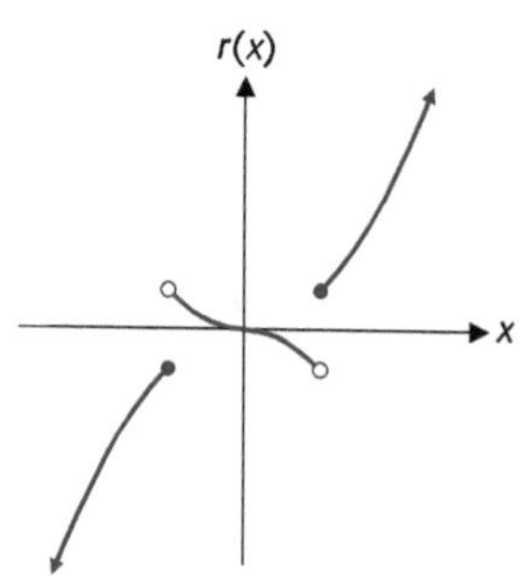

18.

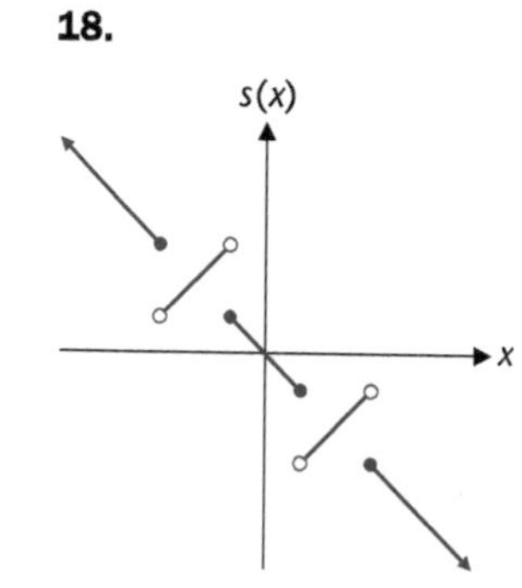

In Problems 19–24, find the inverse of each function, if it exists.

19. $f = \{(2, 3), (3, 4), (4, 5), (5, 6)\}$

20. $g = \{(-5, 10), (-10, 20), (-20, 40), (-40, 80)\}$

21. $h = \{(7, -3), (0, 0), (-7, -3)\}$

22. $k = \{(3, -8), (0, 8), (-3, -8)\}$

23. $F = \{(a, 7), (c, 11), (e, -9), (g, -13)\}$

24. $G = \{(1, x), (3, y), (-5, z), (-7, w)\}$

25. When a function is defined by ordered pairs, how can you tell if it is one-to-one?

26. When you have the graph of a function, how can you tell if it is one-to-one?

27. Why does a function fail to have an inverse if it is not one-to-one? Give an example using ordered pairs to illustrate your answer.

28. True or False: Any function whose graph changes direction is not one-to-one. Explain.

29. What is the result of composing a function with its inverse? Why does this make sense?

30. What is the relationship between the graphs of two functions that are inverses?

In Problems 31–36, use Theorem 1 to determine which functions are one-to-one.

31. $F(x) = \frac{1}{2}x + 2$ **32.** $G(x) = -\frac{1}{3}x + 1$

33. $H(x) = 4 - x^2$ **34.** $K(x) = \sqrt{4 - x}$

35. $M(x) = \sqrt{x + 1}$ **36.** $N(x) = x^2 - 1$

In Problems 37–44, use the horizontal line test (Theorem 2) to determine which functions are one-to-one.

37. $f(x) = \dfrac{7}{x}$ **38.** $g(x) = \dfrac{-11}{x^3}$

39. $f(x) = 0.3x^3 - 3.8x^2 + 12x + 11$

40. $g(x) = -0.4x^3 + 0.1x^2 + 2x - 20$

41. $f(x) = \dfrac{x^2 + |x|}{x}$ **42.** $f(x) = \dfrac{x^2 - |x|}{x}$

43. $f(x) = \dfrac{x^2 - 4}{|x - 2|}$ **44.** $f(x) = \dfrac{1 - x^2}{|x + 1|}$

In Problems 45–50, use Theorem 5 to determine if g is the inverse of f.

45. $f(x) = 3x + 5$; $g(x) = \frac{1}{3}x - \frac{5}{3}$

46. $f(x) = 2x - 4$; $g(x) = \frac{1}{2}x - 2$

47. $f(x) = 2 - (x + 1)^3$; $g(x) = \sqrt[3]{3 - x} - 1$

48. $f(x) = (x - 3)^3 + 4$; $g(x) = \sqrt[3]{x - 4} + 3$

49. $f(x) = \dfrac{2x - 3}{x + 4}$; $g(x) = \dfrac{3 + 4x}{2 - x}$

50. $f(x) = \dfrac{x + 1}{2x - 3}$; $g(x) = \dfrac{3x + 1}{2x + 1}$

Because the inverse of a function reverses the action of the original function, if you can write a step-by-step description of what a function does to numbers in its domain, you can reverse those steps to find the inverse. In Problems 51–56, write a step-by-step description of the given function, then reverse that description and use your result to write an equation for the inverse function.

51. $h(x) = 3x - 7$ **52.** $k(x) = 6 - 9x$

53. $m(x) = \sqrt[3]{x + 11}$ **54.** $n(x) = \sqrt[5]{2 + x}$

55. $s(x) = (3x + 17)^5$ **56.** $t(x) = (2x + 7)^3$

In Problems 57–60, use the graph of the one-to-one function f to sketch the graph of f^{-1}. State the domain and range of f^{-1}.

57.

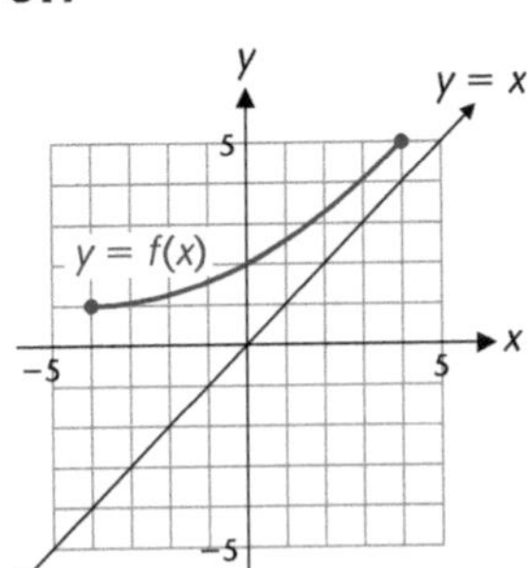

58.

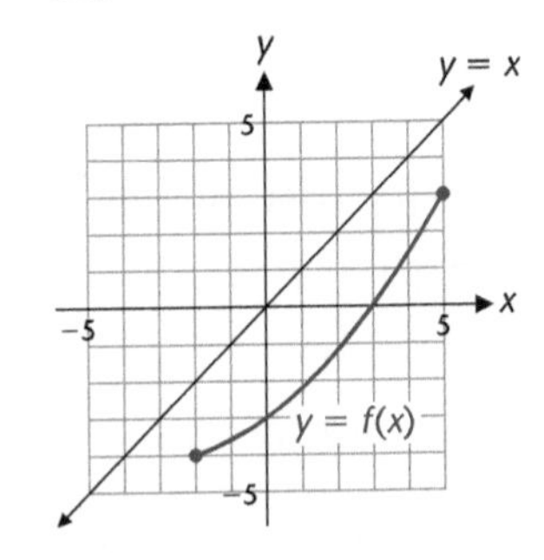

59.

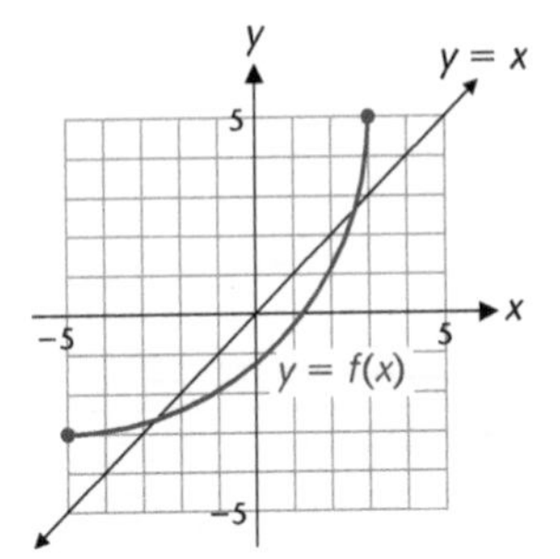

60.

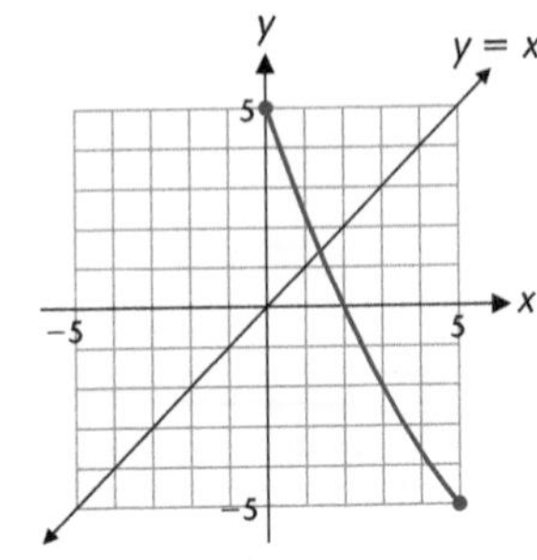

In Problems 61–66, verify that g is the inverse of the one-to-one function f. Sketch the graphs of f, g, and y = x in the same coordinate system and identify each graph.

61. $f(x) = 3x + 6$; $g(x) = \frac{1}{3}x - 2$

62. $f(x) = -\frac{1}{2}x + 2$; $g(x) = -2x + 4$

63. $f(x) = 4 + x^2, x \geq 0$; $g(x) = \sqrt{x - 4}$

64. $f(x) = \sqrt{x + 2}$; $g(x) = x^2 - 2, x \geq 0$

65. $f(x) = -\sqrt{x - 2}$; $g(x) = x^2 + 2, x \leq 0$

66. $f(x) = 6 - x^2, x \leq 0$; $g(x) = -\sqrt{6 - x}$

The functions in Problems 67–86 are one-to-one. Find f^{-1}.

67. $f(x) = 3x$ **68.** $f(x) = \frac{1}{2}x$

69. $f(x) = 4x - 3$ **70.** $f(x) = -\frac{1}{3}x + \frac{5}{3}$

71. $f(x) = \frac{1}{10}x + \frac{3}{5}$

72. $f(x) = -2x - 7$

73. $f(x) = \dfrac{2}{x - 1}$

74. $f(x) = \dfrac{3}{x + 4}$

75. $f(x) = \dfrac{x}{x + 2}$

76. $f(x) = \dfrac{x - 3}{x}$

77. $f(x) = \dfrac{2x + 5}{3x - 4}$

78. $f(x) = \dfrac{5 - 3x}{7 - 4x}$

79. $f(x) = x^3 + 1$

80. $f(x) = x^5 - 2$

81. $f(x) = 4 - \sqrt[5]{x + 2}$

82. $f(x) = \sqrt[3]{x + 3} - 2$

83. $f(x) = \frac{1}{2}\sqrt{16 - x}$

84. $f(x) = -\frac{1}{3}\sqrt{36 - x}$

85. $f(x) = 3 - \sqrt{x - 2}$

86. $f(x) = 4 + \sqrt{5 - x}$

87. How are the x and y intercepts of a function and its inverse related?

88. Does a constant function have an inverse? Explain.

89. Are the functions $f(x) = x^2$ and $g(x) = \sqrt{x}$ inverses? Why or why not?

90. Are the functions $f(x) = x^3$ and $g(x) = \sqrt[3]{x}$ inverses? Why or why not?

The functions in Problems 91–94 are one-to-one. Find f^{-1}.

91. $f(x) = (x - 1)^2 + 2, x \geq 1$

92. $f(x) = 3 - (x - 5)^2, x \leq 5$

93. $f(x) = x^2 + 2x - 2, x \leq -1$

94. $f(x) = x^2 + 8x + 7, x \geq -4$

In Problems 95–100, find f^{-1}, find the domain and range of f^{-1}, sketch the graphs of f, f^{-1}, and $y = x$ in the same coordinate system, and identify each graph.

95. $f(x) = -\sqrt{9 - x^2}, 0 \leq x \leq 3$

96. $f(x) = \sqrt{9 - x^2}, 0 \leq x \leq 3$

97. $f(x) = \sqrt{9 - x^2}, -3 \leq x \leq 0$

98. $f(x) = -\sqrt{9 - x^2}, -3 \leq x \leq 0$

99. $f(x) = 1 + \sqrt{1 - x^2}, 0 \leq x \leq 1$

100. $f(x) = 1 - \sqrt{1 - x^2}, 0 \leq x \leq 1$

In Problems 101–104, the function f is not one-to-one. Find the inverses of the functions formed by restricting the domain of f as indicated. Check by graphing f, f^{-1}, and the line $y = x$ in a squared viewing window on a graphing calculator. [Hint: To restrict the graph of $y = f(x)$ to an interval of the form $a \leq x \leq b$, enter $y = f(x)/((a \leq x)*(x \leq b))$.]

101. $f(x) = (2 - x)^2$: (A) $x \leq 2$ (B) $x \geq 2$

102. $f(x) = (1 + x)^2$: (A) $x \leq -1$ (B) $x \geq -1$

103. $f(x) = \sqrt{4x - x^2}$: (A) $0 \leq x \leq 2$ (B) $2 \leq x \leq 4$

104. $f(x) = \sqrt{6x - x^2}$: (A) $0 \leq x \leq 3$ (B) $3 \leq x \leq 6$

APPLICATIONS

105. PRICE AND DEMAND The number q of CD players consumers are willing to buy per week from a retail chain at a price of \$$p$ is given approximately by

$$q = d(p) = \frac{3{,}000}{0.2p + 1} \qquad 10 \leq p \leq 70$$

(A) Find the range of d.
(B) Find $p = d^{-1}(q)$, and find its domain and range.
(C) Should you interchange p and q in part B? Explain.

106. PRICE AND SUPPLY The number q of CD players a retail chain is willing to supply at a price of \$$p$ is given approximately by

$$q = s(p) = \frac{900p}{p + 20} \qquad 10 \leq p \leq 70$$

(A) Find the range of s.
(B) Find $p = s^{-1}(q)$, and find its domain and range.
(C) Should you interchange p and q in part B? Explain.

107. REVENUE The demand x and the price p (in dollars) for a certain product are related by

$$x = f(p) = 2{,}000 - 40p \qquad 0 \leq p \leq 50$$

Express the revenue as a function of x.

108. REVENUE The demand x and the price p (in dollars) for a certain product are related by

$$x = f(p) = 3{,}000 - 30p \qquad 0 \leq p \leq 100$$

Express the revenue as a function of x.

CHAPTER 1 Review

1-1 Using Graphing Calculators

A **graphing utility** is any electronic device capable of displaying the graph of an equation. The smallest darkened rectangular area that a graphing calculator can display is called a **pixel.** The **window variables** for a **standard viewing window** are

$$\text{Xmin} = -10, \text{Xmax} = 10, \text{Xscl} = 1, \text{Ymin} = -10, \text{Ymax} = 10, \text{Yscl} = 1$$

Other viewing windows can be defined by assigning different values to these variables. Most graphing calculators will construct a table of ordered pairs that satisfy an equation. A grid can be added to a graph to aid in reading the graph. A **cursor** is used to locate a single pixel on the screen. The coordinates of the pixel at the cursor location, called **screen coordinates,** approximate the mathematical coordinates of all the points close to the pixel. The **TRACE** command constrains cursor movement to the graph of an equation and displays coordinates of points that satisfy the equation. The **ZOOM** command enlarges or reduces the viewing window. The **INTERSECT** or **ISECT** command finds the intersection points of two curves.

Mathematical Modeling

The term **mathematical modeling** refers to the process of using an equation or equations to describe data from the real world.

1-2 Functions

A **relation** is a correspondence that matches up two sets of objects. The first set is called the **domain** and the set of all corresponding elements in the second set is called the **range.** A relation where every element in the domain gets matched with only one element of the range is called a **function**. Equivalently, a *function* is a set of ordered pairs with the property that no two ordered pairs have the same first component and different second components. The *domain* is the set of all first components and the *range* is the set of all second components. An equation in two variables defines a function if to each value of the independent variable, the placeholder for domain values, there corresponds exactly one value of the **dependent variable**, the placeholder for range values. A vertical line will intersect the graph of a function in at most one point. Unless otherwise specified, the domain of a function defined by an equation is assumed to be the set of all real number replacements for the independent variable that produce real values for the dependent variable. The symbol $f(x)$ represents the real number in the range of the function f that is paired with the domain value x. Equivalently, the ordered pair $(x, f(x))$ belongs to the function f. The **STAT** editor on a graphing calculator is used to enter data and the **STAT PLOT** command will produce a **scatter plot** of the data.

1-3 Functions: Graphs and Properties

The **graph of a function** f is the set of all points $(x, f(x))$, where x is in the domain of f and $f(x)$ is the associated output. This is also the same as the graph of the equation $y = f(x)$. The first coordinate of a point where the graph of a function intersects the x axis is called an ***x* intercept** or **real zero** of the function. The x intercept is also a real solution or **root** of the equation $f(x) = 0$. The second coordinate of a point where the graph of a function crosses the y axis is called the ***y* intercept** of the function. The y intercept is given by $f(0)$, provided 0 is in the domain of f. Most graphing utilities contain a built-in command, usually called **ROOT** or **ZERO,** for approximating x intercepts. A solid dot on a graph of a function indicates a point that belongs to the graph and an open dot indicates a point that does not belong to the graph. Dots are also used to indicate that a graph terminates at a point, and arrows are used to indicate that the graph continues indefinitely with no significant changes in direction.

Let I be an open interval in the domain of a function f. Then,

1. f is **increasing** on I and the graph of f is **rising** on I if $f(a) < f(b)$ whenever $a < b$ in I.
2. f is **decreasing** on I and the graph of f is **falling** on I if $f(a) > f(b)$ whenever $a < b$ in I.
3. f is **constant** on I and the graph of f is **horizontal** on I if $f(a) = f(b)$ whenever $a < b$ in I.

The functional value $f(c)$ is called a **local maximum** if there is an interval (a, b) containing c such that $f(x) \le f(c)$ for all x in (a, b) and a **local minimum** if there is an interval (a, b) containing c such that $f(x) \ge f(c)$ for all x in (a, b). The functional value $f(c)$ is called a **local extremum** if it is either a local maximum or a local minimum. Most graphing calculators have a **MAXIMUM** command and a **MINIMUM** command for finding local extrema.

A **piecewise-defined function** is a function that is defined by different formulas for different domain values. Graphs of piecewise-defined functions may have **sharp corners.** A function is **continuous** if its graph has no holes or breaks and **discontinuous** at any point where it has a hole or break. Intuitively, the graph of a continuous function can be sketched without lifting a pen from the paper. The **greatest**

integer of a real number x, denoted by $[\![x]\!]$, is the largest integer less than or equal to x; that is, $[\![x]\!] = n$, where n is an integer, $n \le x < n + 1$.

The **greatest integer function** f is defined by the equation $f(x) = [\![x]\!]$. Changing the mode on a graphing calculator from **connected mode** to **dot mode** makes discontinuities on some graphs more apparent.

1-4 Functions: Graphs and Transformations

The first six basic functions in our library of elementary functions are defined by $f(x) = x$ (identity function), $g(x) = |x|$ (absolute value function), $h(x) = x^2$ (square function), $m(x) = x^3$ (cube function), $n(x) = \sqrt{x}$ (square root function), and $p(x) = \sqrt[3]{x}$ (cube root function) (see Figure 1 in this section). Performing an operation on a function produces a transformation of the graph of the function. The basic transformations are the following:

Vertical Translation:

$$y = f(x) + k \begin{cases} k > 0 & \text{Shift graph of } y = f(x) \text{ up } k \text{ units} \\ k < 0 & \text{Shift graph of } y = f(x) \text{ down } |k| \text{ units} \end{cases}$$

Horizontal Translation:

$$y = f(x + h) \begin{cases} h > 0 & \text{Shift graph of } y = f(x) \text{ left } h \text{ units} \\ h < 0 & \text{Shift graph of } y = f(x) \text{ right } |h| \text{ units} \end{cases}$$

Vertical Stretch and Shrink:

$$y = Af(x) \begin{cases} A > 1 & \text{Vertically stretch the graph of } y = f(x) \text{ by multiplying each } y \text{ value by } A \\ 0 < A < 1 & \text{Vertically shrink the graph of } y = f(x) \text{ by multiplying each } y \text{ value by } A \end{cases}$$

Horizontal Stretch and Shrink:

$$y = f(Ax) \begin{cases} A > 1 & \text{Horizontally shrink the graph of } y = f(x) \text{ by multiplying each } x \text{ value by } \frac{1}{A} \\ 0 < A < 1 & \text{Horizontally stretch the graph of } y = f(x) \text{ by mltiplying each } x \text{ value by } \frac{1}{A} \end{cases}$$

Reflection:

$y = -f(x)$ Reflect the graph of $y = f(x)$ in the x axis
$y = f(-x)$ Reflect the graph of $y = f(x)$ in the y axis
$y = -f(-x)$ Reflect the graph of $y = f(x)$ in the origin

A function f is called an **even function** if $f(x) = f(-x)$ for all x in the domain of f and an **odd function** if $f(-x) = -f(x)$ for all x in the domain of f. The graph of an even function is said to be **symmetric with respect to the y axis** and the graph of an odd function is said to be **symmetric with respect to the origin.**

1-5 Operations on Functions; Composition

The **sum, difference, product,** and **quotient** of the functions f and g are defined by

$$(f + g)(x) = f(x) + g(x) \qquad (f - g)(x) = f(x) - g(x)$$

$$(fg)(x) = f(x)g(x) \qquad \left(\frac{f}{g}\right)(x) = \frac{f(x)}{g(x)} \quad g(x) \ne 0$$

The **domain** of each function is the intersection of the domains of f and g, with the exception that values of x where $g(x) = 0$ must be excluded from the domain of f/g.

The **composition** of functions f and g is defined by $(f \circ g)(x) = f(g(x))$. The **domain** of $f \circ g$ is the set of all real numbers x in the domain of g such that $g(x)$ is in the domain of f. The domain of $f \circ g$ is always a subset of the domain of g. Composition is not a commutative process: the order of functions is important.

1-6 Inverse Functions

A function is **one-to-one** if no two ordered pairs in the function have the same second component and different first components. A **horizontal line** will intersect the graph of a one-to-one function in at most one point. A function that is increasing (or decreasing) throughout its domain is one-to-one. The **inverse** of the one-to-one function f is the function f^{-1} formed by reversing all the ordered pairs in f.

If f is a one-to-one function, then:

1. f^{-1} is one-to-one.

2. Domain of f^{-1} = Range of f.

3. Range of f^{-1} = Domain of f.

4. $x = f^{-1}(y)$ if and only if $y = f(x)$.

5. $f^{-1}(f(x)) = x$ for all x in the domain of f.

6. $f(f^{-1}(x)) = x$ for all x in the domain of f^{-1}.

7. To find f^{-1}, replace $f(x)$ with y, then interchange x and y and solve for y. (In some applications, it may not be appropriate to interchange variables, in which case you simply solve for the independent variable of f.)

8. The graphs of $y = f(x)$ and $y = f^{-1}(x)$ are symmetric with respect to the line $y = x$.

CHAPTER 1 Review Exercises

Work through all the problems in this review and check answers in the back of the book. Answers to most review problems are there, and following each answer is a number in italics indicating the section in which that type of problem is discussed. Where weaknesses show up, review appropriate sections in the text.

1. Find the smallest viewing window that will contain all the points in the table. State your answer in terms of the window variables.

x	-3	5	-4	0	9
y	2	-6	7	-5	1

2. Indicate whether each relation defines a function. Indicate whether any of the functions are one-to-one. Find the domain and range of each function. Find the inverse of any one-to-one functions. Find the domain and range of any inverse functions.

(A) $\{(1, 1), (2, 4), (3, 9)\}$

(B) $\{(1, 1), (1, -1), (2, 2), (2, -2)\}$

(C) $\{(-2, 2), (-1, 2), (0, 2), (1, 2), (2, 2)\}$

(D) $\{(-2, 2), (-1, 3), (0, -1), (1, -2), (2, 1)\}$

3. Indicate whether each graph specifies a function:

(A) (B)

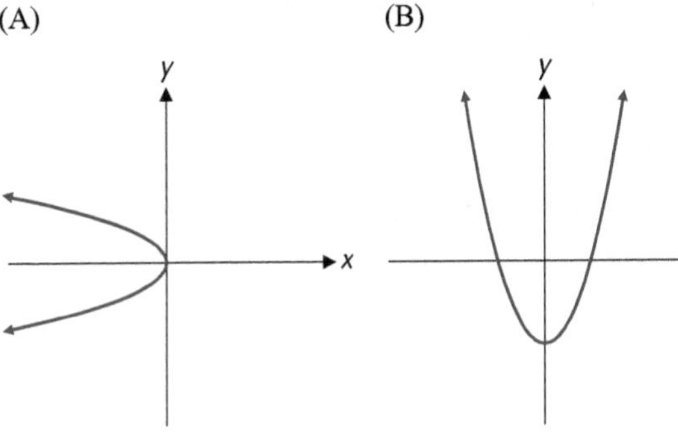

(C) (D)

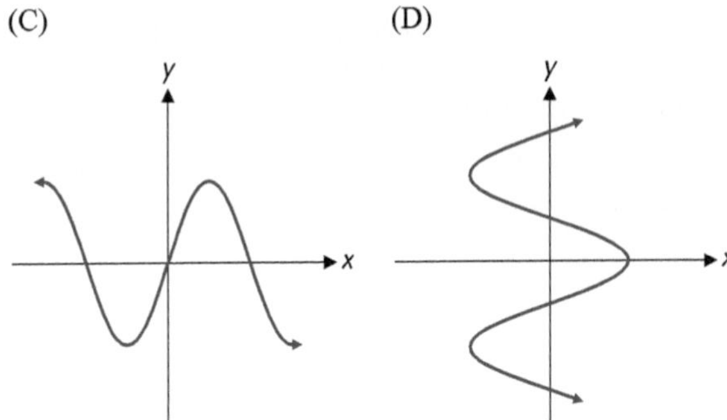

4. For $f(x) = x^2 - 2x$, find:

(A) $f(1)$ (B) $f(-4)$ (C) $f(2) \cdot f(-1)$ (D) $\dfrac{f(0)}{f(3)}$

Problems 5–12 refer to the graphs of f and g shown below.

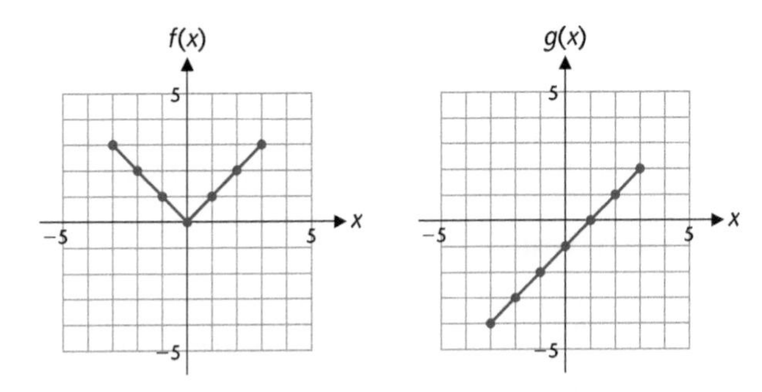

5. Construct a table of values of $(f - g)(x)$ for $x = -3, -2, -1, 0, 1, 2,$ and 3, and sketch the graph of $f - g$.

6. Construct a table of values of $(fg)(x)$ for $x = -3, -2, -1, 0, 1, 2,$ and 3, and sketch the graph of fg.

In Problems 7–10, use the graphs of f and g to find:

7. $(f \circ g)(-1)$ **8.** $(g \circ f)(-2)$ **9.** $f(g(1))$

10. $g(f(-3))$ **11.** Is f a one-to-one function?

12. Is g a one-to-one function?

13. Functions f and g are defined by Table 1. Find $(f \circ g)(-11)$, $(f \circ g)(1)$, and $(f \circ g)(6)$.

Table 1

x	$f(x)$	$g(x)$
-11	12	-4
-4	8	16
1	-4	-11
6	-10	9
9	1	0

14. Indicate whether each function is even, odd, or neither:

(A) $f(x) = x^5 + 6x$ (B) $g(t) = t^4 + 3t^2$

(C) $h(z) = z^5 + 4z^2$

Problems 15–25 refer to the function f given by the following graph.

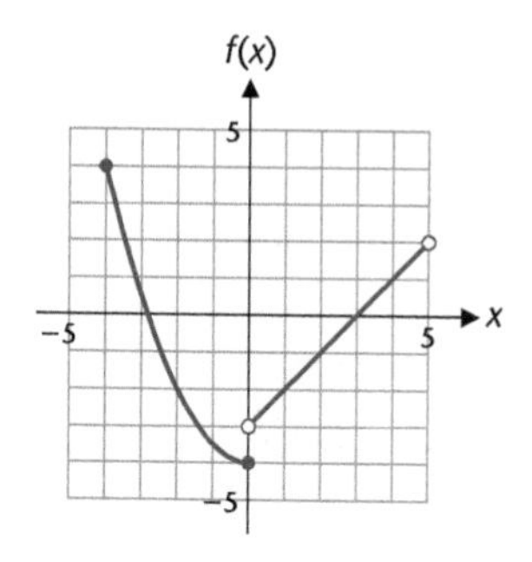

15. Find $f(-4), f(0), f(3)$, and $f(5)$.

16. Find all values of x for which $f(x) = -2$.

17. Find the domain and range of f.

18. Find the intervals over which f is increasing and decreasing.

19. Find any points of discontinuity.

Sketch the graph of each of the following,

20. $f(x) + 1$ **21.** $f(x + 1)$ **22.** $-f(x)$

23. $0.5f(x)$ **24.** $f(2x)$ **25.** $-f(-x)$

26. Match each equation with a graph of one of the functions f, g, m, or n in the figure. Each graph is a graph of one of the equations.

(A) $y = (x - 2)^2 - 4$ (B) $y = -(x + 2)^2 + 4$

(C) $y = -(x - 2)^2 + 4$ (D) $y = (x + 2)^2 - 4$

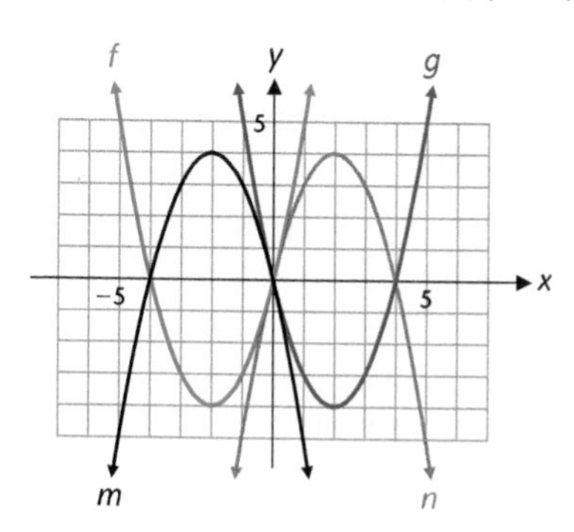

27. Let $f(x) = x^2 - 4$ and $g(x) = x + 3$. Find each of the following functions and find their domains.

(A) f/g (B) g/f (C) $f \circ g$ (D) $g \circ f$

Problems 28–34 refer to the function q given by the following graph.

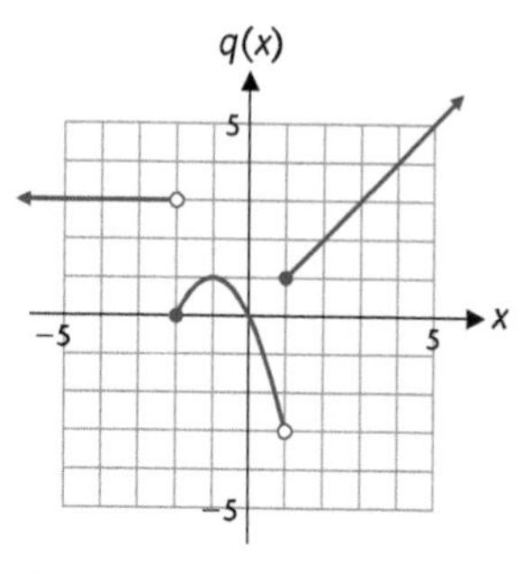

28. Find y to the nearest integer:

(A) $y = q(0)$ (B) $y = q(1)$

(C) $y = q(2)$ (D) $y = q(-2)$

29. Find x to the nearest integer:

(A) $q(x) = 0$ (B) $q(x) = 1$

(C) $q(x) = -3$ (D) $q(x) = 3$

30. Find the domain and range of q.

31. Find the intervals over which q is increasing.

32. Find the intervals over which q is decreasing.

33. Find the intervals over which q is constant.

34. Identify any points of discontinuity.

The graphs of each pair of equations in Problems 35 and 36 intersect in exactly two points. Find a viewing window that clearly shows both points of intersection. Use INTERSECT to find the coordinates of each intersection point to two decimal places.

35. $y = x^2 - 20x, y = 4x - 15$

36. $y = \sqrt{10x + 50}, y = 0.3x + 4$

37. Solve the following equation for the indicated values of b. Round answers to two decimal places.

$$0.1x^3 - 2x^2 - 6x + 80 = b$$

(A) $b = 0$ (B) $b = 100$

(C) $b = -50$ (D) $b = -150$

In Problems 38 and 39, determine if the indicated equation defines a function. Justify your answer.

38. $x + 2y = 10$ **39.** $x + 2y^2 = 10$

40. Find the domain of each of the following functions:

(A) $f(x) = x^2 - 4x + 5$ (B) $g(t) = \dfrac{t + 2}{t - 5}$

(C) $h(w) = 2 + 3\sqrt{w}$

41. If $g(t) = 2t^2 - 3t + 6$, find $\dfrac{g(2 + h) - g(2)}{h}$.

42. The function f multiplies the cube of the domain element by 4 and then subtracts the square root of the domain element. Write an algebraic definition of f.

43. Write a verbal description of the function $f(x) = 3x^2 + 4x - 6$.

In Problems 44 and 45, find the x intercepts, y intercept, local extrema, domain, and range. Round answers to two decimal places.

44. $g(x) = 6\sqrt{x} - x^2$ **45.** $s(x) = x^3 + 27x^2 - 300$

46. Let $f(x) = \begin{cases} -x - 5 & \text{for } -4 \le x < 0 \\ 0.2x^2 & \text{for } 0 \le x \le 5 \end{cases}$

(A) Sketch the graph of $y = f(x)$.

(B) Find the domain and range.

(C) Find any points of discontinuity.

(D) Find the intervals over which f is increasing, decreasing, and constant.

47. Let $f(x) = 0.1x^3 - 6x + 5$. Write a verbal description of the graph of f using increasing and decreasing terminology and indicating any local maximum and minimum values. Approximate to two decimal places the coordinates of any points used in your description.

48. How are the graphs of the following related to the graph of $y = x^2$?

(A) $y = -x^2$ (B) $y = x^2 - 3$

(C) $y = (x + 3)^2$ (D) $y = (2x)^2$

49. Each of the following graphs is the result of applying one or more transformations to the graph of one of the six basic functions in Figure 1, Section 1.4. Find an equation for the graph. Check by graphing the equation on a graphing utility.

(A)

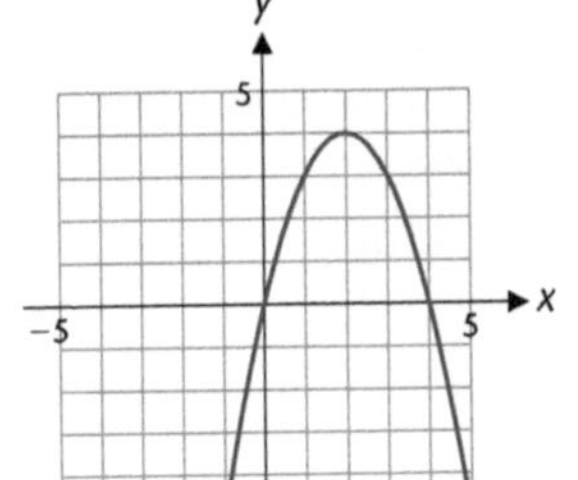

(B)

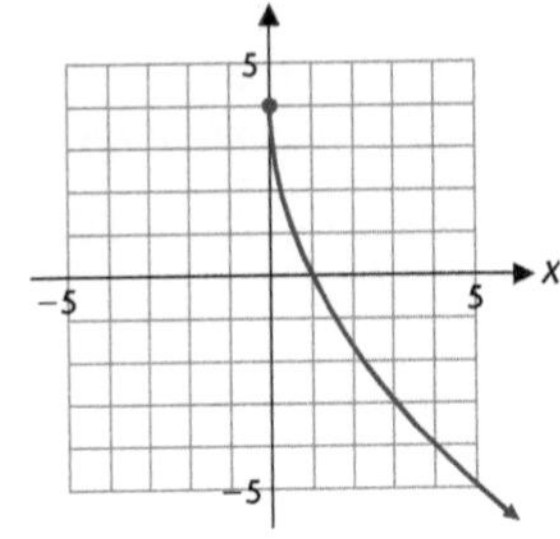

50. The graph of $f(x) = |x|$ is stretched vertically by a factor of 3, reflected in the x axis, shifted four units to the right and eight units up to form the graph of the function g. Find an equation for the function g and graph g.

51. The graph of $m(x) = x^2$ is stretched horizontally by a factor of 2, shifted two units to the left and four units down to form the graph of the function t. Find an equation for the function t and graph t.

52. Is $u(x) = 4x - 8$ the inverse of $v(x) = 0.25x + 2$?

53. Let $k(x) = x^3 + 5$. Write a verbal description of k, reverse your description, and write the resulting algebraic equation. Verify that the result is the inverse of the original function.

54. Find the domain of $f(x) = \dfrac{x}{\sqrt{x} - 3}$.

55. Given $f(x) = \sqrt{x} - 8$ and $g(x) = |x|$,

(A) Find $f \circ g$ and $g \circ f$.

(B) Find the domains of $f \circ g$ and $g \circ f$.

56. Which of the following functions are one-to-one?

(A) $f(x) = x^3$ (B) $g(x) = (x - 2)^2$

(C) $h(x) = 2x - 3$ (D) $F(x) = (x + 3)^2, x \ge -3$

(E) $f(x) = 0.3x^2 - 7x$

In Problems 57–59, find f^{-1}, find the domain and range of f^{-1}, sketch the graphs of f, f^{-1}, and $y = x$ in the same coordinate system, and identify each graph.

57. $f(x) = 3x - 7$ **58.** $f(x) = \sqrt{x - 1}$

59. $f(x) = x^2 - 1, x \ge 0$

60. Sketch by hand the graph of a function that is consistent with the given information.

(A) The function f is continuous on $[-5, 5]$, increasing on $[-5, -3]$, decreasing on $[-3, 1]$, constant on $[1, 3]$, and increasing on $[3, 5]$.

(B) The function f is continuous on $[-5, 1)$ and $[1, 5]$, $f(-2) = -1$ is a local maximum, and $f(3) = 2$ is a local minimum.

61. Write a verbal description of the function g and then find an equation for $g(t)$.

$$g(t + h) = 2(t + h)^2 - 4(t + h) + 5$$

62. Graph in the standard viewing window:

$$f(x) = 0.1(x - 2)^2 + \frac{|3x - 6|}{x - 2}$$

Assuming the graph continues as indicated beyond the part shown in this viewing window, find the domain, range, and any points of discontinuity. [*Hint:* Use the dot mode on your graphing calculator, if it has one.]

63. A partial graph of the function f is shown in the figure. Complete the graph of f over the interval [0, 5] given that:

(A) f is an even function. (B) f is an odd function.

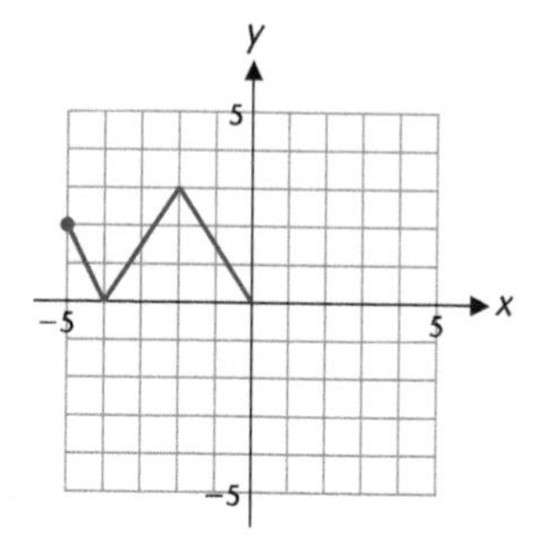

64. For $f(x) = 3x^2 - 5x + 7$, find and simplify:

(A) $\dfrac{f(x + h) - f(x)}{h}$ (B) $\dfrac{f(x) - f(a)}{x - a}$

65. The function f is decreasing on $[-5, 5]$ with $f(-5) = 4$ and $f(5) = -3$.

(A) If f is continuous on $[-5, 5]$, how many times can the graph of f cross the x axis? Support your conclusion with examples and/or verbal arguments.

(B) Repeat part A if the function does not have to be continuous.

66. Let $f(x) = [\![|x|]\!]$.

(A) Write a piecewise definition of f. Include sufficient intervals to clearly illustrate the definition.

(B) Sketch by hand the graph of $y = f(x)$, using a graphing calculator as an aid. Include sufficient intervals to clearly illustrate the graph.

(C) Find the range of f. (D) Find any points of discontinuity.

(E) Indicate whether f is even, odd, or neither.

APPLICATIONS

67. PRICE AND DEMAND The price $\$p$ per hot dog at which q hot dogs can be sold during a baseball game is given approximately by

$$p = g(q) = \frac{9}{1 + 0.002q} \qquad 1{,}000 \le q \le 4{,}000$$

(A) Find the range of g.

(B) Find $q = g^{-1}(p)$ and find its domain and range.

(C) Express the revenue as a function of p.

(D) Express the revenue as a function of q.

68. MARKET RESEARCH If x units of a product are produced each week and sold for a price of $\$p$ per unit, then the weekly demand, revenue, and cost equations are, respectively,

$$x = 500 - 10p$$
$$R(x) = 50x - 0.1x^2$$
$$C(x) = 10x + 1{,}500$$

Express the weekly profit as a function of the price p and find the price that produces the largest profit.

69. PHYSICS: POSITION OF A MOVING OBJECT In flight shooting distance competitions, archers are capable of shooting arrows 600 meters or more. An archer standing on the ground shoots an arrow. After x seconds, the arrow is y meters above the ground as given approximately by

$$y = 55x - 4.88x^2$$

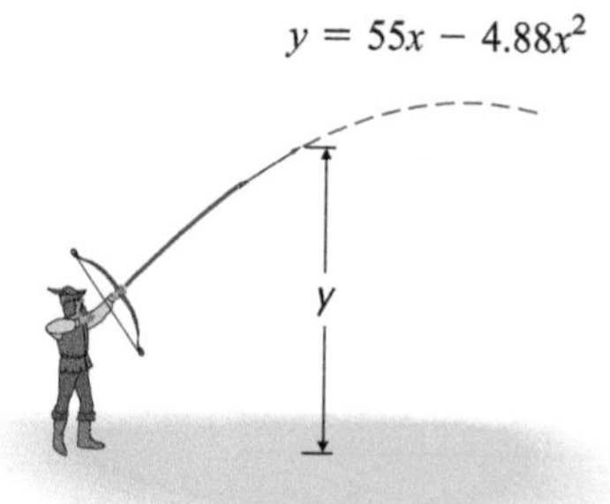

(A) Find the time (to the nearest tenth of a second) the arrow is airborne.

(B) Find the maximum altitude (to the nearest meter) the arrow reaches during its flight.

70. PHYSICS: HEIGHT OF A BUNGEE JUMPER The world's highest bungee jumping bridge is the Bloukrans River Bridge in South Africa, at a height of 708.7 feet. The height in feet of one jumper can be modeled by the function $h(x) = 9.5x^2 - 152x + 708.7$ $0 \le x \le 10$, where x is seconds after he jumps.

(A) How long does it take for the jumper to reach height 300 feet? Round to the nearest tenth of a second.

(B) How high above the ground is the jumper when he reaches the lowest point of the jump? How many seconds pass until he reaches the low point?

71. MANUFACTURING A box with four flaps on each end is to be made out of a piece of cardboard that measures 48 by 72 inches. The width of each flap is x inches and the length of one pair of opposite flaps is $2x$ inches to ensure that the other pair of flaps will meet when folded over to close the box (see the figure).

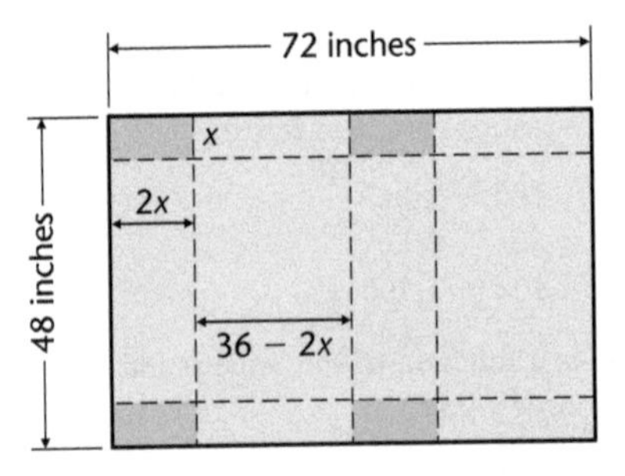

(A) Find the width of the flap (to two decimal places) that will produce a box with maximum volume. What is the maximum volume?

(B) How wide should the flap be if a manufacturer needs the box to have a volume of 9,200 cubic inches?

72. EFFECTS OF ALTITUDE The percentage of oxygen in the air depends on the altitude of a given location. This percentage can be modeled by the function $f(x) = -0.000767x + 21.6$ $0 \le x \le 8000$, where x is the elevation in feet.

(A) Complete the table of values for f.

Elevation	Oxygen Level (%)
0	
2,000	
4,000	
6,000	
8,000	

(B) Based on the information in the table, write a brief verbal description of the relationship between elevation and oxygen level.

(C) The elevation of the summit of Mt. Everest is 29,035 feet. According to the model, what is the oxygen level there? Is your answer reasonable? Why do you suppose this happened?

73. CELL PHONE CHARGES A local cell phone provider calculates monthly usage charges in dollars using the function $c(x) = 19 + 0.012x$, where x is minutes used. Translate this algebraic statement into a verbal description that a sales representative could use to explain the monthly charges to a potential customer.

74. REVENUE The revenue in dollars made by a banquet facility when hosting a wedding is modeled by the function $R(x) = C + 22.50x$, where x is the number of guests and C is the flat fee charged for hosting.

(A) Graph R for $C = 200$, 900, and 1,500 simultaneously in the viewing window Xmin = 0, Xmax = 600, Ymin = 0, Ymax = 15,000. Write a brief verbal description of this collection of functions.

(B) What is the maximum flat fee the facility can charge if they want their price to be no higher than a competing facility that offers a wedding with 300 guests for $7,500?

75. MEDICINE Proscar is a drug produced by Merck & Co., Inc., to treat symptomatic benign prostate enlargement. One of the long-term effects of the drug is to increase urine flow rate. Results from a 3-year study show that

$$f(x) = 0.00005x^3 - 0.007x^2 + 0.255x$$

is a mathematical model for the average increase in urine flow rate in cubic centimeters per second where x is time taking the drug in months.

(A) Graph this function for $0 \le x \le 36$.

(B) Write a brief verbal description of the graph using increasing, decreasing, local maximum, and local minimum as appropriate. Approximate to two decimal places the coordinates of any points used in your description.

76. COMPUTER SCIENCE In computer programming, it is often necessary to check numbers for certain properties (even, odd, perfect square, etc.). The greatest integer function provides a convenient method for determining some of these properties. Consider the function

$$f(x) = x - ([\![\sqrt{x}]\!])^2$$

(A) Evaluate f for $x = 1, 2, \ldots, 16$.

(B) Find $f(n^2)$, where n is a positive integer.

(C) What property of x does this function determine?

MODELING AND DATA ANALYSIS

77. DATA ANALYSIS Winning times in the men's Olympic 400-meter freestyle event in minutes for selected years are given in Table 2 on the next page. A mathematical model for these data is

$$f(x) = -0.021x + 5.57$$

where x is years since 1900.

(A) Compare the model and the data graphically and numerically.

(B) Estimate (to three decimal places) the winning time in 2008.

Table 2

Year	Time
1912	5.41
1932	4.81
1952	4.51
1972	4.00
1992	3.75

78. Use the schedule in Table 3 to construct a piecewise-defined model for the taxes due for a single taxpayer in Virginia with a taxable income of x dollars. Find the tax on the following incomes: \$2,000, \$4,000, \$10,000, \$30,000.

Table 3 Virginia Tax Rate Schedule

Status	Taxable Income Over	But Not Over	Tax Is	Of the Amount Over
Single	\$ 0	\$ 3,000	2%	\$ 0
	\$ 3,000	\$ 5,000	\$ 60 + 3%	\$ 3,000
	\$ 5,000	\$17,000	\$120 + 5%	\$ 5,000
	\$17,000	......	\$720 + 5.75%	\$17,000

CHAPTER 1

››› GROUP ACTIVITY Mathematical Modeling: Choosing a Cell Phone Provider

The number of companies offering cellular telephone service has grown rapidly in recent years. The plans they offer vary greatly and it can be difficult to select the plan that is best for you. Here are five typical plans:

Plan 1: A flat fee of \$50 per month for unlimited calls.
Plan 2: A \$30 per month fee for a total of 30 hours of calls and an additional charge of \$0.01 per minute for all minutes over 30 hours.
Plan 3: A \$5 per month fee and a charge of \$0.04 per minute for all calls.
Plan 4: A \$2 per month fee and a charge of \$0.045 per minute for all calls; the fee is waived if the charge for calls is \$20 or more.
Plan 5: A charge of \$0.05 per minute for all calls; there are no additional fees.

(A) Construct a mathematical model for each plan that gives the total monthly cost in terms of the total number of minutes of calls placed in a month. Graph each model on a graphing calculator. You may find dividing by expressions like $(x > a)$ helpful in entering your model in a graphing calculator (see Example 7 in Section 1-6).
(B) Compare plans 1 and 2. Determine how many minutes per month would make plan 1 cheaper and how many would make plan 2 cheaper.
(C) Repeat part (B) for plans 1 and 3; plans 1 and 4; plans 1 and 5.
(D) Repeat part (B) for plans 2 and 3; plans 2 and 4; plans 2 and 5.
(E) Repeat part (B) for plans 3 and 4; plans 3 and 5.
(F) Repeat part (B) for plans 4 and 5.
(G) Is there one plan that is always better than all the others? Based on your personal calling history, which plan would you choose and why?

Modeling with Linear and Quadratic Functions

CHAPTER

2

Modeling with Linear and Quadratic Functions

IN Chapter 1, we investigated the general concept of functions using graphs, tables, and algebraic equations. Now it's time to get specific: most of the remainder of the book is devoted to studying particular categories of functions in detail. Our goal is to develop a library of functions that we can work with and understand comfortably. The types of functions we will study are used with great frequency in almost any place where mathematics is used: the physical, social, and life sciences; business; computers, engineering, and most technical fields; and of course in any math course you might take beyond this one.

In this chapter, we study two basic types of functions, the linear and quadratic functions. As you will see, many significant real-world problems can be represented by these functions.

OUTLINE

2-1 Linear Functions

The straight line is a very simple geometric object, but it is also an important tool in mathematical modeling. In this section, we will add linear functions to our library of functions and explore the relationship between graphs of linear functions and straight lines. We will also determine how to find the equation of a line, given information about that line. This will be a big help in modeling many quantities. We will conclude the section with a look at how slope is used to model quantities that have a constant rate of change.

Constant and Linear Functions

One of the elementary functions introduced in Section 1-4 was the identity function $f(x) = x$ (Fig. 1).

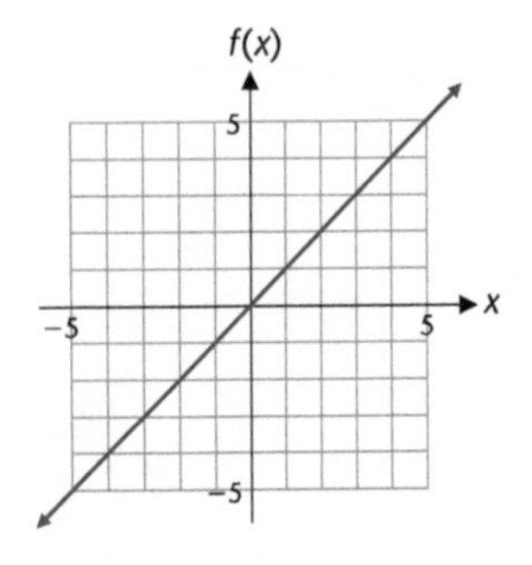

Figure 1 Identity function: $f(x) = x$.

EXPLORE-DISCUSS 1

Use the transformations discussed in Section 1-4 to describe verbally the relationship between the graph of $f(x) = x$ and each of the following functions. Graph each function.

(A) $g(x) = 3x + 1$ **(B)** $h(x) = 0.5x - 2$ **(C)** $k(x) = -x + 1$

If we apply a sequence of translations, reflections, expansions, and/or contractions to the identity function, the result is always a function whose graph is a straight line. Because of this, functions like g, h, and k in Explore-Discuss 1 are called *linear functions*. There's one thing that all such functions will have in common: the independent variable will appear only to the first power.

> **DEFINITION 1 Linear and Constant Functions**
>
> A function f is a **linear function** if
>
> $$f(x) = mx + b \qquad m \neq 0$$
>
> where m and b are real numbers. The domain is the set of all real numbers and the range is also the set of all real numbers.
>
> If $m = 0$, then f is called a **constant function,**
>
> $$f(x) = b$$
>
> which has the set of all real numbers as its domain and the constant b as its range.

Figure 2 shows the graphs of two linear functions f and g, and a constant function h.

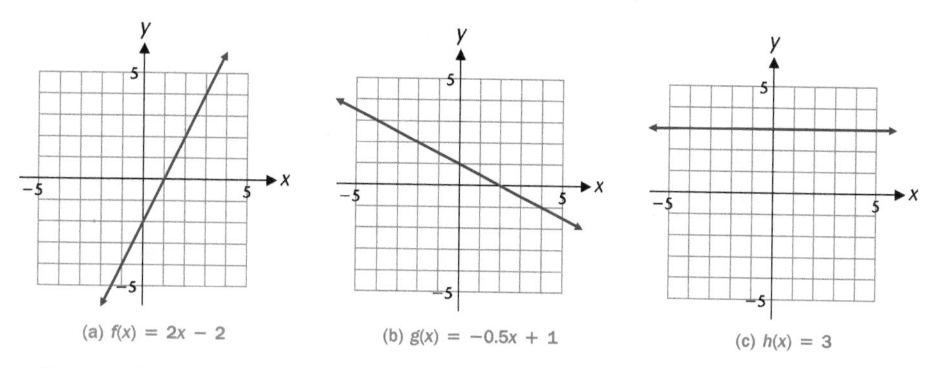

› **Figure 2** Two linear functions and a constant function.

It can be shown that

> **The graph of a linear function is a straight line that is neither horizontal nor vertical. The graph of a constant function is a horizontal straight line.**

What about vertical lines? Recall from Chapter 1 that the graph of a function cannot contain two points with the same x coordinate and different y coordinates. Because *all* the points on a vertical line have the same x coordinate, the graph of a function can never be a vertical line. Later in this section, we will discuss equations of vertical lines, but these equations never define functions.

Recall from Section 1-3 that the y intercept of a function f is $f(0)$, provided $f(0)$ exists, and the x intercepts are the solutions of the equation $f(x) = 0$.

››› EXPLORE-DISCUSS 2

(A) Is it possible for a linear function to have two x intercepts? No x intercept? If either of your answers is yes, give an example.

(B) Is it possible for a linear function to have two y intercepts? No y intercept? If either of your answers is yes, give an example.

(C) Discuss the possible numbers of x and y intercepts for a constant function.

EXAMPLE 1 Finding x and y Intercepts

Find the x and y intercepts for $f(x) = \frac{2}{3}x - 3$.

SOLUTION

The y intercept is $f(0) = -3$. The x intercept can be found algebraically using standard equation-solving techniques (Appendix B, Section B-1), or graphically using the ZERO command on a graphing calculator (Section 1-1).

Algebraic Solution

$$f(x) = 0$$

$$\frac{2}{3}x - 3 = 0 \quad \text{Add 3 to both sides.}$$

$$\frac{2}{3}x = 3 \quad \text{Multiply both sides by } \tfrac{3}{2}.$$

$$x = \frac{9}{2} = 4.5$$

Graphical Solution

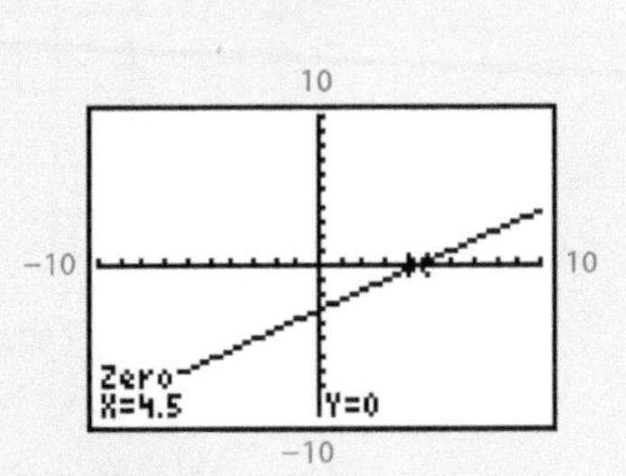

MATCHED PROBLEM 1

Find the x and y intercepts of $g(x) = -\frac{4}{3}x + 5$.

› Exploring the Graph of $Ax + By = C$

››› EXPLORE-DISCUSS 3

Graph each of the following cases of $Ax + By = C$ in the same coordinate system:

1. $3x + 2y = 6$

2. $0x - 3y = 12$

3. $2x + 0y = 10$

Which cases define functions? Explain why or why not.

Graph each case using a graphing utility (check your manual on how to graph vertical lines).

We will now investigate graphs of linear equations in two variables, like

$$Ax + By = C \qquad (1)$$

where at least one of A and B is not zero. Keep in mind that x and y are variables in this setting, while A, B, and C are just numbers. Depending on the values of A and B, this equation can define a linear function, a constant function, or no function at all.

If A and B are both nonzero, then we can solve equation (1) for y:

$$\begin{aligned} Ax + By &= C && \text{Subtract } Ax \text{ from both sides.} \\ By &= C - Ax && \text{Divide both sides by } B. \\ y &= -\frac{A}{B}x + \frac{C}{B} \end{aligned}$$

This fits the form $f(x) = mx + B$ since $A/B \neq 0$. Based on Definition 1, this is a linear function.

If A is zero and B is nonzero, equation (1) becomes

$$\begin{aligned} 0x + By &= C && \text{Divide both sides by } B. \\ y &= \frac{C}{B} \end{aligned}$$

This fits the form $g(x) = b$ (remember, C/B is just a number), so it is a constant function.

If A is nonzero and B is zero, equation (1) becomes

$$\begin{aligned} Ax + 0y &= C && \text{Divide both sides by } A. \\ x &= \frac{C}{A} \end{aligned}$$

This equation specifies the same x value (the number C/A) for every possible y value. This tells us two things: The equation does not define a function, and the graph is a vertical line since every point has the same x coordinate.

The following theorem summarizes the preceding discussion:

› THEOREM 1 Graph of a Linear Equation in Two Variables

The graph of any equation of the form

$$Ax + By = C \qquad \text{Standard form} \qquad (2)$$

where A, B, and C are real numbers (A and B not both 0) is a straight line. Every straight line in a Cartesian coordinate system is the graph of an equation of this type. Vertical and horizontal lines are special cases of equation (2):

Horizontal line with y intercept b: $y = b$

Vertical line with x intercept a: $x = a$

To sketch the graph of an equation of the form

$$Ax + By = C \qquad \text{or} \qquad y = mx + b$$

all that is necessary is to plot any two points from the solution set and use a straightedge to draw a line through these two points. The x and y intercepts are often the easiest points to find, but any two points will do.

EXAMPLE 2 Sketching Graphs of Lines

(A) Describe the graphs of $x = -2$ and $y = 3$ verbally. Graph both equations in the same rectangular coordinate system by hand and in the same viewing window on a graphing calculator.

(B) Write the equations of the vertical and horizontal lines that pass through the point $(1, -4)$.

(C) Graph the equation $3x - 2y = 6$ by hand and on a graphing calculator.

SOLUTIONS

(A) The graph of $x = -2$ is a vertical line with x intercept -2 and the graph of $y = 3$ is a horizontal line with y intercept 3 (Fig. 3 and Fig. 4).

Hand-Drawn Solution

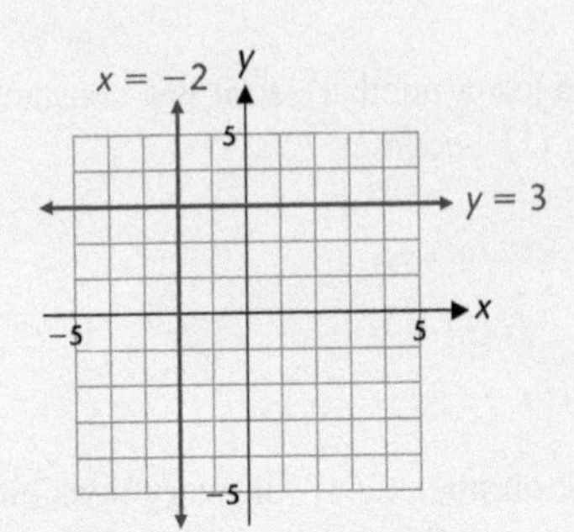

› Figure 3

Graphing Calculator Solution

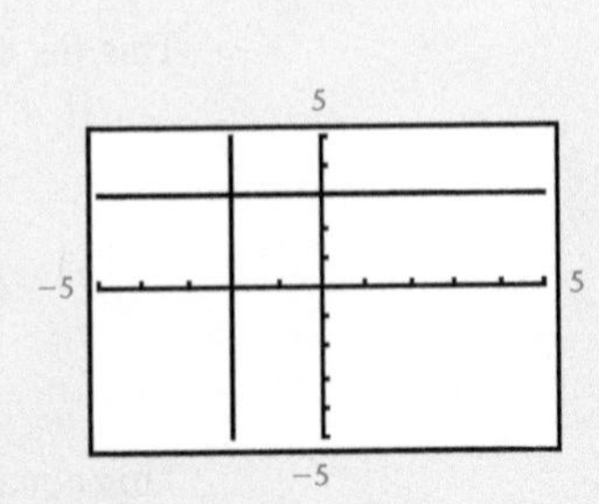

› Figure 4

(B) The y coordinate of every point on a horizontal line through $(1, -4)$ is -4, so the equation is $y = -4$. The x coordinate of every point on a vertical line through $(1, -4)$ is 1, so the equation is $x = 1$.

(C) Hand-Drawn Solution
Find the x intercept by substituting $y = 0$ and solving for x, and then find the y intercept by substituting $x = 0$ and solving for y.

x intercept	y intercept
$3x - 2(0) = 6$	$3(0) - 2y = 6$
$3x = 6$	$-2y = 6$
$x = 2$	$y = -3$

To confirm our work, we'll also plot a third point and make sure that all three points appear to be on the same line.

Additional point:

$$3(4) - 2y = 6 \quad \text{Substitute } x = 4.$$
$$-2y = -6$$
$$y = 3$$

$(4, 3)$

Now we draw a line through all three points (Fig. 5).

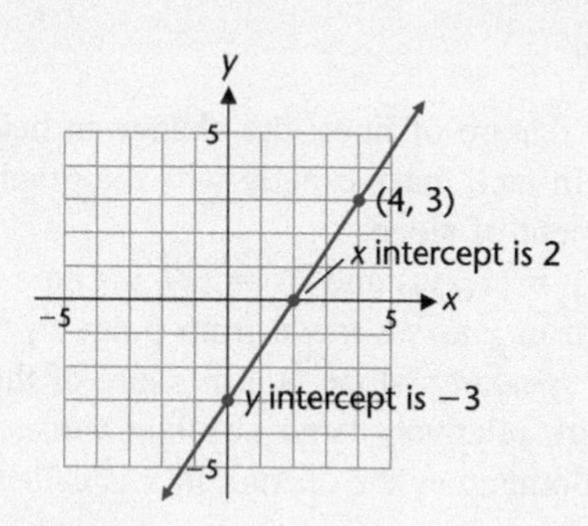

› Figure 5

(C) Graphing Calculator Solution
To enter the equation in the equation editor of a graphing calculator, we'll first need to solve for y.

$$3x - 2y = 6$$
$$-2y = -3x + 6$$
$$y = 1.5x - 3$$

Now enter the result in the equation editor, and graph (Fig. 6).

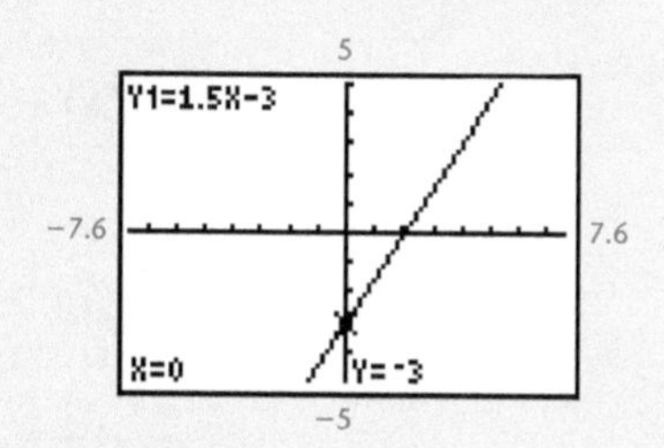

› Figure 6

Note that we used a *squared viewing window* in Figure 6 to produce units of the same length on both axes. This makes it easier to compare the hand sketch with the graphing calculator graph.

>>> **CAUTION** >>>

Even though finding two points is sufficient to graph a line, it's always a good idea to find three. If the three you find do not line up, you know you made a mistake somewhere.

MATCHED PROBLEM 2

(A) Describe the graphs of $x = 4$ and $y = -3$ verbally. Graph both equations in the same rectangular coordinate system by hand and in the same viewing window on a graphing calculator.

(B) Write the equations of the vertical and horizontal lines that pass through the point $(-7, 5)$.

(C) Graph the equation $4x + 3y = 12$ by hand and on a graphing calculator.

Defining the Slope of a Line

EXPLORE-DISCUSS 4

(A) For the linear function $f(x) = 3x - 5$, fill in the table of values.

x	-3	-2	-1	0	1	2	3
$f(x)$							

(B) Do you notice a pattern in the outputs as x gets bigger by 1 unit?

(C) Repeat for $g(x) = -3x - 5$. What do you notice?

x	-3	-2	-1	0	1	2	3
$g(x)$							

Explore-Discuss 4 illustrates the key feature of lines: the change in height is always the same for any 1-unit change in x. In fact, that's exactly why the graph is a straight line! This leads to the important concept of slope.

If we take two different points $P_1 = (x_1, y_1)$ and $P_2 = (x_2, y_2)$ on a line, then the ratio of the change in y to the change in x as we move from point P_1 to point P_2 is called the **slope** of the line. Roughly speaking, slope is a measure of the "steepness" of a line. Steep lines have slopes with relatively large absolute values, and gradual lines have slopes that are near zero. Sometimes the change in x is called the **run** and the change in y the **rise.**

DEFINITION 2 Slope of a Line

If a line passes through two distinct points $P_1 = (x_1, y_1)$ and $P_2 = (x_2, y_2)$, then its slope m is given by the formula

$$m = \frac{y_2 - y_1}{x_2 - x_1} \qquad x_1 \neq x_2$$

$$= \frac{\text{Vertical change (rise)}}{\text{Horizontal change (run)}}$$

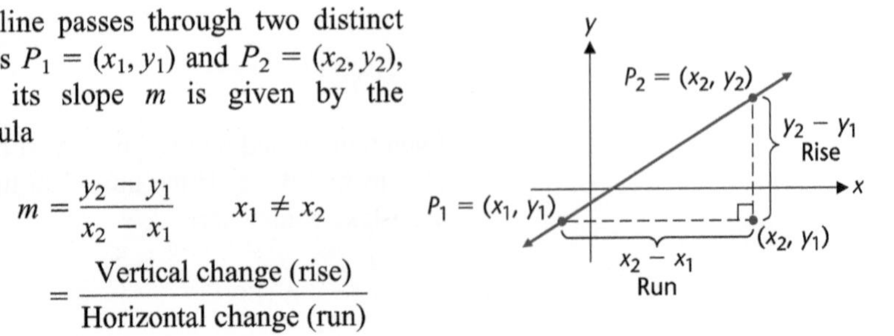

For a horizontal line, y doesn't change as x changes, so its slope is 0. For a vertical line, x doesn't change as y changes, so $x_1 = x_2$, the denominator in the slope formula is 0, and its slope is not defined. In general, the slope of a line can be positive, negative, zero, or not defined. Each case is illustrated geometrically in Table 1.

Table 1 Geometric Interpretation of Slope

Line	Slope	Example
Rising as x moves from left to right	Positive	
Falling as x moves from left to right	Negative	
Horizontal	0	
Vertical	Not defined	

In using the formula to find the slope of the line through two points, it doesn't matter which point is labeled P_1 or P_2, because changing the labeling will change the sign in both the numerator and denominator of the slope formula:

$$\frac{y_2 - y_1}{x_2 - x_1} = \frac{y_1 - y_2}{x_1 - x_2}$$

For example, the slope of the line through the points (3, 2) and (7, 5) is

$$\frac{5 - 2}{7 - 3} = \frac{3}{4} \quad \text{or} \quad \frac{2 - 5}{3 - 7} = \frac{-3}{-4} = \frac{3}{4}$$

In addition, it is important to note that the definition of slope doesn't depend on the two points chosen on the line as long as they are distinct. Lines are straight exactly because the slope at every point on the line is the same.

EXAMPLE 3 Finding Slopes

For each line in Figure 7 on the next page, find the run, the rise, and the slope. (All the horizontal and vertical line segments have integer lengths.)

SOLUTION

In Figure 7(a), the run is 3, the rise is 6 and the slope is $\frac{6}{3} = 2$. In Figure 7(b), the run is 6, the rise is -4 and the slope is $\frac{-4}{6} = -\frac{2}{3}$.

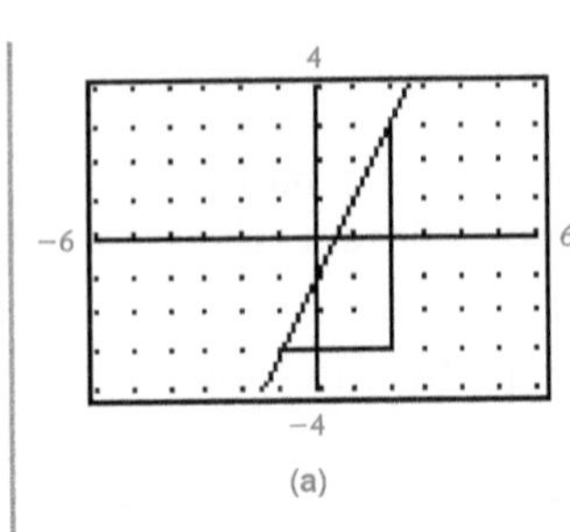

(a)

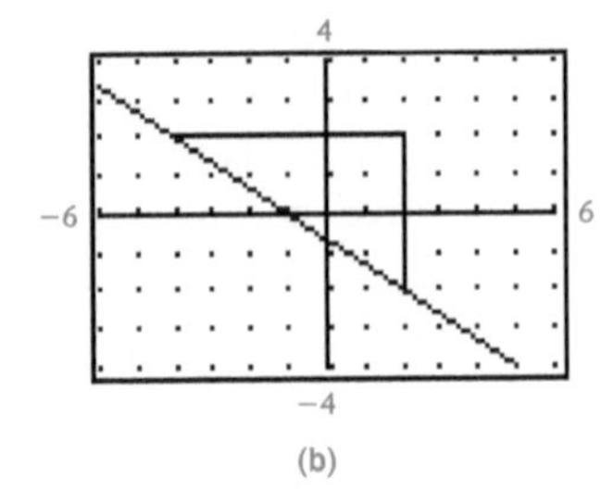

(b)

› **Figure 7**

MATCHED PROBLEM 3

For each line in Figure 8, find the run, the rise, and the slope. (All the horizontal and vertical line segments have integer lengths.)

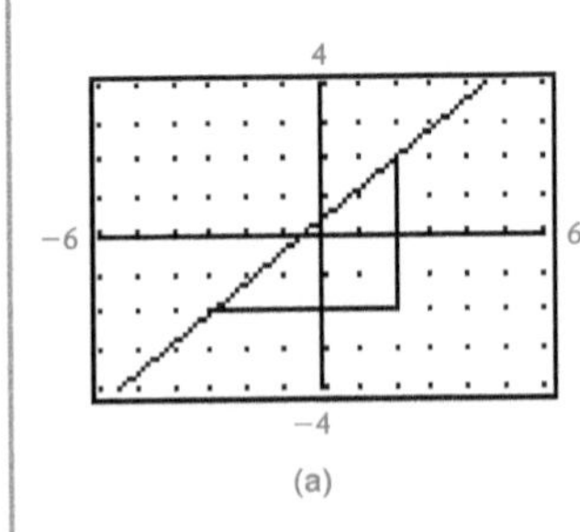

(a)

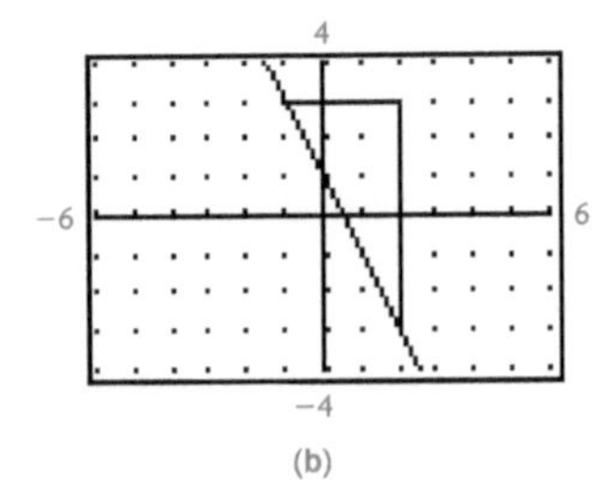

(b)

› **Figure 8**

EXAMPLE 4 Finding Slopes

Sketch a line through each pair of points and find the slope of each line.

(A) $(-3, -4), (3, 2)$ (B) $(-2, 3), (1, -3)$
(C) $(-4, 2), (3, 2)$ (D) $(2, 4), (2, -3)$

SOLUTIONS

(A)

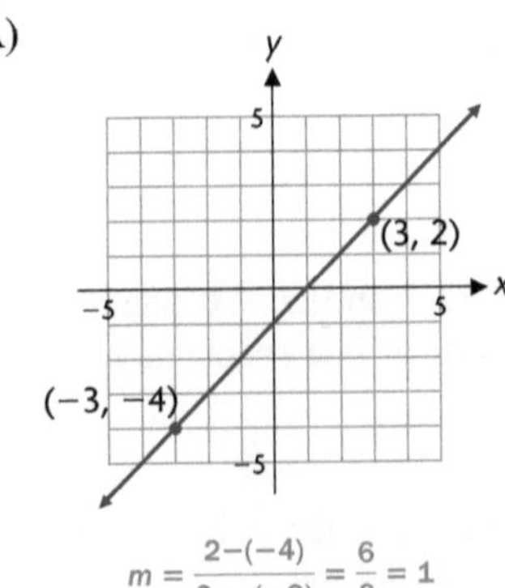

$$m = \frac{2-(-4)}{3-(-3)} = \frac{6}{6} = 1$$

(B)

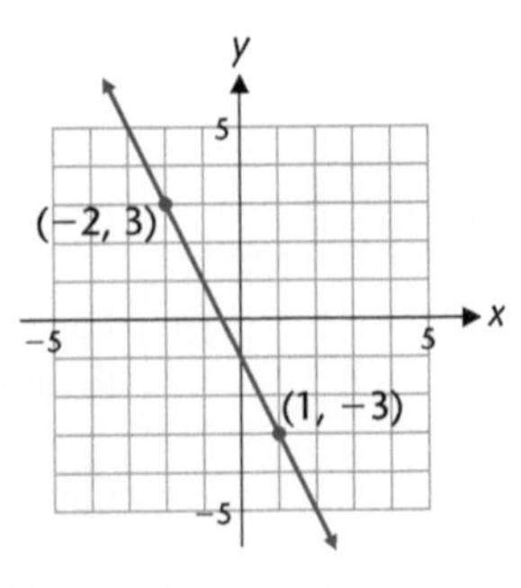

$$m = \frac{-3-3}{1-(-2)} = \frac{-6}{3} = -2$$

(C)

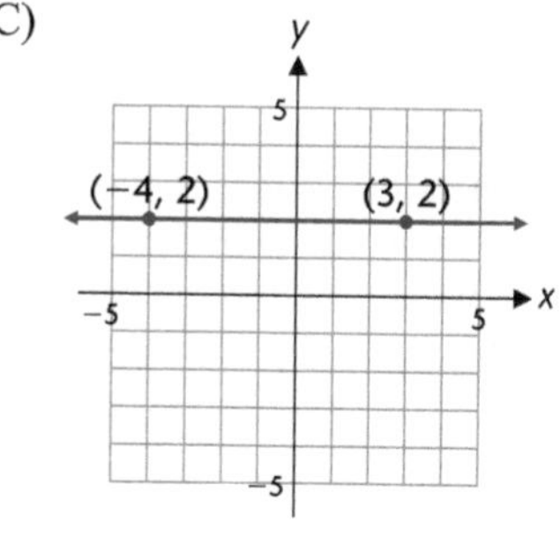

$m = \frac{2-2}{3-(-4)} = \frac{0}{7} = 0$

(D)

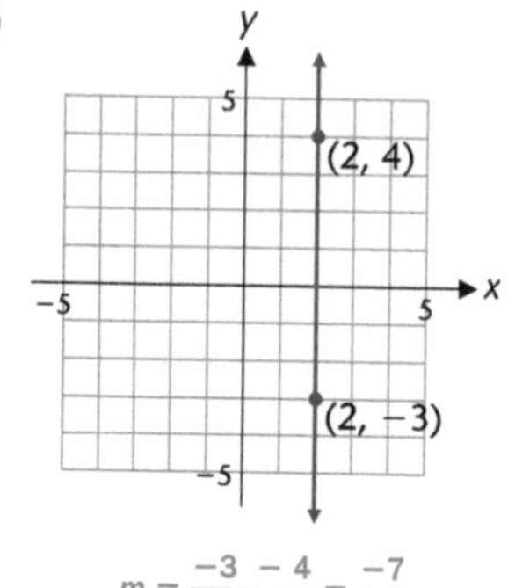

$m = \frac{-3-4}{2-2} = \frac{-7}{0}$

slope is not defined

MATCHED PROBLEM 4

Sketch a line through each pair of points and find the slope of each line.

(A) $(-3, -3), (2, -3)$ (B) $(-2, -1), (1, 2)$
(C) $(0, 4), (2, -4)$ (D) $(-3, 2), (-3, -1)$

The graphs in Example 4 serve to illustrate the summary in Table 2:

Table 2 Graph Properties of Linear and Constant Functions

Linear Functions		**Constant Function**
$f(x) = mx + b, m > 0$	$f(x) = mx + b, m < 0$	$f(x) = b$
Domain $= (-\infty, \infty)$	Domain $= (-\infty, \infty)$	Domain $= (-\infty, \infty)$
Range $= (-\infty, \infty)$	Range $= (-\infty, \infty)$	Range $= \{b\}$
Increasing on $(-\infty, \infty)$	Decreasing on $(-\infty, \infty)$	Constant on $(-\infty, \infty)$

› Using Special Forms of Linear Equations

Let's start by investigating why $y = mx + b$ is called the *slope–intercept form* for a line.

››› EXPLORE-DISCUSS 5

(A) Using a graphing calculator, graph $y = x + b$ for $b = -5, -3, 0, 3$, and 5 simultaneously in a standard viewing window. Verbally describe the geometric significance of b.

(B) Using a graphing calculator, graph $y = mx - 1$ for $m = -2, -1, 0, 1$, and 2 simultaneously in a standard viewing window. Verbally describe the geometric significance of m.

Both constants (m and b) in $y = mx + b$ have special geometric significance, which we now explicitly state.

Explore-Discuss 4 and 5 both suggest that for an equation of the form $y = mx + b$, the number m is the slope of the line. (See Exercise 84 for a proof.) If we let $x = 0$, then $y = m \cdot 0 + b = b$ and the graph of $y = mx + b$ crosses the y axis at $(0, b)$. This tells us that the constant b is the y intercept. For example, the y intercept of the graph of $y = 2x - 7$ is -7.

To summarize:

> **THEOREM 2 Slope–Intercept Form**
>
> The equation
>
> $$y = mx + b$$
>
> is called the **slope–intercept form** of the equation of a line. The slope is m, and the y intercept is b.

EXAMPLE 5 Using the Slope–Intercept Form

Graph the line with y intercept -2 and slope $\frac{5}{4}$.

SOLUTION

Hand-Drawn Solution

If we start at the point $(0, -2)$ and move four units to the right (run), then the y coordinate of a point on the line must move up five units (rise) to the point $(4, 3)$. Drawing a line through these two points produces the graph shown in Figure 9.

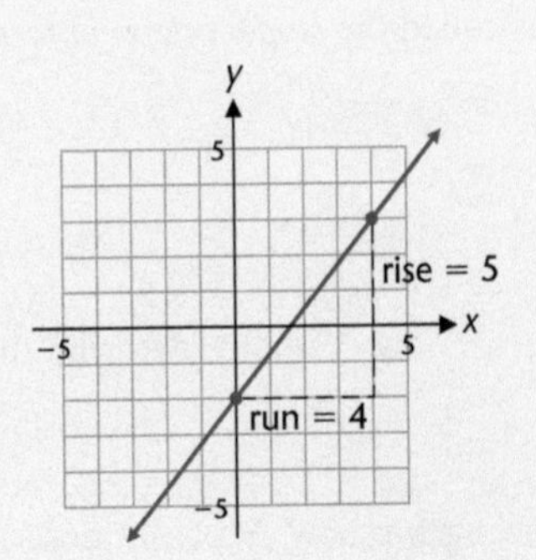

Figure 9

Graphing Calculator Solution

To graph the line on a graphing calculator, we first use the slope–intercept form to find the equation of the line. The equation of a line with y intercept -2 and slope $\frac{5}{4}$ is

$$y = \frac{5}{4}x - 2$$

Graphing this equation on a graphing calculator produces the graph in Figure 10.

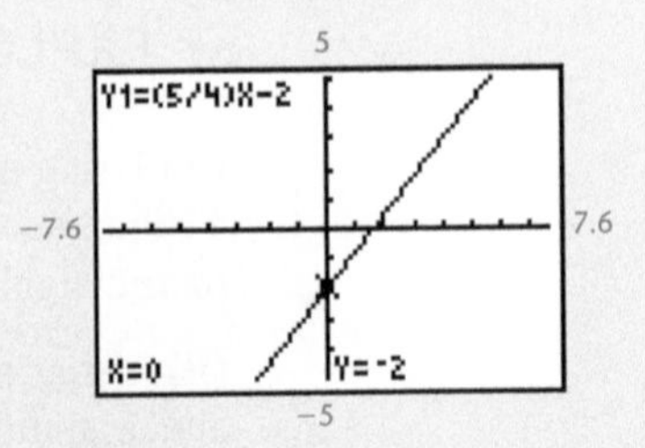

Figure 10

MATCHED PROBLEM 5

Graph the line with y intercept 3 and slope $-\frac{3}{4}$ by hand and on a graphing calculator.

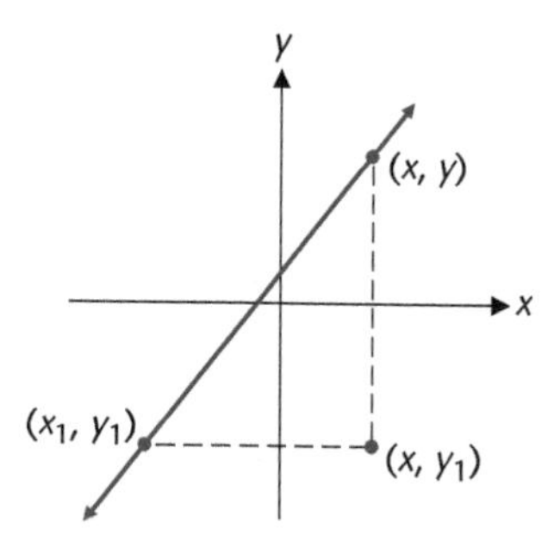

› Figure 11

Next, we will examine the *point–slope form* of a line.

Suppose a line has slope m and passes through the point (x_1, y_1). If (x, y) is any other point on the line (Fig. 11), then the slope formula gives us

$$\frac{y - y_1}{x - x_1} = m$$

Multiplying both sides by $(x - x_1)$, we get

$$y - y_1 = m(x - x_1) \tag{3}$$

Because the point (x_1, y_1) also satisfies equation (3), we can conclude that equation (3) is an equation of a line with slope m that passes through (x_1, y_1).

› THEOREM 3 Point–Slope Form

An equation of a line with slope m that passes through (x_1, y_1) is

$$y - y_1 = m(x - x_1)$$

which is called the **point–slope form** of an equation of a line.

Note that x and y are variables, while m, x_1, and y_1 are all numbers.

The point–slope form is especially useful because it provides a simple way to find the equation of a line. To do so, we need two pieces of information: the slope and any point on the line.

EXAMPLE 6 Point–Slope Form

(A) Find an equation for the line that has slope $\frac{2}{3}$ and passes through the point $(-2, 1)$. Write your answer in slope–intercept form.

(B) Find an equation for the line that passes through the two points $(4, -1)$ and $(-8, 5)$. Write your answer in slope–intercept form.

SOLUTIONS

(A) If $m = \frac{2}{3}$ and $(x_1, y_1) = (-2, 1)$, then

$$y - y_1 = m(x - x_1) \qquad \text{Substitute } m = \tfrac{2}{3},\ x_1 = -2, \text{ and } y_1 = 1.$$

$$y - 1 = \frac{2}{3}[x - (-2)] \qquad \text{Subtract.}$$

$$y - 1 = \frac{2}{3}(x + 2) \qquad \text{Distribute } \tfrac{2}{3}.$$

$$y - 1 = \frac{2}{3}x + \frac{4}{3} \qquad \text{Add 1 to each side.}$$

$$y = \frac{2}{3}x + \frac{7}{3}$$

(B) First use the slope formula to find the slope of the line:

$$m = \frac{y_2 - y_1}{x_2 - x_1} = \frac{5 - (-1)}{-8 - 4} = \frac{6}{-12} = -\frac{1}{2}$$

Now we choose $(x_1, y_1) = (4, -1)$ and proceed as in part A:

$$y - y_1 = m(x - x_1) \qquad \text{Substitute } m = -\tfrac{1}{2},\ x_1 = 4, \text{ and } y_1 = -1.$$

$$y - (-1) = -\frac{1}{2}(x - 4) \qquad \text{Subtract.}$$

$$y + 1 = -\frac{1}{2}(x - 4) \qquad \text{Distribute } -\tfrac{1}{2}.$$

$$y + 1 = -\frac{1}{2}x + 2 \qquad \text{Subtract 1 from each side.}$$

$$y = -\frac{1}{2}x + 1$$

You might want to verify that choosing the other given point $(x_1, y_1) = (-8, 5)$ produces the same equation.

MATCHED PROBLEM 6

(A) Find an equation for the line that has slope $-\frac{2}{5}$ and passes through the point $(3, -2)$. Write your answer in slope–intercept form.

(B) Find an equation for the line that passes through the two points $(-3, 1)$ and $(7, -3)$. Write your answer in slope–intercept form.

The various forms of the equation of a line that we have discussed are summarized in Table 3 for convenient reference. Note that the standard form includes all the other forms as special cases.

Table 3 Equations of a Line

Standard form	$Ax + By = C$	A and B not both 0
Slope–intercept form	$y = mx + b$	Slope: m; y intercept: b
Point–slope form	$y - y_1 = m(x - x_1)$	Slope: m; point: (x_1, y_1)
Horizontal line	$y = b$	Slope: 0
Vertical line	$x = a$	Slope: undefined

Recognizing Parallel and Perpendicular Lines

EXPLORE-DISCUSS 6

(A) Graph all of the following lines in the same viewing window. Discuss the relationship between these graphs and the slopes of the lines.

$$y = 2x - 5 \qquad y = 2x - 1 \qquad y = 2x + 3$$

(B) Graph each pair of lines in the same *squared* viewing window. Discuss the relationship between each pair of lines and their respective slopes.

$$y = 2x \quad \text{and} \quad y = -0.5x$$
$$y = -3x \quad \text{and} \quad y = \frac{1}{3}x$$
$$y = \frac{4}{5}x \quad \text{and} \quad y = -\frac{5}{4}x$$

From geometry, we know that two vertical lines are parallel and that a horizontal line and a vertical line are perpendicular to each other. But how can we tell when two nonvertical lines are parallel or perpendicular to each other? The key is slope. Slope determines the steepness of a line, so if two lines are parallel (i.e., have the same steepness), they also have the same slope. If two lines are perpendicular, it turns out that the slopes have opposite signs and are reciprocals (see Explore-Discuss 6).

Theorem 4, which we state without proof, explicitly states these relationships.

THEOREM 4 Parallel and Perpendicular Lines

Given two nonvertical lines L_1 and L_2, with slopes m_1 and m_2, respectively, then

$$L_1 \| L_2 \quad \text{if and only if } m_1 = m_2$$
$$L_1 \perp L_2 \quad \text{if and only if } m_1 m_2 = -1$$

The symbols $\|$ and $\perp$ mean, respectively, "is parallel to" and "is perpendicular to."

In words, two lines are parallel when their slopes are equal, and perpendicular when their slopes are negative reciprocals.

EXAMPLE 7

Parallel and Perpendicular Lines

Given the line L with equation $3x - 2y = 5$ and the point P with coordinates $(-3, 5)$, find an equation of a line through P that is

(A) Parallel to L (B) Perpendicular to L

SOLUTIONS

We already know a point on the lines, so all we need is the slope of each.

First we write the equation for L in the slope–intercept form to find the slope of L:

$$3x - 2y = 5 \quad \text{Subtract 3x from each side.}$$
$$-2y = -3x + 5 \quad \text{Divide both sides by } -2.$$
$$y = \tfrac{3}{2}x - \tfrac{5}{2}$$

The coefficient of x is $\frac{3}{2}$, so this is the slope of L. The slope of a line parallel to L will also be $\frac{3}{2}$, and the slope of a line perpendicular to L will be $-\frac{2}{3}$. We can now find the equations of the two lines in parts A and B using the point–slope form.

(A) Parallel ($m = \frac{3}{2}$):

$$y - y_1 = m(x - x_1)$$
$$y - 5 = \tfrac{3}{2}(x + 3)$$
$$y - 5 = \tfrac{3}{2}x + \tfrac{9}{2}$$
$$y = \tfrac{3}{2}x + \tfrac{19}{2}$$

(B) Perpendicular ($m = -\frac{2}{3}$):

$$y - y_1 = m(x - x_1)$$
$$y - 5 = -\tfrac{2}{3}(x + 3)$$
$$y - 5 = -\tfrac{2}{3}x - 2$$
$$y = -\tfrac{2}{3}x + 3$$

MATCHED PROBLEM 7

Given the line L with equation $4x + 2y = 3$ and the point P with coordinates $(2, -3)$, find an equation of a line through P that is

(A) Parallel to L (B) Perpendicular to L

› Mathematical Modeling: Slope as a Rate of Change

In 2006 in the United States, babies were born at the rate of about 11,600 per day. At this rate, in 1 day 11,600 would be born; in 2 days, 23,200; in 3 days, 34,800; and so forth. In general, the function $b(x) = 11{,}600x$ describes the number of births after x days. Note that this is a linear function with slope 11,600. This illustrates an interesting point: The slope of a linear function tells us the **rate of change** of the function with respect to the independent variable.

This interpretation of slope can be applied to a wide variety of everyday situations. If you're driving at an average speed of 50 miles/hour, the rate of change of your position with respect to time is 50, and $y = 50x$ is the mileage driven in x hours. If you make $8.00 per hour at a part-time job, the rate of change of money earned with respect to hours worked is 8, and $y = 8x$ describes the amount earned in x hours.

The study of rates of change is pretty simple for linear functions, when the rate of change is constant. For others, computing rates of change is one of the fundamental goals of calculus.

EXAMPLE 8 Rates of Change

The average price in dollars of a gallon of gas in Cincinnati, Ohio, between January 3 and January 18, 2007, can be modeled by the function $P(x) = -0.024x + 2.31$, $0 \leq x \leq 15$, where x is days after January 3.

(A) At what rate was the price changing during that time period? Was the price going up or down?

(B) What was the price on January 3? On January 18? Do your results from parts A and B agree?

SOLUTIONS

(A) $P(x)$ is a linear function with slope -0.024, so the rate of change is -0.024 dollars per day, or -2.4 cents per day. The negative sign indicates that the price was dropping.

(B) January 3 and January 18 are zero and 15 days after January 3, respectively.

$$P(0) = -0.024(0) + 2.31 = \$2.31 \text{ on January 3}$$
$$P(15) = -0.024(15) + 2.31 = \$1.95 \text{ on January 18}$$

With a decrease of 2.4 cents per day, after 15 days the price would have gone down by $2.4 \cdot 15 = 36$ cents. This matches the calculated difference from January 3 to January 18.

MATCHED PROBLEM 8

The average price in dollars of a gallon of gas in Allentown, Pennsylvania, between January 2 and January 22, 2007, can be modeled by the function $P(x) = -0.007x + 2.39$, $0 \leq x \leq 20$, where x is days after January 2.

(A) At what rate was the price changing during that time period? Was the price going up or down?

(B) What was the price on January 2? On January 22? Do your results from parts A and B agree?

››› CAUTION ›››

When interpreting the rate of change of a function, don't forget to consider the sign. A negative rate of change always means that the value of the function is decreasing.

EXAMPLE 9 **Underwater Pressure**

The atmospheric pressure at sea level is 14.7 pounds per square inch. As you descend into the ocean, the pressure increases at a constant rate of about 0.445 pounds per square inch per foot.

(A) Find the pressure p at a depth of d feet.

(B) If a diver's equipment is rated to be safe up to a pressure of 40 pounds per square inch, is it safe to use this equipment at a depth at 60 feet?

SOLUTIONS

(A) The rate of change of pressure is 0.445, so that will be the slope. The equation should look like $p = 0.445d + b$. We know that the pressure at depth zero (the surface) is 14.7, so when $d = 0$, we get

$$p = 0.445(0) + b = b = 14.7$$

The pressure at a depth of d feet is given by

$$p = 0.445d + 14.7$$

(B) The pressure at a depth of 60 feet is given by

$$p = 0.445(60) + 14.7 = 41.4$$

It's not safe to use the equipment at this depth.

MATCHED PROBLEM 9

The rate of change of pressure in freshwater is 0.432 pounds per square inch per foot. Repeat Example 9 for a body of freshwater.

ANSWERS TO MATCHED PROBLEMS

1. x intercept: $\frac{15}{4} = 3.75$; y intercept: 5
2. (A) The graph of $x = 4$ is a vertical line with x intercept 4. The graph of $y = -3$ is a horizontal line with y intercept -3.

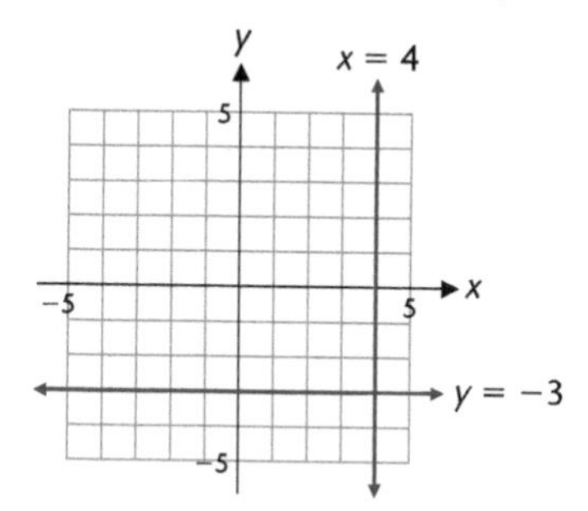

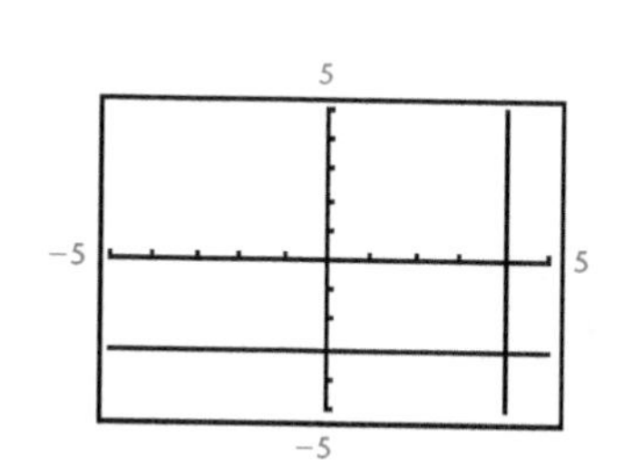

(B) Vertical: $x = -7$; horizontal: $y = 5$

(C)

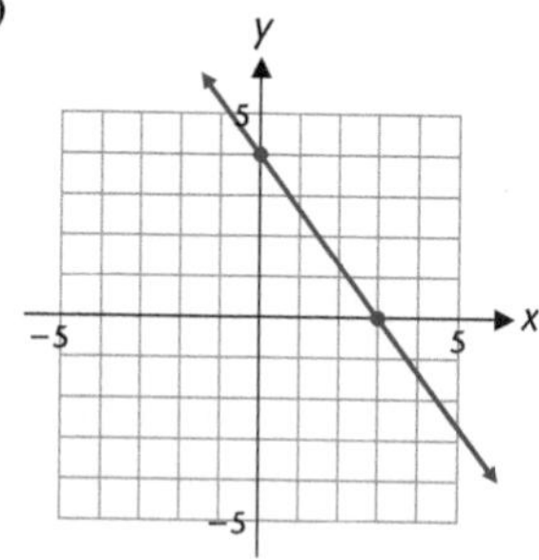

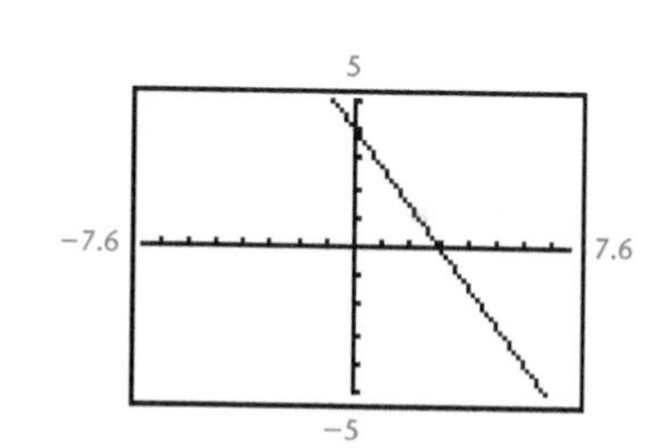

3. (A) Run = 5, rise = 4, slope = $\frac{4}{5} = 0.8$
   (B) Run = 3, rise = −6, slope = $\frac{-6}{3} = -2$
4. (A) $m = 0$ (B) $m = 1$

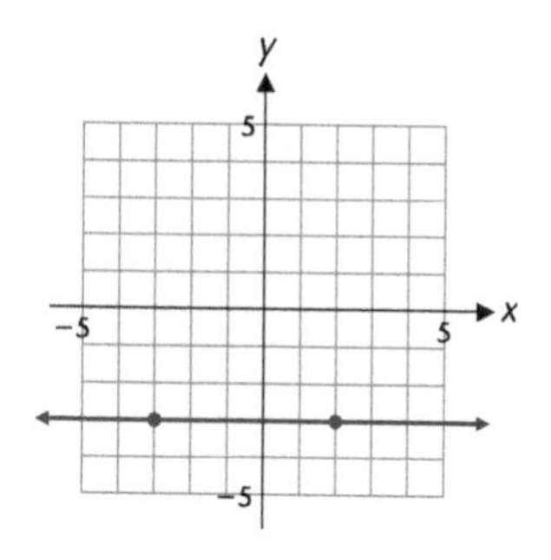

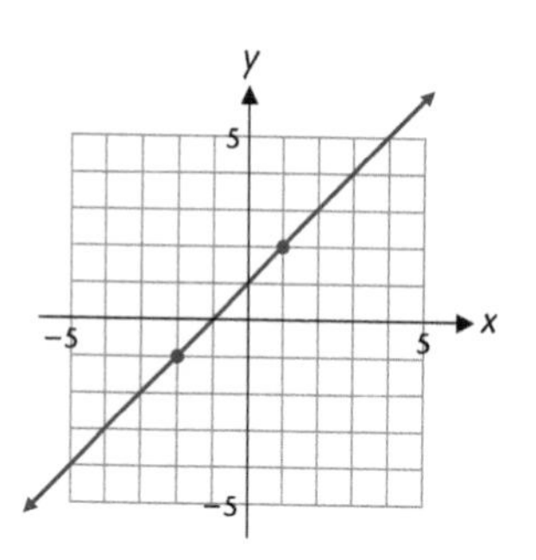

(C) $m = -4$

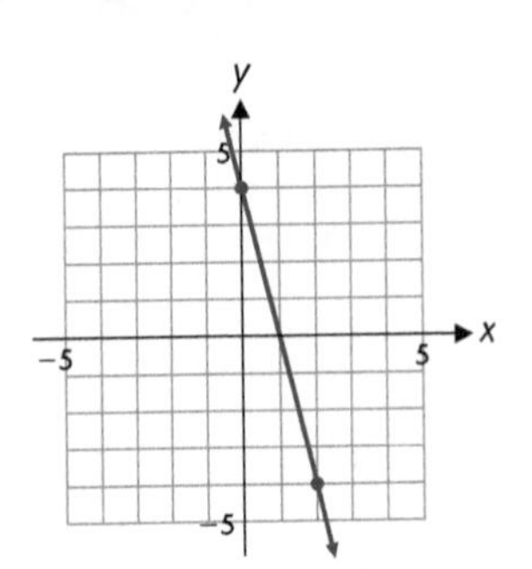

(D) m is not defined

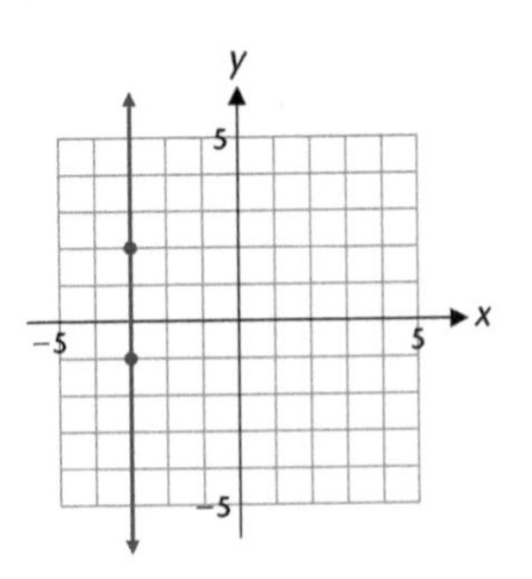

5.

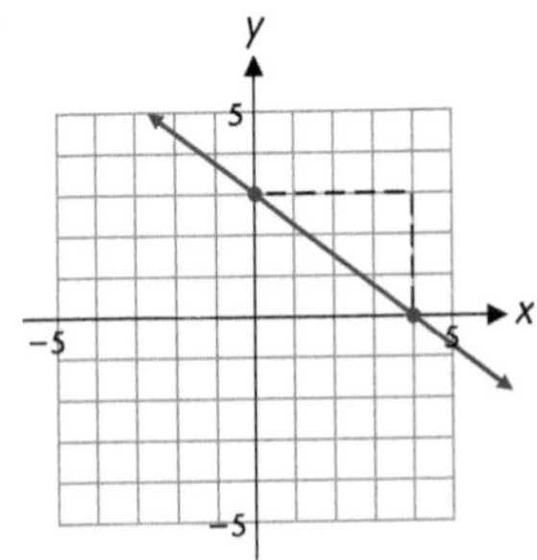

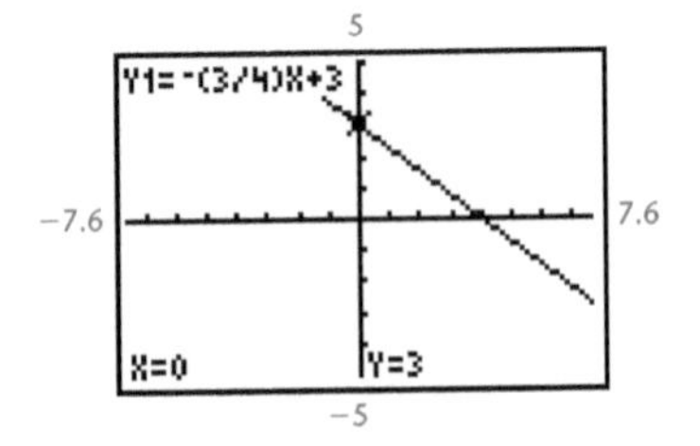

6. (A) $y = -\frac{2}{5}x - \frac{4}{5}$ (B) $y = -\frac{2}{5}x - \frac{1}{5}$

7. (A) $y = -2x + 1$ (B) $y = \frac{1}{2}x - 4$

8. (A) The price was going down by 0.7 cents per day.

(B) The price was \$2.39 on January 2 and \$2.25 on January 22. This matches a decrease of 0.7 cents per day.

9. (A) $p = 0.432d + 14.7$ (B) It is not safe.

2-1 Exercises

1. What is the slope–intercept form of a line? Why is it given that name?

2. What is the point–slope form of a line? Why is it given that name?

3. Explain in your own words what the slope of a line tells us about the graph.

4. If a linear function describes the height in feet of a model rocket in terms of seconds after it was launched, what information would the slope of the line provide? Why?

5. Given a function defined by a formula, how can you tell if it's a linear function?

6. Explain why the graph of a constant function is a horizontal line.

In Problems 7–12, use the graph of each linear function to find the rise, run, and slope. Write the equation of each line in the standard form $Ax + By = C, A \geq 0$. (All the horizontal and vertical line segments have integer lengths.)

7.

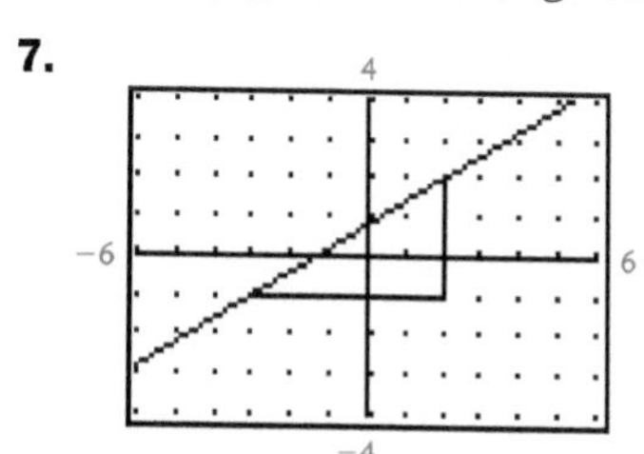

8.

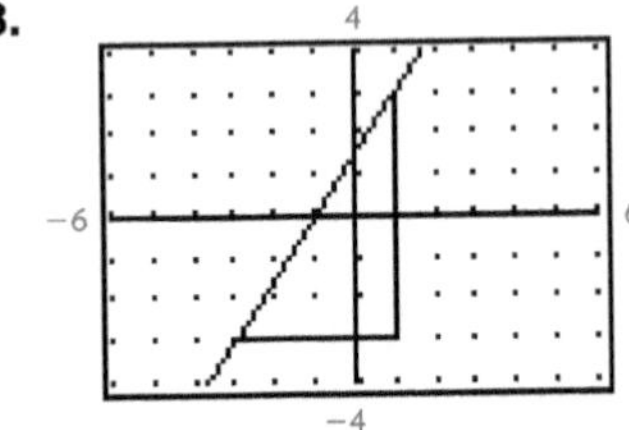

9.

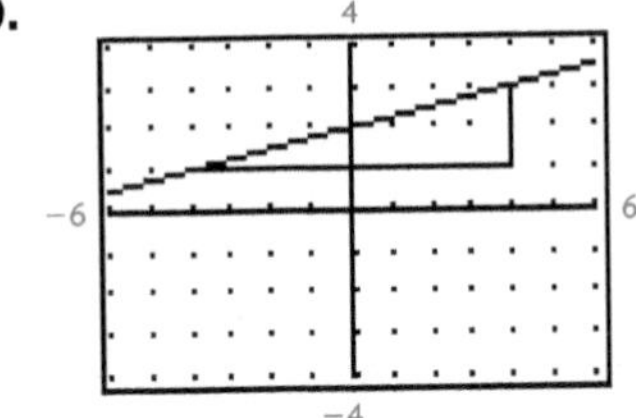

10.

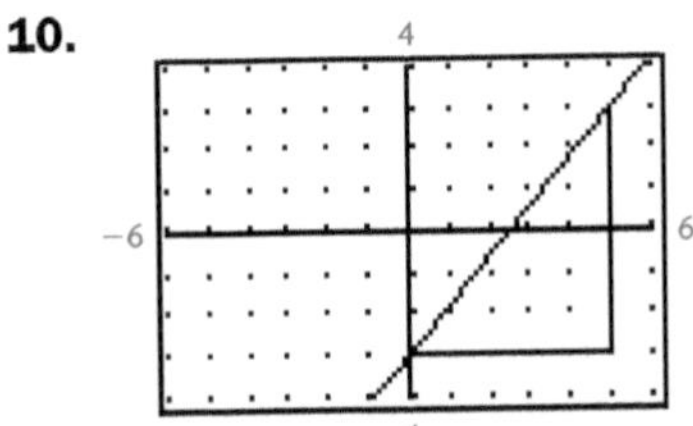

11.

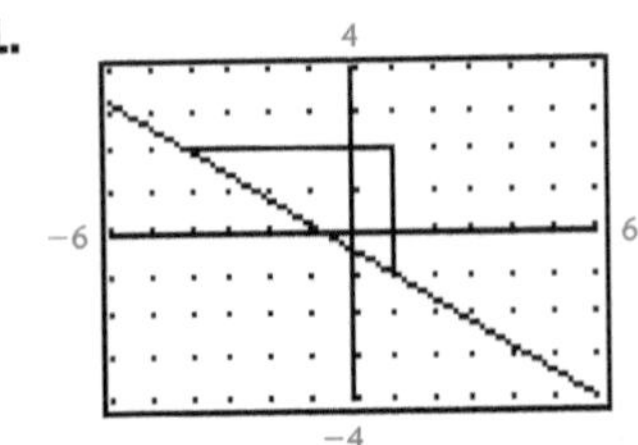

12.

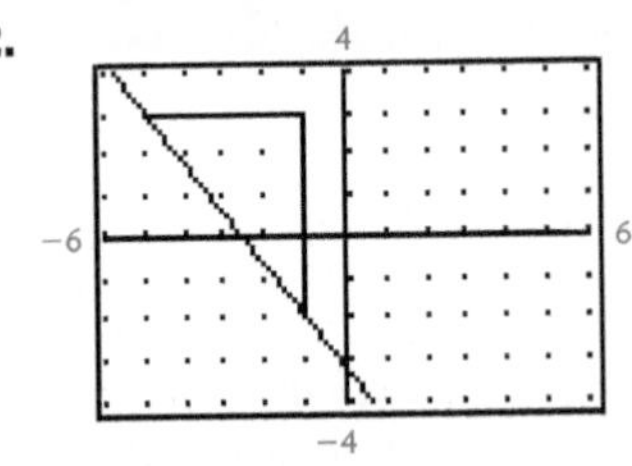

In Problems 13–18, use the graph of each linear function to find the x intercept, y intercept, and slope. Write the slope–intercept form of the equation of each line.

13.

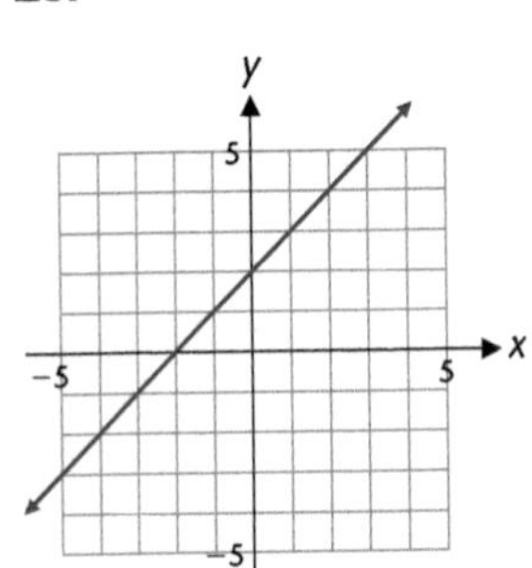

14.

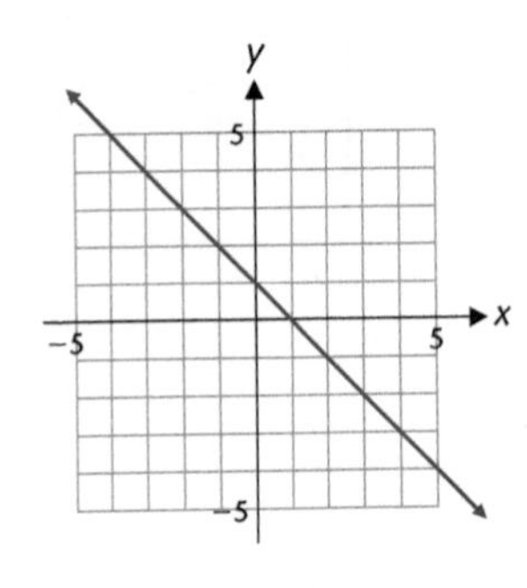

15.

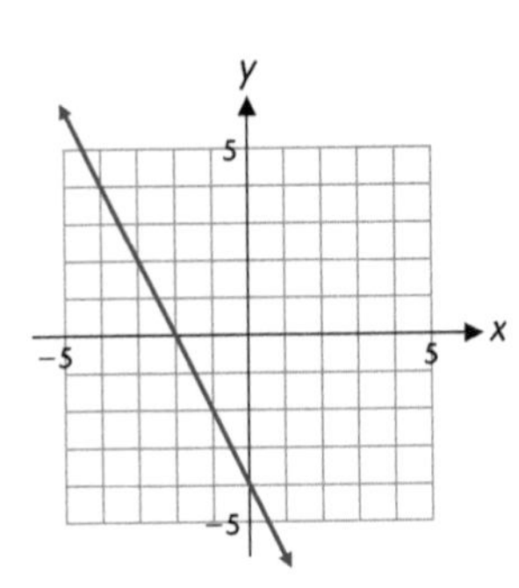

16.

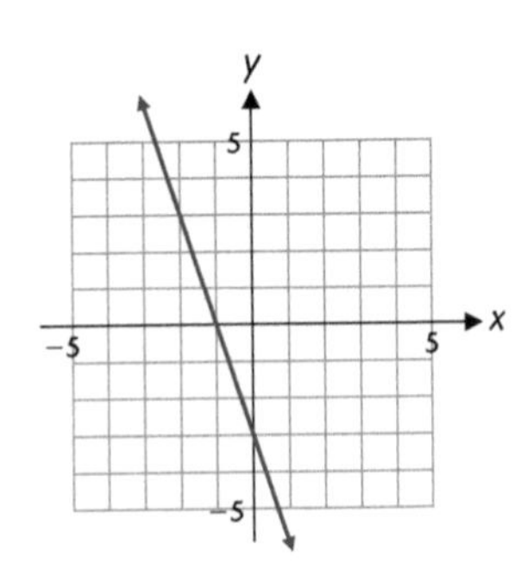

17.

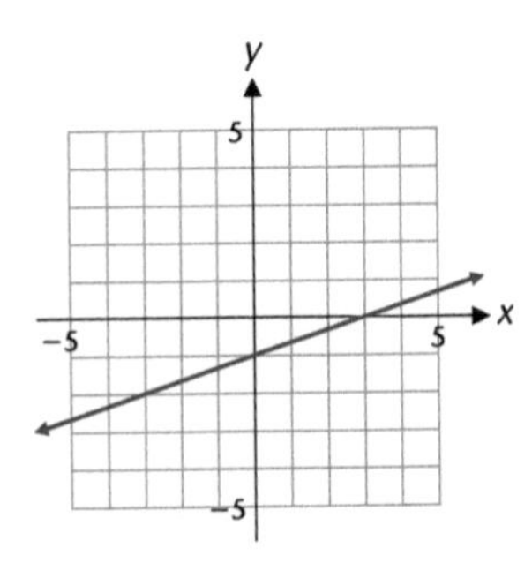

18.

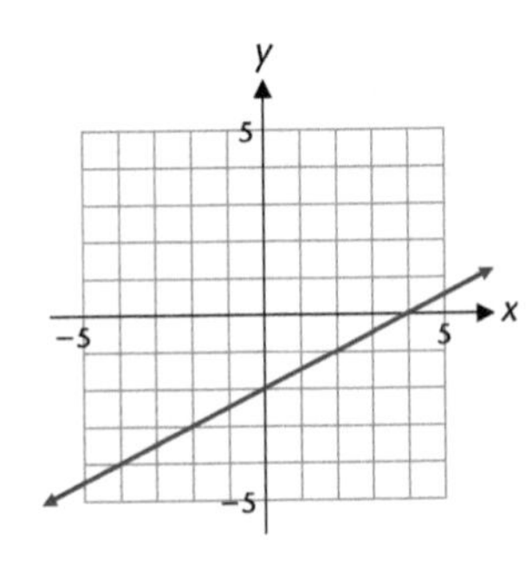

Which equations in Problems 19–28 define linear functions? Justify your answer.

19. $y = 2x^2$

20. $y = 5 - 3x^3$

21. $y = \dfrac{x - 5}{3}$

22. $y = \dfrac{3 - x}{2}$

23. $y = \frac{2}{3}(x - 7) - \frac{1}{2}(3 - x)$

24. $y = -\frac{1}{5}(2 - 3x) + \frac{2}{7}(x + 8)$

25. $y = \frac{1}{4}(2x + 2) + \frac{1}{2}(4 - x)$

26. $y = \frac{4}{3}(2 - x) + \frac{2}{3}(x + 2)$

27. $y = \dfrac{3}{x - 5}$

28. $y = \dfrac{2}{3 - x}$

In Problems 29–40, find the x intercept, y intercept, and slope, if they exist, and graph each equation.

29. $y = -\frac{3}{5}x + 4$

30. $y = -\frac{3}{2}x + 6$

31. $y = -\frac{3}{4}x$

32. $y = \frac{2}{3}x - 3$

33. $2x - 3y = 15$

34. $4x + 3y = 24$

35. $\dfrac{y}{8} - \dfrac{x}{4} = 1$

36. $\dfrac{y}{6} - \dfrac{x}{5} = 1$

37. $x = -3$

38. $y = -2$

39. $y = 3.5$

40. $x = 2.5$

In Problems 41–48, write the equation of the line described.

41. Vertical, goes through $(2, -4)$

42. Vertical, goes through $(-7, 12)$

43. Horizontal, goes through $(2, -4)$

44. Horizontal, goes through $(-7, 12)$

45. Goes through $(-3, 4)$ and $(5, 4)$

46. Goes through $(0, -2)$ and $(4, -2)$

47. Goes through $(4, 6)$ and $(4, -3)$

48. Goes through $(-3, 1)$ and $(-3, 4)$

In Problems 49–52, write the slope–intercept form of the equation of the line with indicated slope and y intercept. Then write the equation in the standard form $Ax + By = C$, where A, B, and C are integers, and $A \geq 0$.

49. Slope $= 1$; y intercept $= 0$

50. Slope $= -1$; y intercept $= 7$

51. Slope $= -\frac{2}{3}$; y intercept $= -4$

52. Slope $= \frac{5}{3}$; y intercept $= 6$

In Problems 53–70, find the equation of the line described. Write your answer in slope–intercept form.

53. Slope -3, goes through $(0, 4)$

54. Slope 2, goes through $(2, 0)$

55. Slope $-\frac{2}{5}$, goes through $(-5, 4)$

56. Slope $\frac{1}{2}$, goes through $(-4, -2)$

57. Goes through $(1, 6)$ and $(5, -2)$

58. Goes through $(-3, 4)$ and $(6, 1)$

59. Goes through $(-4, 8)$ and $(2, 0)$

60. Goes through $(2, -1)$ and $(10, 5)$

61. Has x intercept -4 and y intercept 3

62. Has x intercept -4 and y intercept -5

63. Goes through $(-3, 4)$; parallel to $y = 3x - 5$

64. Goes through $(-4, 0)$; parallel to $y = -2x + 1$

65. Goes through $(2, -3)$; perpendicular to $y = -\frac{1}{3}x$

66. Goes through $(-2, -4)$; perpendicular to $y = \frac{2}{3}x - 5$

67. Goes through $(5, 0)$; parallel to $3x - 2y = 4$

68. Goes through $(3, 5)$; parallel to $3x + 4y = 8$

69. Goes through $(0, -4)$; perpendicular to $x + 3y = 9$

70. Goes through $(-2, 4)$; perpendicular to $4x + 5y = 0$

71. Discuss the relationship between the graphs of the lines with equation $y = mx + 2$, where m is any real number.

72. Discuss the relationship between the graphs of the lines with equation $y = -0.5x + b$, where b is any real number.

73. (A) Find the linear function f whose graph passes through the points $(-1, -3)$ and $(7, 2)$.
(B) Find the linear function g whose graph passes through the points $(-3, -1)$ and $(2, 7)$.
(C) Graph both functions and discuss how they are related.

74. (A) Find the linear function f whose graph passes through the points $(-2, -3)$ and $(10, 5)$.
(B) Find the linear function g whose graph passes through the points $(-3, -2)$ and $(5, 10)$.
(C) Graph both functions and discuss how they are related.

Problems 75–80 are calculus related. A line connecting two points on a graph is called a ***secant line.*** *For the graph of the function $f(x) = \frac{1}{2}x^2$, find the slope of each secant line.*

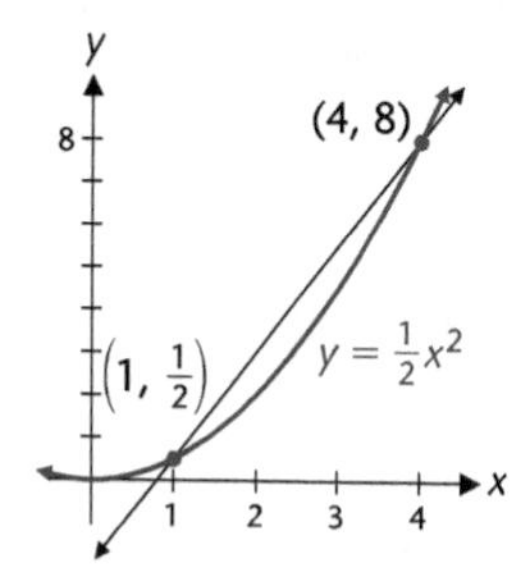

75. Connecting the points at $x = 1$ and $x = 4$. (See the figure.)

76. Connecting the points at $x = 1$ and $x = 3$.

77. Connecting the points at $x = 1$ and $x = 2$.

78. Connecting the points at $x = 1$ and $x = \frac{3}{2}$.

79. Connecting the points at $x = 1$ and $x = \frac{5}{4}$.

80. As the right-hand point gets closer and closer to $(1, \frac{1}{2})$ (see Figure A), the secant lines approach a line that intersects the graph only at $(1, \frac{1}{2})$ (see Figure B). This line is called the **tangent line** at $x = 1$. Use your answers from Problems 75–79 to estimate the slope of the tangent line at $x = 1$. (Note that Figure A contains only the secant lines for Problems 75–77.)

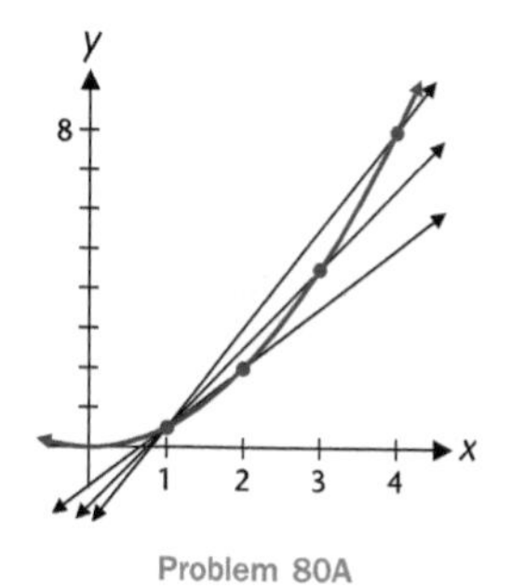

Problem 80A

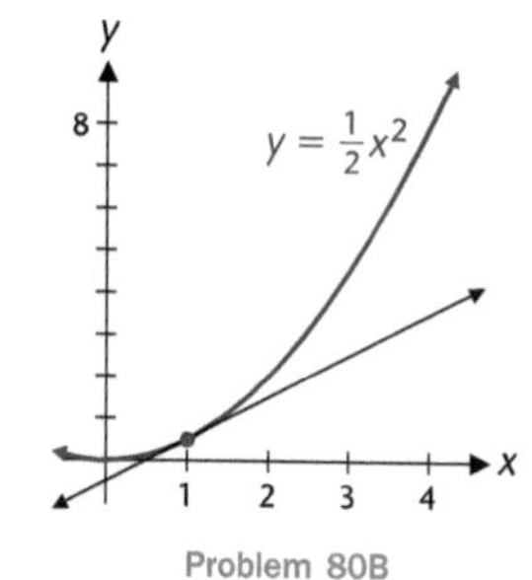

Problem 80B

81. (A) Graph the following equations in a squared viewing window:

$$3x + 2y = 6 \qquad 3x + 2y = 3$$
$$3x + 2y = -6 \qquad 3x + 2y = -3$$

(B) From your observations in part A, describe the family of lines obtained by varying C in $Ax + By = C$ while holding A and B fixed.
(C) Verify your conclusions in part B with a proof.

82. (A) Graph the following two equations in a squared viewing window:

$$3x + 4y = 12 \qquad 4x - 3y = 12$$

(B) Graph the following two equations in a squared viewing window:

$$2x + 3y = 12 \qquad 3x - 2y = 12$$

(C) From your observations in parts A and B, describe the apparent relationship of the graphs of

$$Ax + By = C \text{ and } Bx - Ay = C.$$

(D) Verify your conclusions in part C with a proof.

83. Prove that if a line L has x intercept $(a, 0)$ and y intercept $(0, b)$, then the equation of L can be written in the **intercept form**

$$\frac{x}{a} + \frac{y}{b} = 1 \qquad a, b \neq 0$$

84. For $y = mx + b$, prove that the slope is m by using Definition 2 to find the slope of the line connecting any two points on the graph. [*Hint:* Find the points corresponding to two x values x_1 and x_2.]

APPLICATIONS

85. POLITICS The *Washington Post*/ABC News approval rating for the president of the United States between October 2001 and January 2003 can be modeled by the function $A(x) = -2.13x + 91$, $0 \leq x \leq 15$, where x is months after October 2001, and A is the percentage of those polled that approved of the president's job performance.
(A) At what rate was the approval rating changing during that time period? Was it going up or down?
(B) What was the approval rating in October 2001? In January 2003? Do your results from parts A and B agree?

86. THE STOCK MARKET The price in dollars of one share of Apple Computer stock over the span of 108 days from August 15 to December 1, 2006, can be modeled by the function $P(x) = 0.23x + 66.45$, $0 \leq x \leq 108$, where x is days after August 15.
(A) At what rate was the price changing during that time period? Was it going up or down?
(B) What was the price on August 15? On December 1? Do your results from parts A and B agree?

87. IMMIGRATION The number of immigrants (in millions) living in the United States from 1996 to 2004 can be modeled by the function $N(x) = 1.04x + 25.95$, $0 \leq x \leq 8$, where x is years after 1996.
(A) At what rate was the number of immigrants changing during that time period? Was it going up or down?
(B) How many immigrants were there in 1996? In 2004? Do your results from parts A and B agree?

88. GLOBAL WARMING The average global temperature in degrees Celsius from 1965 to 2001 can be modeled by the function $T(x) = 0.0183x + 13.86$, $0 \leq x \leq 36$, where x is years after 1965.
(A) At what rate was the temperature changing during that time period? Was it going up or down?
(B) What was the average global temperature in 1965? In 2001? Do your results from parts A and B agree?
(Source: www.giss.nasa.gov/data)

89. METEOROLOGY A meteorologist tracking a storm finds that it is 145 miles away at 11 P.M. and moving toward her city at the rate of 23 miles per hour. Find a linear function describing the distance d of the storm from the city h hours after 11 P.M. Will the storm arrive by the beginning of rush hour at 6 A.M. the next morning?

90. GEOLOGY A geologist is alerted to a seismic disturbance at sea that caused a tsunami headed toward the coast of Japan. At that time, the tsunami is moving at the rate of 235 miles per hour, and is 700 miles away. Find a linear function describing the distance d of the tsunami from Japan h hours later. If it would take $2\frac{1}{2}$ hours to evacuate the coastal communities, will they be able to accomplish this before the tsunami reaches Japan?

91. PHYSICS The two temperature scales Fahrenheit (F) and Celsius (C) are linearly related. It is known that water freezes at 32°F or 0°C and boils at 212°F or 100°C.
(A) Find a linear equation that expresses F in terms of C.
(B) If a European house thermostat is set at 20°C, what is the setting in degrees Fahrenheit? If the outside temperature in Milwaukee is 86°F, what is the temperature in degrees Celsius?
(C) What is the slope of the graph of the linear equation found in part A? Interpret verbally.

92. PHYSICS Hooke's law states that the relationship between the stretch s of a spring and the weight w causing the stretch is linear (a principle on which all spring scales are constructed). For a particular spring, a 5-pound weight causes a stretch of 2 inches, whereas with no weight the stretch of the spring is 0.
(A) Find a linear equation that expresses s in terms of w.
(B) What weight will cause a stretch of 3.6 inches?
(C) What is the slope of the graph of the equation? Interpret verbally.

93. BUSINESS–DEPRECIATION A copy machine was purchased by a law firm for \$8,000 and is assumed to have a depreciated value of \$0 after 5 years. The firm takes straight-line depreciation over the 5-year period.
(A) Find a linear equation that expresses value V in dollars in terms of time t in years.
(B) What is the depreciated value after 3 years?
(C) What is the slope of the graph of the equation found in part A? Interpret verbally.

94. BUSINESS–MARKUP POLICY A clothing store sells a shirt costing \$20 for \$33 and a jacket costing \$60 for \$93.
(A) If the markup policy of the store for items costing over \$10 is assumed to be linear, write an equation that expresses retail price R in terms of cost C (wholesale price).
(B) What does a store pay for a suit that retails for \$240?
(C) What is the slope of the graph of the equation found in part A? Interpret verbally.

95. COST ANALYSIS A plant can manufacture 80 golf clubs per day for a total daily cost of \$8,147 and 100 golf clubs per day for a total daily cost of \$9,647.
(A) Assuming that the daily cost function is linear, find the total daily cost of producing x golf clubs.
(B) Write a brief verbal interpretation of the slope and y intercept of this cost function.

96. COST ANALYSIS A plant can manufacture 50 tennis rackets per day for a total daily cost of \$4,174 and 60 tennis rackets per day for a total daily cost of \$4,634.
(A) Assuming that the daily cost function is linear, find the total daily cost of producing x tennis rackets.
(B) Write a brief verbal interpretation of the slope and y intercept of this cost function.

97. MEDICINE Cardiovascular research has shown that above the 210 cholesterol level, each 1% increase in cholesterol level increases coronary risk 2%. For a particular age group, the coronary risk at a 210 cholesterol level is found to be 0.160 and at a level of 231 the risk is found to be 0.192.
(A) Find a linear equation that expresses risk R in terms of cholesterol level C.
(B) What is the risk for a cholesterol level of 260?
(C) What is the slope of the graph of the equation found in part A? Interpret verbally.
Express all calculated quantities to three significant digits.

98. DEMOGRAPHICS The average number of persons per household in the United States has been shrinking steadily for as long as such statistics have been kept and is approximately linear with respect to time. In 1900, there were about 4.76 persons per household and in 1990, about 2.5.
(A) If N represents the average number of persons per household and t represents the number of years since 1900, write a linear equation that expresses N in terms of t.
(B) What is the predicted household size in the year 2015?
Express all calculated quantities to three significant digits.

99. METEOROLOGY In stable air, as the altitude of a weather balloon increases, the temperature drops at a rate of about 5°F for each 1,000-foot rise in altitude.
(A) If the temperature at sea level is 70°F, write a linear equation that expresses the temperature T in terms of altitude A (in thousands of feet above sea level).
(B) What would the temperature be at an altitude of 10,000 feet?
(C) What is the slope of the graph of the equation found in part A? What does the slope describe physically?

100. FLIGHT NAVIGATION An airspeed indicator on some aircraft is affected by the changes in atmospheric pressure at different altitudes. A pilot can estimate the true airspeed by observing the indicated airspeed and adding to it about 2% for every 1,000 feet of altitude.
(A) If a pilot maintains a constant reading of 200 miles per hour on the airspeed indicator as the aircraft climbs from sea level to an altitude of 10,000 feet, write a linear equation that expresses true airspeed T (miles per hour) in terms of altitude A (thousands of feet).
(B) What would be the true airspeed of the aircraft at 6,500 feet?
(C) What is the slope of the graph of the equation found in part A? Interpret verbally.

2-2 Linear Equations and Models

- Solving Linear Equations
- Modeling with Linear Equations
- Modeling Distance-Rate-Time Problems
- Modeling Mixture Problems
- Data Analysis and Linear Regression

In this section, we will discuss methods for solving equations that involve linear functions. Some problems are best solved using algebraic techniques, while others benefit from a graphical approach. Because graphs often give additional insight into relationships, especially in applications, we will usually emphasize graphical techniques over algebraic methods. But mastering both will lead to a far greater understanding of linear equations and how they are used. Some of the problems in this section can only be solved algebraically, and near the end of the section, we are going to introduce an important new tool—linear regression—that will be one of the most useful applications of a graphing calculator.

Solving Linear Equations

We will begin with a quick review of solving a basic linear equation. For a more detailed coverage, see Appendix B, Section B-1.

EXAMPLE 1 Solving an Equation

Solve $5x - 8 = 2x + 1$.

SOLUTION

Algebraic Solution

We will use the familiar properties of equality to transform the given equation into an equivalent equation with an obvious solution.

$5x - 8 = 2x + 1$	Subtract $2x$ from both sides.
$5x - 8 - 2x = 2x + 1 - 2x$	Combine like terms.
$3x - 8 = 1$	Add 8 to both sides.
$3x - 8 + 8 = 1 + 8$	Combine like terms.
$3x = 9$	Divide both sides by 3.
$\frac{3x}{3} = \frac{9}{3}$	Simplify.
$x = 3$	

Graphical Solution

Enter each side of the equation in the equation editor of a graphing calculator (Fig. 1) and use the INTERSECT command (Fig. 2).

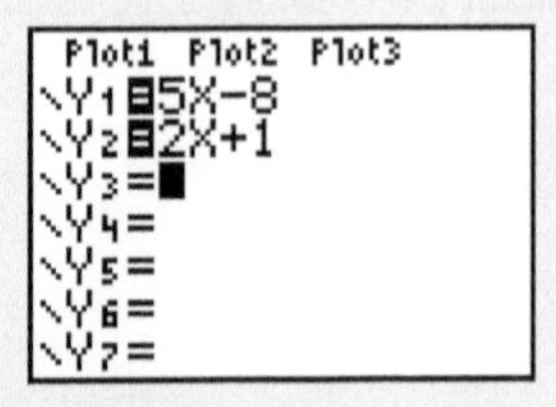

Figure 1

It follows from the properties of equality that $x = 3$ is also the solution set of all the preceding equations in our solution, including the original equation.

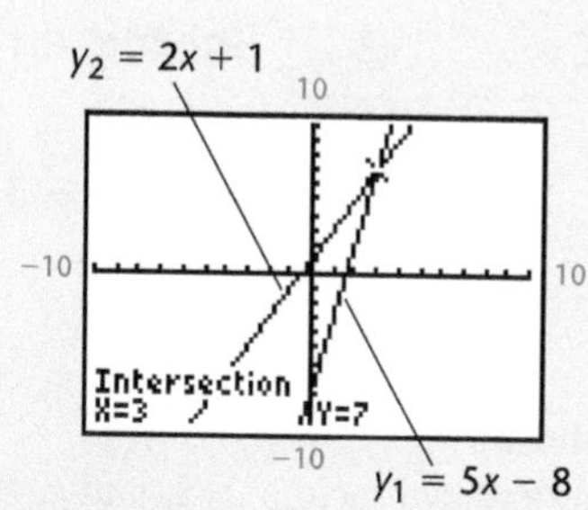

› Figure 2

We see that $x = 3$ is the solution to the original equation.

MATCHED PROBLEM 1

Solve $2x + 1 = 4x + 5$.

In the solution of Example 1, notice that we used the informal notation $x = 3$ for the solution set rather than the more formal statement: solution set = $\{3\}$.

››› EXPLORE-DISCUSS 1

An equation that is true for all values of the variable for which both sides of the equation are defined is called an **identity.** An equation that is true for some values of the variable and false for others is called a **conditional equation.** An equation that is false for all permissible values of the variable is called a **contradiction.** Use algebraic and/or graphical techniques to classify each of the following as an identity, a conditional equation, or a contradiction. Solve any conditional equations.

(A) $2(x - 4) = 2x - 12$ **(B)** $2(x - 4) = 3x - 12$

(C) $2(x - 4) = 2x - 8$ **(D)** $\dfrac{2}{x - 1} + 3 = \dfrac{x}{x - 1}$

(E) $\dfrac{1}{x - 1} + 3 = \dfrac{x}{x - 1}$ **(F)** $\dfrac{1}{x - 1} + 1 = \dfrac{x}{x - 1}$

When an equation is an identity, we say that the solution is all real numbers for which the equation is defined. When an equation is a contradiction, we say that it has no solution.

When equations involve fractions, it's always a good idea to begin by removing all of the fractions. This can be accomplished with a two-step procedure: (1) Find the least common denominator (LCD) for all fractions, and (2) multiply both sides of the equation by that LCD.

EXAMPLE 2 Solving an Equation

Solve $\frac{7}{2x} - 3 = \frac{8}{3} - \frac{15}{x}$.

SOLUTION

Algebraic Solution

The denominators have factors 2, 3, and x, so the LCD is $2 \cdot 3 \cdot x$, or $6x$.

$$\frac{7}{2x} - 3 = \frac{8}{3} - \frac{15}{x}$$ Multiply both sides by 6x.

$$6x\left(\frac{7}{2x} - 3\right) = 6x\left(\frac{8}{3} - \frac{15}{x}\right)$$ Distribute.

$$6x \cdot \frac{7}{2x} - 6x \cdot 3 = 6x \cdot \frac{8}{3} - 6x \cdot \frac{15}{x}$$ Simplify each fraction. The equation is now free of fractions.

$$21 - 18x = 16x - 90$$ Subtract 16x from both sides.

$$21 - 18x - 16x = 16x - 90 - 16x$$ Combine like terms.

$$21 - 34x = -90$$ Subtract 21 from both sides.

$$21 - 34x - 21 = -90 - 21$$ Combine like terms.

$$-34x = -111$$ Divide both sides by −34.

$$\frac{-34x}{-34} = \frac{-111}{-34}$$ Simplify.

$$x = \frac{111}{34}$$

Graphical Solution

Enter $y_1 = \frac{7}{2x} - 3$ and $y_2 = \frac{8}{3} - \frac{15}{x}$ (Fig. 3) in the equation editor of a graphing calculator. Note the use of parentheses in Figure 3 to be certain that $\frac{7}{2x}$ is evaluated correctly. After looking at various viewing windows to convince ourselves that the graphs only cross once, we use the INTERSECT command (Fig. 4).

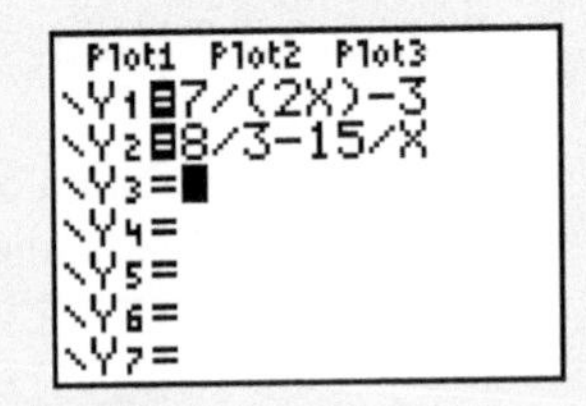

› Figure 3

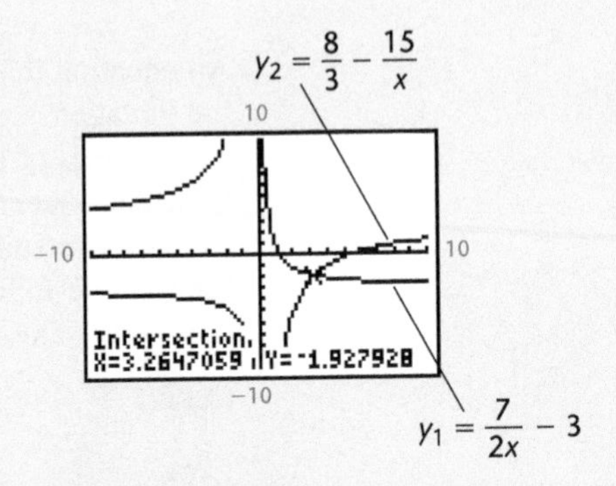

› Figure 4

We see that $x = 3.2647059$ is the solution of the original equation. Note that $\frac{111}{34} \approx 3.2647059$ to seven decimal places.

MATCHED PROBLEM 2

Solve $\frac{7}{3x} + 2 = \frac{1}{x} - \frac{3}{5}$.

››› CAUTION ›››

1. When multiplying both sides of an equation by the LCD, make sure you multiply by *every* term. Students often forget to multiply by terms with no denominator.
2. When entering fractional expressions in a graphing calculator, you should get in the habit of putting parentheses around any numerator or denominator that consists of more than one symbol.

The equation in Example 2 has a factor of x in the denominator, so a value of $x = 0$ has to be excluded. Fortunately, that wasn't an issue, since the solution is $x = \frac{111}{34}$. But it brings up an important point: When solving an equation with a variable denominator, you always need to make sure that any potential solution does not result in a zero denominator.

EXAMPLE 3 Solving an Equation

Solve $\dfrac{x}{x+2} = 4 - \dfrac{2}{x+2}$.

SOLUTION

Algebraic Solution

There is only one denominator, $x + 2$, so it's the LCD.

$$\frac{x}{x+2} = 4 - \frac{2}{x+2} \quad \text{Multiply both sides by } x + 2.$$

$$(x+2)\frac{x}{x+2} = (x+2)\left(4 - \frac{2}{x+2}\right) \quad \text{Distribute.}$$

$$(x+2)\frac{x}{x+2} = 4(x+2) - (x+2)\frac{2}{x+2} \quad \text{Simplify each term.}$$

$$x = 4x + 8 - 2 \quad \text{Subtract } 4x \text{ from each side.}$$

$$x - 4x = 4x + 8 - 2 - 4x \quad \text{Combine like terms.}$$

$$-3x = 6 \quad \text{Divide both sides by } -3.$$

$$\frac{-3x}{-3} = \frac{6}{-3} \quad \text{Simplify.}$$

$$x = -2$$

Graphical Solution

Enter $y_1 = \frac{x}{x+2}$ and $y_2 = 4 - \frac{2}{x+2}$ into the equation editor of a graphing calculator. (Fig. 5). The graph in a standard window (Fig. 6) shows that the graphs might intersect near $x = -2$ (Fig. 7). Using the INTERSECT command with a guess near $x = -2$ results in an error screen (Fig. 8). This indicates that the graphs do not intersect, and there is no solution. (This should be repeated for an x value slightly less than -2.)

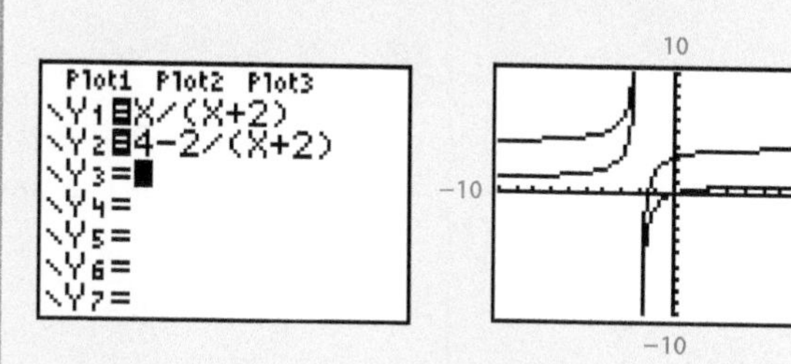

› Figure 5 › Figure 6

It appears that $x = -2$ is the solution. But $x = -2$ makes the original equation undefined, so we conclude that the equation has no solution.

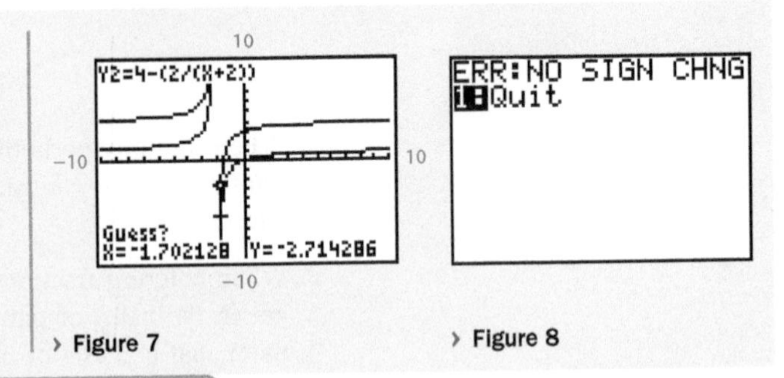

› **Figure 7**

› **Figure 8**

MATCHED PROBLEM 3

Solve $\dfrac{2x}{x + 10} = 3 - \dfrac{20}{x + 10}$.

In practical applications, we frequently encounter equations involving more than one variable. For example, if L and W are the length and width of a rectangle, respectively, the area of the rectangle is given by (Fig. 9)

$$A = LW$$

› **Figure 9** Area of a rectangle.

Depending on the situation, we may want to solve this equation for L or W. To solve for W, we simply treat A and L as constants and W as the variable. Then the equation $A = LW$ becomes a linear equation with variable W, which can be solved easily by dividing both sides by L:

$$W = \frac{A}{L} \qquad L \neq 0$$

EXAMPLE 4 Solving an Equation with More than One Variable

Solve for P in terms of the other variables: $A = P + Prt$.

SOLUTION

$$A = P + Prt \qquad \text{Think of } A, r, \text{ and } t \text{ as constants. Factor to isolate } P.$$

$$A = P(1 + rt) \qquad \text{Divide both sides by } 1 + rt.$$

$$P = \frac{A}{1 + rt} \qquad \text{Restriction: } 1 + rt \neq 0$$

MATCHED PROBLEM 4

Solve for r in terms of the other variables: $A = P + Prt$.

Modeling with Linear Equations

Linear equations can be used to model a wide variety of real-world situations. In the remainder of the section, we'll study a sampling of these applications. To construct models for word problems, we translate verbal statements into mathematical statements. Explore-Discuss 2 will help you review this process.

EXPLORE-DISCUSS 2

Translate each of the following sentences involving two numbers into an equation.

(A) The first number is 10 more than the second number.

(B) The first number is 15 less than the second number.

(C) The first number is half the second number.

(D) The first number is three times the second number.

(E) Ten times the first number is 15 more than the second number.

EXAMPLE 5 Cost Analysis

A hot dog vendor pays \$25 per day to rent a pushcart and \$1.25 for the ingredients in one hot dog.

(A) Find the cost of selling x hot dogs in 1 day.
(B) What is the cost of selling 200 hot dogs in 1 day?
(C) If the daily cost is \$355, how many hot dogs were sold that day?

SOLUTIONS

(A) The rental charge of \$25 is the vendor's **fixed cost**—a cost that is accrued every day and does not depend on the number of hot dogs sold. The cost of ingredients does depend on the number sold. The cost of the ingredients for x hot dogs is $\$1.25x$ (\$1.25 times the number of hot dogs sold). This is the vendor's **variable cost**—a cost that depends on the number of hot dogs sold. The total cost for selling x hot dogs is

$$C(x) = 1.25x + 25$$ Total cost = Variable cost + Fixed cost

(B) The cost of selling 200 hot dogs in 1 day is

$$C(200) = 1.25(200) + 25 = \$275$$

(C) The number of hot dogs that can be sold for $355 is the solution of the equation

$$1.25x + 25 = 355$$

Algebraic Solution

$$1.25x + 25 = 355 \quad \text{Subtract 25 from each side.}$$
$$1.25x = 330 \quad \text{Divide both sides by 1.25.}$$
$$x = \frac{330}{1.25}$$
$$= 264 \text{ hot dogs}$$

Graphical Solution

Entering $y_1 = 1.25x + 25$ and $y_2 = 355$ in a graphing calculator and using the INTERSECT command (Fig. 10) shows that 264 hot dogs can be sold for $355.

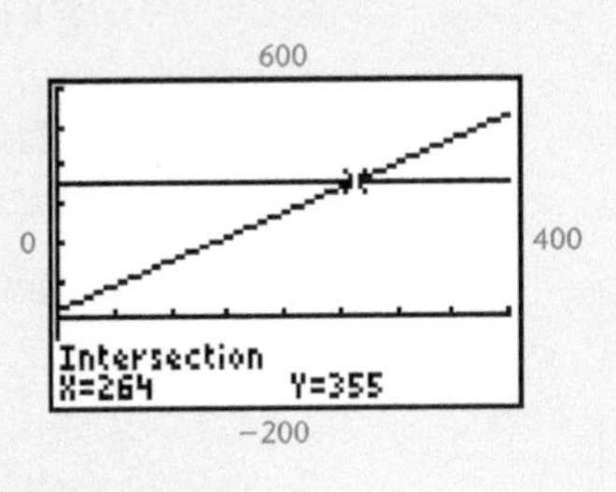

› Figure 10

MATCHED PROBLEM 5

It costs a pretzel vendor $20 per day to rent a cart and $0.75 for each pretzel.

(A) Find the cost of selling x pretzels in 1 day.
(B) What is the cost of selling 150 pretzels in 1 day?
(C) If the daily cost is $275, how many pretzels were sold that day?

In Example 5, the vendor's cost increases at the rate of $1.25 per hot dog. Thus, the rate of change of the cost function $C(x) = 1.25x + 25$ is the slope $m = 1.25$. This constant rate can also be viewed as the cost of selling one additional hot dog. In economics, this quantity is referred to as the **marginal cost.**

› Modeling Distance-Rate-Time Problems

If you drive for 2 hours and cover 120 miles, what was your average speed? If you answered 60 miles per hour, you already know our next important formula. To get that result, we used the formula

$$\text{Average speed} = \frac{\text{Distance traveled}}{\text{Time passed}}$$

When the speed of an object is constant, we can write this as

$$r = \frac{d}{t} \quad \text{Rate is distance divided by time.}$$

or, equivalently, $d = rt$. Distance is rate times time.

››› EXPLORE-DISCUSS 3

A bus leaves Milwaukee at 12:00 noon and travels due west on Interstate 94 at a constant rate of 55 miles per hour. A passenger that was left behind leaves Milwaukee in a taxicab at 1:00 P.M. in pursuit of the bus. The taxicab travels at a constant rate of 65 miles per hour. Let t represent time in hours after 12:00 noon.

(A) How far has the bus traveled after t hours?

(B) If $t \geq 1$, how far has the taxicab traveled after t hours?

(C) When will the taxicab catch up with the bus?

EXAMPLE 6 A Distance-Rate-Time Problem

An excursion boat takes 1.5 times as long to go 60 miles up a river as it does to return. If the boat cruises at 16 miles per hour in still water, what is the rate of the current in the river?

SOLUTION

It's usually helpful in distance-rate-time problems to build a table that helps to organize the information. We were asked to find the speed of the current, so we let x = rate of current (in mph). Then the rate of the boat upstream (against the current) is $16 - x$ mph, and the rate downstream (with the current) is $16 + x$ mph. The distance in each case is 60 miles.

	Distance	Rate	Time
Upstream	60	$16 - x$	
Downstream	60	$16 + x$	

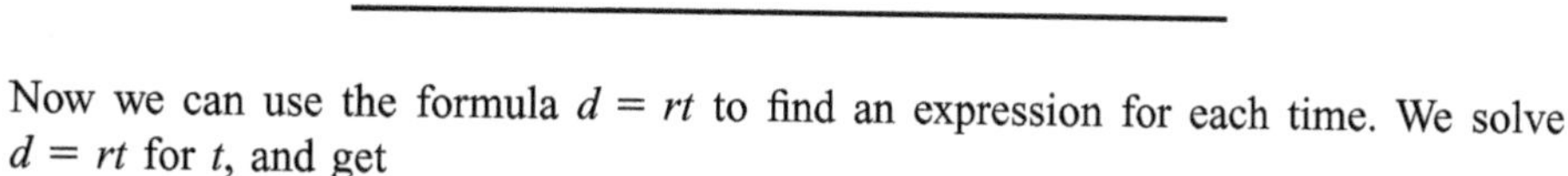

Now we can use the formula $d = rt$ to find an expression for each time. We solve $d = rt$ for t, and get

$$t = \frac{d}{r}$$

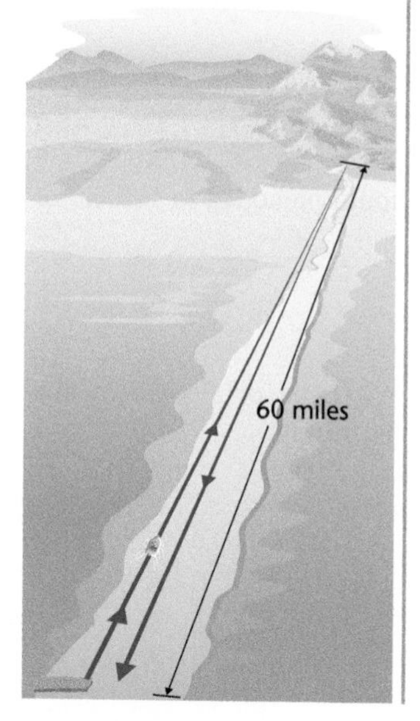

$$\text{Time upstream: } t_u = \frac{60}{16 - x} \quad (x \neq 16)$$

$$\text{Time downstream: } t_d = \frac{60}{16 + x} \quad (x \neq -16)$$

Since the upstream trip took 1.5 times as long,

$$t_u = 1.5t_d$$

$$\frac{60}{16 - x} = 1.5\frac{60}{16 + x}$$

Multiplying out the right side, we get the equation

$$\frac{60}{16 - x} = \frac{90}{16 + x}$$

Algebraic Solution

$$\frac{60}{16 - x} = \frac{90}{16 + x}$$ Multiply both sides by $(16 - x)(16 + x)$.

$$60(16 + x) = 90(16 - x)$$ Distribute.

$$960 + 60x = 1{,}440 - 90x$$ Add $90x$ to each side.

$$960 + 150x = 1{,}440$$ Subtract 960 from each side.

$$150x = 480$$ Divide both sides by 150.

$$x = \frac{480}{150} = 3.2 \text{ mph}$$

Graphical Solution

We first enter $y_1 = \frac{60}{16 - x}$ and $y_2 = \frac{90}{16 + x}$. Since x is a speed and y is a time, we restrict our viewing window to positive values. The INTERSECT command (Fig. 11) shows that $x = 3.2$ mph is the solution.

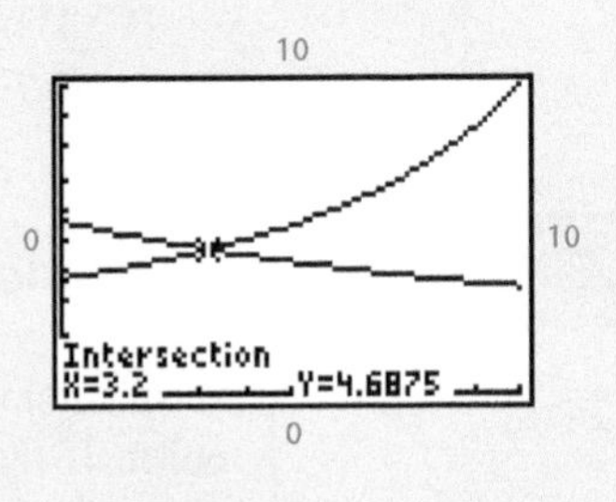

› Figure 11

MATCHED PROBLEM 6

A jetliner takes 1.2 times as long to fly from Paris to New York (3,600 miles) as to return. If the jet cruises at 550 miles per hour in still air, what is the average rate of the wind blowing in the direction of Paris from New York?

› Modeling Mixture Problems

A variety of applications can be classified as mixture problems. Although the problems come from different areas, their mathematical treatment is essentially the same.

EXAMPLE 7 A Mixture Problem

How many liters of a mixture containing 80% alcohol should be added to 5 liters of a 20% solution to yield a 30% solution?

SOLUTION

Let x = amount of 80% solution used. Then $0.8x$ is the amount of alcohol in that solution, and $x + 5$ is the amount of the 30% solution that results.

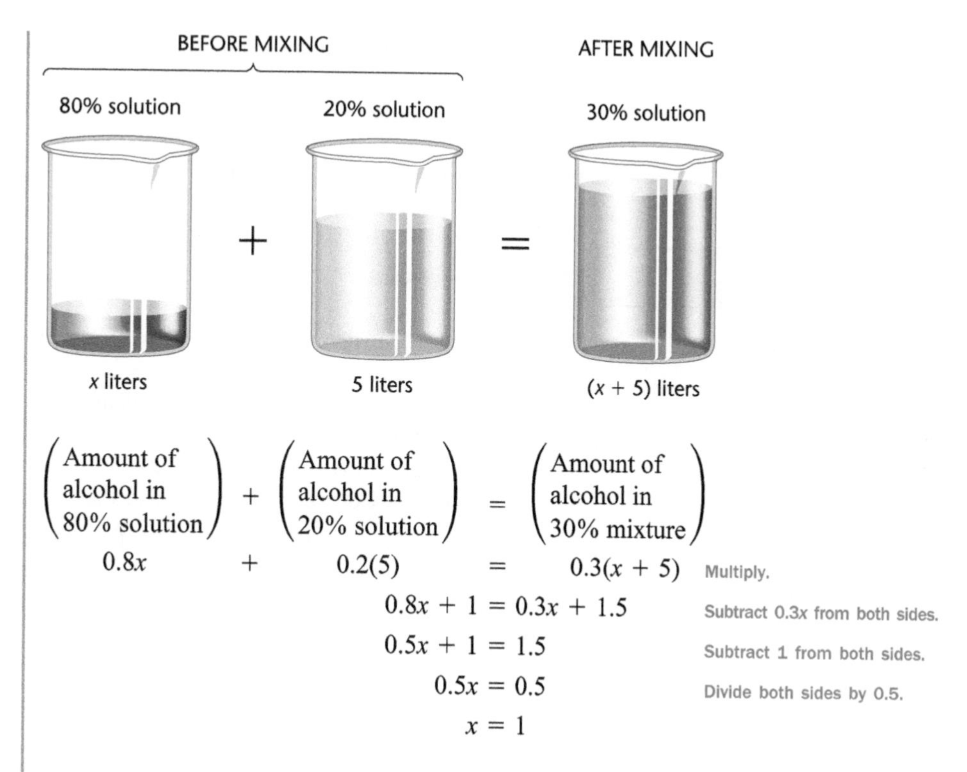

$$\begin{pmatrix}\text{Amount of}\\ \text{alcohol in}\\ \text{80\% solution}\end{pmatrix} + \begin{pmatrix}\text{Amount of}\\ \text{alcohol in}\\ \text{20\% solution}\end{pmatrix} = \begin{pmatrix}\text{Amount of}\\ \text{alcohol in}\\ \text{30\% mixture}\end{pmatrix}$$

$$0.8x + 0.2(5) = 0.3(x + 5) \quad \text{Multiply.}$$

$$0.8x + 1 = 0.3x + 1.5 \quad \text{Subtract } 0.3x \text{ from both sides.}$$

$$0.5x + 1 = 1.5 \quad \text{Subtract 1 from both sides.}$$

$$0.5x = 0.5 \quad \text{Divide both sides by 0.5.}$$

$$x = 1$$

Add 1 liter of the 80% solution.

CHECK

	Liters of solution	Liters of alcohol	Percent alcohol
First solution	1 (Add)	$0.8(1) = 0.8$ (Add)	80%
Second solution	5	$0.2(5) = 1$	20%
Mixture	6	1.8	$1.8/6 = 0.3$, or 30%

MATCHED PROBLEM 7

A chemical storeroom has a 90% acid solution and a 40% acid solution. How many centiliters of the 90% solution should be added to 50 centiliters of the 40% solution to yield a 50% solution?

› Data Analysis and Linear Regression

In most math courses you've taken, there were probably a lot of application problems in which an equation or function was provided that describes some real-world situation. There have been dozens in this book already, and we're only in the second section of Chapter 2! This may have left you wondering where in the world these functions come from.

There is a mathematical technique known as **regression analysis** that is used to find a function that provides a useful model for a set of data points. Graphs of equations are often called **curves** and regression analysis is also referred to as **curve fitting.** In Example 8, we use **linear regression** to construct a mathematical model in the form of a linear function that fits a data set.

EXAMPLE 8 Diamond Prices

Table 1 Round-Cut Diamond Prices

Weight (carats)	Price
0.5	$1,340
0.6	$1,760
0.7	$2,540
0.8	$3,350
0.9	$4,130
1.0	$4,920

Source: www.tradeshop.com

Prices for round-cut diamonds taken from an online trader are given in Table 1.

(A) Use linear regression on a graphing calculator to find a linear model $y = f(x)$ that fits these data, where x is the weight of a diamond (in carats) and y is the associated price of that diamond (in dollars). Round the constants a and b to three significant digits. Compare the model and the data both graphically and numerically.

(B) Use the model to estimate the cost of a 0.85 carat diamond and the cost of a 1.2 carat diamond. Round answers to the nearest dollar.

(C) Use the model to estimate the weight of a diamond that sells for $3,000. Round the answer to two significant digits.

SOLUTIONS

(A) The first step in fitting a curve to a data set is to enter the data in two lists in a graphing calculator, usually by pressing STAT and selecting EDIT (see Fig. 12).* We enter the given values of the independent variable x in L_1 and the corresponding values of the dependent variable y in L_2 (Fig. 13). Next, we select a viewing window that will show all the data (Fig. 14).

EDIT CALC TESTS
1:Edit...
2:SortA(
3:SortD(
4:ClrList
5:SetUpEditor

› Figure 12

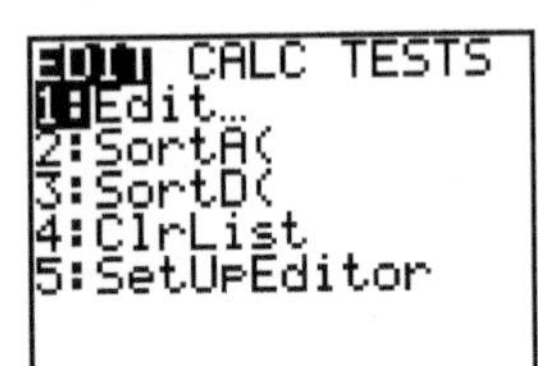

› Figure 13

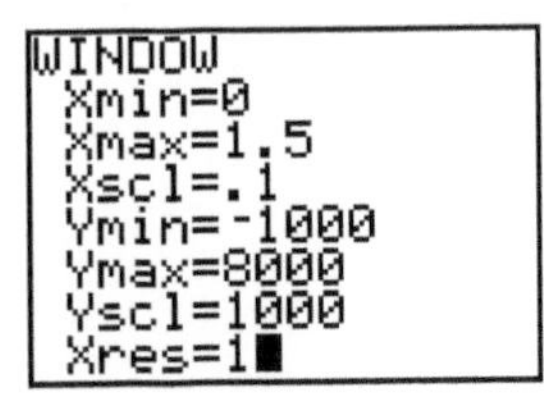

› Figure 14

To check that all the data will be visible in this window, we need to graph the points in the form (x, y), where x is a number in list L_1 and y is the corresponding number in list L_2. This is called a **scatter diagram** or **scatter plot.** On most graphing calculators, a scatter diagram can be drawn by first pressing STAT PLOT and selecting the options displayed in Figure 15 on the next page. Then press GRAPH to display the scatter diagram (Fig. 16).

*Remember, we are using a TI-83 or TI-84 to produce the screen images in this book. Other graphing calculators will produce different images.

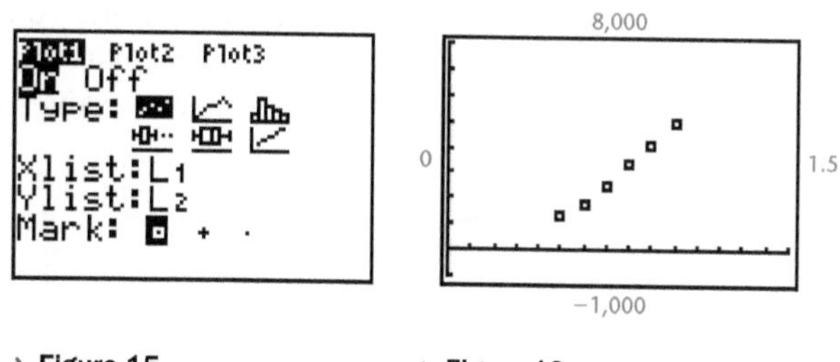

› Figure 15 › Figure 16

Now we are ready to fit a curve to the data graphed in Figure 16. First we find the screen on the graphing calculator that lists the various regression options, usually by pressing STAT and selecting CALC (Fig. 17).

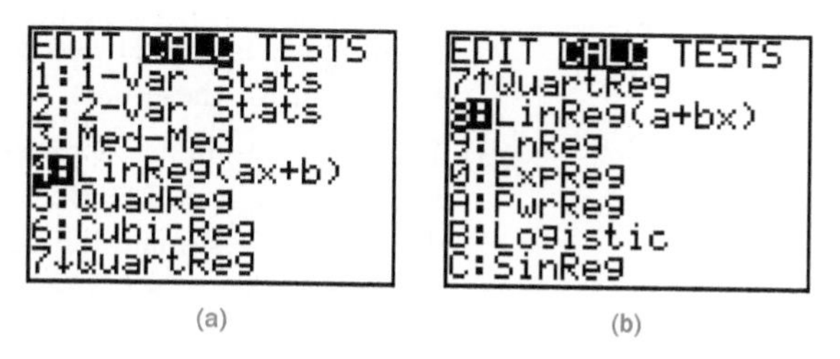

(a) (b)

› Figure 17

Any of options 4 through C in Figure 17 can be used to fit a curve to a data set. As you progress through this text, you will become familiar with most of the choices in Figure 17. In this example, we are directed to select option 4 (or, equivalently, option 8), linear regression (Fig. 18). Notice that we entered the names of the two lists of data, L_1 and L_2, after the command LinReg($ax + b$) in Figure 18. The order in which we enter these two names is important. The name of the list of independent values must precede the name of the list of dependent values. Press ENTER to obtain the results in Figure 19. The values r^2 and r displayed in Figure 19 are called **diagnostics.*** They provide a measure of how well the regression curve fits the data. Values of r close to 1 or -1 indicate a good fit. Values of r close to 0 indicate a poor fit.

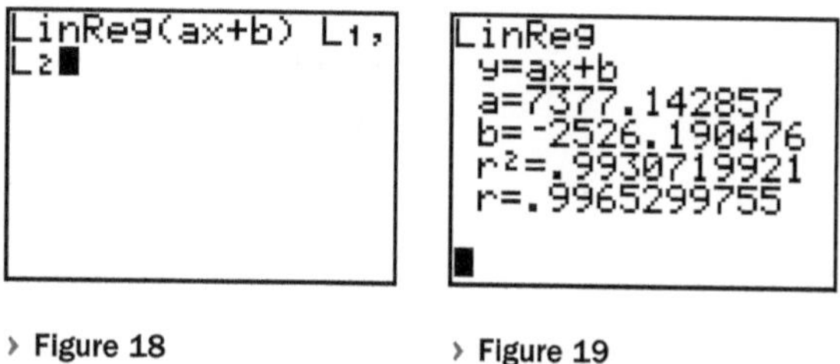

› Figure 18 › Figure 19

After rounding a and b in Figure 19 to three significant digits, the linear regression model for these data is

$$y = f(x) = 7{,}380x - 2{,}530$$

*If your graphing calculators doesn't display values of r, try pressing CATALOG, then selecting "diagnostics on."

Enter this equation in the equation editor (Fig. 20). The graph of the model and the scatter plot of the data are shown in Figure 21 and a table comparing the data and the corresponding values of the model is shown in Figure 22.*

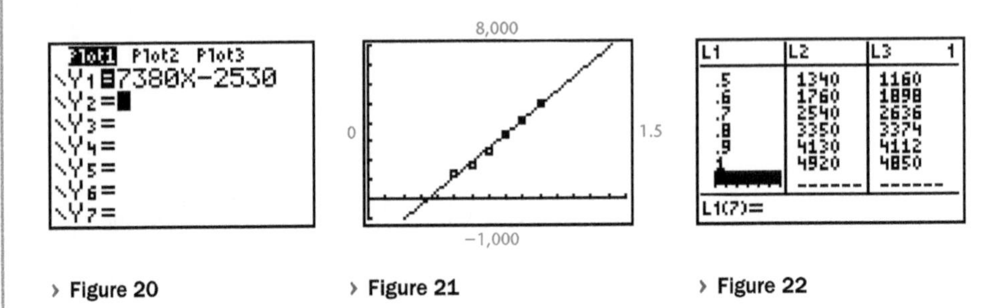

› Figure 20 › Figure 21 › Figure 22

Examining Figures 21 and 22, we see that the model does seem to provide a reasonable fit for these data.

(B) The carat weight is represented by x, so we need to find the dollar values for $x = 0.85$ and $x = 1.2$. Because $x = 0.85$ and $x = 1.2$ are not in Table 1, we use the model to estimate the corresponding prices. From Figure 23 we see that the estimated price of a 0.85-carat diamond is \$3,743. Figure 24 shows that the estimated price of a 1.2-carat diamond is \$6,326. Figure 25 shows how TABLE can be used in place of TRACE to obtain the same results.

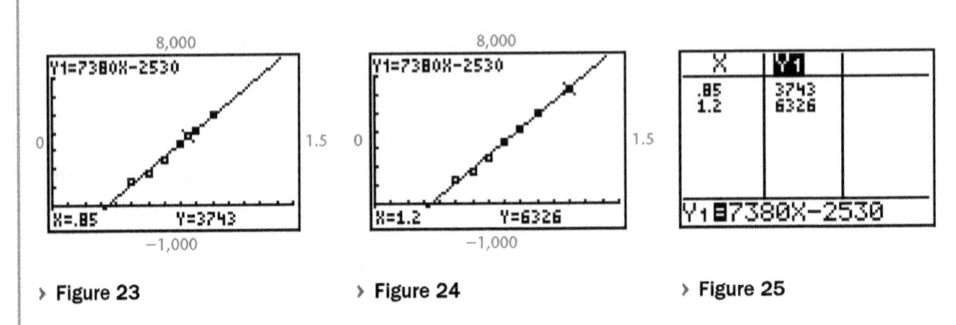

› Figure 23 › Figure 24 › Figure 25

(C) This time we are given a value of the dependent variable y (\$3,000) and asked to solve for the independent variable (carat weight). To find the weight, we add $y_2 = 3{,}000$ to the equation list (Fig. 26) and use the INTERSECT command (Fig. 27).

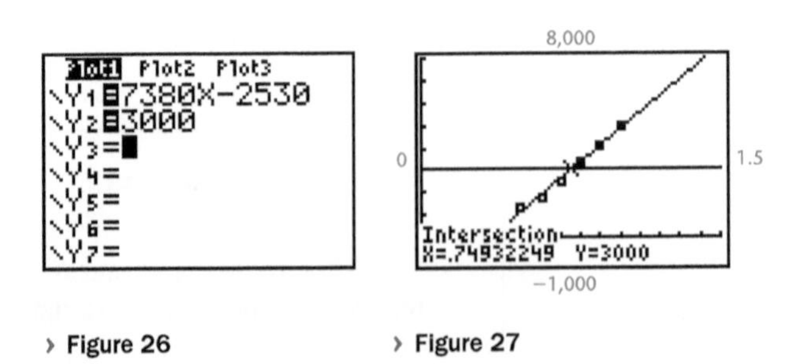

› Figure 26 › Figure 27

*On most graphing calculators, the values of the model displayed as L_3 in Figure 22 can be computed in a single operation by entering $y_1(L_1) \rightarrow L_3$ on the home screen.

From Figure 27 we see that $x = 0.75$ (to two significant digits) when $y = 3{,}000$. Thus, a $3,000 diamond should weigh approximately 0.75 carats.

MATCHED PROBLEM* 8

Prices for emerald-cut diamonds taken from an online trader are given in Table 2. Repeat Example 8 for this data set.

Table 2 Emerald-Cut Diamond Prices

Weight (carats)	Price
0.5	$1,350
0.6	$1,740
0.7	$2,610
0.8	$3,320
0.9	$4,150
1.0	$4,850

Source: www.tradeshop.com

The quantity of a product that consumers are willing to buy during some period depends on its price. Generally, the higher the price, the lower the demand; the lower the price, the greater the demand. Similarly, the quantity of a product that producers are willing to sell during some period also depends on the price. Generally, a producer will be willing to supply more of a product at higher prices and less of a product at lower prices. In Example 9 we use linear regression to analyze supply and demand data and construct linear models.

EXAMPLE 9

Supply and Demand

Table 3 contains supply and demand data for broccoli at various price levels. Express all answers in numbers rounded to three significant digits.

(A) Use the data in Table 3 and linear regression to find a linear supply model $p = f(s)$, where s is the supply (in thousand pounds) and p is the corresponding price of broccoli (in cents).

(B) Use the data in Table 3 and linear regression to find a linear demand model $p = g(d)$, where d is the demand (in thousand pounds) and p is the corresponding price of broccoli (in cents).

*Be certain to delete the old values in the lists L_1 and L_2 before you work Matched Problem 8. Select the list title and push CLEAR, then ENTER.

(C) Graph both functions in the same viewing window and discuss possible interpretations of any intersection points.

Table 3 Supply and Demand for Broccoli

Price (Cents)	Supply (Thousand lb)	Demand (Thousand lb)
76.8	853	1,680
81.5	1,010	1,440
85.2	1,040	1,470
87.5	957	1,280
97.2	1,280	1,040
104	1,620	1,130
105	1,600	1,010

SOLUTIONS

(A) First, we enter the data from Table 3 in the list editor of a graphing utility (Fig. 28). Next we select the linear regression command LinReg($ax + b$) followed by L_2, L_1 (Fig. 29) to make supply the independent variable and price the dependent variable. We also added the variable y_1, which automatically assigns the resulting regression equation into the equation editor as y_1, enabling us to view the graph without having to enter the equation manually. This produces the results shown in Figure 30. Thus, the linear model for the supply function is

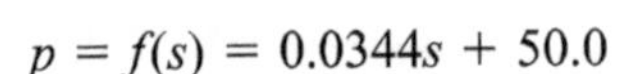

$$p = f(s) = 0.0344s + 50.0$$

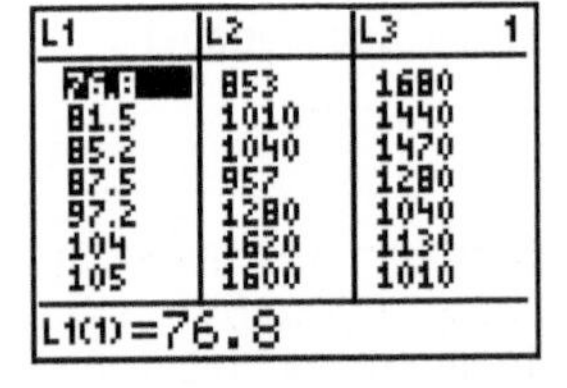

› Figure 28

› Figure 29

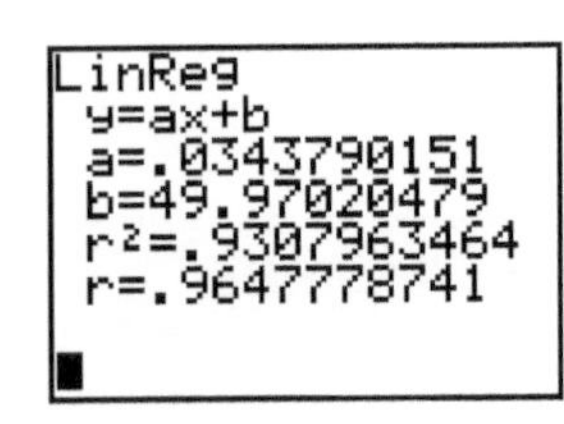

› Figure 30

To graph the supply data we use STAT PLOT, setting Xlist to L_2 and Ylist to L_1 (Fig. 31). Figure 32 shows a graph of the supply data and the supply model.

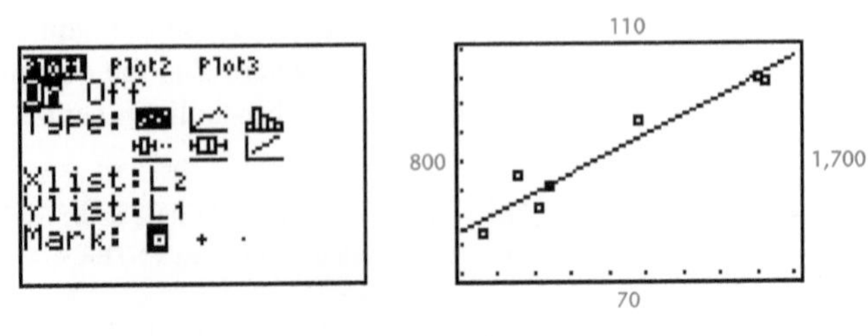

› Figure 31

› Figure 32

(B) This time we use the command LinReg($ax + b$) followed by L_3, L_1 to make demand the independent variable and price the dependent variable. This produces the results shown in Figure 33. Thus, the linear model for the demand function is

$$p = g(d) = -0.0416d + 145$$

To graph the demand data we use STAT PLOT, setting Xlist to L_3 and Ylist to L_1. Figure 34 shows a graph of the demand data and the demand model.

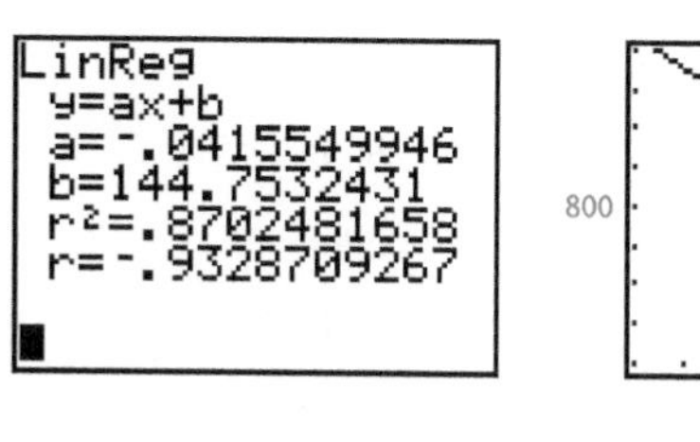

› Figure 33

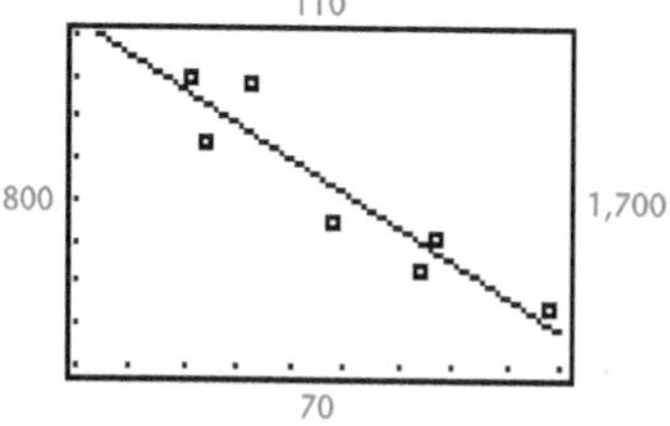

› Figure 34

(C) We graph both models in the same viewing window and use the INTERSECT command to find the intersection point (Fig. 35). The graphs intersect at $p = 93$ and $s = d = 1{,}250$. This point is called the **equilibrium point,** the value of p is called the **equilibrium price,** and the common value of s and d is called the **equilibrium quantity.** To help understand price fluctuations, suppose the current price of broccoli is 100 cents. We add the constant function $p = 100$ to the graph (Fig. 36).

Using the INTERSECT command (details omitted), we find that the constant price line intersects the demand curve at 1,080 thousand pounds and the supply curve at 1,450 thousand pounds. Because the supply at a price level of 100 is greater than the demand, the producers will lower their prices. Suppose the price drops to 80 cents per pound. Changing the constant function to $p = 80$ produces the graph in Figure 37. This time the constant price line intersects the demand curve at 1,560 thousand pounds and the supply curve at 872 thousand pounds. Now supply is less than demand and producers will raise their prices. If the producers set the price at $p = 93$ cents, then, as we saw in Figure 35, the supply and demand are equal.

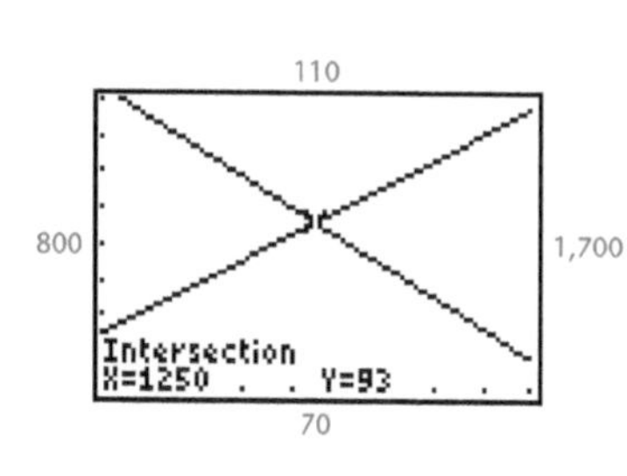

› Figure 35

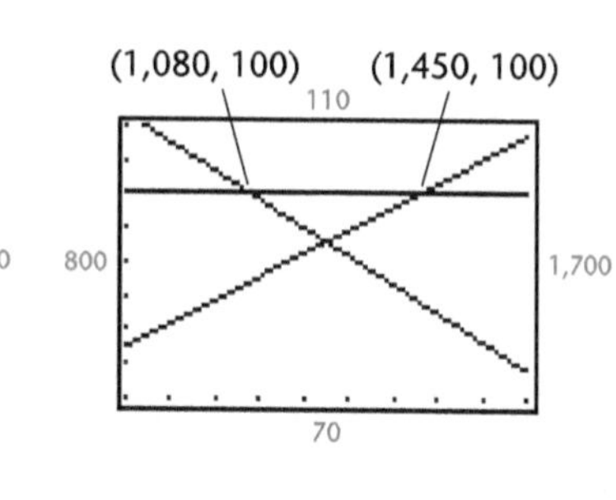

› Figure 36

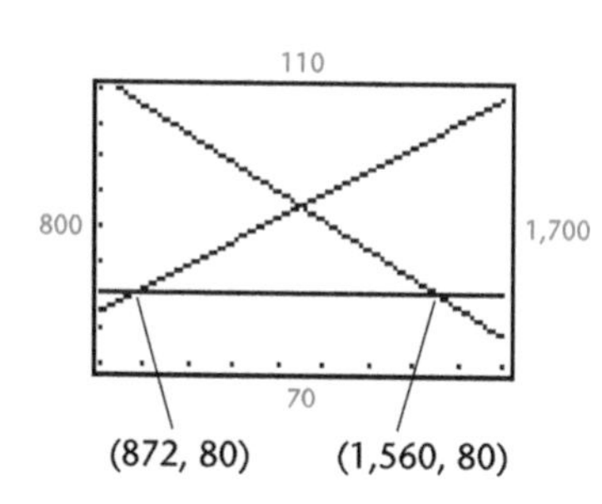

› Figure 37

MATCHED PROBLEM 9

Table 4 contains supply and demand data for cauliflower at various prices. Repeat Example 9 with these data.

Table 4 Supply and Demand for Cauliflower

Price (Cents)	Supply (Thousand lb)	Demand (Thousand lb)
26.5	583	653
27.1	607	629
27.2	596	635
27.4	627	631
27.5	604	638
28.1	661	610
28.6	682	599

ANSWERS TO MATCHED PROBLEMS

1. $x = -2$ **2.** $x = -\frac{20}{39} \approx -0.5128205$ **3.** No solution

4. $r = \frac{A - P}{Pt}$ $Pt \neq 0$ **5.** (A) $C(x) = 0.75x + 20$ (B) \$132.50 (C) 340 pretzels

6. 50 miles per hour **7.** 12.5 centiliters

8. (A) $y = 7{,}270x - 2{,}450$ (B) \$3,730; \$6,270 (C) 0.75 carats

9. (A) $p = 0.0180s + 16.3$ (B) $p = -0.0362d + 50.2$
(C) The price stabilizes at the equilibrium price of 27.6 cents.

2-2 Exercises

1. What exactly does it mean to solve an equation?
2. Explain why the following does not make sense: Solve the equation $P = 2l + 2w$.
3. Explain the difference between a conditional equation, an identity, and a contradiction.
4. Think of a real-world situation that would likely be modeled accurately with a linear function, and one that would not.
5. Explain how you could decide that an equation is an identity using a graphing calculator.
6. Explain how you could decide that an equation is a contradiction using a graphing calculator.
7. Why is it so important to check your answer when solving equations that contain fractions?
8. What is meant by the term "linear regression"?

Use the graphs of functions u and v in the figure to solve the equations in Problems 9–12. (Assume the graphs continue as indicated beyond the portions shown here.)

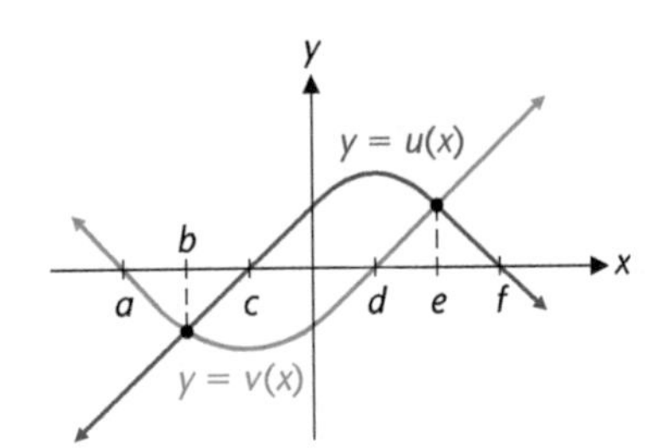

9. $u(x) = 0$

10. $v(x) = 0$

11. $u(x) = v(x)$

12. $u(x) - v(x) = 0$

In Problems 13–18, classify each equation as an identity, a conditional equation, or a contradiction. Solve each conditional equation.

13. $3(x - 2) - 2(x + 1) = x - 8$

14. $4(x - 1) - 2(x + 2) = 2x + 7$

15. $2(x - 1) - 3(2 - x) = 3x - 8$

16. $4(2 - x) + 2(x - 3) = 5x + 2$

17. $5(x + 2) - 3(x - 1) = 2x + 4$

18. $2(x + 1) + 3(2 - x) = 8 - x$

In Problems 19–30, solve the equation.

19. $10x - 7 = 4x - 25$

20. $11 + 3y = 5y - 5$

21. $3(x + 2) = 5(x - 6)$

22. $5x + 10(x - 2) = 40$

23. $5 + 4(t - 2) = 2(t + 7) + 1$

24. $5w - (7w - 4) - 2 = 5 - (3w + 2)$

25. $\frac{x}{2} - 2 = \frac{x}{5} + \frac{2}{5}$

26. $\frac{2x}{3} + \frac{1}{2} = \frac{3x}{2} - 2$

27. $3 + 5(x - 7) = 3x - 2(16 - x)$

28. $8x - 5(2 + x) = 2 + 3(x - 4)$

29. $5 - \frac{2x - 1}{4} = \frac{x + 2}{3}$

30. $\frac{x + 3}{4} - \frac{x - 4}{2} = \frac{3}{8}$

In Problems 31–46, solve the equation.

31. $\frac{7}{t} + 4 = \frac{2}{t}$

32. $\frac{9}{w} - 3 = \frac{2}{w}$

33. $\frac{1}{m} - \frac{1}{9} = \frac{4}{9} - \frac{2}{3m}$

34. $\frac{2}{3x} + \frac{1}{2} = \frac{4}{x} + \frac{4}{3}$

35. $(x - 2)(x + 3) = (x - 4)(x + 5)$

36. $(x - 2)(x - 4) = (x - 1)(x - 5)$

37. $(x + 2)(x - 3) = (x - 4)(x + 5)$

38. $(x - 2)(x + 4) = (x + 3)(x - 5)$

39. $(x - 2)^2 = (x - 1)(x + 2)$

40. $(x + 3)^2 = (x + 2)(x - 4)$

41. $\frac{2x}{x - 3} = 2 + \frac{6}{x - 3}$

42. $\frac{2x}{x + 4} = 2 - \frac{8}{x + 4}$

43. $\frac{2x}{x - 3} = 7 + \frac{4}{x - 3}$

44. $\frac{2x}{x + 4} = 7 - \frac{6}{x + 4}$

45. $\frac{2x}{x - 3} = 7 + \frac{6}{x - 3}$

46. $\frac{2x}{x + 4} = 7 - \frac{8}{x + 4}$

In Problems 47–56, solve for the indicated variable in terms of the other variables.

47. $P = 2l + 2w$ for w (perimeter of a rectangle)

48. $D = L + 2W + 2H$ for H (shipping dimensions)

49. $a_n = a_1 + (n - 1)d$ for d (arithmetic progressions)

50. $F = \frac{9}{5}C + 32$ for C (temperature scale)

51. $\frac{1}{f} = \frac{1}{d_1} + \frac{1}{d_2}$ for f (simple lens formula)

52. $\frac{1}{R} = \frac{1}{R_1} + \frac{1}{R_2}$ for R_1 (electric circuit)

53. $A = 2ab + 2ac + 2bc$ for a (surface area of a rectangular solid)

54. $A = 2ab + 2ac + 2bc$ for c

55. $y = \frac{2x - 3}{3x + 5}$ for x

56. $x = \frac{3y + 2}{y - 3}$ for y

57. Discuss the relationship between the graphs of $y_1 = x$ and $y_2 = \sqrt{x^2}$. What does this tell you about the equation $\sqrt{x^2} = x$?

58. Discuss the relationship between the graphs of $y_1 = |x|$ and $y_2 = \sqrt{x^2}$. What does this tell you about the equation $\sqrt{x^2} = |x|$?

Problems 59–66 refer to a rectangle with width W and length L (see the figure). Write a mathematical expression in terms of W and L for each of the verbal statements in Problems 59–66.

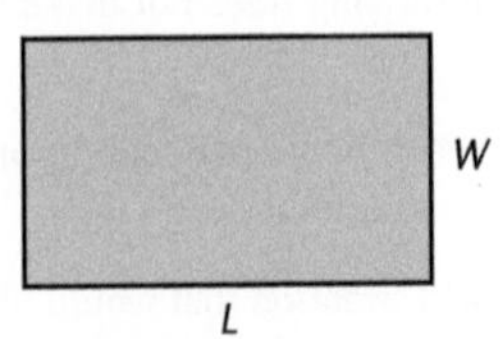

59. The length is twice the width.

60. The width is three times the length.

61. The width is half the length.

62. The length is one-third of the width.

63. The length is three more than the width.

64. The width is five less than the length.

65. The length is four less than the width.

66. The width is ten more than the length.

67. Use linear regression to fit a line to each of the following data sets. How are the graphs of the two functions related? How are the two functions related?

(A)

x	y
−3	−3
1	−1
5	1

(B)

x	y
−3	−3
−1	1
1	5

68. Repeat Problem 67 for the following data sets.

(A)

x	y
−5	−5
−1	0
3	5

(B)

x	y
−5	−5
0	−1
5	3

In Problems 69–72, solve for x.

69. $\dfrac{x - \dfrac{1}{x}}{1 + \dfrac{1}{x}} = 1$

70. $\dfrac{x - \dfrac{1}{x}}{x + 1 - \dfrac{2}{x}} = 1$

71. $\dfrac{x + 1 - \dfrac{2}{x}}{1 - \dfrac{1}{x}} = x + 2$

72. $\dfrac{x - 1 - \dfrac{2}{x}}{1 - \dfrac{2}{x}} = x$

73. Find three consecutive integers whose sum is 84.

74. Find four consecutive integers whose sum is 182.

75. Find four consecutive even integers so that the sum of the first three is 2 more than twice the fourth.

76. Find three consecutive even integers so that the first plus twice the second is twice the third.

77. Find the dimensions of a rectangle if the perimeter is 60 inches and the length is twice the width.

78. Find the dimensions of a rectangle if the perimeter is 60 inches and the length is half the width.

APPLICATIONS

79. COST ANALYSIS A doughnut shop has a fixed cost of $124 per day and a variable cost of $0.12 per doughnut. Find the total daily cost of producing x doughnuts. How many doughnuts can be produced for a total daily cost of $250?

80. COST ANALYSIS A small company manufactures picnic tables. The weekly fixed cost is $1,200 and the variable cost is $45 per table. Find the total weekly cost of producing x picnic tables. How many picnic tables can be produced for a total weekly cost of $4,800?

81. SALES COMMISSIONS One employee of a computer store is paid a base salary of $2,150 a month plus an 8% commission on all sales over $7,000 during the month. How much must the employee sell in 1 month to earn a total of $3,170 for the month?

82. SALES COMMISSIONS A second employee of the computer store in Problem 81 is paid a base salary of $1,175 a month plus a 5% commission on all sales during the month.
(A) How much must this employee sell in 1 month to earn a total of $3,170 for the month?
(B) Determine the sales level at which both employees receive the same monthly income. If employees can select either of these payment methods, how would you advise an employee to make this selection?

83. COMPETITIVE ROWING A two-woman rowing team can row 1,200 meters with the current in a river in the same amount of time it takes them to row 1,000 meters against that same current. In each case, their average rowing speed without the effect of the current is 3 meters per second. Find the speed of the current.

84. COMPETITIVE ROWING The winners of the men's 1,000-meter double sculls event in the 2006 Asian games rowed at an average of 11.3 miles per hour. If this team were to row this speed for a half mile with a current in 80% of the time they were able to row that same distance against the current, what would be the speed of the current?

85. AERONAUTICS The cruising speed of an airplane is 150 miles per hour (relative to the ground). You wish to hire the plane for a 3-hour sightseeing trip. You instruct the pilot to fly north as far as he can and still return to the airport at the end of the allotted time.
(A) How far north should the pilot fly if the wind is blowing from the north at 30 miles per hour?
(B) How far north should the pilot fly if there is no wind?

86. NAVIGATION Suppose you are at a river resort and rent a motor boat for 5 hours starting at 7 A.M. You are told that the boat will travel at 8 miles per hour upstream and 12 miles per hour returning. You decide that you would like to go as far up the river as you can and still be back at noon. At what time should you turn back, and how far from the resort will you be at that time?

87. EARTHQUAKES An earthquake emits a primary wave and a secondary wave. Near the surface of the Earth the primary wave travels at about 5 miles per second, and the secondary wave travels at about 3 miles per second. From the time lag between the two waves arriving at a given seismic station, it is possible to estimate the distance to the quake. Suppose a station measures a time difference of 12 seconds between the arrival of the two waves. How far is the earthquake from the station? (The *epicenter* can be located by obtaining distance bearings at three or more stations.)

88. SOUND DETECTION A ship using sound-sensing devices above and below water recorded a surface explosion 39 seconds sooner on its underwater device than on its above-water device. If sound travels in air at about 1,100 feet per second and in water at about 5,000 feet per second, how far away was the explosion?

89. CHEMISTRY How many gallons of distilled water must be mixed with 50 gallons of 30% alcohol solution to obtain a 25% solution?

90. CHEMISTRY How many gallons of hydrochloric acid must be added to 12 gallons of a 30% solution to obtain a 40% solution?

91. CHEMISTRY A chemist mixes distilled water with a 90% solution of sulfuric acid to produce a 50% solution. If 5 liters of distilled water is used, how much 50% solution is produced?

92. CHEMISTRY A fuel oil distributor has 120,000 gallons of fuel with 0.9% sulfur content, which exceeds pollution control standards of 0.8% sulfur content. How many gallons of fuel oil with a 0.3% sulfur content must be added to the 120,000 gallons to obtain fuel oil that complies with the pollution control standards?

93. EARTH SCIENCE In 1984, the Soviets led the world in drilling the deepest hole in the Earth's crust—more than 12 kilometers deep. They found that below 3 kilometers the temperature T increased 2.5°C for each additional 100 meters of depth.
(A) If the temperature at 3 kilometers is 30°C and x is the depth of the hole in kilometers, write an equation using x that will give the temperature T in the hole at any depth beyond 3 kilometers.
(B) What would the temperature be at 15 kilometers? (The temperature limit for their drilling equipment was about 300°C.)
(C) At what depth (in kilometers) would the temperature reach 280°C?

94. AERONAUTICS Because air is not as dense at high altitudes, planes require a higher ground speed to become airborne. A rule of thumb is 3% more ground speed per 1,000 feet of elevation, assuming no wind and no change in air temperature. (Compute numerical answers to three significant digits.)
(A) Let
V_s = Takeoff ground speed at sea level for a particular plane (in miles per hour)
A = Altitude above sea level (in thousands of feet)
V = Takeoff ground speed at altitude A for the same plane (in miles per hour)
Write a formula relating these three quantities.
(B) What takeoff ground speed would be required at Lake Tahoe airport (6,400 feet), if takeoff ground speed at San Francisco airport (sea level) is 120 miles per hour?
(C) If a landing strip at a Colorado Rockies hunting lodge (8,500 feet) requires a takeoff ground speed of 125 miles per hour, what would be the takeoff ground speed in Los Angeles (sea level)?
(D) If the takeoff ground speed at sea level is 135 miles per hour and the takeoff ground speed at a mountain resort is 155 miles per hour, what is the altitude of the mountain resort in thousands of feet?

DATA ANALYSIS AND LINEAR REGRESSION

In Problems 95–100, use linear regression to construct linear models of the form $y = ax + b$.

95. COLLEGE TUITION Find a linear model for the public college tuition data given in Table 5, where x is years after 1999 and y is the average tuition in dollars. Round a and b to the nearest dollar. Use your model to predict the average public college tuition in 2008, and to estimate when the average public college tuition will reach $15,000 per year.

Table 5 Average Annual Tuition at Public and Private Colleges

School Year Ending	Public	Private
1999	$7,107	$19,368
2000	$7,310	$20,186
2001	$7,586	$21,368
2002	$8,022	$22,413
2003	$8,502	$23,340
2004	$9,249	$24,636
2005	$9,877	$26,025

Source: www.infoplease.com

96. COLLEGE TUITION Find a linear model for the private college tuition data given in Table 5, where x is years after 1999 and y is the average tuition in dollars. Round a and b to the nearest dollar. Use your model to predict the average private college tuition in 2008, and to estimate when the average private college tuition will reach $35,000 per year.

97. OLYMPIC GAMES Find a linear model $y = ax + b$ for the men's 100-meter freestyle data given in Table 6 where x is years since 1968 and y is winning time (in seconds). Do the same for the women's 100-meter freestyle data (round to three decimal places). Do these models indicate that the women will eventually catch up with the men? If so, when? Do you think this will actually occur?

Table 6 Winning Times in Olympic Swimming Events

	100-Meter Freestyle		200-Meter Backstroke	
	Men (seconds)	Women (seconds)	Men (minutes: seconds)	Women (minutes: seconds)
1968	52.20	60.00	2:09.60	2:24.80
1972	51.22	58.59	2:02.82	2:19.19
1976	49.99	55.65	1:59.19	2:13.43
1980	50.40	54.79	2:01.93	2:11.77
1984	49.80	55.92	2:00.23	2:12.38
1988	48.63	54.93	1:59.37	2:09.29
1992	49.02	54.65	1:58.47	2:07.06
1996	48.74	54.50	1.58.54	2:07.83
2000	48.30	53.83	1:56.76	2:08.16
2004	48.17	53.84	1:54.95	2:09.19

Source: www.infoplease.com

98. OLYMPIC GAMES Find a linear model $y = ax + b$ for the men's 200-meter backstroke data given in Table 6, where x is years since 1968 and y is winning time (in seconds). Do the same for the women's 200-meter backstroke data (round to three decimal places). Do these models indicate that the women will eventually catch up with the men? If so, when? Do you think this will actually occur?

99. SUPPLY AND DEMAND Table 7 contains price–supply data and price–demand data for corn. Find a linear model $y = ax + b$ for the price–supply data where x is price (in dollars) and y is supply (in billions of bushels). Do the same for the price–demand data. Find the equilibrium price for corn.

Table 7 Supply and Demand for U.S. Corn

Price $/bu	Supply (billion bu)	Price $/bu	Demand (billion bu)
2.15	6.29	2.07	9.78
2.29	7.27	2.15	9.35
2.36	7.53	2.22	8.47
2.48	7.93	2.34	8.12
2.47	8.12	2.39	7.76
2.55	8.24	2.47	6.98
2.71	9.23	2.59	5.57

Source: www.usda.gov/nass/pubs/histdata.htm

100. SUPPLY AND DEMAND Table 8 contains price–supply data and price–demand data for soybeans. Find a linear model $y = ax + b$ for the price–supply data where x is supply (in billions of bushels) and y is price (in dollars). Do the same for the price–demand data. Find the equilibrium price for soybeans.

Table 8 Supply and Demand for U.S. Soybeans

Price $/bu	Supply (billion bu)	Price $/bu	Demand (billion bu)
5.15	1.55	4.93	2.60
5.79	1.86	5.48	2.40
5.88	1.94	5.71	2.18
6.07	2.08	6.07	2.05
6.15	2.15	6.40	1.95
6.25	2.27	6.66	1.85
6.65	2.53	7.25	1.67

Source: www.usda.gov/nass/pubs/histdata.htm

2-3 Quadratic Functions

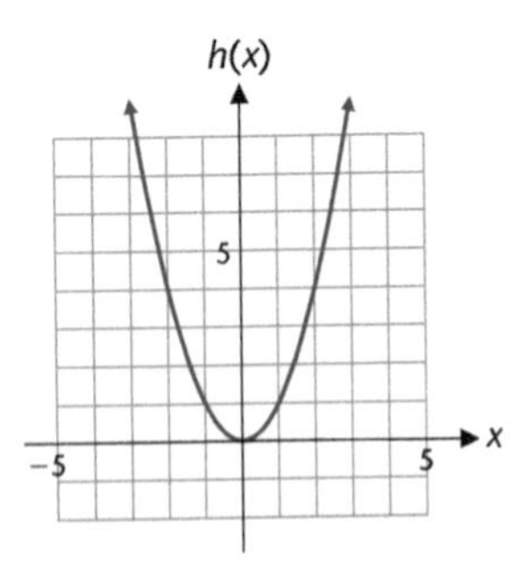

› **Figure 1** Squaring function $h(x) = x^2$.

The graph of the squaring function $h(x) = x^2$ is shown in Figure 1. Notice that h is an even function; that is, the graph of h is symmetrical with respect to the y axis. Also, the lowest point on the graph is (0, 0). Let's explore the effect of applying a sequence of basic transformations to the graph of h. (A brief review of Section 1-4 would be helpful at this point.)

››› EXPLORE-DISCUSS 1

Indicate how the graph of each function is related to the graph of $h(x) = x^2$. Discuss the symmetry of the graphs and find the highest or lowest point, whichever exists, on each graph.

(A) $f(x) = (x - 3)^2 - 7 = x^2 - 6x + 2$

(B) $g(x) = 0.5(x + 2)^2 + 3 = 0.5x^2 + 2x + 5$

(C) $m(x) = -(x - 4)^2 + 8 = -x^2 + 8x - 8$

(D) $n(x) = -3(x + 1)^2 - 1 = -3x^2 - 6x - 4$

› Defining Quadratic Functions

Graphing the functions in Explore-Discuss 1 produces figures similar in shape to the graph of the squaring function in Figure 1. These figures are called *parabolas*. The functions that produced these parabolas are examples of the important class of *quadratic functions*, which we will now define.

› DEFINITION 1 Quadratic Functions

If a, b, and c are real numbers with $a \neq 0$, then the function

$$f(x) = ax^2 + bx + c$$

is called a **quadratic function** and its graph is called a **parabola.*** This is known as the **general form** of a quadratic function.

*A more general definition of a parabola that is independent of any coordinate system is given in Section 8-1.

Because the expression $ax^2 + bx + c$ represents a real number no matter what number we substitute for x,

the domain of a quadratic function is the set of all real numbers.

We will discuss methods for determining the range of a quadratic function later in this section. Typical graphs of quadratic functions are illustrated in Figure 2.

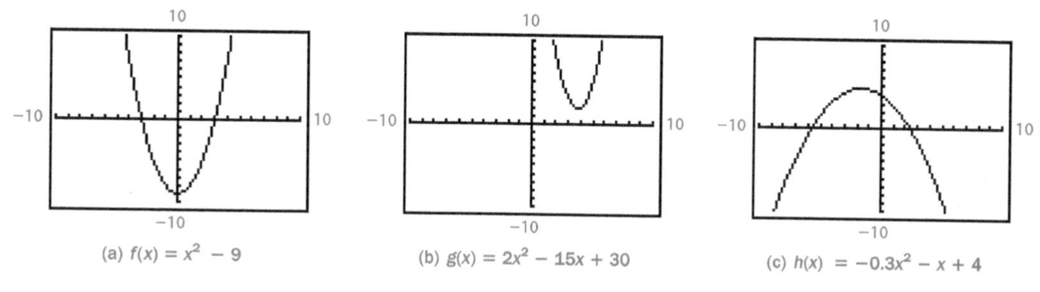

› **Figure 2** Graphs of quadratic functions.

› The Vertex Form of a Quadratic Function

We will begin our detailed study of quadratic functions by examining some in a special form, which we will call the **vertex form:***

$$f(x) = a(x - h)^2 + k$$

We'll see where the name comes from in a bit. For now, refer to Explore-Discuss 1. Any function of this form is a transformation of the basic squaring function $g(x) = x^2$, so we can use transformations to analyze the graph.

EXAMPLE 1 The Graph of a Quadratic Function

Use transformations of $g(x) = x^2$ to graph the function $f(x) = 2(x - 3)^2 + 4$. Use your graph to determine the graphical significance of the constants 2, 3, and 4 in this function.

SOLUTION

Multiplying by 2 vertically stretches the graph by a factor of 2. Subtracting 3 inside the square moves the graph 3 units to the right. Adding 4 outside the square moves the graph 4 units up. The graph of f is shown in Figure 3, along with the graph of $g(x) = x^2$.

*In Problem 63 of Exercises 2-3, you will be asked to show that any function of this form fits the definition of quadratic function in Definition 1.

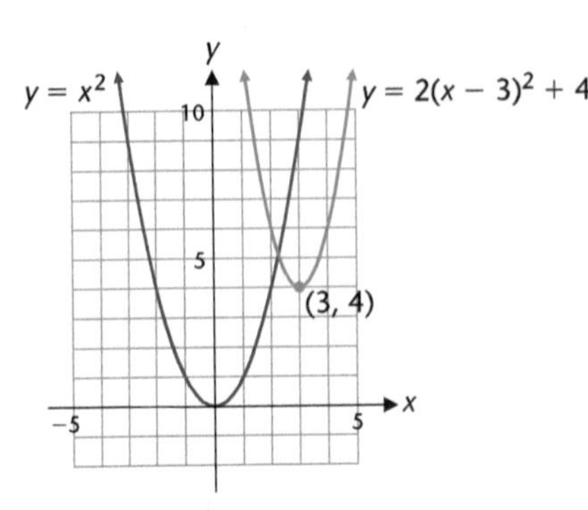

› Figure 3

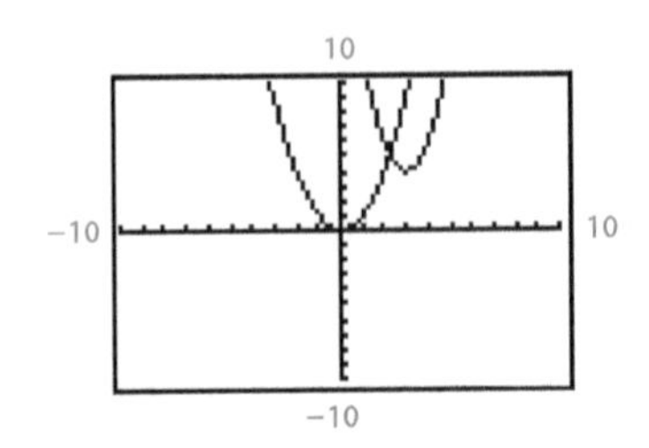

› Figure 4

The lowest point on the graph of f is (3, 4), so $h = 3$ and $k = 4$ determine the key point where the graph changes direction. The constant $a = 2$ affects the width of the parabola. Our results are checked by graphing f and $g(x) = x^2$ with a graphing calculator (Fig. 4).

MATCHED PROBLEM 1

Use transformations of $g(x) = x^2$ to graph the function $f(x) = -\frac{1}{2}(x - 2)^2 + 5$. Use your graph to determine the significance of the constants $-\frac{1}{2}$, 2, and 5 in this function.

Explore-Discuss 2 will help to clarify the significance of the constants a, h, and k in the form $f(x) = a(x - h)^2 + k$.

››› EXPLORE-DISCUSS 2

Explore the effect of changing the constants a, h, and k on the graph of $f(x) = a(x - h)^2 + k$.

(A) Let $a = 1$ and $h = 5$. Graph function f for $k = -4, 0$, and 3 simultaneously in the same viewing window. Explain the effect of changing k on the graph of f.

(B) Let $a = 1$ and $k = 2$. Graph function f for $h = -4, 0$, and 5 simultaneously in the same viewing window. Explain the effect of changing h on the graph of f.

(C) Let $h = 5$ and $k = -2$. Graph function f for $a = 0.25, 1$, and 3 simultaneously in the same viewing window. Then graph function f for $a = 1, -1$, and -0.25 simultaneously in the same viewing window. Explain the effect of changing a on the graph of f.

(D) Can all quadratic functions of the form $y = ax^2 + bx + c$ be rewritten as $a(x - h)^2 + k$?

Every parabola has a point where the graph reaches a maximum or minimum and changes direction. We will call that point the **vertex** of the parabola. Finding the vertex is key to many of the things we'll do with parabolas. Example 1 and Explore-Discuss 2 demonstrate that *if a quadratic function is in the form* $f(x) = a(x - h)^2 + k$, *then the vertex is the point* (h, k).

Next, notice that the graph of $h(x) = x^2$ is symmetric about the y axis. As a result, the transformation $f(x) = 2(x - 3)^2 + 4$ is symmetric about the vertical line $x = 3$ (which runs through the vertex). We will call this vertical line of symmetry the **axis,** or **axis of symmetry** of a parabola. If the page containing the graph of f is folded along the line $x = 3$, the two halves of the graph would match exactly.

Finally, Explore-Discuss 2 illustrates the significance of the constant a in $f(x) = a(x - h)^2 + k$. If a is positive, the graph has a minimum and opens upward. But if a is negative, the graph will be a vertical reflection of $h(x) = x^2$ and will have a maximum and open downward. The size of a determines the width of the parabola: if $|a| > 1$, the graph is narrower than $h(x) = x^2$, and if $|a| < 1$, it is wider.

These properties of a quadratic function in vertex form are summarized next.

PROPERTIES OF A QUADRATIC FUNCTION AND ITS GRAPH

Given a quadratic function in vertex form

$$f(x) = a(x - h)^2 + k \qquad a \neq 0$$

we summarize general properties as follows:

1. The graph of f is a parabola:

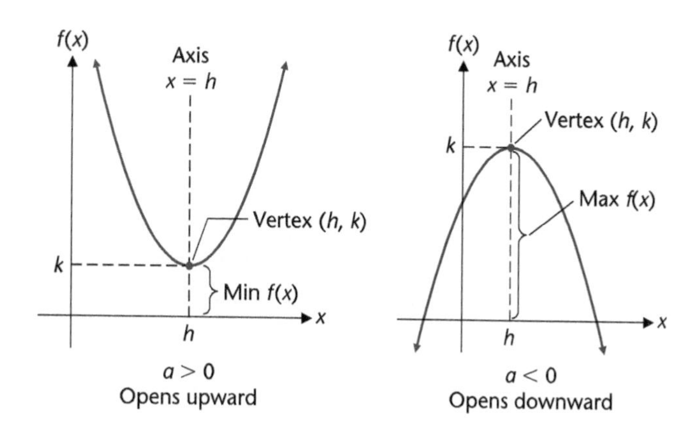

2. Vertex: (h, k) (parabola rises on one side of the vertex and falls on the other).
3. Axis (of symmetry): $x = h$ (parallel to y axis).
4. $f(h) = k$ is the minimum if $a > 0$ and the maximum if $a < 0$.
5. Domain: all real numbers; range: $(-\infty, k]$ if $a < 0$ or $[k, \infty)$ if $a > 0$.
6. The graph of f is the graph of $g(x) = ax^2$ translated horizontally h units and vertically k units.

EXAMPLE 2 Analyzing a Quadratic Function

For the following quadratic function, analyze the graph, and check your results with a graphing calculator:

$$f(x) = -0.5(x + 1)^2 + 5.5$$

SOLUTION

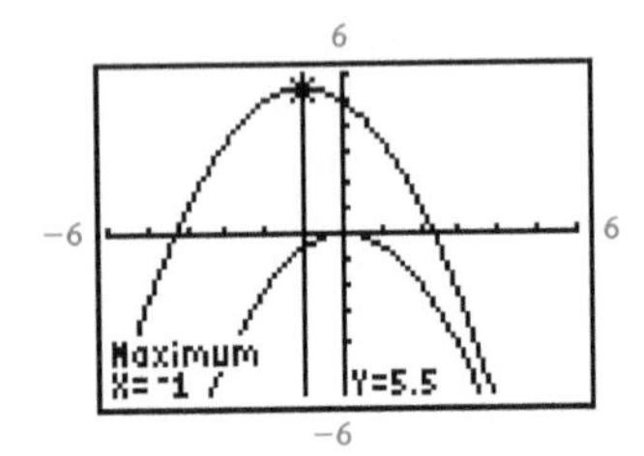

› Figure 5

We can rewrite the function as $f(x) = -0.5[x - (-1)]^2 + 5.5$. Comparing this equation to $y = a(x - h)^2 + k$, we see that $a = -0.5$, $h = -1$, and $k = 5.5$. Therefore, the vertex is $(-1, 5.5)$, the axis of symmetry is $x = -1$, the maximum value is $f(-1) = 5.5$, and the range is $(-\infty, 5.5]$. The function f is increasing on $(-\infty, -1]$ and decreasing on $[-1, \infty)$. The graph of f is the graph of $g(x) = -0.5x^2$ shifted to the left one unit and upward five and one-half units. To check these results, we graph f and g simultaneously in the same viewing window, use the MAXIMUM command to locate the vertex, and add the graph of the axis of symmetry (Fig. 5).

MATCHED PROBLEM 2

For the following quadratic function, analyze the graph, and check your results with a graphing calculator:

$$f(x) = -(x - 1.5)^2 + 1.25$$

››› CAUTION ›››

Be careful with the sign when finding the first coordinate of a vertex. The generic vertex form has $(x - h)^2$ in it, so when we have $(x + 1)^2$, the first coordinate of the vertex is actually *negative* 1.

› Completing the Square

Now that we can recognize the properties of a quadratic function in vertex form, the obvious question is "What if a quadratic function is *not* in vertex form?" More often than not, the quadratic functions we encounter will be in the form $f(x) = ax^2 + bx + c$. The method of *completing the square* can be used to find the vertex form of such a quadratic function. We'll also find this process useful in solving equations later in the chapter.

››› EXPLORE-DISCUSS 3

Replace ? in each of the following with a number that makes the equation valid.

(A) $(x + 1)^2 = x^2 + 2x + ?$ **(B)** $(x + 2)^2 = x^2 + 4x + ?$

(C) $(x + 3)^2 = x^2 + 6x + ?$ **(D)** $(x + 4)^2 = x^2 + 8x + ?$

Replace ? in each of the following with a number that makes the expression a perfect square of the form $(x + h)^2$.

(E) $x^2 + 10x + ?$ **(F)** $x^2 + 12x + ?$

(G) $x^2 + bx + ?$

Given the quadratic expression

$$x^2 + bx$$

what number should be added to this expression to make it a perfect square? To find out, consider the square of the following expression:

$$(x + m)^2 = x^2 + 2mx + m^2$$ m^2 is the square of one-half the coefficient of x.

We see that the third term on the right side of the equation is the square of one-half the coefficient of x in the second term on the right; that is, m^2 is the square of $\frac{1}{2}(2m)$. This observation leads to the following rule:

› COMPLETING THE SQUARE

To **complete the square** of the quadratic expression

$$x^2 + bx$$ Leading coefficient 1

add the square of one-half the coefficient of x; that is, add

$$\left(\frac{b}{2}\right)^2 \quad \text{or} \quad \frac{b^2}{4}$$

The resulting expression can be factored as a perfect square:

$$x^2 + bx + \left(\frac{b}{2}\right)^2 = \left(x + \frac{b}{2}\right)^2$$

EXAMPLE 3 Completing the Square

Complete the square for each of the following:

(A) $x^2 - 6x$ (B) $x^2 + \frac{4}{5}x$ (C) $x^2 - \frac{3}{4}x$

SOLUTIONS

(A) $x^2 - 6x$

$x^2 - 6x + 9 = (x - 3)^2$ Add $\left[\frac{1}{2}(-6)\right]^2$; that is, 9.

(B) $x^2 + \frac{4}{5}x$

$x^2 + \frac{4}{5}x + \frac{4}{25} = \left(x + \frac{2}{5}\right)^2$ Add $\left(\frac{1}{2} \cdot \frac{4}{5}\right)^2$; that is, $\frac{4}{25}$.

(C) $x^2 - \frac{3}{4}x$

$x^2 - \frac{3}{4}x + \frac{9}{64} = \left(x - \frac{3}{8}\right)^2$ Add $\left(\frac{1}{2} \cdot \frac{-3}{4}\right)^2$; that is, $\frac{9}{64}$.

Note: In each case, the quadratic expression ends up factoring as (x + half the coefficient of the x term).

MATCHED PROBLEM 3

Complete the square for each of the following:

(A) $x^2 - 8x$ (B) $x^2 + \frac{7}{4}x$ (C) $x^2 - \frac{2}{3}x$

It is important to note that the rule for completing the square applies to only quadratic expressions in which the coefficient of x^2 is 1. We'll see how to overcome this limitation later.

› Finding the Equation of a Parabola

EXAMPLE 4 Finding the Vertex Form of a Parabola

Find the vertex form of $f(x) = x^2 - 8x + 4$, then write the vertex and axis.

SOLUTION

We will separate $x^2 - 8x$ with parentheses, then use completing the square to factor part of f as a perfect square.

$$\begin{aligned} f(x) &= x^2 - 8x + 4 && \text{Group } x^2 - 8x \text{ together.} \\ &= (x^2 - 8x) + 4 && \text{Find the number needed to complete the square.} \\ &= (x^2 - 8x + ?) + 4 && \left[\tfrac{1}{2}(-8)\right]^2 = 16\text{; add 16, then subtract it at the end.} \\ &= (x^2 - 8x + 16) + 4 - 16 && \text{Factor parentheses; combine like terms.} \\ &= (x - 4)^2 - 12 && f \text{ is now in vertex form.} \end{aligned}$$

The vertex form is $f(x) = (x - 4)^2 - 12$. The vertex is $(4, -12)$ and the axis is $x = 4$.

MATCHED PROBLEM 4

Find the vertex form of $g(x) = x^2 + 10x - 1$, then write the vertex and axis.

When the coefficient of x^2 is not 1, the procedure is just a bit more complicated.

EXAMPLE 5 Finding the Vertex Form of a Parabola

Find the vertex form of $f(x) = -3x^2 + 8x - 5$. Find the vertex and axis, then describe the graph verbally and check your answer with a graphing calculator.

SOLUTION

We need a coefficient of 1 on the x^2, so after grouping the first two terms, we'll factor out -3.

$$\begin{aligned} f(x) &= (-3x^2 + 8x) - 5 && \text{Factor } -3 \text{ out of the first two terms.} \\ &= -3\left(x^2 - \frac{8}{3}x\right) - 5 && \left(\frac{1}{2}\cdot\frac{-8}{3}\right)^2 = \frac{16}{9}\text{; add this number inside the parentheses.} \\ &= -3\left(x^2 - \frac{8}{3}x + \frac{16}{9}\right) - 5 + ? && \text{Because of the } -3 \text{ factor, we actually subtracted } \frac{16}{3}\text{, so we also add } \frac{16}{3}. \\ &= -3\left(x^2 - \frac{8}{3}x + \frac{16}{9}\right) - 5 + \frac{16}{3} && \text{Factor the parentheses; combine like terms.} \\ &= -3\left(x - \frac{4}{3}\right)^2 + \frac{1}{3} && f \text{ is in vertex form.} \end{aligned}$$

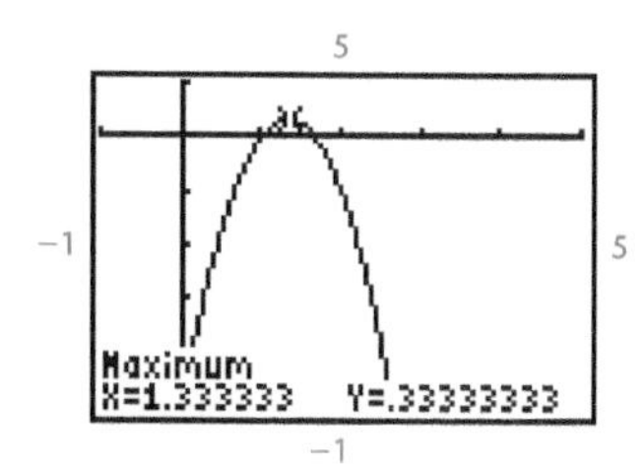

› Figure 6

The vertex is $(\frac{4}{3}, \frac{1}{3})$ and the axis is $x = \frac{4}{3}$. Because $a = -3$ is negative, the parabola opens downward and has a maximum value of $\frac{1}{3}$. The function f is increasing on $(-\infty, \frac{4}{3}]$ and decreasing on $[\frac{4}{3}, \infty)$. The range of f is $(-\infty, \frac{1}{3}]$. The graph is shown in Figure 6.

MATCHED PROBLEM 5

Repeat Example 5 for $g(x) = -2x^2 - 7x + 3$.

››› CAUTION ›››

When completing the square on a quadratic function with $a \neq 1$, the number that you add or subtract at the end will be different from the number you added inside the parentheses.

A key observation based on Examples 4 and 5 will help us to find the vertex of a parabola quickly, without completing the square. In both Example 4 and 5, the first coordinate of the vertex worked out to be $-\frac{b}{2a}$, where the function f was written in the form $f(x) = ax^2 + bx + c$. This provides a simple way to find the vertex of a parabola in that form. (For a proof of this fact, see Problem 64 in Exercises 2-3.)

FINDING THE VERTEX OF A PARABOLA

When a quadratic function is written in the form $f(x) = ax^2 + bx + c$, the first coordinate of the vertex can be found using the formula

$$x = -\frac{b}{2a}$$

The second coordinate can then be found by evaluating f at the first coordinate.

EXAMPLE 6

Finding the Vertex of a Parabola

Find the vertex of the parabola $f(x) = -5x^2 + 30x - 2$.

SOLUTION

The first coordinate is given by

$$x = -\frac{b}{2a} = -\frac{30}{-10} = 3$$

The second coordinate is $f(3)$:

$$f(3) = -5(3)^2 + 30(3) - 2 = 43$$

The vertex is (3, 43).

MATCHED PROBLEM 6

Find the vertex of the parabola $g(x) = 2x^2 - 16x + 10$.

So far we've used the vertex form of a parabola to help us learn all about the graphs of quadratic functions. But it can also be used for something equally as important, especially when it comes to mathematical modeling: finding the equation of a parabola.

EXAMPLE 7 Finding the Equation of a Parabola

Find an equation for the parabola whose graph is shown in Figure 7. Write your answer in the form $y = ax^2 + bx + c$.

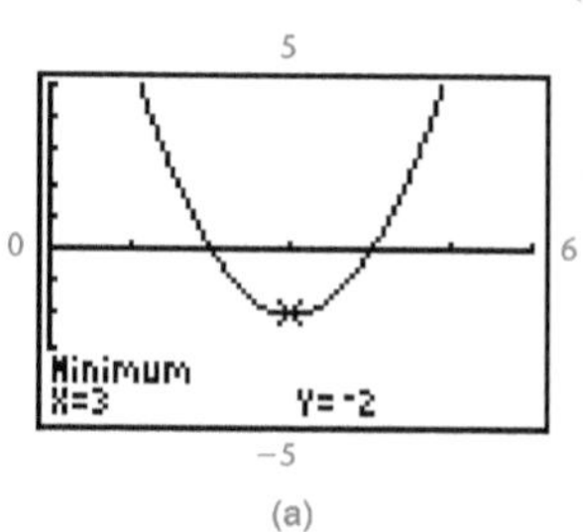

(a)

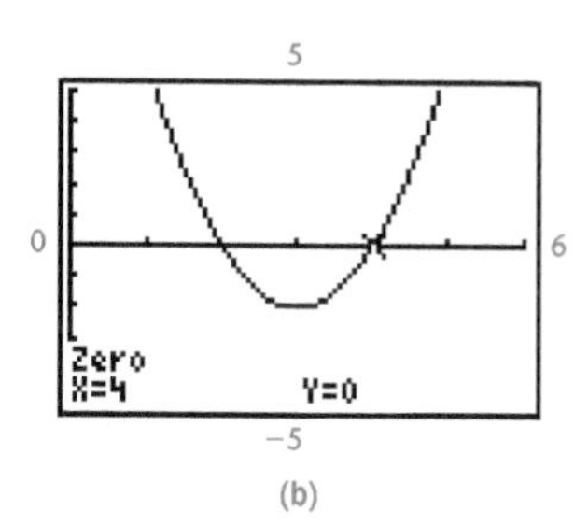

(b)

› **Figure 7**

SOLUTION

Figure 7a shows that the vertex of the parabola is $(h, k) = (3, -2)$. So the vertex form of the parabola must look like

$$f(x) = a(x - 3)^2 - 2 \tag{1}$$

All that remains is to find a. Figure 7b shows that the point $(4, 0)$ is on the graph of f, so $f(4) = 0$. According to equation (1),

$$\begin{aligned} f(4) &= a(4 - 3)^2 - 2 \\ &= a - 2 \end{aligned}$$

Since 0 and $a - 2$ are both $f(4)$, they must be equal:

$$\begin{aligned} a - 2 &= 0 \\ a &= 2 \end{aligned}$$

The equation for the parabola is

$$\begin{aligned} f(x) &= 2(x - 3)^2 - 2 \\ &= 2(x^2 - 6x + 9) - 2 \\ &= 2x^2 - 12x + 16 \end{aligned}$$

MATCHED PROBLEM 7

Find the equation of the parabola with vertex $(2, 4)$ and y intercept $(0, 2)$. Write your answer in the form $y = ax^2 + bx + c$.

EXAMPLE 8 Finding the Equation of a Parabola

Find an equation for the parabola whose graph is shown in Figure 8. Write your answer in the form $y = ax^2 + bx + c$.

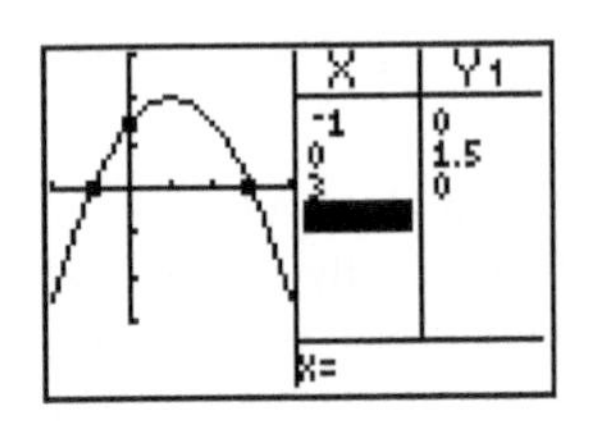

› Figure 8

SOLUTION

Let

$$f(x) = a(x - h)^2 + k$$

Because $f(-1) = f(3)$, the axis of symmetry $x = h$ must contain the midpoint of the interval $[-1, 3]$. That is,

$$h = \frac{-1 + 3}{2} = 1 \qquad \text{and} \qquad f(x) = a(x - 1)^2 + k$$

Now we can use either x intercept to find a relationship between a and k. We choose $f(-1) = 0$.

$$\begin{aligned} f(-1) = a(-1 - 1)^2 + k &= 0 \\ 4a + k &= 0 \\ k &= -4a \end{aligned}$$

Now we can write

$$f(x) = a(x - 1)^2 - 4a$$

and use the y intercept to find a. (We can't use the other x intercept to find a. Try it to see why.)

$$\begin{aligned} f(0) = a(0 - 1)^2 - 4a &= 1.5 \\ a - 4a &= 1.5 \\ -3a &= 1.5 \\ a &= -0.5 \end{aligned}$$

So the equation is

$$f(x) = -0.5(x - 1)^2 + 2 = -0.5x^2 + x + 1.5$$

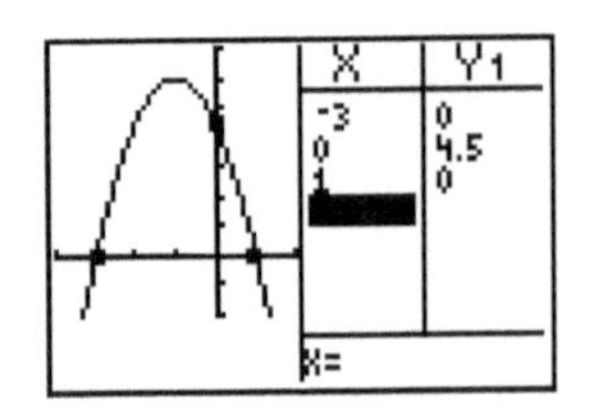

› Figure 9

MATCHED PROBLEM 8

Find an equation for the parabola whose graph is shown in Figure 9. Write your answer in the form $y = ax^2 + bx + c$.

› Modeling with Quadratic Functions

We now look at several applications that can be modeled using quadratic functions.

EXAMPLE 9 Maximum Area

A dairy farm has a barn that is 150 feet long and 75 feet wide. The owner has 240 feet of fencing and wishes to use all of it in the construction of two identical adjacent outdoor pens, with part of the long side of the barn as one side of the pens, and a common fence between the two (Fig. 10). The owner wants the pens to be as large as possible.

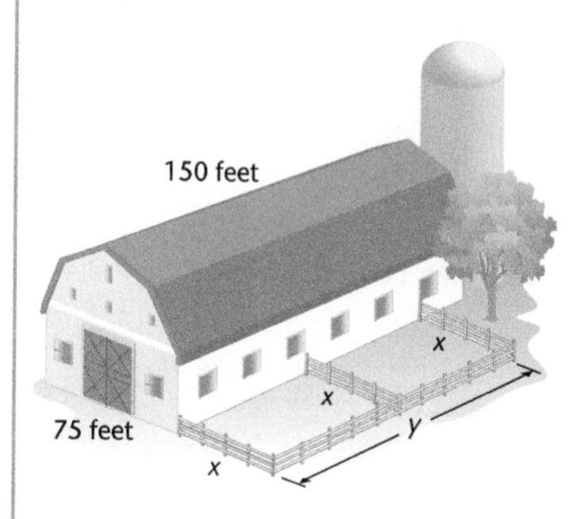

› **Figure 10**

(A) Construct a mathematical model for the combined area of both pens in the form of a function $A(x)$ (see Fig. 10) and state the domain of A.

(B) Find the value of x that produces the maximum combined area.

(C) Find the dimensions and the area of each pen.

SOLUTIONS

(A) The combined area of the two pens is

$$A = xy$$

Adding up the lengths of all four segments of fence, we find that building the pens will require $3x + y$ feet of fencing. We have 240 feet of fence to use, so

$$3x + y = 240$$
$$y = 240 - 3x$$

Because the distances x and y must be nonnegative, x and y must satisfy $x \geq 0$ and $y = 240 - 3x \geq 0$. It follows that $0 \leq x \leq 80$. Substituting for y in the combined area equation, we have the following model for this problem:

$$A(x) = x(240 - 3x) = 240x - 3x^2 \qquad 0 \leq x \leq 80$$

(B) Algebraic Solution
The function $A(x) = 240x - 3x^2$ is a parabola that opens downward, so the maximum value of area will occur at the vertex.

$$x = -\frac{b}{2a} = -\frac{240}{2(-3)} = 40;$$
$$A(40) = 240(40) - 3(40)^2 = 4{,}800$$

A value of $x = 40$ gives a maximum area of 4,800 square feet.

(B) Graphical Solution
Entering $y_1 = 240x - 3x^2$ and using the MAXIMUM command produces the graph in Figure 11. This shows that the maximum combined area of 4,800 square feet occurs at $x = 40$ feet.

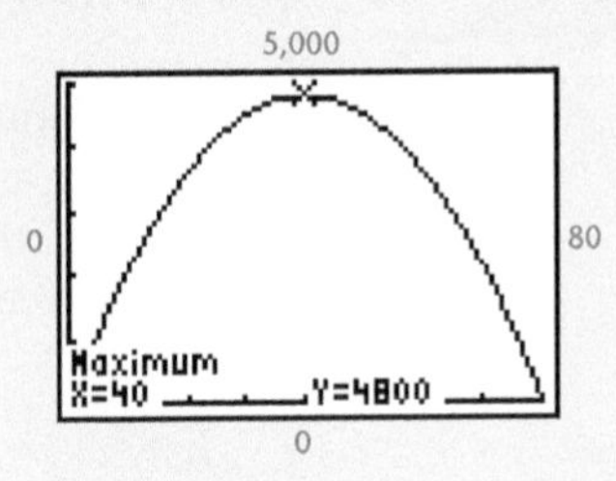

› **Figure 11**

(C) When $x = 40$, $y = 240 - 3(40) = 120$. Each pen is x by $\frac{y}{2}$, or 40 feet by 60 feet. The area of each pen is 40 feet × 60 feet = 2,400 square feet.

MATCHED PROBLEM 9

Repeat Example 9 with the owner constructing three identical adjacent pens instead of two.

The great sixteenth-century astronomer and physicist Galileo was the first to discover that the distance an object falls is proportional to the square of the time it has been falling. This makes quadratic functions a natural fit for modeling falling objects. Neglecting air resistance, the quadratic function

$$h(t) = h_0 - 16t^2$$

represents the *height of an object t* seconds after it is dropped from an initial height of h_0 feet. The constant -16 is related to the force of gravity and is dependent on the units used. That is, -16 only works for distances measured in feet and time measured in seconds. If the object is thrown either upward or downward, the quadratic model will also have a term involving t. (See Problems 87 and 88 in Exercises 2-3.)

EXAMPLE 10 **Projectile Motion**

As a publicity stunt, a late-night talk show host drops a pumpkin from a rooftop that is 200 feet high. When will the pumpkin hit the ground? Round your answer to two decimal places.

SOLUTION

Because the initial height is 200 feet, the quadratic model for the height of the pumpkin is

$$h(t) = 200 - 16t^2$$

Because $h(t) = 0$ when the pumpkin hits the ground, we must solve this equation for t.

Algebraic Solution

$$\begin{aligned} h(t) = 200 - 16t^2 &= 0 \\ 16t^2 &= 200 \\ t^2 &= \frac{200}{16} = 12.5 \\ t &= \sqrt{12.5} \\ &= 3.54 \text{ seconds} \end{aligned}$$

Graphical Solution

Graphing $y_1 = 200 - 16x^2$ and using the ZERO command (Fig. 12) shows that $h = 0$ at $t = 3.54$ seconds.

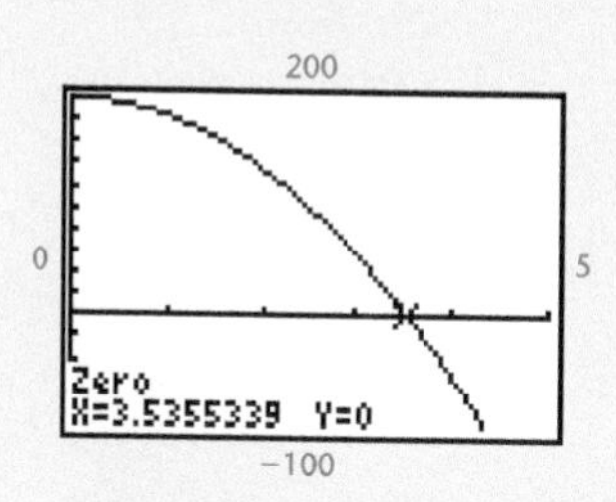

› Figure 12

MATCHED PROBLEM 10

A watermelon is dropped from a rooftop that is 300 feet high. When will the melon hit the ground? Round your answer to two decimal places.

ANSWERS TO MATCHED PROBLEMS

1.

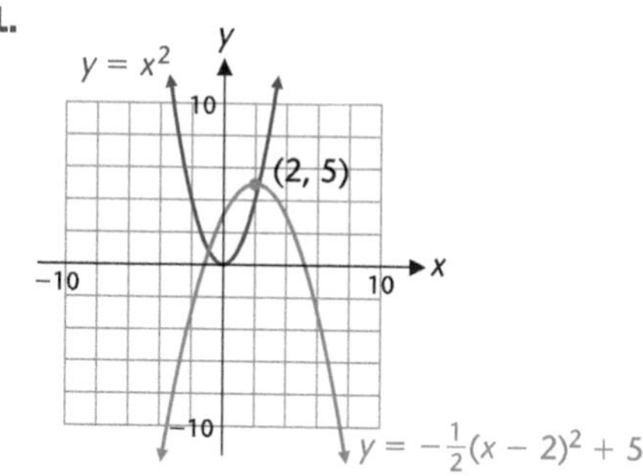

The $-\frac{1}{2}$ makes the graph open downward and vertically shrinks it by a factor of $\frac{1}{2}$, the 2 moves it 2 units right, and the 5 moves it 5 units up.

2. Vertex form: $f(x) = -(x - 1.5)^2 + 1.25$. The vertex is $(1.5, 1.25)$, the axis of symmetry is $x = 1.5$, the maximum value of $f(x)$ is 1.25, and the range of f is $(-\infty, 1.25]$. The function f is increasing on $(-\infty, 1.5]$ and decreasing on $[1.5, \infty)$. The graph of f is the graph of $g(x) = -x^2$ shifted one and a half units to the right and one and a quarter units upward.

3. (A) $x^2 - 8x + 16 = (x - 4)^2$ (B) $x^2 + \frac{7}{4}x + \frac{49}{64} = \left(x + \frac{7}{8}\right)^2$
(C) $x^2 - \frac{2}{3}x + \frac{1}{9} = \left(x - \frac{1}{3}\right)^2$

4. $g(x) = (x + 5)^2 - 26$; vertex is $(-5, -26)$, axis is $x = -5$.

5. $g(x) = -2\left(x + \frac{7}{2}\right)^2 + \frac{55}{2}$; vertex is $(-\frac{7}{2}, \frac{55}{2})$, axis is $x = -\frac{7}{2}$. The parabola opens downward, has a maximum value of $\frac{55}{2}$, and a range of $(-\infty, \frac{55}{2}]$. The function g is increasing on $(-\infty, -\frac{7}{2}]$ and decreasing on $[-\frac{7}{2}, \infty)$.

6. $(4, -22)$ **7.** $f(x) = -0.5x^2 + 2x + 2$ **8.** $f(x) = -1.5x^2 - 3x + 4.5$

9. (A) $A(x) = (240 - 4x)x$, $0 \le x \le 60$ (B) The maximum combined area of 3,600 ft^2 occurs at $x = 30$ feet. (C) Each pen is 30 feet by 40 feet with area 1,200 ft^2. **10.** 4.33 seconds

2-3 Exercises

1. Describe the graph of any quadratic function.

2. How can you tell from a quadratic function whether its graph opens up or down?

3. True or False: every quadratic function has a maximum. Explain.

4. Using transformations, explain why the vertex of $f(x) = a(x - h)^2 + k$ is (h, k).

5. What information does the constant a provide about the graph of a function of the form $f(x) = ax^2 + bx + c$?

6. Explain how to find the maximum or minimum value of a quadratic function.

In Problems 7–12, find the vertex and axis of the parabola, then draw the graph by hand and verify with a graphing calculator.

7. $f(x) = (x + 3)^2 - 4$ **8.** $f(x) = (x + 2)^2 - 2$

9. $f(x) = -\left(x - \frac{3}{2}\right)^2 - 5$ **10.** $f(x) = -\left(x - \frac{11}{2}\right)^2 + 3$

11. $f(x) = 2(x + 10)^2 + 20$ **12.** $f(x) = -\frac{1}{2}(x + 8)^2 + 12$

In Problems 13–18, write a brief verbal description of the relationship between the graph of the indicated function and the graph of $y = x^2$.

13. $f(x) = (x - 2)^2 + 1$ **14.** $g(x) = -(x + 1)^2 - 2$

15. $h(x) = -(x + 1)^2$ **16.** $k(x) = (x - 2)^2$

17. $m(x) = (x - 2)^2 - 3$ **18.** $n(x) = -(x + 1)^2 + 4$

In Problems 19–24, match each graph with one of the functions in Problems 13–18.

19.

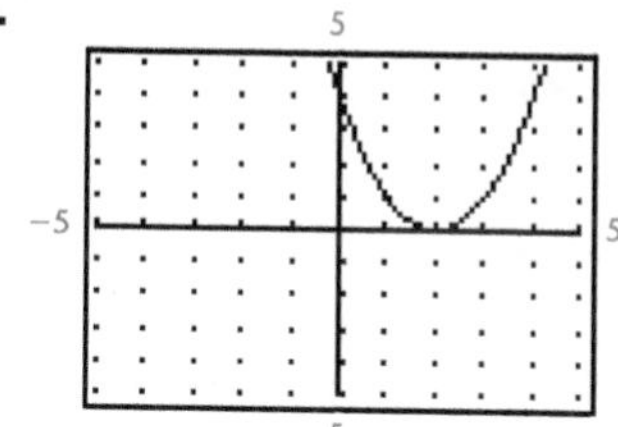

20.

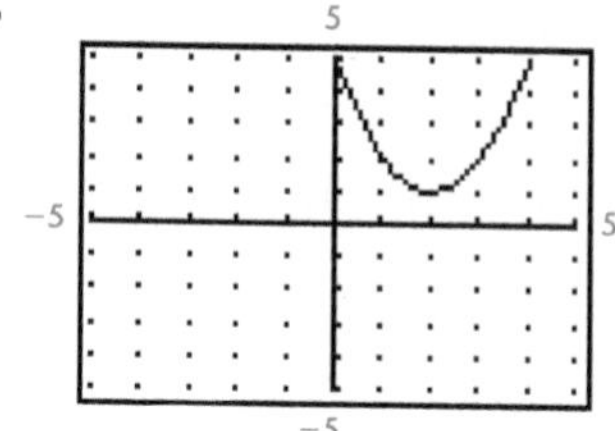

21.

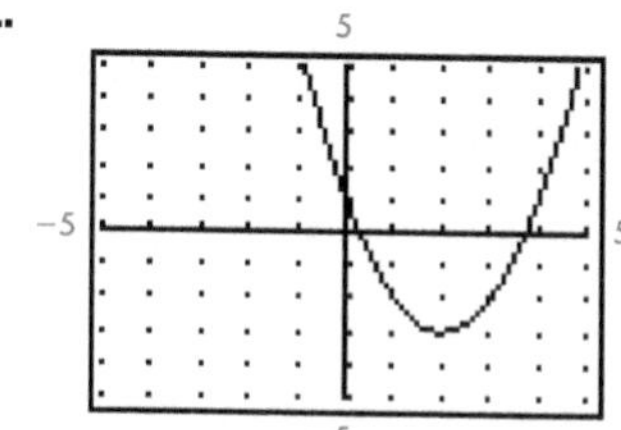

22.

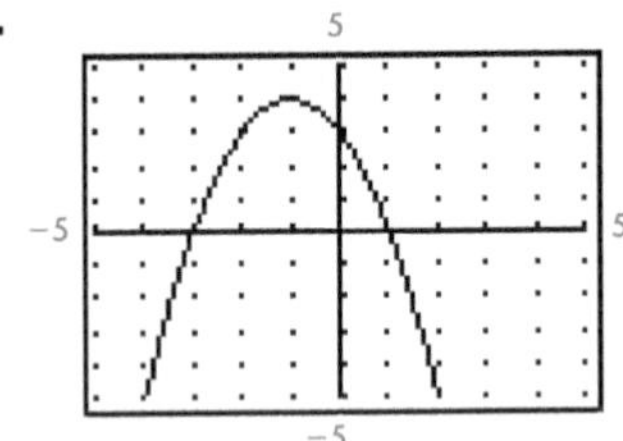

23.

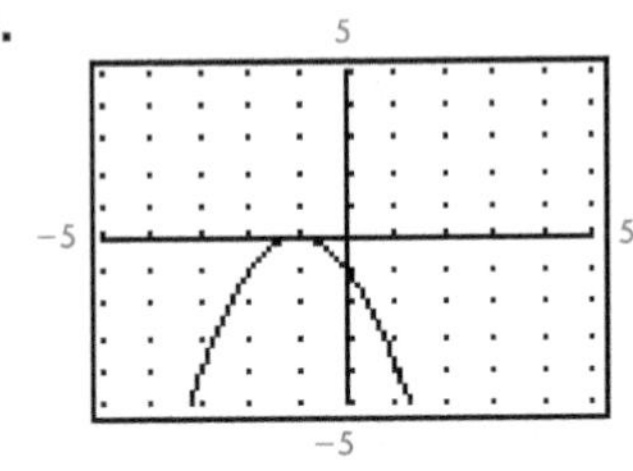

24.

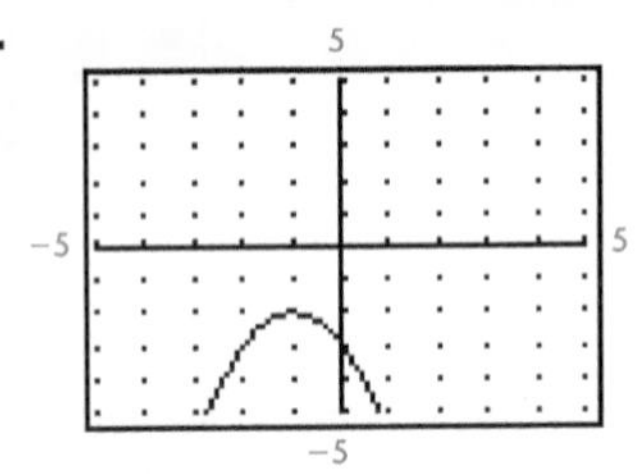

In Problems 25–30, complete the square for each expression.

25. $x^2 + 10x$

26. $x^2 + 8x$

27. $x^2 - 7x$

28. $x^2 - 3x$

29. $x^2 + \frac{7}{5}x$

30. $x^2 + \frac{11}{3}x$

In Problems 31–40, complete the square and find the vertex form of each quadratic function, then write the vertex and the axis.

31. $f(x) = x^2 - 4x + 5$

32. $g(x) = x^2 - 6x + 1$

33. $h(x) = -x^2 - 2x - 3$

34. $k(x) = -x^2 - 10x + 3$

35. $m(x) = 2x^2 - 12x + 22$

36. $n(x) = 3x^2 + 6x - 2$

37. $f(x) = \frac{1}{2}x^2 + 3x - \frac{7}{2}$

38. $g(x) = -\frac{3}{2}x^2 + 9x + \frac{11}{2}$

39. $f(x) = 2x^2 - 24x + 90$

40. $g(x) = 3x^2 + 24x + 30$

In Problems 41–48, use the formula $x = -\frac{b}{2a}$ to find the vertex. Then write a description of the graph using all of the following words: axis, increases, decreases, range, and maximum or minimum. Check your answer with a graphing calculator.

41. $f(x) = x^2 + 8x + 8$

42. $f(x) = x^2 + 10x + 10$

43. $f(x) = -x^2 - 7x + 4$

44. $f(x) = -x^2 - 11x + 1$

45. $f(x) = 4x^2 - 18x + 25$

46. $f(x) = 5x^2 + 30x - 17$

47. $f(x) = -10x^2 + 50x + 12$

48. $f(x) = -8x^2 - 24x + 16$

In problems 49–54, find the equation of a quadratic function whose graph satisfies the given conditions.

49. Vertex: (4, 8); x intercept: 6

50. Vertex: (−2, −12); x intercept: −4

51. Vertex: (−4, 12); y intercept: 4

52. Vertex: (5, 8); y intercept: −2

53. Vertex: (−5, −25); additional point on graph: (−2, 20)

54. Vertex: (6, −40); additional point on graph: (3, 50)

In Problems 55–62, use the graph of the parabola to find the equation of the corresponding quadratic function.

55.

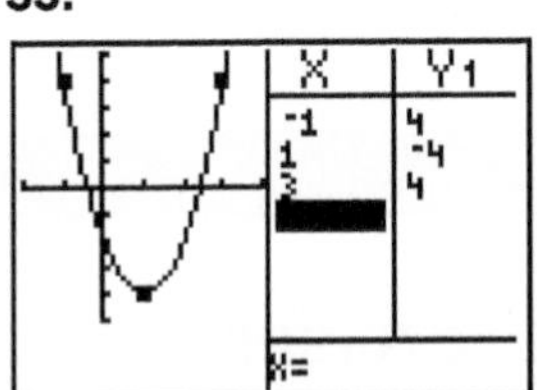

56.

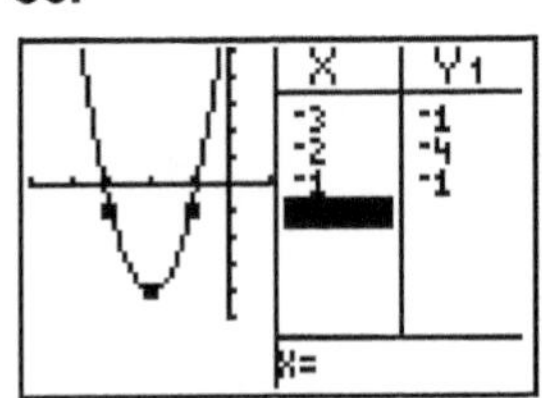

57.

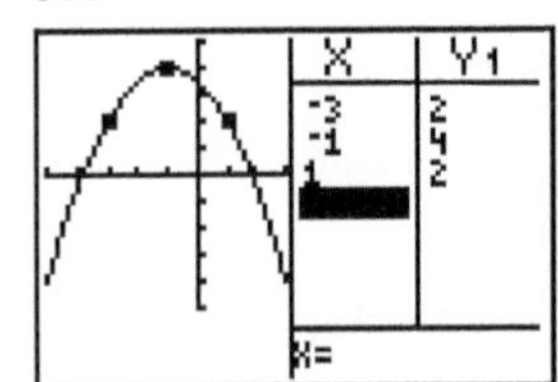

58.

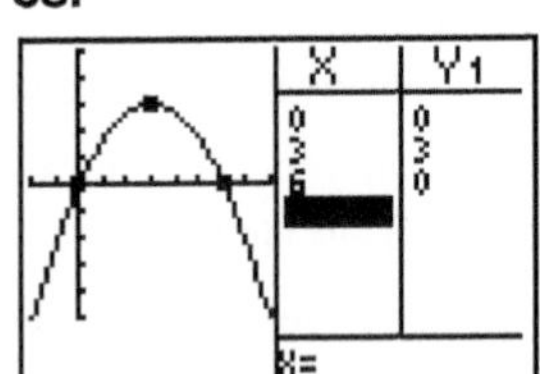

59.

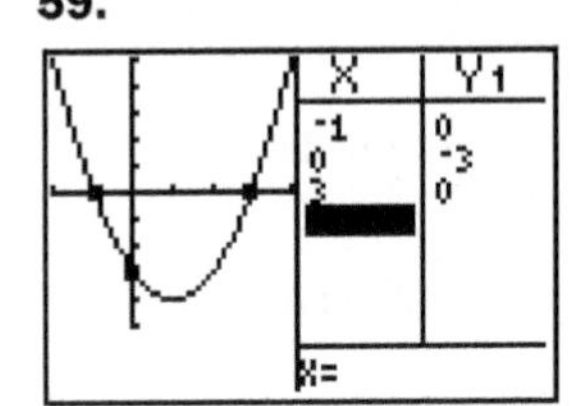

60.

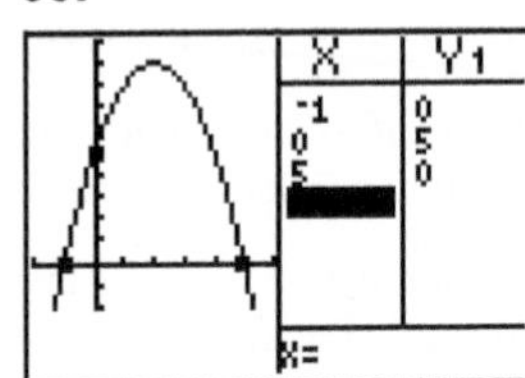

61.

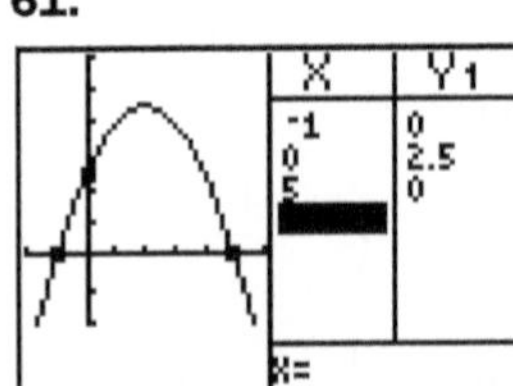

62.

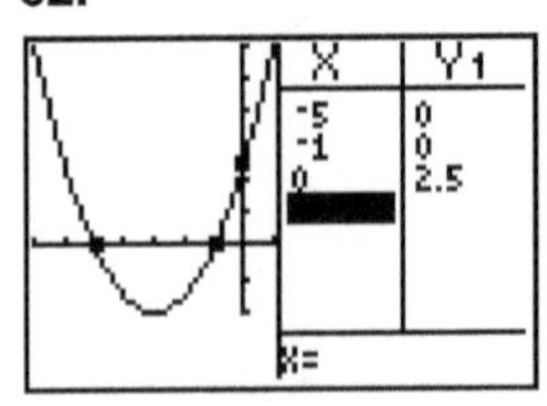

63. For $f(x) = a(x - h)^2 + k$, expand the parentheses and simplify to write in the form $f(x) = ax^2 + bx + c$. This proves that any function in vertex form is a quadratic function as defined in Definition 1.

64. For $f(x) = ax^2 + bx + c$:

(A) Group the first two terms, then factor out a.

(B) Multiply the coefficient of the middle term by $\frac{1}{2}$ and square the result.

(C) Add your result from (B) inside the parentheses, and subtract an appropriate number outside the parentheses so that the function is unchanged.

(D) Factor the parentheses. [*Hint:* The number you squared in (B) is important here!] What is the x coordinate of the vertex for any function of the form $f(x) = ax^2 + bx + c$?

65. Let $g(x) = x^2 + kx + 1$. Graph g for several different values of k and discuss the relationship among these graphs.

66. Confirm your conclusions in Problem 65 by finding the vertex form for g.

67. Let $f(x) = (x - 1)^2 + k$. Discuss the relationship between the values of k and the number of x intercepts for the graph of f. Generalize your comments to any function of the form

$$f(x) = a(x - h)^2 + k, a > 0$$

68. Let $f(x) = -(x - 2)^2 + k$. Discuss the relationship between the values of k and the number of x intercepts for the graph of f. Generalize your comments to any function of the form

$$f(x) = a(x - h)^2 + k, a < 0$$

69. Let $f(x) = a(x - h)^2 + k$. Compare the values of $f(h + r)$ and $f(h - r)$ for any real number r. Interpret the results in terms of the graph of f.

70. For the equation $x = y^2 - 2y + 1$:

(A) Plot points corresponding to $y = -2, -1, 0, 1, 2, 3$, and 4. Use these points to sketch the graph of the equation.

(B) Is your graph a function? Explain.

(C) Use your results to describe the graph of any equation of the form $x = ay^2 + by + c$.

Problems 71–74 are calculus related. In geometry, a line that intersects a circle in two distinct points is called a secant line, as shown in figure (a). In calculus, the line through the points $(x_1, f(x_1))$ and $(x_2, f(x_2))$ is called a ***secant line*** *for the graph of the function f, as shown in figure (b).*

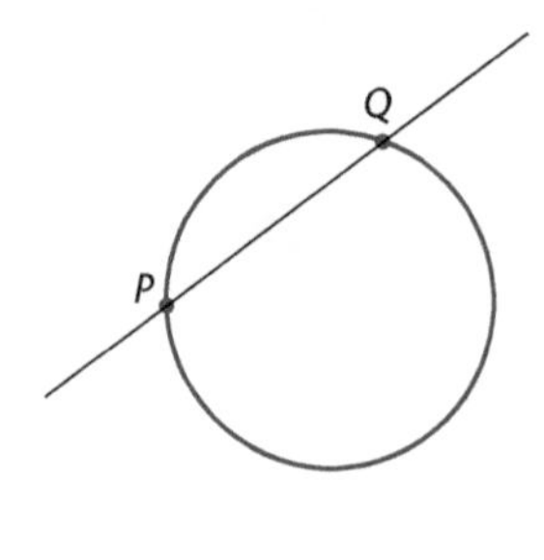

Secant line for a circle
(a)

Secant line for the graph of a function
(b)

In Problems 71 and 72, find the equation of the secant line through the indicated points on the graph of f. Graph f and the secant line on the same coordinate system.

71. $f(x) = x^2 - 4$; $(-1, -3)$, $(3, 5)$

72. $f(x) = 9 - x^2$; $(-2, 5)$, $(4, -7)$

73. Let $f(x) = x^2 - 3x + 5$. If h is a nonzero real number, then $(2, f(2))$ and $(2 + h, f(2 + h))$ are two distinct points on the graph of f.

(A) Find the slope of the secant line through these two points.

(B) Evaluate the slope of the secant line for $h = 1$, $h = 0.1$, $h = 0.01$, and $h = 0.001$. What value does the slope seem to be approaching?

74. Repeat Problem 73 for $f(x) = x^2 + 2x - 6$.

75. Find the minimum product of two numbers whose difference is 30. Is there a maximum product? Explain.

76. Find the maximum product of two numbers whose sum is 60. Is there a minimum product? Explain.

APPLICATIONS

77. PROFIT ANALYSIS A consultant hired by a small manufacturing company informs the company owner that their annual profit can be modeled by the function $P(x) = -1.2x^2 + 62.5x - 491$, where x represents the number of employees and P is profit in thousands of dollars. How many employees should the company have to maximize annual profit? What is the maximum annual profit they can expect in that case?

78. PROFIT ANALYSIS The annual profits (in thousands of dollars) from 1998 to 2007 for the company in Problem 77 can be modeled by the function $P(t) = 6.8t^2 - 80.5t + 427.3$, $0 \leq t \leq 9$, where t is years after 1998. How much profit did the company make in their worst year?

79. MOVIE INDUSTRY REVENUE The annual U.S. box office revenue in billions of dollars for a span of years beginning in 2000 can be modeled by the function $B(x) = -0.19x^2 + 1.2x + 7.6$, $0 \leq x \leq 7$, where x is years after 2000.

(A) In what year was box office revenue at its highest in that time span?

(B) Explain why you should not use the exact vertex in answering part A in this problem.

80. GAS MILEAGE The speed at which a car is driven can have a big effect on gas mileage. Based on EPA statistics for compact cars, the function $m(x) = -0.025x^2 + 2.45x - 30$, $30 \leq x \leq 65$, models the average miles per gallon for compact cars in terms of the speed driven x (in miles per hour).

(A) At what speed should the owner of a compact car drive to maximize miles per gallon?

(B) If one compact car has a 14-gallon gas tank, how much farther could you drive it on one tank of gas driving at the speed you found in part A than if you drove at 65 miles per hour?

81. CONSTRUCTION A horse breeder wants to construct a corral next to a horse barn that is 50 feet long, using all of the barn as one side of the corral (see the figure). He has 250 feet of fencing available and wants to use all of it.

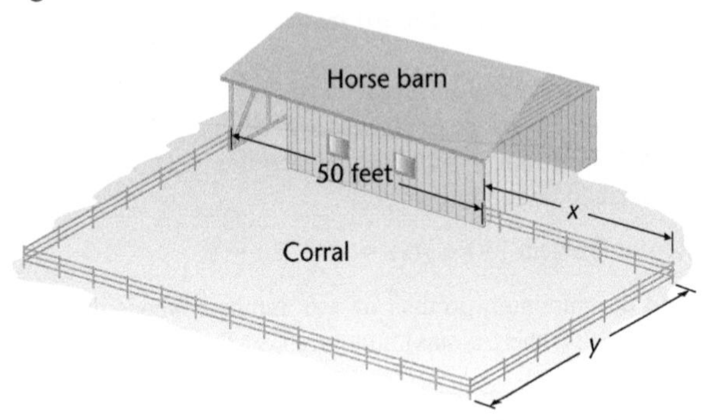

(A) Express the area $A(x)$ of the corral as a function of x and indicate its domain.
(B) Find the value of x that produces the maximum area.
(C) What are the dimensions of the corral with the maximum area?

82. CONSTRUCTION Repeat Problem 81 if the horse breeder has only 140 feet of fencing available for the corral. Does the maximum value of the area function still occur at the vertex? Explain.

83. FALLING OBJECT A sandbag is dropped off a high-altitude balloon at an altitude of 10,000 ft. When will the sandbag hit the ground?

84. FALLING OBJECT A prankster drops a water balloon off the top of a 144-foot-high building. When will the balloon hit the ground?

85. FALLING OBJECT A cliff diver hits the water 2.5 seconds after diving off the cliff. How high is the cliff?

86. FALLING OBJECT A forest ranger drops a coffee cup off a fire watchtower. If the cup hits the ground 1.5 seconds later, how high is the tower?

87. PROJECTILE FLIGHT An arrow shot vertically into the air from ground level with a crossbow reaches a maximum height of 484 feet after 5.5 seconds of flight. Let the quadratic function $d(t)$ represent the distance above ground (in feet) t seconds after the arrow is released. (If air resistance is neglected, a quadratic model provides a good approximation for the flight of a projectile.)
(A) Find $d(t)$ and state its domain.
(B) At what times (to two decimal places) will the arrow be 250 feet above the ground?

88. PROJECTILE FLIGHT Repeat Problem 87 if the arrow reaches a maximum height of 324 feet after 4.5 seconds of flight.

89. ENGINEERING The arch of a bridge is in the shape of a parabola 14 feet high at the center and 20 feet wide at the base (see the figure).

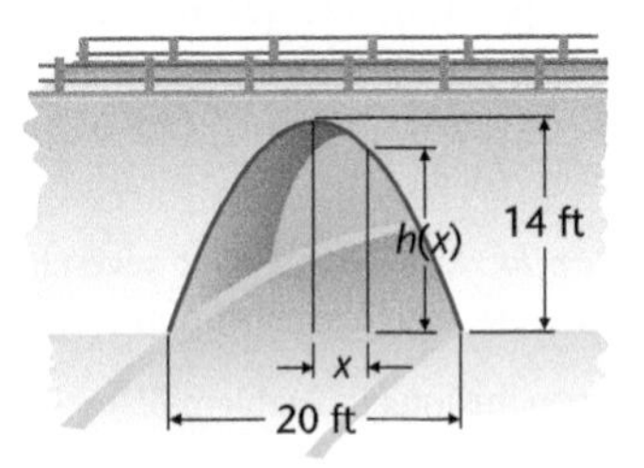

(A) Express the height of the arch $h(x)$ in terms of x and state its domain.
(B) Can a truck that is 8 feet wide and 12 feet high pass through the arch?
(C) What is the tallest 8-foot-wide truck that can pass through the arch?
(D) What (to two decimal places) is the widest 12-foot-high truck that can pass through the arch?

90. ENGINEERING The roadbed of one section of a suspension bridge is hanging from a large cable suspended between two towers that are 200 feet apart (see the figure). The cable forms a parabola that is 60 feet above the roadbed at the towers and 10 feet above the roadbed at the lowest point.

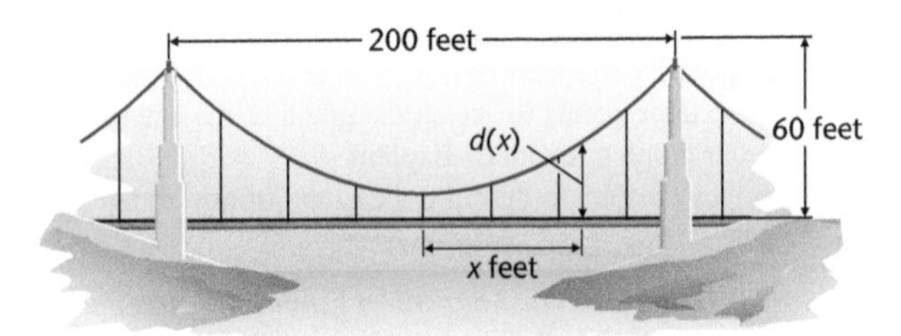

(A) Express the vertical distance $d(x)$ (in feet) from the roadbed to the suspension cable in terms of x and state the domain of d.
(B) The roadbed is supported by seven equally spaced vertical cables (see the figure). Find the combined total length of these supporting cables.

MODELING AND LINEAR REGRESSION

91. MAXIMIZING REVENUE A company that manufactures flashlights has collected the price–demand data in Table 1 on the next page. Round all numbers to three significant digits.
(A) Use the data in Table 1 and linear regression to find a linear price–demand function $p = d(x)$, where x is the number of flashlights (in thousands) that the company can sell at a price of p dollars.
(B) Find the price that maximizes the company's revenue from the sale of flashlights. Recall that revenue = price times quantity sold.

Table 1

Price	Demand
$3.55	45,800
$3.95	40,500
$4.13	37,900
$4.85	34,700
$5.19	30,400
$5.55	28,900
$6.15	25,400

92. MAXIMIZING REVENUE A company that manufactures pencil sharpeners has collected the price–demand data in Table 2. Round all numbers to three significant digits.
(A) Use the data in Table 2 and linear regression to find a linear price–demand function $p = d(x)$, where x is the number of pencil sharpeners (in thousands) that the company can sell at a price of p dollars.
(B) Find the price that maximizes the company's revenue from the sale of pencil sharpeners. Recall that revenue = price times quantity sold.

Table 2

Price	Demand
$4.23	47,800
$4.89	45,600
$5.43	42,700
$5.97	39,600
$6.47	34,700
$7.12	31,600
$7.84	27,800

2-4 Complex Numbers

The idea of inventing new numbers may sound very odd to you, but it's not as strange as you might think. Consider the simple quadratic equation

$$x^2 - 2 = 0 \tag{1}$$

The solution is a number whose square is 2, so you are probably thinking "the square root of two." But there was a time when square roots had not yet been defined. Twenty-six hundred years ago, early mathematicians would have told you that there was no number whose square is 2. They only knew about rational numbers, and around 500 B.C. a group of mathematicians known as the Pythagoreans found that it is impossible to square a rational number and get 2. For equation (1) to have a solution, a new kind of number had to be invented—an irrational number. The study of irrational numbers didn't get a firm mathematical foundation for over 2,000 years after that!

We now accept $\sqrt{2}$ as a number because we can approximate it very well with technology, but at one time almost everyone would have said that it was just made up, and didn't *really* exist. In this section, we ask this question: Is there any reason to invent any other kinds of numbers?

››› EXPLORE-DISCUSS 1

Graph $g(x) = x^2 - 1$ in a standard viewing window and discuss the relationship between the real zeros of the function and the x intercepts of its graph. Do the same for $f(x) = x^2 + 1$.

Does the simple quadratic equation

$$x^2 + 1 = 0 \tag{2}$$

have a solution? If equation (2) is to have a solution, x^2 has to be negative. But the square of a real number is never negative. Therefore, equation (2) cannot have any real-number solutions. Once again, a new type of number must be invented—a number whose square is negative one. The concept of square roots of negative numbers had been kicked around for a couple of centuries, but in 1748, the Swiss mathematician Euler used the letter i to represent a square root of -1. From this simple beginning, it's possible to build a new system of numbers called the complex number system, which we explore in this section.

› Imaginary Numbers

We begin with imaginary numbers, one of which we know already: i is a square root of -1. The number i is called the **imaginary unit**. Explore-Discuss 2 will help you to become acquainted with this number.

››› EXPLORE-DISCUSS 2

Natural number powers of i take on particularly simple forms:

$$\begin{aligned} &i & &i^5 = i^4 \cdot i = (1)i = i \\ &i^2 = -1 & &i^6 = i^4 \cdot i^2 = 1(-1) = -1 \\ &i^3 = i^2 \cdot i = (-1)i = -i & &i^7 = i^4 \cdot i^3 = 1(-i) = -i \\ &i^4 = i^2 \cdot i^2 = (-1)(-1) = 1 & &i^8 = i^4 \cdot i^4 = 1 \cdot 1 = 1 \end{aligned}$$

In general, what are the possible values for i^n, n a natural number? Explain how you could easily evaluate i^n for any natural number n. Then evaluate each of the following:

(A) i^{17} **(B)** i^{24} **(C)** i^{38} **(D)** i^{47}

If your graphing calculator can perform complex arithmetic, use it to check your calculations in parts A–D.

A **pure imaginary number** is defined to be any multiple of the imaginary unit i, that is, any number of the form bi, where b is a real number.

EXAMPLE 1 Finding Powers of Pure Imaginary Numbers

Find the requested power of each pure imaginary number:

(A) $(5i)^2$ (B) $(-3i)^3$ (C) $(2i)^4$

SOLUTIONS

Algebraic Solutions

(A) $(5i)^2 = 5^2 \cdot i^2 = 25(-1) = -25$
(B) $(-3i)^3 = (-3)^3 \cdot i^3 = -27 \cdot (-i) = 27i$
(C) $(2i)^4 = 2^4 \cdot i^4 = 16(1) = 16$

Graphical Solutions
Most graphing calculators can do arithmetic with the imaginary unit i (Fig. 1). On the TI-84, i is entered with the key combination 2nd decimal point.

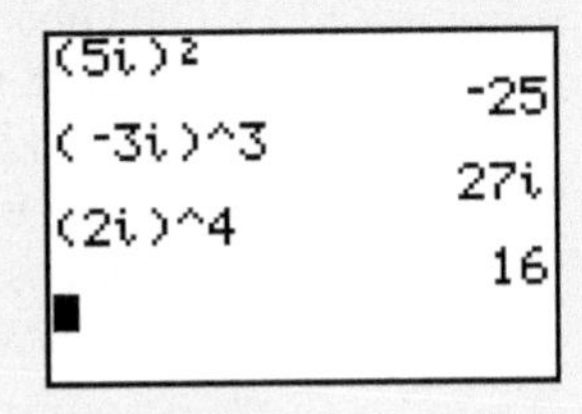

› Figure 1

MATCHED PROBLEM 1

Find the requested power of each pure imaginary number:

(A) $(-7i)^2$ (B) $(4i)^3$ (C) $(-2i)^4$

As we will see in the next section, to solve many equations that would otherwise not have solutions, we will need to go a bit beyond pure imaginary numbers. With the imaginary unit as starting point, we can build a new system of numbers called the complex number system. The complex numbers evolved over a long period, but, like the real numbers, it was not until the nineteenth century that they were given a firm mathematical foundation. Table 1 gives a brief history of the evolution of complex numbers.

Table 1 Brief History of Complex Numbers

Approximate Date A.D.	Person	Event
50	Heron of Alexandria	First recorded encounter of a square root of a negative number.
850	Mahavira of India	Said that a negative has no square root, because it is not a square.
1545	Cardano of Italy	Solutions to cubic equations involved square roots of negative numbers.
1637	Descartes of France	Introduced the terms *real* and *imaginary*.
1748	Euler of Switzerland	Used i for $\sqrt{-1}$.
1832	Gauss of Germany	Introduced the term *complex number*.

The Complex Number System

We start our development of the complex number system by defining what we mean by a complex number, and several special types of complex numbers.

DEFINITION 1 Complex Number

A **complex number** is a number of the form

$$a + bi \quad \text{Standard form}$$

where a and b are real numbers and i is the **imaginary unit,** a square root of -1.

For a complex number $a + bi$, a is called the **real part** and bi is called the **imaginary part.**

Some examples of complex numbers are

$$\begin{array}{ccc} 3 - 2i & \frac{1}{2} + 5i & 2 - \frac{1}{3}i \\ 0 + 3i & 5 + 0i & 0 + 0i \end{array}$$

Particular kinds of complex numbers are given special names as follows:

DEFINITION 2 Names for Particular Kinds of Complex Numbers

Imaginary Unit:	i	(A square root of -1)
Complex Number:	$a + bi$	a and b real numbers
Imaginary Number:	$a + bi$	$b \neq 0$ (The imaginary part is nonzero.)
Pure Imaginary Number:	$0 + bi = bi$	$b \neq 0$ (The real part is zero.)
Real Number:	$a + 0i = a$	(The imaginary part is zero.)
Zero:	$0 + 0i = 0$	
Conjugate of $a + bi$:	$a - bi$	

EXAMPLE 2 Special Types of Complex Numbers

Given the list of complex numbers:

$$\begin{array}{ccc} 3 - 2i & \frac{1}{2} + 5i & 2 - \frac{1}{3}i \\ 0 + 3i = 3i & 5 + 0i = 5 & 0 + 0i = 0 \end{array}$$

(A) List all the imaginary numbers, pure imaginary numbers, real numbers, and zero.

(B) Write the conjugate of each.

SOLUTIONS

(A) Imaginary numbers: $3 - 2i, \frac{1}{2} + 5i, 2 - \frac{1}{3}i, 3i$
Pure imaginary numbers: $0 + 3i = 3i$
Real numbers: $5 + 0i = 5, 0 + 0i = 0$
Zero: $0 + 0i = 0$

(B) $3 + 2i$ $\quad \frac{1}{2} - 5i$ $\quad 2 + \frac{1}{3}i$
$0 - 3i = -3i$ $\quad 5 - 0i = 5$ $\quad 0 - 0i = 0$

MATCHED PROBLEM 2

Given the list of complex numbers:

$$6 + 7i \qquad \sqrt{2} - \tfrac{1}{3}i \qquad 0 - i = -i$$
$$0 + \tfrac{2}{3}i = \tfrac{2}{3}i \qquad -\sqrt{3} + 0i = -\sqrt{3} \qquad 0 - 0i = 0$$

(A) List all the imaginary numbers, pure imaginary numbers, real numbers, and zero.
(B) Write the conjugate of each.

In Definition 2, notice that we identify a complex number of the form $a + 0i$ with the real number a. This means that every real number is also a complex number; in other words, the set of real numbers is contained in the set of complex numbers, just as the set of rational numbers is contained in the set of real numbers. Any complex number that is not a real number is called an **imaginary number.** If we combine the set of all real numbers with the set of all imaginary numbers, we obtain ***C*, the set of complex numbers.** The relationship of the complex number system to the other number systems we have studied is shown in Figure 2. In each column, adding a new set of numbers to the set on top produces a bigger set containing the one listed before it.

Figure 2

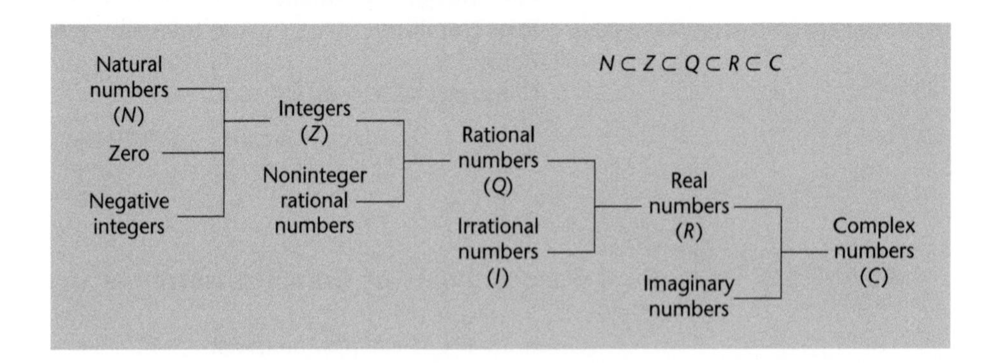

If we are going to work with this new type of number, it seems reasonable to begin by considering the basic operations of addition, subtraction, multiplication, and division. But first, we should make sure we are clear on what exactly it means for two complex numbers to be equal.

› DEFINITION 3 Equality and Basic Operations

1. Two complex numbers are equal exactly when their real and imaginary parts are equal. That is,

$$a + bi = c + di \text{ if and only if } a = c \text{ and } b = d$$

2. To add complex numbers, add their real and imaginary parts separately. That is,

$$(a + bi) + (c + di) = (a + c) + (b + d)i$$

3. Multiplication of complex numbers is defined by the following formula:

$$(a + bi)(c + di) = (ac - bd) + (ad + bc)i$$

Using the definitions of addition and multiplication of complex numbers (Definition 3), it can be shown that basic properties of the real number system* extend to the following basic properties of the complex number system.

› BASIC PROPERTIES OF THE COMPLEX NUMBER SYSTEM

1. Addition and multiplication of complex numbers are commutative and associative operations.
2. There is an additive identity and a multiplicative identity for complex numbers.
3. Every complex number has an additive inverse or negative.
4. Every nonzero complex number has a multiplicative inverse or reciprocal.
5. Multiplication distributes over addition.

This is actually really good news: it tells us that we don't have to memorize the formulas for adding and multiplying complex numbers in Definition 3. Instead:

We can treat complex numbers of the form $a + bi$ exactly as we treat algebraic expressions of the form $a + bx$. We just need to remember that in this case, i stands for the imaginary unit; it is not a variable that represents a real number.

The first two arithmetic operations we consider are **addition** and **subtraction.**

*Basic properties of the real number system are discussed in Appendix A, Section A-1.

EXAMPLE 3 Addition and Subtraction of Complex Numbers

Carry out each operation and express the answer in standard form:

(A) $(2 - 3i) + (6 + 2i)$ (B) $(-5 + 4i) + (0 + 0i)$
(C) $(7 - 3i) - (6 + 2i)$ (D) $(-2 + 7i) + (2 - 7i)$

SOLUTIONS

Algebraic Solutions

(A) We could apply the definition of addition directly, but it is easier to use complex number properties.

$$(2 - 3i) + (6 + 2i) = 2 - 3i + 6 + 2i \quad \text{Remove parentheses.}$$
$$= (2 + 6) + (-3 + 2)i \quad \text{Combine like terms.}$$
$$= 8 - i$$

(B) $(-5 + 4i) + (0 + 0i) = -5 + 4i + 0 + 0i$
$= -5 + 4i$

(C) $(7 - 3i) - (6 + 2i) = 7 - 3i - 6 - 2i$
$= 1 - 5i$

(D) $(-2 + 7i) + (2 - 7i) = -2 + 7i + 2 - 7i = 0$

Graphical Solutions

```
(2-3i)+(6+2i)
                8-i
(-5+4i)+(0+0i)
              -5+4i
(7-3i)-(6+2i)
               1-5i
(-2+7i)+(2-7i)
                  0
```

› Figure 3

››› CAUTION ›››

When subtracting complex numbers, the parentheses around the second number are crucial. Make sure that you distribute the negative sign.

MATCHED PROBLEM 3

Carry out each operation and express the answer in standard form:

(A) $(3 + 2i) + (6 - 4i)$ (B) $(0 + 0i) + (7 - 5i)$
(C) $(3 - 5i) - (1 - 3i)$ (D) $(-4 + 9i) + (4 - 9i)$

Not all graphing calculators make use of the $a + bi$ notation for complex numbers. For example, on the TI-86, the complex number $a + bi$ is entered as the ordered pair (a, b). Figure 4 shows the solution to parts A and B of Example 2 on a TI-86.

```
(2,-3)+(6,2)
                (8,-1)
(-5,4)+(0,0)
                (-5,4)
```

› **Figure 4** Complex number arithmetic on a TI-86.

Example 2, part B, illustrates the following general result: For any complex number $a + bi$,

$$(a + bi) + (0 + 0i) = (0 + 0i) + (a + bi) = a + bi$$

Thus, $0 + 0i$ is the **additive identity** or **zero** for the complex numbers. We anticipated this result in Definition 2 when we identified the complex number $0 + 0i$ with the real number 0.

Example 2, part D, illustrates a different result: In general, the **additive inverse** or **negative** of $a + bi$ is $-a - bi$ because

$$(a + bi) + (-a - bi) = (-a - bi) + (a + bi) = 0$$

Now we turn our attention to multiplication. Just like addition and subtraction, **multiplication of complex numbers** can be carried out by treating $a + bi$ in the same way we treat the algebraic expression $a + bx$. The key difference is that we replace i^2 with -1 each time it occurs.

EXAMPLE 4 Multiplying Complex Numbers

Carry out each operation and express the answer in standard form:

(A) $(2 - 3i)(6 + 2i)$ (B) $1(3 - 5i)$

(C) $i(1 + i)$ (D) $(3 + 4i)(3 - 4i)$

SOLUTIONS

Algebraic Solutions

(A) $(2 - 3i)(6 + 2i) = 12 + 4i - 18i - 6i^2$ Combine like terms; replace i^2 with -1.

$= 12 - 14i - 6(-1)$

$= 18 - 14i$

(B) $1(3 - 5i) = 1 \cdot 3 - 1 \cdot 5i = 3 - 5i$

(C) $i(1 + i) = i + i^2 = i - 1 = -1 + i$

(D) $(3 + 4i)(3 - 4i) = 9 - 12i + 12i - 16i^2$ $-16i^2 = -16(-1) = 16$

$= 9 + 16 = 25$

Graphical Solutions

```
(2-3i)(6+2i)
              18-14i
1(3-5i)
                3-5i
i(1+i)
               -1+i
(3+4i)(3-4i)
                  25
```

› **Figure 5**

MATCHED PROBLEM 4

Carry out each operation and express the answer in standard form:

(A) $(5 + 2i)(4 - 3i)$
(B) $3(-2 + 6i)$
(C) $i(2 - 3i)$
(D) $(2 + 3i)(2 - 3i)$

Notice that for any complex number $a + bi$,

$$1(a + bi) = (a + bi)1 = a + bi$$

(see Example 4, part B). This tells us that 1 is the **multiplicative identity** for complex numbers, just as it is for real numbers.

Part D of Example 4 illustrates an important property of the conjugate of a complex number.

› THEOREM 1 Product of a Complex Number and Its Conjugate

$$(a + bi)(a - bi) = a^2 + b^2 \quad \text{A real number}$$

You will be asked to prove this theorem in the exercises. Theorem 1 comes in very handy in finding reciprocals and **dividing complex numbers.**

Earlier we stated that every nonzero complex number has a multiplicative inverse or reciprocal. We will denote this as a fraction, just as we do with real numbers. The **reciprocal** of $a + bi$ is

$$\frac{1}{a + bi} \text{ (for } a + bi \neq 0\text{)}.$$

As before, when dividing we can manipulate $a + bi$ in the same way we manipulate the real binomial form $a + bx$, except we replace i^2 with -1 each time it occurs. The trick to dividing and writing the result in standard form is to multiply numerator and denominator by the conjugate of the denominator.

EXAMPLE 5 Reciprocals and Quotients

Carry out each operation and express the answer in standard form:

(A) $\frac{1}{2 + 3i}$ (B) $\frac{7 - 3i}{1 + i}$

SOLUTIONS

Algebraic Solutions

(A) Multiply numerator and denominator by the conjugate of the denominator:

$$\frac{1}{2+3i} = \frac{1}{2+3i} \cdot \frac{2-3i}{2-3i} = \frac{2-3i}{4-9i^2} = \frac{2-3i}{4+9}$$

$$= \frac{2-3i}{13} \quad \text{Write in standard form.}$$

$$= \frac{2}{13} - \frac{3}{13}i$$

(B) $$\frac{7-3i}{1+i} = \frac{7-3i}{1+i} \cdot \frac{1-i}{1-i} = \frac{7-7i-3i+3i^2}{1-i^2}$$

$$= \frac{4-10i}{2} \quad \text{Write in standard form.}$$

$$= 2 - 5i$$

Graphical Solutions

```
1/(2+3i)
.1538461538-.23…
Ans►Frac
         2/13-3/13i
(7-3i)/(1+i)
               2-5i
```

› **Figure 6**

In Figure 6, note that we used the FRACTION command to convert the decimal form to the fraction form.

MATCHED PROBLEM 5

Carry out each operation and express the answer in standard form:

(A) $\frac{1}{4 + 2i}$ (B) $\frac{6 + 7i}{2 - i}$

EXAMPLE 6 Combined Operations

Carry out the indicated operations and write each answer in standard form:

(A) $(3 - 2i)^2 - 6(3 - 2i) + 13$ (B) $\frac{2 - 3i}{2i}$

SOLUTIONS

Algebraic Solutions

(A) $(3 - 2i)^2 - 6(3 - 2i) + 13$
$= 9 - 12i + 4i^2 - 18 + 12i + 13$
$= 9 - 12i - 4 - 18 + 12i + 13$
$= 0$

(B) If a complex number is divided by a pure imaginary number, we can make the denominator real by multiplying numerator and denominator by i. (We could also multiply by the conjugate of $2i$, which is $-2i$.)

$$\frac{2 - 3i}{2i} \cdot \frac{i}{i} = \frac{2i - 3i^2}{2i^2} = \frac{2i + 3}{-2} = -\frac{3}{2} - i$$

Graphical Solutions

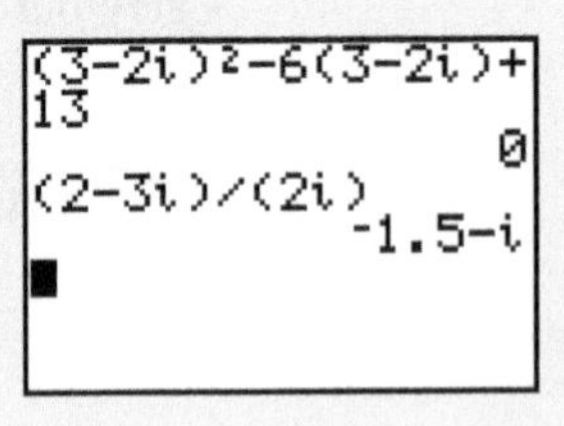

› Figure 7

MATCHED PROBLEM 6

Carry out the indicated operations and write each answer in standard form:

(A) $(3 + 2i)^2 - 6(3 + 2i) + 13$ (B) $\dfrac{4 - i}{3i}$

› Complex Numbers and Radicals

Recall that we say that a is a square root of b if $a^2 = b$. If x is a positive real number, then x has two square roots, the principal square root, denoted by $\sqrt{x}$, and its negative, $-\sqrt{x}$. If x is a negative real number, we would previously have said that x didn't have any square roots. Now we can find two square roots for negative real numbers: They will both be imaginary numbers.

››› EXPLORE-DISCUSS 3

(A) Find the square of each expression.

$(i\sqrt{3})^2 =$ ______ $(5i)^2 =$ ______ $(i\sqrt{11})^2 =$ ______
$(-i\sqrt{3})^2 =$ ______ $(-5i)^2 =$ ______ $(-i\sqrt{11})^2 =$ ______

(B) What are the two square roots of -3? Of -5? Of -11?

> **DEFINITION 4 Principal Square Root of a Negative Real Number**

The **principal square root of a negative real number,** denoted by $\sqrt{-a}$, where a is positive, is defined by

$$\sqrt{-a} = i\sqrt{a} \qquad \sqrt{-3} = i\sqrt{3} \qquad \sqrt{-9} = i\sqrt{9} = 3i$$

The other square root of $-a$, $a > 0$, is $-\sqrt{-a} = -i\sqrt{a}$.

Note in Definition 4 that we wrote $i\sqrt{a}$ and $i\sqrt{3}$ in place of the standard forms $\sqrt{a}i$ and $\sqrt{3}i$. We follow this convention to avoid confusion over whether the i should or should not be under the radical. (Notice that $\sqrt{3}i$ and $\sqrt{3i}$ look a lot alike, but are not the same number.)

EXAMPLE 7 Complex Numbers and Radicals

Write in standard form:

(A) $\sqrt{-4}$ (B) $4 + \sqrt{-5}$ (C) $\dfrac{-3 - \sqrt{-5}}{2}$ (D) $\dfrac{1}{1 - \sqrt{-9}}$

SOLUTIONS

Algebraic Solutions

(A) $\sqrt{-4} = i\sqrt{4} = 2i$

(B) $4 + \sqrt{-5} = 4 + i\sqrt{5}$

(C) $\dfrac{-3 - \sqrt{-5}}{2} = \dfrac{-3 - i\sqrt{5}}{2} = -\dfrac{3}{2} - \dfrac{\sqrt{5}}{2}i$

(D) $\dfrac{1}{1 - \sqrt{-9}} = \dfrac{1}{1 - 3i} = \dfrac{1 \cdot (1 + 3i)}{(1 - 3i) \cdot (1 + 3i)}$

$= \dfrac{1 + 3i}{1 - 9i^2} = \dfrac{1 + 3i}{10}$

$= \dfrac{1}{10} + \dfrac{3}{10}i$

Graphical Solutions

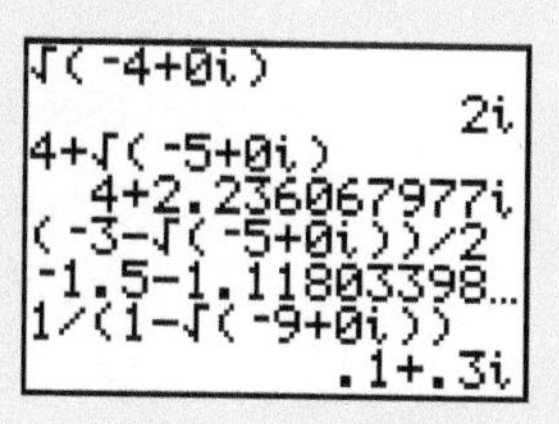

> Figure 8

Note that principal square roots like $\sqrt{-4}$ must be entered as $\sqrt{-4 + 0i}$ to indicate that we want to perform complex arithmetic rather than real arithmetic (see Fig. 8). Press the right arrow key to display the i in the answer to part C.

MATCHED PROBLEM 7

Write in standard form:

(A) $\sqrt{-16}$ (B) $5 + \sqrt{-7}$ (C) $\dfrac{-5 - \sqrt{-2}}{2}$ (D) $\dfrac{1}{3 - \sqrt{-4}}$

››› EXPLORE-DISCUSS 4

From basic algebra, we know that if a and b are positive real numbers, then

$$\sqrt{a}\sqrt{b} = \sqrt{ab} \tag{3}$$

So, we can evaluate expressions like $\sqrt{9}\,\sqrt{4}$ two ways:

$$\sqrt{9}\,\sqrt{4} = \sqrt{(9)(4)} = \sqrt{36} = 6 \quad \text{and} \quad \sqrt{9}\,\sqrt{4} = (3)(2) = 6$$

Evaluate each of the following in two ways. Is equation (3) a valid property to use in all cases?

(A) $\sqrt{9}\,\sqrt{-4}$ **(B)** $\sqrt{-9}\,\sqrt{-4}$ **(C)** $\sqrt{-9}\,\sqrt{-4}$

››› CAUTION ›››

Note that in Example 7, part D, we wrote $1 - \sqrt{-9} = 1 - 3i$ before proceeding with the simplification. This is a necessary step because some of the properties of radicals that are true for real numbers turn out not to be true for complex numbers. In particular, for positive real numbers a and b,

$$\sqrt{a}\sqrt{b} = \sqrt{ab} \quad \text{but} \quad \sqrt{-a}\,\sqrt{-b} \neq \sqrt{(-a)(-b)}$$

(See Explore-Discuss 4.)

To avoid having to worry about this, always convert expressions of the form $\sqrt{-a}$ to the equivalent form in terms of i before performing any operations.

› Solving Equations Involving Complex Numbers

EXAMPLE 8 **Solving Equations Involving Complex Numbers**

(A) Solve for real numbers x and y:

$$(3x + 2) + (2y - 4)i = -4 + 6i$$

(B) Solve for complex number z:

$$(3 + 2i)z - 3 + 6i = 8 - 4i$$

SOLUTIONS

(A) This equation is really a statement that two complex numbers are equal: $(3x + 2) + (2y - 4)i$, and $-4 + 6i$. In order for these numbers to be equal, the real parts must be the same, and the imaginary parts must be the same as well.

$$\begin{aligned} 3x + 2 &= -4 & 2y - 4 &= 6 \\ 3x &= -6 & 2y &= 10 \\ x &= -2 & y &= 5 \end{aligned}$$

(B) Solve for z, then write the answer in standard form.

$$\begin{aligned} (3 + 2i)z - 3 + 6i &= 8 - 4i && \text{Add 3 and subtract } 6i \text{ from both sides.} \\ (3 + 2i)z &= 11 - 10i && \text{Divide both sides by } 3 + 2i. \\ z &= \frac{11 - 10i}{3 + 2i} && \text{Multiply numerator and denominator by the conjugate of the denominator.} \\ &= \frac{(11 - 10i)(3 - 2i)}{(3 + 2i)(3 - 2i)} && \text{Simplify.} \\ &= \frac{13 - 52i}{13} && \text{Write in standard form.} \\ &= 1 - 4i \end{aligned}$$

A check is left to the reader.

MATCHED PROBLEM 8

(A) Solve for real numbers x and y:

$$(2y - 7) + (3x + 4)i = 1 + i$$

(B) Solve for complex number z:

$$(1 + 3i)z + 4 - 5i = 3 + 2i$$

The truth is that the types of numbers we studied in this section weren't received very well when they were invented. (It could have been worse, though. According to legend, the first mathematician to accept irrational numbers was sentenced to drowning!) In fact, the names given to these numbers are indicative of this resistance to accept them: *complex* and *imaginary*. These are not exactly names that would be given to widely accepted ideas!

In spite of this early resistance, complex numbers have come into widespread use in both pure and applied mathematics. They are used extensively, for example, in electrical engineering, physics, chemistry, statistics, and aeronautical engineering. Our first use of them will be in connection with solutions of second-degree equations in the next section.

ANSWERS TO MATCHED PROBLEMS

1. (A) -49 (B) $-64i$ (C) 16
2. (A) Imaginary numbers: $6 + 7i$, $\sqrt{2} - \frac{1}{3}i$, $0 - i = -i$, $0 + \frac{2}{3}i = \frac{2}{3}i$
Pure imaginary numbers: $0 - i = -i$, $0 + \frac{2}{3}i = \frac{2}{3}i$
Real numbers: $-\sqrt{3} + 0i = -\sqrt{3}$, $0 - 0i = 0$
Zero: $0 - 0i = 0$
(B) $6 - 7i$, $\sqrt{2} + \frac{1}{3}i$, $0 + i = i$, $0 - \frac{2}{3}i = -\frac{2}{3}i$, $-\sqrt{3} - 0i = -\sqrt{3}$, $0 + 0i = 0$
3. (A) $9 - 2i$ (B) $7 - 5i$ (C) $2 - 2i$ (D) 0 **4.** (A) $26 - 7i$ (B) $-6 + 18i$
(C) $3 + 2i$ (D) 13 **5.** (A) $\frac{1}{5} - \frac{1}{10}i$ (B) $1 + 4i$ **6.** (A) 0 (B) $-\frac{1}{3} - \frac{4}{3}i$
7. (A) $4i$ (B) $5 + i\sqrt{7}$ (C) $-\frac{5}{2} - (\sqrt{2}/2)i$ (D) $\frac{3}{13} + \frac{2}{13}i$ **8.** (A) $x = -1$, $y = 4$
(B) $z = 2 + i$

2-4 Exercises

1. Do negative real numbers have square roots? Explain.

2. Arrange the following sets of numbers so that each one contains the one that comes before it in the list: rational numbers, complex numbers, integers, real numbers, natural numbers

3. Is it possible to square an imaginary number and get a real number? Explain.

4. What is the conjugate of a complex number? How do we use conjugates?

5. Which statement is false, and which is true? Justify your response.
(A) Every real number is a complex number
(B) Every complex number is a real number

6. Is it possible to add a real number and an imaginary number? If so, what kind of number is the result?

In Problems 7–12, classify each number into one or more of the following types: imaginary, pure imaginary, real, complex.

7. $2 + 5i$ **8.** $-3 + 0i$ **9.** $0 + 7i$

10. $14 - \frac{1}{2}i$ **11.** $100 + 0i$ **12.** $0 - \pi i$

In Problems 13–46, perform the indicated operations and write each answer in standard form.

13. i^2 **14.** i^3 **15.** $(4i)^2$ **16.** $(11i)^2$

17. $(-i\sqrt{3})^2$ **18.** $(-i\sqrt{17})^2$

19. $(4i)(6i)$ **20.** $(3i)(8i)$

21. $(2 + 4i) + (5 + i)$ **22.** $(3 + i) + (4 + 2i)$

23. $(-2 + 6i) + (7 - 3i)$ **24.** $(6 - 2i) + (8 - 3i)$

25. $(6 + 7i) - (4 + 3i)$ **26.** $(9 + 8i) - (5 + 6i)$

27. $(3 + 5i) - (-2 - 4i)$ **28.** $(8 - 4i) - (11 - 2i)$

29. $(4 - 5i) + 2i$ **30.** $6 + (3 - 4i)$

31. $-3i(2 - 4i)$ **32.** $-2i(5 - 3i)$

33. $(3 + 3i)(2 - 3i)$ **34.** $(-2 - 3i)(3 - 5i)$

35. $(2 - 3i)(7 - 6i)$ **36.** $(3 + 2i)(2 - i)$

37. $(7 + 4i)(7 - 4i)$ **38.** $(5 + 3i)(5 - 3i)$

39. $(4 - 3i)^2$ **40.** $(-2 + 8i)^2$

41. $\dfrac{1}{2 + i}$ **42.** $\dfrac{1}{3 - i}$ **43.** $\dfrac{3 + i}{2 - 3i}$

44. $\dfrac{2 - i}{3 + 2i}$ **45.** $\dfrac{13 + i}{2 - i}$ **46.** $\dfrac{15 - 3i}{2 - 3i}$

In Problems 47–54, evaluate and express results in standard form.

47. $\sqrt{2}\sqrt{8}$ **48.** $\sqrt{3}\sqrt{12}$ **49.** $\sqrt{2}\sqrt{-8}$

50. $\sqrt{-3}\sqrt{12}$ **51.** $\sqrt{-2}\sqrt{8}$ **52.** $\sqrt{3}\sqrt{-12}$

53. $\sqrt{-2}\sqrt{-8}$ **54.** $\sqrt{-3}\sqrt{-12}$

In Problems 55–64, convert imaginary numbers to standard form, perform the indicated operations, and express answers in standard form.

55. $(2 - \sqrt{-4}) + (5 - \sqrt{-9})$

56. $(3 - \sqrt{-4}) + (-8 + \sqrt{-25})$

57. $(9 - \sqrt{-9}) - (12 - \sqrt{-25})$

58. $(-2 - \sqrt{-36}) - (4 + \sqrt{-49})$

59. $(3 - \sqrt{-4})(-2 + \sqrt{-49})$

60. $(2 - \sqrt{-1})(5 + \sqrt{-9})$

61. $\frac{5 - \sqrt{-4}}{7}$

62. $\frac{6 - \sqrt{-64}}{2}$

63. $\frac{1}{2 - \sqrt{-9}}$

64. $\frac{1}{3 - \sqrt{-16}}$

Write Problems 65–70 in standard form.

65. $\frac{2}{5i}$ **66.** $\frac{1}{3i}$ **67.** $\frac{1 + 3i}{2i}$ **68.** $\frac{2 - i}{3i}$

69. $(2 - 3i)^2 - 2(2 - 3i) + 9$

70. $(2 - i)^2 + 3(2 - i) - 5$

71. Let $f(x) = x^2 - 2x + 2$.
(A) Show that the conjugate complex numbers $1 + i$ and $1 - i$ are both zeros of f.
(B) Does f have any real zeros? Any x intercepts? Explain.

72. Let $g(x) = -x^2 + 4x - 5$.
(A) Show that the conjugate complex numbers $2 + i$ and $2 - i$ are both zeros of g.
(B) Does g have any real zeros? Any x intercepts? Explain.

73. Simplify: i^{18}, i^{32}, and i^{67}.

74. Simplify: i^{21}, i^{43}, and i^{52}.

In Problems 75–78, solve for x and y.

75. $(2x - 1) + (3y + 2)i = 5 - 4i$

76. $3x + (y - 2)i = (5 - 2x) + (3y - 8)i$

77. $\frac{(1 + x) + (y - 2)i}{1 + i} = 2 - i$

78. $\frac{(2 + x) + (y + 3)i}{1 - i} = -3 + i$

In Problems 79–82, solve for z. Express answers in standard form.

79. $(2 + i)z + i = 4i$

80. $(3 - i)z + 2 = i$

81. $3iz + (2 - 4i) = (1 + 2i)z - 3i$

82. $(2 - i)z + (1 - 4i) = (-1 + 3i)z + (4 + 2i)$

83. Show that $2 - i$ and $-2 + i$ are square roots of $3 - 4i$.

84. Show that $-3 + 2i$ and $3 - 2i$ are square roots of $5 - 12i$.

85. Explain what is wrong with the following "proof" that $-1 = 1$:

$$-1 = i^2 = \sqrt{-1}\sqrt{-1} = \sqrt{(-1)(-1)} = \sqrt{1} = 1$$

86. Explain what is wrong with the following "proof" that $1/i = i$. What is the correct value of $1/i$?

$$\frac{1}{i} = \frac{1}{\sqrt{-1}} = \frac{\sqrt{1}}{\sqrt{-1}} = \sqrt{\frac{1}{-1}} = \sqrt{-1} = i$$

87. Prove that the product of any complex number and its conjugate is a real number by multiplying a generic complex number $a + bi$ by its conjugate.

88. Is the sum of a complex number and its conjugate always a real number? What about the difference? The quotient?

In Problems 89–94, perform the indicated operations, and write each answer in standard form.

89. $(a + bi) + (c + di)$ **90.** $(a + bi) - (c + di)$

91. $(a + bi)(a - bi)$ **92.** $(u - vi)(u + vi)$

93. $(a + bi)(c + di)$ **94.** $\frac{a + bi}{c + di}$

95. Show that $i^{4k} = 1$, for any natural number k.

96. Show that $i^{4k-1} = -i$, for any natural number k.

97. Let $S_n = i + i^2 + i^3 + \cdots + i^n$, $n \geq 1$. Describe the possible values of S_n.

98. Let $T_n = i^2 + i^4 + i^6 + \cdots + i^{2n}$, $n \geq 1$. Describe the possible values of T_n.

Supply the reasons in the proofs for the theorems stated in Problems 99 and 100.

99. *Theorem:* The complex numbers are commutative under addition.

Proof: Let $a + bi$ and $c + di$ be two arbitrary complex numbers; then,

Statement
1. $(a + bi) + (c + di) = (a + c) + (b + d)i$
2. $= (c + a) + (d + b)i$
3. $= (c + di) + (a + bi)$

Reason
1.
2.
3.

100. *Theorem:* The complex numbers are commutative under multiplication.

Proof: Let $a + bi$ and $c + di$ be two arbitrary complex numbers; then,

Statement
1. $(a + bi) \cdot (c + di) = (ac - bd) + (ad + bc)i$
2. $= (ca - db) + (da + cb)i$
3. $= (c + di) \cdot (a + bi)$

Reason
1.
2.
3.

2-5 Quadratic Equations and Models

- Solving by Factoring
- Solving by Completing the Square
- Solving Using the Quadratic Formula
- Mathematical Modeling
- Data Analysis and Regression

Now that we are familiar with quadratic functions, we turn our attention to quadratic equations. A **quadratic equation** is an equation that can be written in the form $ax^2 + bx + c = 0$, where a, b, and c are real numbers, and a is not zero. (This is called the **general form** for a quadratic equation.) In this book, we are mostly interested in functions that have real-number domains and ranges. But we saw in the last section that some equations don't have solutions unless we expand our thinking to consider imaginary numbers.

Back in Chapter 1, we defined a *zero* of a function $f(x)$ as any real number solution, or *root,* of the equation $f(x) = 0$. To fully understand the zeros of a function, or the roots of an equation, we will need to extend these definitions to allow for complex zeros and roots. We already know that real zeros of a function are x intercepts of its graph. But this does not extend to imaginary zeros: they are never x intercepts.

››› EXPLORE-DISCUSS 1

Match the zeros of each function on the left with one of the sets A, B, or C on the right:

Function	**Zeros**
$f(x) = x^2 - 1$	$A = \{1\}$
$g(x) = x^2 + 1$	$B = \{-1, 1\}$
$h(x) = (x - 1)^2$	$C = \{-i, i\}$

Which of these sets of zeros can be found using graphical approximation techniques? Which cannot? Why?

A graphing calculator can be used to approximate the real roots of an equation, but not the imaginary roots; they simply don't appear on the graph. So in this section, we will focus on algebraic techniques for finding the exact value of the roots of a quadratic equation. In some cases, the roots will be real numbers, and in others they will be imaginary numbers. In the process, we will derive the *quadratic formula,* another essential tool for our mathematical toolbox.

› Solving by Factoring

Throughout our remaining study of solving equations, factoring plays a tremendously important role. Simply put, it's unlikely that you will be successful in the remainder of this course unless you are comfortable with the basic techniques of factoring. We strongly recommend that you review factoring in Appendix A, Section A-5, before moving on.

There is one single reason why factoring is so important in solving equations. It's called the **zero product property.**

››› EXPLORE-DISCUSS 2

(A) Write down a pair of numbers whose product is zero. Is one of them zero? Can you think of two nonzero numbers whose product is zero?

(B) Choose any number other than zero and call it a. Write down a pair of numbers whose product is a. Is one of them a? Can you think of a pair, neither of which is a, whose product is a?

› ZERO PRODUCT PROPERTY

If m and n are complex numbers, then

$$m \cdot n = 0 \quad \text{if and only if} \quad m = 0 \text{ or } n = 0 \text{ (or both)}$$

It is very helpful to think about what this says in words: If the product of two factors is zero, then *at least one of those factors has to be zero*. It's also helpful to observe that *zero is the only number for which this is true.*

EXAMPLE 1 Solving Quadratic Equations by Factoring

Solve by factoring:

(A) $(x - 5)(x + 3) = 0$ (B) $6x^2 - 19x - 7 = 0$

(C) $x^2 - 6x + 5 = -4$ (D) $2x^2 = 3x$

SOLUTIONS

(A) The product of two factors is zero, so by the zero product property, one of the two must be zero. This enables us to write two easier equations to solve.

$$(x - 5)(x + 3) = 0$$
$$x - 5 = 0 \quad \text{or} \quad x + 3 = 0$$
$$x = 5 \qquad\qquad x = -3$$

The solution set is $\{-3, 5\}$.

(B)
$$6x^2 - 19x - 7 = 0 \qquad \text{Factor the left side.}$$
$$(2x - 7)(3x + 1) = 0 \qquad \text{Use the zero product property.}$$
$$2x - 7 = 0 \quad \text{or} \quad 3x + 1 = 0$$
$$x = \tfrac{7}{2} \qquad\qquad x = -\tfrac{1}{3}$$

The solution set is $\{-\frac{1}{3}, \frac{7}{2}\}$.

(C)
$$x^2 - 6x + 5 = -4 \qquad \text{Add 4 to both sides.}$$
$$x^2 - 6x + 9 = 0 \qquad \text{Factor left side.}$$
$$(x - 3)(x - 3) = 0 \qquad \text{Use the zero product property.}$$
$$x - 3 = 0$$
$$x = 3$$

The solution set is $\{3\}$. The equation has one root, 3. But because it came from two factors, we call 3 a *double root* or a *root of multiplicity 2*.

(D)
$$2x^2 = 3x \qquad \text{Subtract } 3x \text{ from both sides.}$$
$$2x^2 - 3x = 0 \qquad \text{Factor the left side.}$$
$$x(2x - 3) = 0 \qquad \text{Use the zero product property.}$$
$$x = 0 \quad \text{or} \quad 2x - 3 = 0$$
$$x = \tfrac{3}{2}$$

Solution set: $\{0, \frac{3}{2}\}$

MATCHED PROBLEM 1

Solve by factoring:

(A) $(2x + 4)(x - 7) = 0$ (B) $3x^2 + 7x - 20 = 0$
(C) $4x^2 + 12x + 9 = 0$ (D) $4x^2 = 5x$

››› CAUTION ›››

1. One side of an equation must be 0 before the zero product property can be applied. So

$$x^2 - 6x + 5 = -4$$
$$(x - 1)(x - 5) = -4$$

does not imply that $x - 1 = -4$ or $x - 5 = -4$. See Example 1, part C, for the correct solution of this equation.

2. The equations

$$2x^2 = 3x \qquad \text{and} \qquad 2x = 3$$

are not equivalent. The first has solution set $\{0, \frac{3}{2}\}$, but the second has solution set $\{\frac{3}{2}\}$. The root $x = 0$ is lost when each member of the first equation is divided by the variable x. See Example 1, part D, for the correct solution of this equation.

Never divide both sides of an equation by an expression containing the variable for which you are solving. You may be dividing by 0, which of course is not allowed.

REMARK: It is common practice to represent solutions of quadratic equations informally by the last equation (such as $x = 3$) rather than by writing a solution set using set notation (see Example 1). From now on, we will follow this practice unless a particular emphasis is necessary.

› Solving by Completing the Square

Factoring is a very efficient method for solving equations when the factors can be quickly identified. But often, that is not the case.* We next turn to an approach that will be able to solve any quadratic equation. But first, we must become acquainted with a simple method for solving certain quadratic equations.

› SQUARE ROOT PROPERTY

If r is a complex number, s is a real number, and $r^2 = s$, then $r = \pm\sqrt{s}$.

*As we will see in Chapter 3, every quadratic expression *can* be factored, but doing so directly is often extremely difficult.

EXAMPLE 2 Solving Using the Square Root Property

Solve using the square root property:

(A) $(2x - 3)^2 = 9$ (B) $(x + 5)^2 = -3$ (C) $\left(x + \frac{1}{2}\right)^2 - \frac{5}{4} = 0$

SOLUTIONS

(A) According to the square root property, if the square of $2x - 3$ is 9, then $2x - 3$ is either $\sqrt{9}$ or $-\sqrt{9}$.

$$(2x - 3)^2 = 9 \quad \text{Apply the square root property.}$$
$$2x - 3 = \pm 3 \quad \text{Add 3 to both sides.}$$
$$2x = 3 + 3 \quad \text{or} \quad 2x = 3 - 3$$
$$2x = 6 \quad \text{or} \quad 2x = 0$$
$$x = 3 \qquad\qquad x = 0$$

(B)
$$(x + 5)^2 = -3 \quad \text{Apply the square root property.}$$
$$x + 5 = \pm\sqrt{-3} \quad \text{Simplify } \sqrt{-3}.$$
$$x + 5 = \pm i\sqrt{3} \quad \text{Subtract 5 from both sides.}$$
$$x = -5 \pm i\sqrt{3}$$

(C)
$$\left(x + \frac{1}{2}\right)^2 - \frac{5}{4} = 0 \quad \text{Add } \tfrac{5}{4} \text{ to both sides.}$$
$$\left(x + \frac{1}{2}\right)^2 = \frac{5}{4} \quad \text{Apply the square root property.}$$
$$x + \frac{1}{2} = \pm\sqrt{\frac{5}{4}} \quad \text{Subtract } \tfrac{1}{2} \text{ from both sides; simplify } \sqrt{\tfrac{5}{4}}.$$
$$x = -\frac{1}{2} \pm \frac{\sqrt{5}}{2}$$
$$x = \frac{-1 \pm \sqrt{5}}{2}$$

MATCHED PROBLEM 2

Solve using the square root property:

(A) $(7 - 5x)^2 = 25$ (B) $(x - 7)^2 = -6$ (C) $\left(\frac{1}{2}x - 4\right)^2 - 10 = 0$

››› CAUTION ›››

1. Before applying the square root property, make sure to isolate the squared expression.
2. The single most common mistake that students make in solving quadratic equations is forgetting the "±" when applying the square root property.

Now we will see how completing the square will enable us to rewrite quadratic equations of the form $ax^2 + bx + c = 0$ into a form that can be solved using the square root property.

EXAMPLE 3 Solving by Completing the Square

Use completing the square and the square root property to solve each of the following:

(A) $x^2 + 6x - 2 = 0$ (B) $2x^2 - 4x + 3 = 0$

SOLUTIONS

(A) We can speed up the process of completing the square by taking advantage of the fact that we are working with a quadratic equation, not a quadratic expression.

$x^2 + 6x - 2 = 0$	Isolate the squared and first power terms.
$x^2 + 6x = 2$	$(\frac{1}{2} \cdot 6)^2 = 9$; Add 9 to both sides to complete the square.
$x^2 + 6x + 9 = 2 + 9$	Factor the left side.
$(x + 3)^2 = 11$	Use the square root property.
$x + 3 = \pm\sqrt{11}$	Subtract 3 from both sides.
$x = -3 \pm \sqrt{11}$	

(B) $2x^2 - 4x + 3 = 0$	Divide both sides by 2 to make 1 the coefficient of x^2.
$x^2 - 2x + \frac{3}{2} = 0$	Isolate the squared and first power terms.
$x^2 - 2x = -\frac{3}{2}$	$(\frac{1}{2} \cdot (-2))^2 = 1$; Add 1 to both sides to complete the square.
$x^2 - 2x + 1 = -\frac{3}{2} + 1$	Factor the left side.
$(x - 1)^2 = -\frac{1}{2}$	Use the square root property.
$x - 1 = \pm\sqrt{-\frac{1}{2}}$	Add 1 to both sides; simplify $\sqrt{-\frac{1}{2}}$.
$x = 1 \pm i\sqrt{\frac{1}{2}}$	Rationalize the denominator.
$= 1 \pm \frac{\sqrt{2}}{2}i$	Answer in $a + bi$ form.

MATCHED PROBLEM 3

Solve by completing the square:

(A) $x^2 + 8x - 3 = 0$ (B) $3x^2 - 12x + 13 = 0$

››› CAUTION ›››

Do not confuse completing the square in a quadratic function with completing the square in a quadratic equation. For functions, we add and subtract $\frac{b^2}{4}$ on the same side. For equations, we add $\frac{b^2}{4}$ to both sides of the equation.

Function	**Equation**
$f(x) = x^2 - 6x - 4$	$x^2 - 6x - 4 = 0$
$= x^2 - 6x + 9 - 9 - 4$	$x^2 - 6x + 9 = 4 + 9$
$= (x - 3)^2 - 13$	$(x - 3)^2 = 13$

››› EXPLORE-DISCUSS 3

Graph the quadratic functions associated with the two quadratic equations in Example 3. Approximate the x intercepts of each function and compare with the roots found in Example 3. Which of these equations has roots that cannot be approximated graphically?

› Solving Using the Quadratic Formula

The value of completing the square as a method of solving is that it works for *every* quadratic equation. But it is a bit cumbersome to use on a regular basis. Fortunately, the fact that it works for any quadratic equation leads to a very clever idea: We will try to reproduce the process of completing the square on the general quadratic equation $ax^2 + bx + c = 0$ (recall that $a \neq 0$). If all goes well, we will have solved *every* quadratic equation all at once!

Note that the steps we follow are exactly the same as the steps used in Example 3, part B.

$$ax^2 + bx + c = 0$$
Divide both sides by a to make 1 the coefficient of x^2.

$$x^2 + \frac{b}{a}x + \frac{c}{a} = 0$$
Isolate the squared and first power terms.

$$x^2 + \frac{b}{a}x = -\frac{c}{a}$$
$\left(\frac{1}{2} \cdot \frac{b}{a}\right)^2 = \frac{b^2}{4a^2}$; add $\frac{b^2}{4a^2}$ to both sides.

$$x^2 + \frac{b}{a}x + \frac{b^2}{4a^2} = \frac{b^2}{4a^2} - \frac{c}{a}$$
Factor the left side as $(x$ + half the coefficient of $x)^2$; subtract on the right side.

$$\left(x + \frac{b}{2a}\right)^2 = \frac{b^2 - 4ac}{4a^2}$$
Use the square root property.

$$x + \frac{b}{2a} = \pm\sqrt{\frac{b^2 - 4ac}{4a^2}}$$
Subtract $\frac{b}{2a}$ from both sides.

$$x = \frac{-b}{2a} \pm \sqrt{\frac{b^2 - 4ac}{4a^2}}$$ Simplify the radical. (See Problem 93 in Exercises 2-5.)

$$x = \frac{-b}{2a} \pm \frac{\sqrt{b^2 - 4ac}}{2a}$$ Write as a single fraction.

$$x = \frac{-b \pm \sqrt{b^2 - 4ac}}{2a}$$

We were successful in solving, and the result is a formula that provides the solution of any quadratic equation in standard form. This is known as the **quadratic formula.**

› THEOREM 1 Quadratic Formula

If $ax^2 + bx + c = 0, a \neq 0$, then

$$x = \frac{-b \pm \sqrt{b^2 - 4ac}}{2a}$$

The quadratic formula and completing the square are equivalent methods. Either can be used to find the exact value of the roots of any quadratic equation, although in most cases the quadratic formula is easier to use.

EXAMPLE 4 Using the Quadratic Formula

Solve $2x + \frac{3}{2} = x^2$ using the quadratic formula. Leave the answer in simplest radical form.

SOLUTION

$$2x + \tfrac{3}{2} = x^2$$ Multiply both sides by 2 to clear fractions.

$$4x + 3 = 2x^2$$ Write in standard form.

$$2x^2 - 4x - 3 = 0$$ Use the quadratic formula.

$$x = \frac{-b \pm \sqrt{b^2 - 4ac}}{2a}$$ Substitute $a = 2, b = -4, c = -3$.

$$= \frac{-(-4) \pm \sqrt{(-4)^2 - 4(2)(-3)}}{2(2)}$$

$$= \frac{4 \pm \sqrt{40}}{4} = \frac{4 \pm 2\sqrt{10}}{4} = \frac{2 \pm \sqrt{10}}{2}$$

››› CAUTION ›››

There are a number of common mistakes to watch out for when using the quadratic formula.

1. Make sure the equation is written in the form $ax^2 + bx + c = 0$ before deciding on values for a, b, and c.
2. $-4^2 \neq (-4)^2$ $\quad -4^2 = -16$ and $(-4)^2 = 16$
3. $2 + \dfrac{\sqrt{10}}{2} \neq \dfrac{2 + \sqrt{10}}{2}$ $\quad 2 + \dfrac{\sqrt{10}}{2} = \dfrac{4 + \sqrt{10}}{2}$
4. $\dfrac{4 \pm 2\sqrt{10}}{4} \neq \pm 2\sqrt{10}$ $\quad \dfrac{4 \pm 2\sqrt{10}}{4} = \dfrac{2(2 \pm \sqrt{10})}{4} = \dfrac{2 \pm \sqrt{10}}{2}$

MATCHED PROBLEM 4

Solve $x^2 - \frac{5}{2} = -3x$ using the quadratic formula. Leave the answer in simplest radical form.

››› EXPLORE-DISCUSS 4

Given the quadratic function $f(x) = ax^2 + bx + c$, let $D = b^2 - 4ac$. How many real zeros does f have if

(A) $D > 0$ **(B)** $D = 0$ **(C)** $D < 0$

In each of these three cases, what type of roots does the quadratic equation $f(x) = 0$ have?

Match each of the three cases with one of the following graphs.

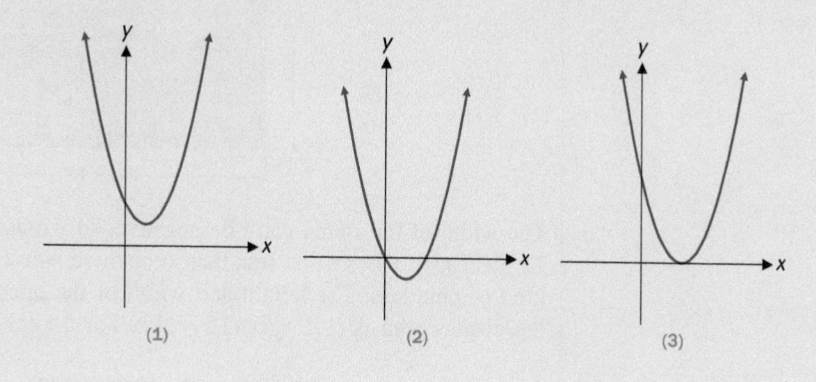

The quantity $b^2 - 4ac$ in the quadratic formula is called the **discriminant** and gives us information about the roots of the corresponding equation and the zeros of the associated quadratic function. This information is summarized in Table 1.

Table 1 Discriminants, Roots, and Zeros

Discriminant $b^2 - 4ac$	Roots of $ax^2 + bx + c = 0$*	Number of Real Zeros of $f(x) = ax^2 + bx + c$*
Positive	Two distinct real roots	2
0	One real root (a double root)	1
Negative	Two imaginary roots, one the conjugate of the other†	0

*a, b, and c are real numbers with $a \neq 0$.
†See Problem 94 in Exercises 2-5 for a justification.

Mathematical Modeling

Now we will use our new skills in some applications that involve quadratic equations.

EXAMPLE 5 Design

A rectangular picture frame of uniform width has outer dimensions of 12 inches by 18 inches. How wide (to the nearest tenth of an inch) must the frame be to display an area of 140 square inches?

SOLUTION

Constructing the Model

We begin by drawing and labeling a figure:

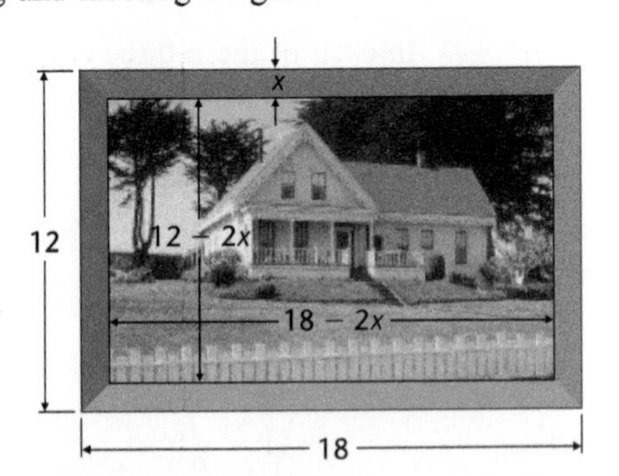

The width of the frame can't be negative, so x must satisfy $x \geq 0$. The total height is 12 inches, so x has to be less than 6 or there won't be an opening, making the frame kind of pointless. The height and width of the opening are $12 - 2x$ and $18 - 2x$, so the display area is $(12 - 2x)(18 - 2x)$. For a total of 140 square inches, we need

$$(12 - 2x)(18 - 2x) = 140 \qquad 0 \leq x < 6$$

Algebraic Solution

$$(18 - 2x)(12 - 2x) = 140 \quad \text{Multiply parentheses.}$$
$$216 - 36x - 24x + 4x^2 = 140 \quad \text{Write in standard form.}$$
$$4x^2 - 60x + 76 = 0 \quad \text{Divide both sides by 4.}$$
$$x^2 - 15x + 19 = 0 \quad a = 1, b = -15, c = 19$$

$$x = \frac{15 \pm \sqrt{225 - 4(1)(19)}}{2(1)}$$
$$= \frac{15 \pm \sqrt{149}}{2}$$

The quadratic equation has two solutions (rounded to one decimal place):

$$x = \frac{15 + \sqrt{149}}{2} = 13.6$$

and

$$x = \frac{15 - \sqrt{149}}{2} = 1.4$$

The first must be discarded because x must satisfy $x < 6$. So the width of the frame is 1.4 inches.

Graphical Solution

Entering $y_1 = (18 - 2x)(12 - 2x)$ and $y_2 = 140$ in the equation editor (Fig. 1) and using the INTERSECT command (Fig. 2) shows that the width of the frame is $x = 1.4$ inches.

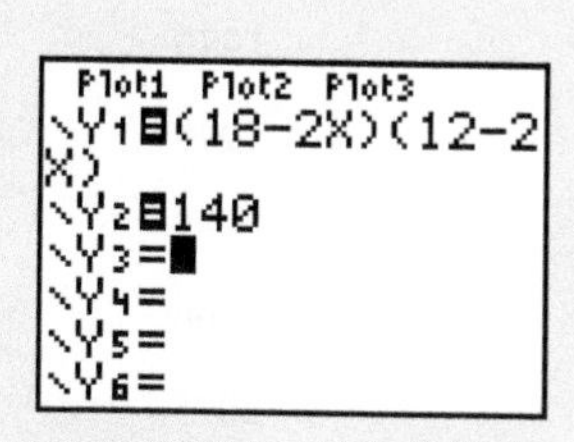

› **Figure 1**

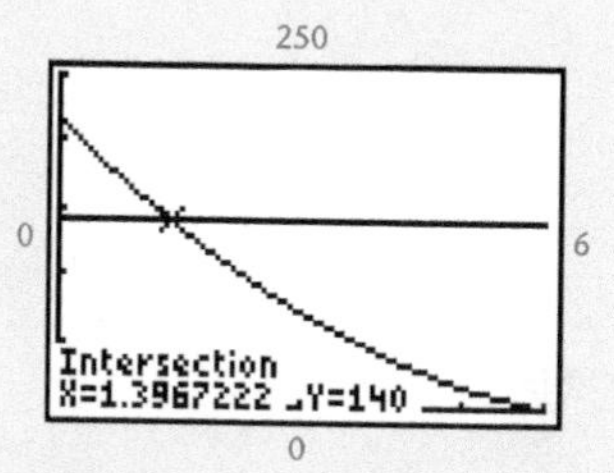

› **Figure 2**

Note: A graphical solution is sufficient in this setting since x is a length, and imaginary solutions wouldn't be of interest.

MATCHED PROBLEM 5

A poster promoting a concert is being designed to fit on 24- by 36-inch pieces of paper. If the printer requires a margin of uniform width around all four sides, how wide (to the nearest tenth of an inch) should the margin be if the artist requires 730 square inches of printable area?

› Data Analysis and Regression

Now that we have added quadratic functions to our mathematical toolbox, we can use this new tool in conjunction with another tool discussed previously—regression analysis. In Example 6, we use both of these tools to investigate the effect of recycling efforts on solid waste disposal.

EXAMPLE 6 **Solid Waste Disposal**

Franklin Associates, Ltd. of Prairie Village, Kansas, reported the data in Table 2 to the U.S. Environmental Protection Agency.

Table 2 Municipal Solid Waste Disposal

Year	Annual landfill disposal (millions of tons)	Per Person per Day (pounds)
1960	55.5	1.68
1970	88.2	2.37
1980	123.3	2.97
1990	131.6	2.90
1995	118.4	2.50
2000	113.6	2.16
2005	109.1	2.03

(A) Let x represent time in years with $x = 0$ corresponding to 1950, and let y represent the corresponding annual landfill disposal. Use regression analysis on a graphing calculator to find a quadratic function $y = ax^2 + bx + c$ that models these data. (Round the constants a, b, and c to three significant digits.)

(B) If landfill disposal continues to follow the trend exhibited in Table 2, when (to the nearest year) will the annual landfill disposal return to the 1960 level?

(C) Is it reasonable to expect the annual landfill disposal to follow this trend indefinitely? Explain.

SOLUTIONS

(A) The y values in the annual landfill disposal column increase from 1960 to 1990 but then begin to decrease, so a linear regression model will not fit the data well. But a quadratic model seems like a reasonable alternative. See Section 2-2 for a refresher on entering data and calculating a regression model. The only difference now is that we choose QUADREG from the CALC menu. Figure 3 shows the details of constructing the model on a graphing calculator.

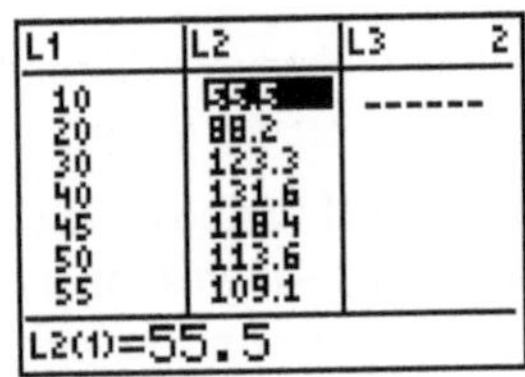

(a) Data

QuadReg
y=ax²+bx+c
a=-.0836154579
b=6.606514436
c=-4.25507545
R²=.9648988782

(b) Regression equation

Plot1 Plot2 Plot3
\Y1=-.0836X²+6.61X-4.26
\Y2=
\Y3=
\Y4=
\Y5=
\Y6=

(c) Regression equation entered in equation editor

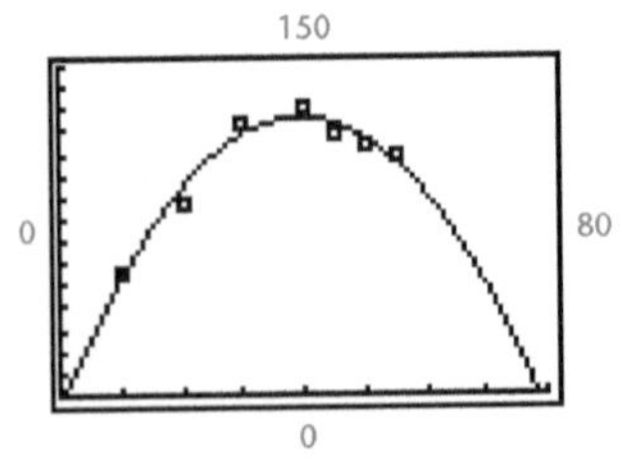

(d) Graph of data and regression equation

› **Figure 3**

Rounding the constants to three significant digits, a quadratic regression equation for these data is

$$y_1 = -0.0836x^2 + 6.61x - 4.26$$

The graph in Figure 3(d) indicates that this is a reasonable model for these data.

(B) To determine when the annual landfill disposal returns to the 1960 level, we add the graph of $y_2 = 55.5$ to the graph (Fig. 4).

The graphs of y_1 and y_2 intersect twice, once at $x = 10$ (1960), and again at a later date. Using the INTERSECT command (Fig. 5) shows that the x coordinate of the second intersection point (to the nearest integer) is 69. Thus, the annual landfill disposal returns to the 1960 level of 55.5 million tons in 2019.

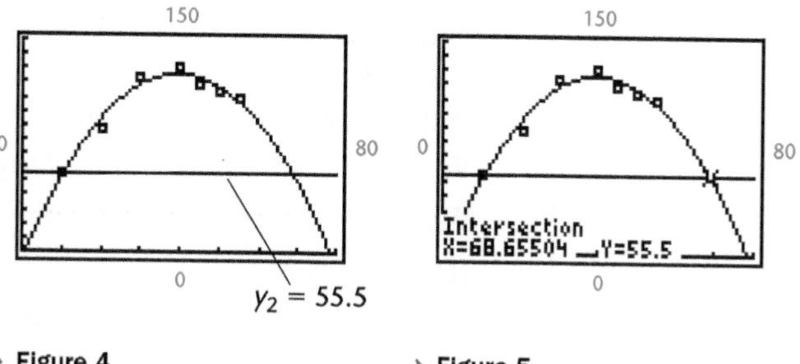

› Figure 4 › Figure 5

(C) The graph of y_1 continues to decrease and reaches 0 somewhere between $x = 78$ and 79 (2028 and 2029). It is highly unlikely that the annual landfall disposal will ever reach 0. As time goes by and more data become available, new models will have to be constructed to better predict future trends.

MATCHED PROBLEM 6

Refer to Table 2.

(A) Let x represent time in years with $x = 0$ corresponding to 1950, and let y represent the corresponding landfill disposal per person per day. Use regression analysis on a graphing calculator to find a quadratic function of the form $y = ax^2 + bx + c$ that models these data. (Round the constants a, b, and c to three significant digits.)

(B) If landfill disposal per person per day continues to follow the trend exhibited in Table 2, when (to the nearest year) will it fall below 1 pound per person per day?

(C) Is it reasonable to expect the landfill disposal per person per day to follow this trend indefinitely? Explain.

Most gasoline engines are more fuel efficient at a midrange speed than at either extremely high or extremely low speeds. Example 7 uses quadratic regression to determine the most economical speed for a speedboat.

EXAMPLE 7 Optimal Speed

Table 3

mph	mpg
4.6	3.07
7.3	3.17
21.0	6.77
29.8	6.62
40.2	2.77
44.6	2.37

Source: www.yamaha-motor.com

Table 3 contains performance data for a speedboat powered by a Yamaha outboard motor. In the work that follows, round all numbers to three significant digits.

(A) Let x be the speed of the boat in miles per hour (mph) and y the associated mileage in miles per gallon (mpg). Use the data in Table 3 to find a quadratic regression function $y = ax^2 + bx + c$ for this boat.

(B) A marina rents this boat for \$20 per hour plus the cost of the gasoline used. If gasoline costs \$2.30 per gallon and you take a 100-mile trip in this boat, construct a mathematical model and use it to answer the following questions:

What speed should you travel to minimize the rental charges?

What mileage will the boat get?

How long is the trip?

How much gasoline will you use?

How much will the trip cost you?

SOLUTIONS

L1	L2	L3 3
4.6	3.07	
7.3	3.17	
21	6.77	
29.8	6.62	
40.2	2.77	
44.6	2.37	

L3(1)=

› **Figure 6**

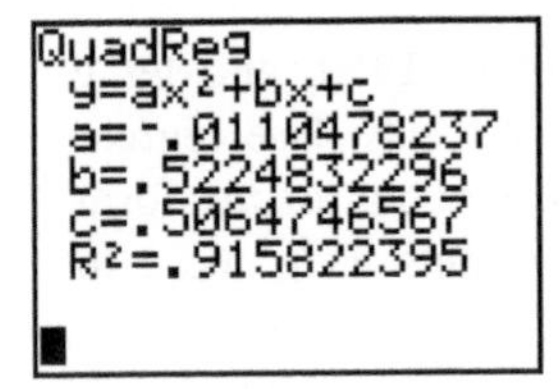

› **Figure 7**

(A) Entering the data in the statistics editor (Fig. 6) and selecting the QUADREG option (Fig. 7) produces the following quadratic function relating speed and mileage:

$$y = -0.0110x^2 + 0.522x + 0.506$$

(B) If t is the number of hours the boat is rented and g is the number of gallons of gasoline used, then the cost of the rental (in dollars) is

$$C = 20t + 2.3g \qquad \text{\$20 per hour + \$2.30 per gallon}$$

If x is the speed of the boat and y is the associated mileage, then

$$xt = 100 \qquad \text{rate} \cdot \text{time} = \text{distance} \tag{1}$$

and

$$yg = 100 \qquad \text{(miles/gallon)(gallons) = distance} \tag{2}$$

Solving equation (1) for t, we get

$$t = \frac{100}{x}$$

Next, we solve equation (2) for y, and use the quadratic regression function from part A to represent y.

$$g = \frac{100}{y} = \frac{100}{-0.0110x^2 + 0.522x + 0.506}$$

Now that we have expressions for both gallons and hours in terms of x, we return to the cost equation,

$$\begin{aligned} C &= 20t + 2.3g \\ &= 20\frac{100}{x} + 2.3\frac{100}{-0.0110x^2 + 0.522x + 0.506} \\ &= \frac{2,000}{x} + \frac{230}{-0.0110x^2 + 0.522x + 0.506} \end{aligned}$$

```
Plot1 Plot2 Plot3
\Y1■(2000/X)+(23
0/(-.0110X²+.522
X+.506)
\Y2=■
\Y3=
\Y4=
\Y5=
```

› Figure 8

This is the mathematical model for the total cost of the trip. Our first objective is to find the speed x that produces the minimum cost. Entering the cost function in the equation editor (Fig. 8) and using the MINIMUM command (Fig. 9), we see that the minimum cost occurs when the boat speed is 34.1 miles per hour. Evaluating the quadratic function in part A at 34.1, we find that the corresponding mileage is $y = 5.52$ miles per gallon. The trip will take $\frac{1000}{34.1} = 2.93$ hours and consume $\frac{1000}{5.52} = 18.1$ gallons of gas. We can see from Figure 9 that the trip will cost \$100. To check this, we can compute the cost directly

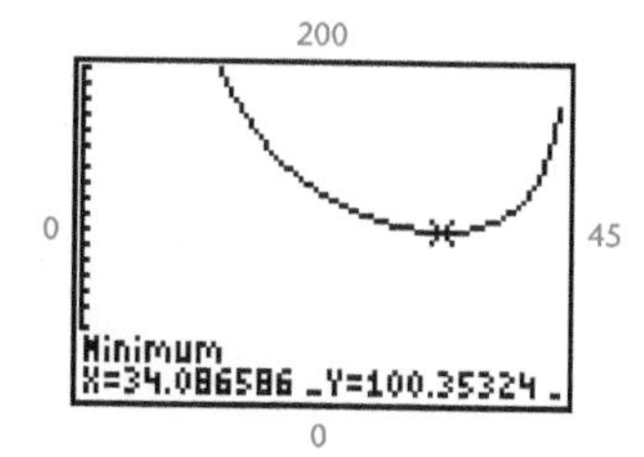

› Figure 9

$$C = \underset{\text{Rent}}{20(2.93)} \underset{\text{plus}}{+} \underset{\text{Gasoline}}{2.3(18.1)} = \$100 \text{ (to nearest dollar)}$$

MATCHED PROBLEM 7

Table 4 contains performance data for a speedboat powered by a Yamaha outboard motor. In the work that follows, round all numbers to three significant digits.

Table 4

mph	mpg
4.8	2.67
8.9	2.12
18.5	2.89
34.4	3.78
43.8	3.40
48.6	2.63

Source: www.yamaha-motor.com

(A) Let x be the speed of the boat in miles per hour (mph) and y the associated mileage in miles per gallon (mpg). Use the data in Table 4 to find a quadratic regression function $y = ax^2 + bx + c$ for this boat.

(B) A marina rents this boat for \$15 per hour plus the cost of the gasoline used. If gasoline costs \$2.50 per gallon and you take a 200-mile trip in this boat, construct a mathematical model and use it to answer the following questions:

What speed should you travel to minimize the rental charges?

What mileage will the boat get?

How long does the trip take?

How much gasoline will you use?

How much will the trip cost you?

ANSWERS TO MATCHED PROBLEMS

1. (A) $\{-2, 7\}$ (B) $\{-4, \frac{5}{3}\}$ (C) $\{-\frac{3}{2}\}$ (a double root) (D) $\{0, \frac{5}{4}\}$

2. (A) $x = \frac{2}{5}, \frac{12}{5}$ (B) $x = 7 \pm i\sqrt{6}$ (C) $x = 8 \pm 2\sqrt{10}$

3. (A) $x = -4 \pm \sqrt{19}$ (B) $x = (6 \pm i\sqrt{3})/3$ or $2 \pm (\sqrt{3}/3)i$

4. $x = (-3 \pm \sqrt{19})/2$ **5.** 1.2 inches

6. (A) $y = -0.00217x^2 + 0.146x + 0.412$ (B) 2013

7. (A) $y = -0.00176x^2 + 0.110x + 1.72$

(B) The boat should travel at 41.6 miles per hour. The mileage is 3.25 miles per gallon. The trip will take 4.81 hours and will consume 61.5 gallons of gasoline. The trip will cost $225.95.

2-5 Exercises

1. Explain what the zero product property says in your own words.

2. Explain what the square root property says in your own words.

3. If you could only use one of factoring, completing the square, and quadratic formula on an important test featuring a variety of quadratic equations, which would you choose, and why?

4. Does every quadratic equation have two solutions? Explain.

5. Explain why the real roots of the quadratic equation $ax^2 + bx + c = 0$ are equivalent to the x intercepts of the function $f(x) = ax^2 + bx + c$.

6. Explain why the imaginary roots of the $ax^2 + bx + c = 0$ do not correspond to x intercepts of the function $f(x) = ax^2 + bx + c$.

In Problems 7–16, solve by factoring.

7. $(x - 8)(2x + 3) = 0$ **8.** $(x + 4)(3x - 10) = 0$

9. $x^2 - 3x - 10 = 0$ **10.** $x^2 + 6x + 8 = 0$

11. $4u^2 = 8u$ **12.** $3A^2 = -12A$

13. $9y^2 = 12y - 4$ **14.** $16x^2 + 8x = -1$

15. $11x = 2x^2 + 12$ **16.** $8 - 10x = 3x^2$

In Problems 17–28, solve by completing the square.

17. $x^2 - 6x - 3 = 0$ **18.** $y^2 - 10y - 3 = 0$

19. $t^2 - 4t + 8 = 0$ **20.** $w^2 - 6w + 25 = 0$

21. $m^2 + 2m + 9 = 0$ **22.** $n^2 + 8n + 34 = 0$

23. $2d^2 + 5d - 25 = 0$ **24.** $2u^2 + 7u + 3 = 0$

25. $2v^2 - 2v + 1 = 0$ **26.** $9x^2 - 12x + 5 = 0$

27. $4y^2 + 3y + 9 = 0$ **28.** $5t^2 + 2t + 5 = 0$

In Problems 29–38, solve using the quadratic formula.

29. $x^2 - 10x - 3 = 0$ **30.** $x^2 - 6x - 3 = 0$

31. $x^2 + 8 = 4x$ **32.** $y^2 + 3 = 2y$

33. $2x^2 + 1 = 4x$ **34.** $2m^2 + 3 = 6m$

35. $5x^2 + 2 = 2x$ **36.** $7x^2 + 6x + 4 = 0$

37. $4(x^2 + 2x) - 4 = 0$ **38.** $-2(5 - x^2) + 2 = 0$

For each equation in Problems 39–44, use the discriminant to determine the number and type of zeros.

39. $2.4x^2 + 6.4x - 4.3 = 0$ **40.** $0.4x^2 - 3.2x + 6.4 = 0$

41. $6.5x^2 - 7.4x + 3.4 = 0$ **42.** $3.4x^2 - 2.5x - 1.5 = 0$

43. $0.3x^2 + 3.6x + 10.8 = 0$ **44.** $1.7x^2 + 2.4x + 1.4 = 0$

For each equation in Problems 45–50, use a graph to determine the number and type of zeros.

45. $0.2x^2 - 3.2x + 12.8 = 0$ **46.** $4.5x^2 + 1.7x - 0.4 = 0$

47. $3.4x^2 - 9.1x - 4.7 = 0$ **48.** $1.3x^2 - 1.5x + 0.8 = 0$

49. $2.4x^2 + 3.7x + 1.5 = 0$ **50.** $0.6x^2 + 6x + 15 = 0$

In Problems 51–60, solve algebraically and confirm with a graphing calculator, if possible.

51. $x^2 - 6x - 3 = 0$

52. $y^2 - 10y - 3 = 0$

53. $2y^2 - 6y + 3 = 0$

54. $2d^2 - 4d + 1 = 0$

55. $3x^2 - 2x - 2 = 0$

56. $3x^2 + 5x - 4 = 0$

57. $12x^2 + 7x = 10$

58. $9x^2 + 9x = 4$

59. $x^2 = 3x + 1$

60. $x^2 + 2x = 2$

In Problems 61–64, solve for the indicated variable in terms of the other variables. Use positive square roots only.

61. $s = \frac{1}{2}gt^2$ for t

62. $a^2 + b^2 = c^2$ for a

63. $P = EI - RI^2$ for I

64. $A = P(1 + r)^2$ for r

In Problems 65–80, solve by any algebraic method and confirm graphically, if possible. Round any approximate solutions to three decimal places.

65. $x^2 - \sqrt{7}x + 2 = 0$

66. $x^2 + \sqrt{11}x + 3 = 0$

67. $x^2 - 2\sqrt{3}x + 3 = 0$

68. $x^2 - \sqrt{5}x - 5 = 0$

69. $x^2 + \sqrt{3}x - 4 = 0$

70. $x^2 + 2\sqrt{5}x + 5 = 0$

71. $1 + \frac{9}{x^2} = \frac{5}{x}$

72. $1 + \frac{25}{x^2} = \frac{9}{x}$

73. $1 + \frac{9}{x^2} = \frac{6}{x}$

74. $1 + \frac{25}{x^2} = \frac{10}{x}$

75. $1 + \frac{9}{x^2} = \frac{7}{x}$

76. $1 + \frac{25}{x^2} = \frac{11}{x}$

77. $3 + \frac{5}{x - 4} = \frac{7}{x + 4}$

78. $5 + \frac{6}{x - 2} = \frac{4}{x + 2}$

79. $\frac{8}{x - 5} = \frac{3}{x + 5} - 2$

80. $\frac{6}{x - 3} = \frac{4}{x + 3} - 3$

81. Consider the quadratic equation

$$x^2 + 4x + c = 0$$

where c is a real number. Discuss the relationship between the values of c and the three types of roots listed in Table 1 on page 215.

82. Consider the quadratic equation

$$x^2 - 2x + c = 0$$

where c is a real number. Discuss the relationship between the values of c and the three types of roots listed in Table 1 on page 215.

In Problems 83–86, solve and express your answer in $a + bi$ form.

83. $x^2 + 3ix - 2 = 0$

84. $x^2 - 7ix - 10 = 0$

85. $x^2 + 2ix = 3$

86. $x^2 = 2ix - 3$

In Problems 87 and 88, find all solutions. [Hint: Factor using special formulas.]

87. $x^3 - 1 = 0$

88. $x^4 - 1 = 0$

89. Can a quadratic equation with rational coefficients have one rational root and one irrational root? Explain.

90. Can a quadratic equation with real coefficients have one real root and one imaginary root? Explain.

91. Show that if r_1 and r_2 are the two roots of $ax^2 + bx + c = 0$, then $r_1r_2 = c/a$.

92. For r_1 and r_2 in Problem 91, show that $r_1 + r_2 = -b/a$.

93. In one stage of the derivation of the quadratic formula, we replaced the expression

$$\pm\sqrt{(b^2 - 4ac)/4a^2}$$

with

$$\pm\sqrt{b^2 - 4ac}/2a$$

What justifies using $2a$ in place of $|2a|$?

Problem 94 addresses the claim in Table 1 on page 215 that imaginary solutions to quadratic equations come in conjugate pairs.

94. If $ax^2 + bx + c = 0$ has two imaginary solutions, then the discriminant $b^2 - 4ac$ is negative.

(A) Write $\sqrt{b^2 - 4ac}$ as i times a root in this case. [*Hint:* Try writing $\sqrt{-3}$ as i times a root, then apply the result to $\sqrt{b^2 - 4ac}$, where $b^2 - 4ac < 0$.]

(B) Rewrite the quadratic formula with your answer to part A in place of $\sqrt{b^2 - 4ac}$.

(C) Split the quadratic formula into two separate solutions, one for the positive root and one for the negative. Then write the right side of each in $a + bi$ form. What do you notice about the two solutions in this case?

95. Find two numbers such that their sum is 21 and their product is 104.

96. Find all numbers with the property that when the number is added to itself the sum is the same as when the number is multiplied by itself.

97. Find two consecutive positive even integers whose product is 168.

98. Find two consecutive positive integers whose product is 600.

APPLICATIONS

99. AIR SEARCH A search plane takes off from an airport at 6:00 A.M. and travels due north at 200 miles per hour. A second plane takes off at 6:30 A.M. and travels due east at 170 miles per hour. The planes carry radios with a maximum range of 500 miles. When (to the nearest minute) will these planes no longer be able to communicate with each other?

100. NAVIGATION A speedboat takes 1 hour longer to go 24 miles up a river than to return. If the boat cruises at 10 miles per hour in still water, what is the rate of the current?

101. CONSTRUCTION A gardener has a 30 foot by 20 foot rectangular plot of ground. She wants to build a brick walkway of uniform width on the border of the plot (see the figure). If the gardener wants to have 400 square feet of ground left for planting, how wide (to two decimal places) should she build the walkway?

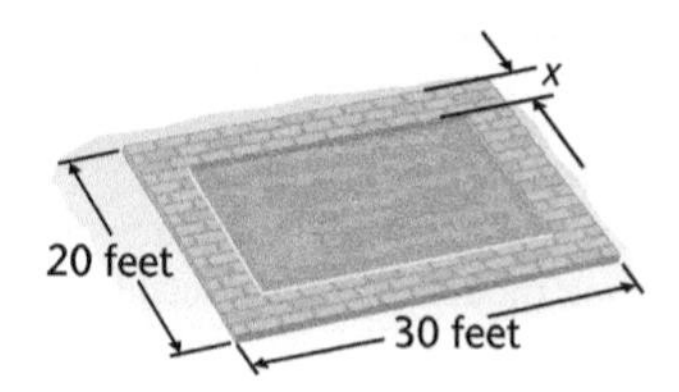

102. CONSTRUCTION Refer to Problem 101. The gardener buys enough bricks to build 160 square feet of walkway. Is this sufficient to build the walkway determined in Problem 101? If not, how wide (to two decimal places) can she build the walkway with these bricks?

103. CONSTRUCTION A 1,200 square foot rectangular garden is enclosed with 150 feet of fencing. Find the dimensions of the garden to the nearest tenth of a foot.

104. CONSTRUCTION The intramural fields at a small college will cover a total area of 140,000 square feet, and the administration has budgeted for 1,600 feet of fence to enclose the rectangular field. Find the dimensions of the field.

105. ARCHITECTURE A developer wants to erect a rectangular building on a triangular-shaped piece of property that is 200 feet wide and 400 feet long (see the figure).

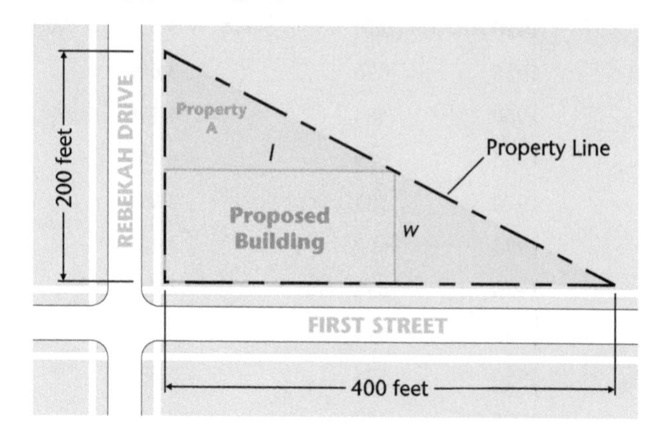

(A) Express the area $A(w)$ of the footprint of the building as a function of the width w and state the domain of this function. [*Hint:* Use Euclid's theorem* to find a relationship between the length l and width w.]
(B) Building codes require that this building have a footprint of at least 15,000 square feet. What are the widths of the building that will satisfy the building codes?
(C) Can the developer construct a building with a footprint of 25,000 square feet? What is the maximum area of the footprint of a building constructed in this manner?

106. ARCHITECTURE An architect is designing a small A-frame cottage for a resort area. A cross-section of the cottage is an isosceles triangle with a base of 5 meters and an altitude of 4 meters. The front wall of the cottage must accommodate a sliding door positioned as shown in the figure.

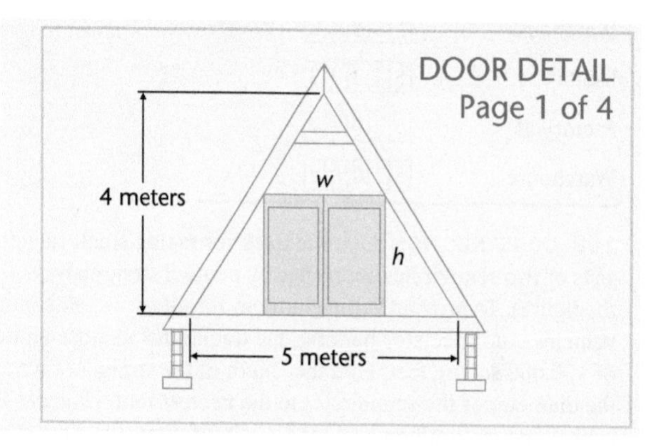

(A) Express the area $A(w)$ of the door as a function of the width w and state the domain of this function. [See the hint for Problem 105.]
(B) A provision of the building code requires that doorways must have an area of at least 4.2 square meters. Find the width of the doorways that satisfy this provision.
(C) A second provision of the building code requires all doorways to be at least 2 meters high. Discuss the effect of this requirement on the answer to part B.

107. TRANSPORTATION A delivery truck leaves a warehouse and travels north to factory A. From factory A the truck travels east to factory B and then returns directly to the warehouse (see the figure on the next page). The driver recorded the truck's odometer reading at the warehouse at both the beginning and the end of the trip and also at factory B, but forgot to record it at factory A (see the table on the next page). The driver does recall that it was farther from the warehouse to factory A than it was from factory A to factory B. Because delivery charges are based

Euclid's theorem: If two triangles are similar, their corresponding sides are proportional:

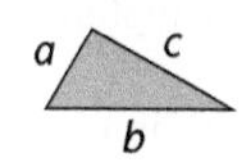

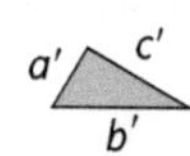

$$\frac{a}{a'} = \frac{b}{b'} = \frac{c}{c'}$$

on distance from the warehouse, the driver needs to know how far factory A is from the warehouse. Find this distance.

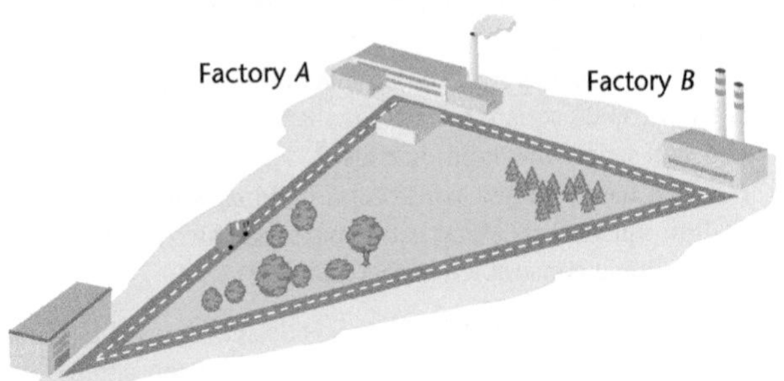

Odometer Readings	
Warehouse	52846
Factory A	52???
Factory B	52937
Warehouse	53002

108. CONSTRUCTION A $\frac{1}{4}$-mile track for racing stock cars consists of two semicircles connected by parallel straightaways (see the figure). To provide sufficient room for pit crews, emergency vehicles, and spectator parking, the track must enclose an area of 100,000 square feet. Find the length of the straightaways and the diameter of the semicircles to the nearest foot. [*Recall:* The area A and circumference C of a circle of diameter d are given by $A = \pi d^2/4$ and $C = \pi d$.]

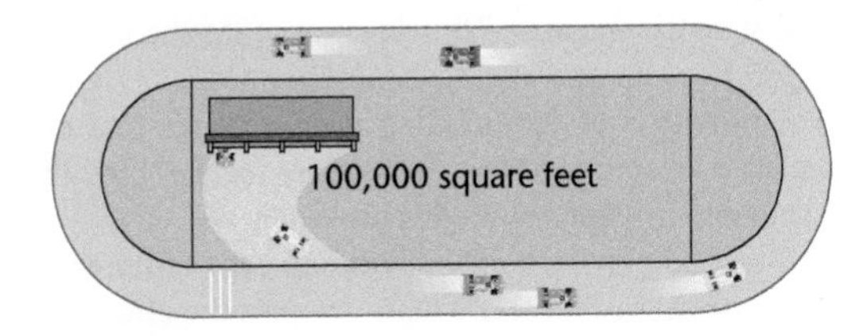

DATA ANALYSIS AND QUADRATIC REGRESSION

In Problems 109–116, unless directed otherwise, round all numbers to three significant digits.

109. ALCOHOL CONSUMPTION Table 5 contains data related to the per capita alcohol consumption in the United States from 1960 to 2000.
(A) Let the independent variable x represent years since 1960. Find a quadratic regression model for the per capita beer consumption.
(B) If beer consumption continues to follow the trend exhibited in Table 5, when (to the nearest year) will the consumption return to the 1960 level?
(C) What does your model predict for beer consumption in the year 2005? Use the Internet or a library to compare your predicted results with the actual results.

Table 5 Per Capita Alcohol Consumption (in Gallons)

Year	Beer	Wine
1960	0.99	0.22
1965	1.04	0.24
1970	1.14	0.27
1975	1.26	0.32
1980	1.38	0.34
1985	1.33	0.38
1990	1.34	0.33
1995	1.25	0.29
2000	1.22	0.31

Source: NIAAA

110. ALCOHOL CONSUMPTION Refer to Table 5.
(A) Let the independent variable x represent years since 1960. Find a quadratic regression model for the per capita wine consumption.
(B) If wine consumption continues to follow the trend exhibited in Table 5, when (to the nearest year) will the consumption return to the 1960 level?
(C) What does your model predict for wine consumption in the year 2005? Use the Internet or a library to compare your predicted results with the actual results.

111. CIGARETTE PRODUCTION Table 6 contains data related to the total production and per capita consumption of cigarettes in the United States from 1950 to 2000.
(A) Let the independent variable x represent years since 1950. Find a quadratic regression model for the total cigarette production.

Table 6 Cigarette Consumption

Year	Production (billions)	Per Capita Annual Consumption
1950	370	3,550
1955	396	3,600
1960	484	4,170
1965	529	4,260
1970	537	3,990
1975	607	4,120
1980	632	3,850
1985	594	3,370
1990	525	2,830
1995	487	2,520
2000	430	2,080

Source: CDC

(B) If cigarette production continues to follow the trend exhibited in Table 6, when (to the nearest year) will the production return to the 1950 level?
(C) What does your model predict for cigarette production in the year 2005? Use the Internet or a library to compare your predicted results with the actual results.

112. CIGARETTE CONSUMPTION Refer to Table 6.
(A) Let the independent variable x represent years since 1950. Find a quadratic regression model for the per capita cigarette consumption.
(B) If per capita cigarette consumption continues to follow the trend exhibited in Table 6, when (to the nearest year) will the per capita consumption drop to 500 cigarettes?
(C) What does your model predict for per capita cigarette consumption in the year 2005? Use the Internet or a library to compare your predicted results with the actual results.

113. STOPPING DISTANCE Table 7 contains data related to the length of the skid marks left by two different automobiles when making emergency stops.
(A) Let x be the speed of the vehicle in miles per hour. Find a quadratic regression model for the braking distance for auto A.
(B) An insurance investigator finds skid marks 200 feet long at the scene of an accident involving auto A. How fast (to the nearest mile per hour) was auto A traveling when it made these skid marks?

Table 7 Skid Marks

Speed (mph)	Length of Skid Marks (in feet)	
	Auto A	Auto B
20	21	29
30	44	53
40	76	86
50	114	124
60	182	193
70	238	263
80	305	332

114. STOPPING DISTANCE Refer to Table 7.
(A) Let x be the speed of the vehicle in miles per hour. Find a quadratic regression model for the braking distance for auto B.
(B) An insurance investigator finds skid marks 165 feet long at the scene of an accident involving auto B. How fast (to the nearest mile per hour) was auto B traveling when it made these skid marks?

115. OPTIMAL SPEED Table 8 contains performance data for two speedboats powered by Yamaha outboard motors.
(A) Let x be the speed of boat A in miles per hour (mph) and y the associated mileage in miles per gallon (mpg). Use the data in Table 8 to find a quadratic regression function $y = ax^2 + bx + c$ for this boat.
(B) A marina rents this boat for $10 per hour plus the cost of the gasoline used. If gasoline costs $2.30 per gallon and you take a 100-mile trip in this boat, construct a mathematical model and use it to answer the following questions:
What speed should you travel to minimize the rental charges?
What mileage will the boat get?
How long does the trip take?
How much gasoline will you use?
How much will the trip cost you?

Table 8 Performance Data

Boat A		Boat B	
mph	mpg	mph	mpg
5.4	2.84	5.1	1.65
12.3	2.86	9.0	1.45
29.3	4.44	23.9	2.30
41.8	3.80	35.0	2.48
53.1	3.28	44.1	2.19
57.4	2.73	49.1	1.81

Source: www.yamaha-motor.com

116. OPTIMAL SPEED Refer to Table 8.
(A) Let x be the speed of boat B in miles per hour (mph) and y the associated mileage in miles per gallon (mpg). Use the data in Table 8 to find a quadratic regression function $y = ax^2 + bx + c$ for this boat.
(B) A marina rents this boat for $15 per hour plus the cost of the gasoline used. If gasoline costs $2.50 per gallon and you take a 200-mile trip in this boat, construct a mathematical model and use it to answer the following questions:
What speed should you travel to minimize the rental charges?
What mileage will the boat get?
How long does the trip take?
How much gasoline will you use?
How much will the trip cost you?

2-6 Additional Equation-Solving Techniques

- Solving Equations Involving Radicals
- Solving Equations of Quadratic Type
- Mathematical Modeling

In this section, we will examine some equations that can be transformed into quadratic equations using various algebraic steps. We will then be able to solve these quadratic equations, and with a little bit of interpretation, use those solutions to solve the original equations.

Solving Equations Involving Radicals

Consider the equation

$$x = \sqrt{x + 2} \tag{1}$$

Figure 1 $y_1 = x$, $y_2 = \sqrt{x + 2}$.

Graphing both sides of the equation and using the INTERSECT command on a graphing calculator shows that $x = 2$ is a solution to the equation (Fig. 1). But is it the only solution?

There may be other solutions not visible in this viewing window. Or there may be imaginary solutions (remember, graphical approximation applies only to real solutions). To solve this equation algebraically, we eliminate the radical by squaring both sides of the equation. The result is a quadratic equation.

$$
\begin{aligned}
x^2 &= (\sqrt{x + 2})^2 && \text{Simplify right side.} \qquad (2)\\
x^2 &= x + 2 && \text{Write in standard form for a quadratic.}\\
x^2 - x - 2 &= 0 && \text{Factor.}\\
(x - 2)(x + 1) &= 0 && \text{Use the zero product property.}\\
x - 2 &= 0 \quad \text{or} \quad x + 1 = 0\\
x &= 2, -1
\end{aligned}
$$

These are the only solutions to the quadratic equation. We have already seen that $x = 2$ is a solution to the original equation. From the graph, it certainly doesn't look like $x = -1$ is a solution. To check, we substitute in equation (1):

$$
\begin{aligned}
x &= \sqrt{x + 2}\\
-1 &\stackrel{?}{=} \sqrt{-1 + 2}\\
-1 &\stackrel{?}{=} \sqrt{1}\\
-1 &\neq 1
\end{aligned}
$$

It turns out that -1 is not a solution to equation (1). What went wrong?

››› EXPLORE-DISCUSS 1

(A) The three statements below are true. Square both sides of each. Are they still true?

$$5 = \frac{10}{2} \qquad 6 = 2 \cdot 3 \qquad -4 = \frac{-12}{3}$$

(B) The three statements below are false. Square both sides of each. Are they still false? What can you conclude?

$$-4 = 4 \qquad 4 = \frac{6}{2} \qquad -2 = 6 - 4$$

Solving equations is all about deciding when an equation is a true statement. Explore-Discuss 1 demonstrates that squaring both sides can turn a false statement into a true one. That's what happened in equation (1). Substituting in $x = -1$ makes the equation the false statement $-1 = 1$, but squaring both sides made it true.

Then what do we gain by squaring both sides of an equation to solve? Theorem 1 provides a clue.

› THEOREM 1 Power Operation on Equations

If both sides of an equation are raised to the same natural number power, then the solution set of the original equation is a subset of the solution set of the new equation.

Equation	Solution Set
$x = 3$	$\{3\}$
$x^2 = 9$	$\{-3, 3\}$

Theorem 1 indicates that when we square both sides of an equation, the resulting equation might have more solutions than the original. But any solutions of the original will be among the solutions of the new equation.

Referring to equations (1) and (2) on page 226, we know that 2 and -1 are the only solutions to the quadratic equation (2). And we checked that -1 is not a solution to equation (1). Theorem 1 now implies that 2 must be the *only* solution to equation (1).

We call -1 an *extraneous solution.* In general, an **extraneous solution** is a solution introduced during the solution process that does not satisfy the original equation.

When raising both sides of an equation to a power, every solution of the new equation must be checked in the original equation to eliminate extraneous solutions.

››› EXPLORE-DISCUSS 2

Figure 2 shows that $x = -1$ is a solution of the equation

$$\sqrt{x + 2} = 0.01x + 1.01$$

Are there any other solutions? Find any additional solutions both algebraically and graphically. What are some advantages and disadvantages of each of these solution methods?

› **Figure 2** $y_1 = \sqrt{x + 2}, y_2 = 0.01x + 1.01.$

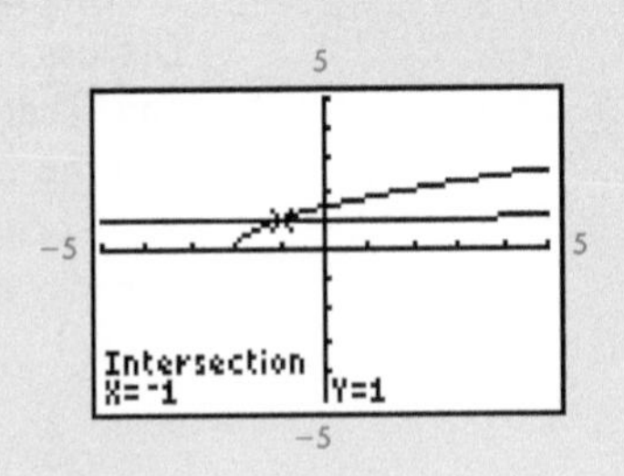

EXAMPLE 1 Solving Equations Involving Radicals

Solve algebraically $\sqrt{4x^2 + 8x + 7} - x = 1.$

SOLUTION

$\sqrt{4x^2 + 8x + 7} - x = 1$	Isolate radical on one side.
$\sqrt{4x^2 + 8x + 7} = x + 1$	Square both sides.
$4x^2 + 8x + 7 = x^2 + 2x + 1$	Collect like terms.
$3x^2 + 6x + 6 = 0$	Divide both sides by 3.
$x^2 + 2x + 2 = 0$	Use the quadratic formula.
$x = \dfrac{-2 \pm \sqrt{-4}}{2}$	
$= -1 + i, -1 - i$	

CHECK

$$x = -1 + i$$
$$\sqrt{4x^2 + 8x + 7} - x = 1$$
$$\sqrt{4(-1+i)^2 + 8(-1+i) + 7} - (-1+i) \stackrel{?}{=} 1 \qquad (-1+i)^2 = 1 - 2i + i^2 = -2i$$
$$\sqrt{-8i - 8 + 8i + 7} + 1 - i \stackrel{?}{=} 1$$
$$\sqrt{-1} + 1 - i \stackrel{?}{=} 1$$
$$1 \stackrel{\checkmark}{=} 1$$

$$x = -1 - i$$
$$\sqrt{4x^2 + 8x + 7} - x = 1$$
$$\sqrt{4(-1-i)^2 + 8(-1-i) + 7} - (-1-i) \stackrel{?}{=} 1 \qquad (-1-i)^2 = 1 + 2i + i^2 = 2i$$
$$\sqrt{8i - 8 - 8i + 7} + 1 + i \stackrel{?}{=} 1$$
$$\sqrt{-1} + 1 + i \stackrel{?}{=} 1$$
$$1 + 2i \neq 1$$

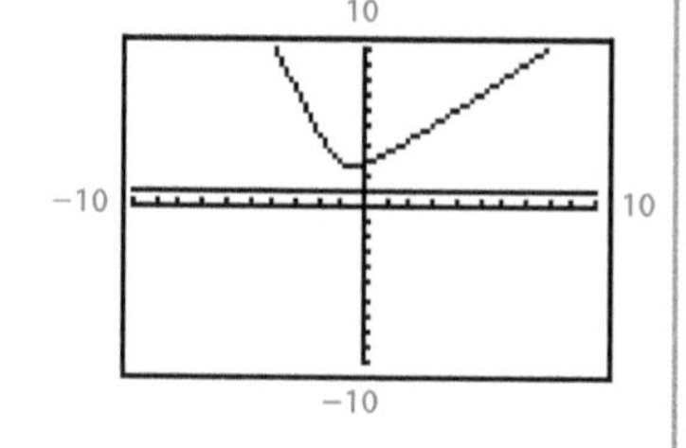

› **Figure 3**
$y_1 = 1,$
$y_2 = \sqrt{4x^2 + 8x + 7} - x.$

The check shows that $-1 + i$ is a solution to the original equation and $-1 - i$ is extraneous. Thus, the only solution is the imaginary number

$$x = -1 + i$$

Graphing both sides of the equation illustrates that there are no intersection points in a standard viewing window (Fig. 3). The algebraic solution shows that the equation has no real solutions, so there cannot be any intersection points anywhere in the plane.

››› CAUTION ›››

1. When solving equations by squaring both sides, it is very important to isolate the radical first.
2. Be sure to square binomials like $x + 1$ by first writing it as $(x + 1)(x + 1)$. Keep in mind that $(x + 1)^2$ is *not* equal to $x^2 + 1^2$.

MATCHED PROBLEM 1

Solve algebraically: $\sqrt{x^2 - 2x - 2} + 2x = 2$.

When an equation has more than one radical, it may be necessary to square both sides more than once. In this case, we begin by isolating one of the radicals.

EXAMPLE 2 Solving Equations Involving Two Radicals

Solve algebraically and graphically: $\sqrt{2x+3} - \sqrt{x-2} = 2$.

SOLUTION

Algebraic Solution

$\sqrt{2x+3} - \sqrt{x-2} = 2$	Isolate one of the radicals.
$\sqrt{2x+3} = \sqrt{x-2} + 2$	Square both sides.
$2x+3 = (\sqrt{x-2}+2)(\sqrt{x-2}+2)$	Multiply parentheses.
$2x+3 = x-2+4\sqrt{x-2}+4$	Isolate the remaining radical.
$x+1 = 4\sqrt{x-2}$	Square both sides.
$x^2+2x+1 = 16(x-2)$	Distribute.
$x^2+2x+1 = 16x-32$	Collect like terms.
$x^2-14x+33 = 0$	Factor.
$(x-3)(x-11) = 0$	Use the zero product property.
$x-3=0 \quad \text{or} \quad x-11=0$	
$x = 3, 11$	

CHECK

$$x = 3$$
$$\sqrt{2x+3} - \sqrt{x-2} = 2$$
$$\sqrt{2(3)+3} - \sqrt{3-2} \stackrel{?}{=} 2$$
$$2 \stackrel{\checkmark}{=} 2$$

$$x = 11$$
$$\sqrt{2x+3} - \sqrt{x-2} = 2$$
$$\sqrt{2(11)+3} - \sqrt{11-2} \stackrel{?}{=} 2$$
$$2 \stackrel{\checkmark}{=} 2$$

Both solutions check. The equation has two solutions.

$$x = 3, 11$$

Graphical Solution
Graphing $y_1 = \sqrt{2x+3} - \sqrt{x-2}$ and $y_2 = 2$ in a standard viewing window produces a graph that is not very useful (Fig. 4).

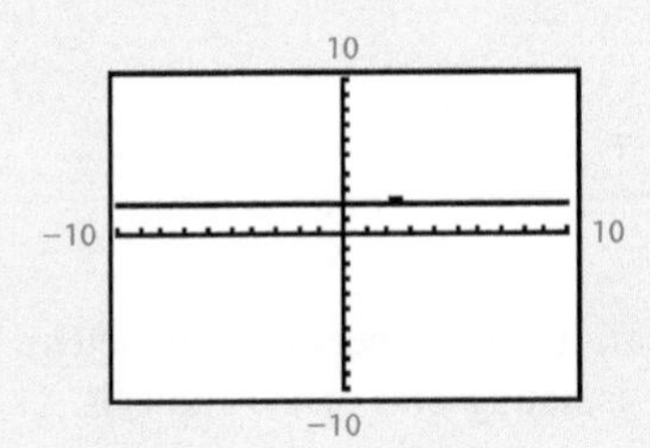

› Figure 4

Examining a table of values (Fig. 5) suggests that choosing Xmin = 2, Xmax = 14, Ymin = 1.5, Ymax = 3 is likely to produce a graph that shows two intersection points.

X	Y1	Y2
2	2.6458	2
4	1.9024	2
6	1.873	2
8	1.9094	2
10	1.9674	2
12	2.0339	2
14	2.1037	2

Y1=√(2X+3)−√(X−...

› Figure 5

Using the INTERSECT command, the x coordinates of the intersection points are $x = 3$ (Fig. 6) and $x = 11$ (Fig. 7).

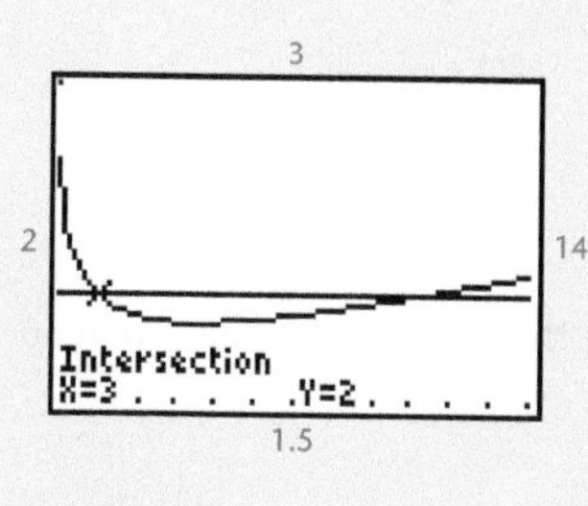

› Figure 6

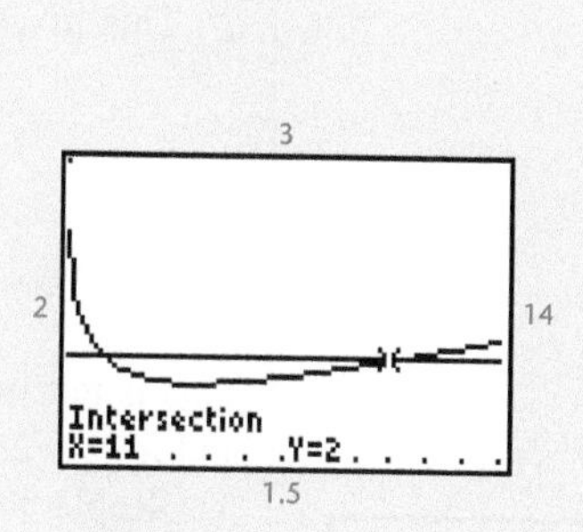

› Figure 7

MATCHED PROBLEM 2

Solve algebraically and graphically: $\sqrt{2x + 5} + \sqrt{x + 2} = 5$.

How do you choose between algebraic and graphical solution methods? It depends on the type of solutions you want. If you want to find real and complex solutions, you must use algebraic methods, as we did in Example 1. If you are only interested in real solutions, then either method can be used, as in Example 2. To get the most out of this topic, we recommend that you solve each equation algebraically and, when possible, confirm your solutions graphically.

› Solving Equations of Quadratic Type

Quadratic equations in standard form have two terms with the variable; one has power 2, the other power 1. When equations have two variable terms where the larger power is twice the smaller, we can use quadratic solving techniques.

EXAMPLE 3 **Solving an Equation of Quadratic Type**

Solve $x^{2/3} - x^{1/3} - 6 = 0$.

SOLUTIONS

Method I. Direct solution:

Note that the larger power (2/3) is twice the smaller. Using the properties of exponents from basic algebra, we can write $x^{2/3}$ as $(x^{1/3})^2$ and solve by factoring.

$$(x^{1/3})^2 - x^{1/3} - 6 = 0 \quad \text{Factor left side.}$$
$$(x^{1/3} - 3)(x^{1/3} + 2) = 0 \quad \text{Use the zero product property.}$$
$$x^{1/3} = 3 \quad \text{or} \quad x^{1/3} = -2 \quad \text{Cube both sides.}$$
$$(x^{1/3})^3 = 3^3 \qquad (x^{1/3})^3 = (-2)^3$$
$$x = 27 \qquad x = -8$$

The solution is $x = 27, -8$

Method II. Using substitution:

Replace $x^{1/3}$ (the smaller power) with a new variable u. Then the larger power $x^{2/3}$ is u^2. This gives us a quadratic equation with variable u.

$$u^2 - u - 6 = 0 \qquad \text{Factor.}$$
$$(u - 3)(u + 2) = 0 \qquad \text{Use the zero product property.}$$
$$u = 3, -2$$

This is not the solution! We still need to find the values of x that correspond to $u = 3$ and $u = -2$.

Replacing u with $x^{1/3}$, we obtain

$$x^{1/3} = 3 \quad \text{or} \quad x^{1/3} = -2 \qquad \text{Cube both sides.}$$
$$x = 27 \qquad\qquad x = -8$$

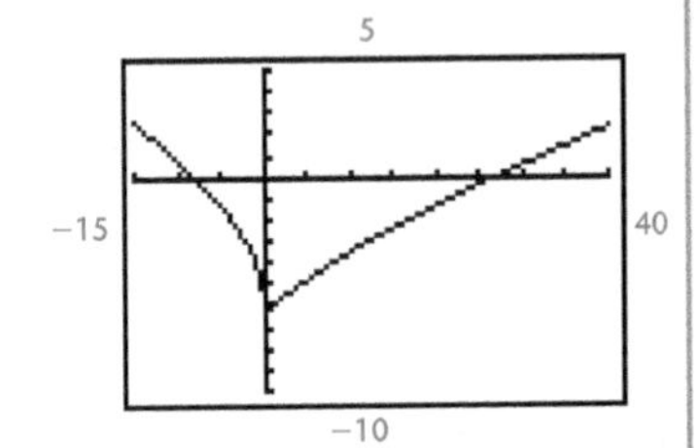

› **Figure 8**
$y_1 = x^{2/3} - x^{1/3} - 6.$

The solution is $x = 27, -8$.

The graph in Figure 8 confirms these results. [*Note:* In some graphing calculators you may have to enter the left side of the equation in the form $y_1 = (x^2)^{1/3} - x^{1/3} - 6$ rather than $y_1 = x^{2/3} - x^{1/3} - 6$. Try both forms to see what happens.]

MATCHED PROBLEM 3

Solve algebraically using both Method I and Method II and confirm graphically $x^{1/2} - 5x^{1/4} + 6 = 0$.

In general, if an equation that is not quadratic can be transformed to the form

$$au^2 + bu + c = 0$$

where u is an expression in some other variable, then the equation is called an **equation of quadratic type.** Equations of quadratic type often can be solved using quadratic methods.

››› EXPLORE-DISCUSS 3

Which of the following can be transformed into a quadratic equation by making a substitution of the form $u = x^n$? What is the resulting quadratic equation?

(A) $3x^{-4} + 2x^{-2} + 7 = 0$ **(B)** $7x^5 - 3x^2 + 3 = 0$

(C) $2x^5 + 4x^2\sqrt{x} - 6 = 0$ **(D)** $8x^{-2}\sqrt{x} - 5x^{-1}\sqrt{x} - 2 = 0$

In general, if a, b, c, m, and n are nonzero real numbers, when can an equation of the form $ax^m + bx^n + c = 0$ be transformed into an equation of quadratic type?

EXAMPLE 4 Solving Equations of Quadratic Type

Solve algebraically and graphically: $3x^{-2/5} - 6x^{-1/5} + 2 = 0$.

SOLUTION

Algebraic Solution

The larger power $(-2/5)$ is twice the smaller $(-1/5)$. We substitute $u = x^{-1/5}$; then $u^2 = x^{-2/5}$

$$3u^2 - 6u + 2 = 0 \qquad \text{Use the quadratic formula.}$$

$$u = \frac{6 \pm \sqrt{12}}{6}$$

$$u = \frac{3 \pm \sqrt{3}}{3}$$

We now replace u with $x^{-1/5}$.

$$x^{-1/5} = \frac{3 \pm \sqrt{3}}{3} \qquad \text{Raise both sides to the } -5 \text{ power.}$$

$$x = \left(\frac{3 \pm \sqrt{3}}{3}\right)^{-5} \qquad \text{Apply the negative exponent.}$$

$$x = \left(\frac{3}{3 \pm \sqrt{3}}\right)^{5} \qquad \text{Use a calculator.}$$

$$\approx 0.102414, 74.147586$$

Graphical Solution

The graph of $y_1 = 3x^{-2/5} - 6x^{-1/5} + 2$ is the thick curve in Figure 9. The graph crosses the x axis near $x = 0$ and again near $x = 75$. The solution near $x = 75$ is easily approximated in this viewing window. The solution near the origin can be approximated in the same viewing window, but it's much easier to see if we change the limits on the x axis (Fig. 10).

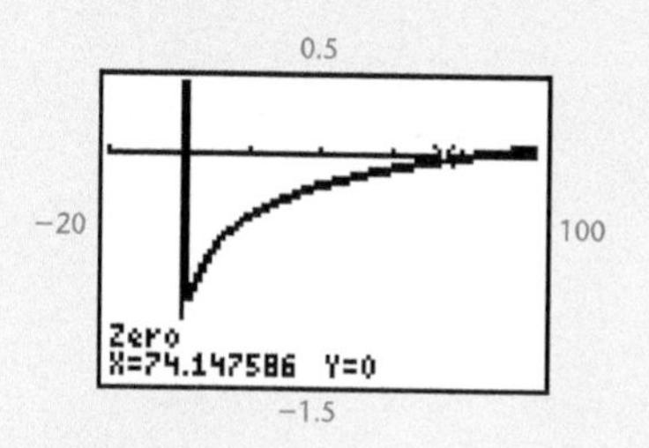

› Figure 9

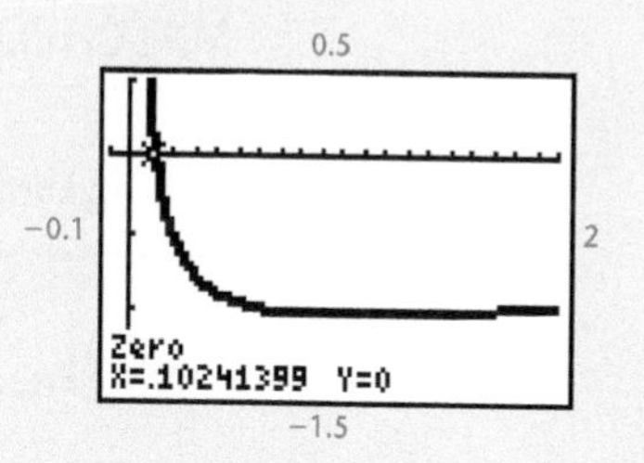

› Figure 10

MATCHED PROBLEM 4

Solve algebraically and graphically: $3x^{-2/5} - x^{-1/5} - 2 = 0$.

EXAMPLE 5 Solving Equations of Quadratic Type

Solve algebraically and confirm graphically, if possible: $x^4 - 3x^2 - 4 = 0$.

SOLUTION

Algebraic Solution

In this case, we will use Method 1 and factor directly.

$$(x^2)^2 - 3x^2 - 4 = 0 \quad \text{Factor.}$$
$$(x^2 - 4)(x^2 + 1) = 0 \quad \text{Use the zero product property.}$$
$$x^2 = 4 \quad \text{or} \quad x^2 = -1$$
$$x = \pm 2 \quad \text{or} \quad x = \pm i$$

Because we did not raise each side of the equation to a natural number power, we do not have to check for extraneous solutions. (But you should still check the accuracy of the solutions.)

Graphical Confirmation

Figures 11 and 12 show the two real solutions. The imaginary solutions cannot be confirmed graphically.

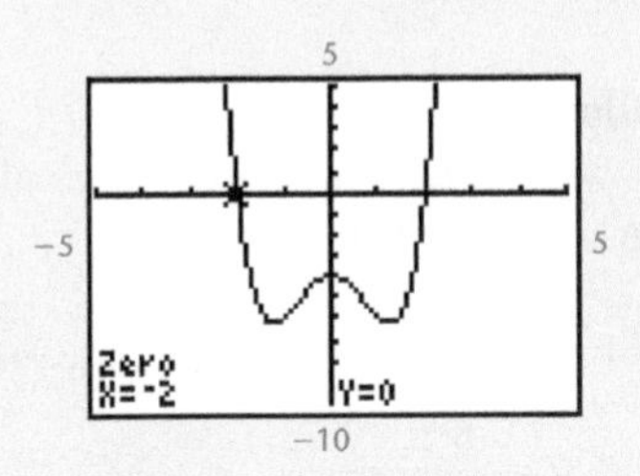

› Figure 11

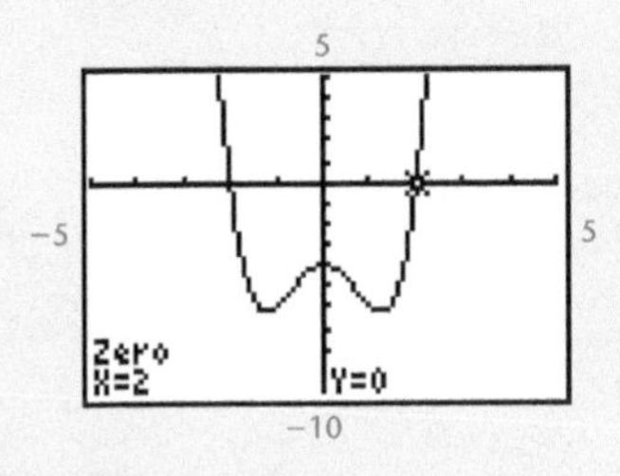

› Figure 12

MATCHED PROBLEM 5

Solve algebraically and confirm graphically, if possible: $x^4 + 3x^2 - 4 = 0$.

› Mathematical Modeling

Examples 6 and 7 illustrate the use of radicals in constructing mathematical models.

EXAMPLE 6 **Depth of a Well**

The splash from a stone dropped into a deep well is heard 5 seconds after the stone is released (Fig. 13). If sound travels through air at 1,100 feet per second, how deep is the well? Round answer to the nearest foot.

SOLUTION

Constructing the Model

The time between the instant the stone is released and the instant the splash is heard can be broken down into two parts:

t_1 = Time in seconds stone is falling through the air

t_2 = Time in seconds sound of splash travels back to surface

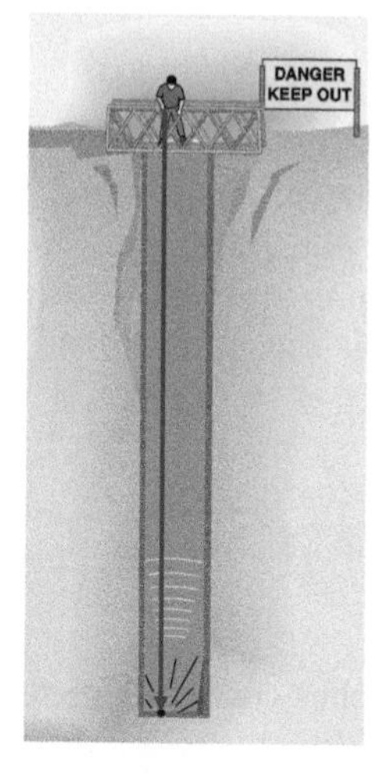

› Figure 13

From the section before last, the distance traveled by the stone in free fall is $x = 16t_1^2$. Using distance = rate · time, the sound of the splash traveling back up is $x = 1{,}100t_2$. Solving these two equations for t_1 and t_2, we get

$$t_1^2 = \frac{x}{16} \qquad t_2 = \frac{x}{1{,}100}$$

$$t_1 = \frac{\sqrt{x}}{4} \qquad t_1 \text{ is a time, so we disregard the negative solution.}$$

If we combine t_1 and t_2, we have a model for the total time t between releasing the stone and hearing the splash in terms of the depth of the well x:

$$t = t_1 + t_2 = \frac{\sqrt{x}}{4} + \frac{x}{1{,}100}$$

We are asked to find x when $t = 5$ seconds.

Algebraic Solution

$$\frac{\sqrt{x}}{4} + \frac{x}{1{,}100} = 5 \qquad \text{Multiply both sides by 1,100.}$$

$$275\sqrt{x} + x = 5{,}500 \qquad \text{Subtract 5,500 from both sides; rearrange.}$$

$$x + 275x^{1/2} - 5{,}500 = 0 \qquad \text{Let } u = x^{1/2};\ u^2 = x$$

$$u^2 + 275u - 5{,}500 = 0 \qquad \text{Use the quadratic formula.}$$

$$u = \frac{-275 \pm \sqrt{275^2 - 4(-5{,}500)}}{2}$$

$$= \frac{-275 \pm \sqrt{97{,}625}}{2}$$

$$= 18.724998 \quad \text{or} \quad -293.724998$$

Because $u = x^{1/2} > 0$, the second solution is discarded.

$$x = u^2$$

$$= 18.724998^2 \qquad \text{Round to the nearest foot.}$$

$$= 351$$

The well is 351 feet deep.

Graphical Solution

Enter $y_1 = \frac{\sqrt{x}}{4} + \frac{x}{1{,}100}$ and $y_2 = 5$. To determine the window variables, examine a table of values (Fig. 14) with fairly large x values (remember, x is the depth of the well and wells can be thousands of feet deep).

X	Y1	Y2
0	0	5
100	2.5909	5
200	3.7174	5
300	4.6029	5
400	5.3636	5
500	6.0447	5
600	6.6692	5

Y1=√(X)/4+X/1100

› Figure 14

Now graph y_1 and y_2 and use INTERSECT (Fig. 15).

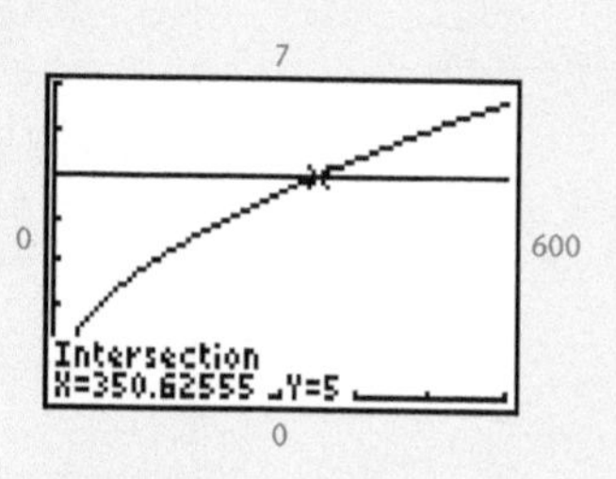

› Figure 15

From Figure 15, we see that the well is 351 feet deep.

MATCHED PROBLEM 6

The speed of sound through air is actually dependent on the air temperature. A deep well above a hot spring has an air temperature of 115 degrees, which makes sound travel at 1,180 feet per second. If the splash from a stone dropped into this well is heard 10 seconds after the stone is released, how deep is the well? Round to the nearest foot.

EXAMPLE 7

Design

› Figure 16

A window in the shape of a semicircle with radius 20 inches contains a rectangular pane of glass as shown in Figure 16.

(A) Find a mathematical model for the area of the rectangle. Use one-half the length of the base of the rectangle for the independent variable in your model.

(B) Find the dimensions of the pane if the area of the pane is 320 square inches.

(C) Find the dimensions and the area of the largest possible rectangular pane of glass.

Round all answers to three significant digits.

SOLUTIONS

(A) Place a rectangular coordinate system on the window (Fig. 17). Let x be one-half the base of the rectangle and y be the height of the rectangle.

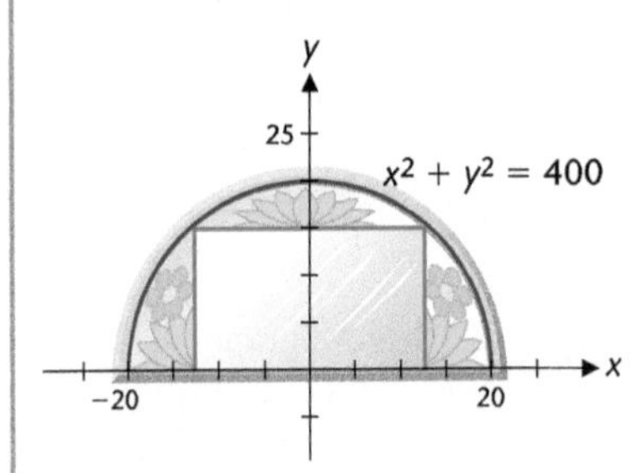

› Figure 17

Because (x, y) are the coordinates of a point on the circle with radius 20 and center $(0, 0)$, x and y must satisfy the equation of the circle*

$$x^2 + y^2 = 400$$
$$y = \sqrt{400 - x^2} \qquad (3)$$

*Circles are reviewed in Appendix B, Section B-3.

The area of the rectangle is

$$A = \text{Base} \cdot \text{Height} = 2xy = 2x\sqrt{400 - x^2}$$

The radius is 20, so x must be less than 20. A model for the area is

$$A(x) = 2x\sqrt{400 - x^2} \qquad 0 < x < 20$$

(B) Solve the equation $A(x) = 320$.

Algebraic Solution

$$2x\sqrt{400 - x^2} = 320 \qquad \text{Divide both sides by 2.}$$

$$x\sqrt{400 - x^2} = 160 \qquad \text{Square both sides.}$$

$$x^2(400 - x^2) = 25{,}600 \qquad \text{Distribute.}$$

$$400x^2 - x^4 = 25{,}600 \qquad \text{Subtract 25,600 from both sides.}$$

$$400x^2 - x^4 - 25{,}600 = 0 \qquad \text{Multiply both sides by } -1\text{; rearrange.}$$

$$x^4 - 400x^2 + 25{,}600 = 0 \qquad \text{Write as a quadratic with variable } x^2.$$

$$(x^2)^2 - 400x^2 + 25{,}000 = 0$$

Use the quadratic formula to solve for x^2:

$$x^2 = \frac{400 \pm \sqrt{400^2 - 4 \cdot 25{,}600}}{2}$$

$$= \frac{400 \pm \sqrt{57{,}600}}{2}$$

$$= \frac{400 \pm 240}{2}$$

$$= 80 \quad \text{or} \quad 320$$

$$x = \sqrt{80} = 8.94 \quad \text{or} \quad x = \sqrt{320} = 17.9$$

A check (which we leave to the reader) shows that neither solution is extraneous.

Graphical Solution

To solve the equation $A(x) = 320$, enter both sides in the equation editor of a graphing calculator (Fig. 18).

The values of x must satisfy $0 \le x \le 20$. Examining a table of values over this interval suggests that $0 \le y \le 500$ will produce a usable window (Fig. 19).

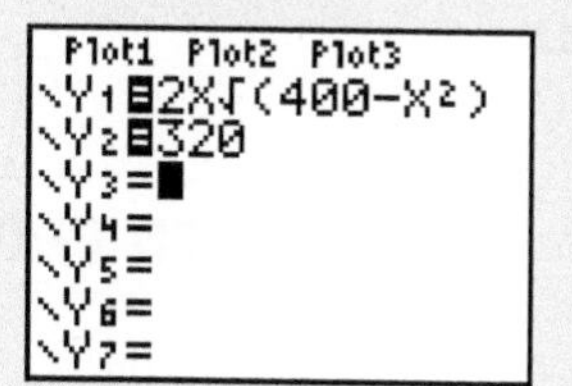

› Figure 18

X	Y1	Y2
0	0	320
4	156.77	320
8	293.28	320
12	384	320
16	384	320
20	0	320

X=

› Figure 19

Graphing y_1 and y_2 and using the INTERSECT command shows that the solutions are $x = 8.94$ (Fig. 20) and $x = 17.9$ (Fig. 21).

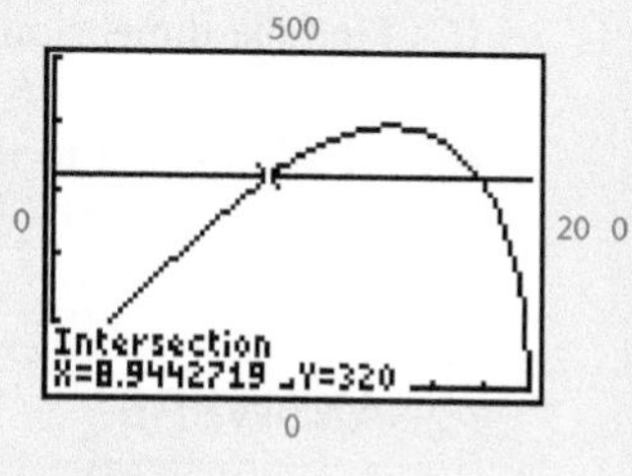

› Figure 20

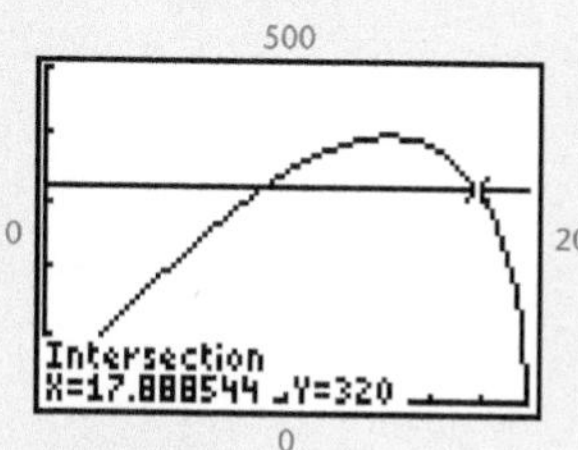

› Figure 21

Now that we have determined the solutions to the equation $A(x) = 320$, we use $y = \sqrt{400 - x^2}$ to find the dimensions of the two rectangles:

$$x = \sqrt{80} = 8.94 \quad \text{and} \quad y = \sqrt{400 - 80} = \sqrt{320} = 17.9$$

$$x = \sqrt{320} = 17.9 \quad \text{and} \quad y = \sqrt{400 - 320} = \sqrt{80} = 8.94$$

Recalling that x is one-half the base, the dimensions of the rectangles are 17.9 inches wide by 17.9 inches high or 35.8 inches wide by 8.94 inches high. Each solution is illustrated in Figure 22.

(C) Using the MAXIMUM command (Fig. 23), the largest rectangle has an area of 400 square inches when $x = 14.1$ inches. The dimensions of this rectangle are 28.2 inches wide and 14.2 inches high.

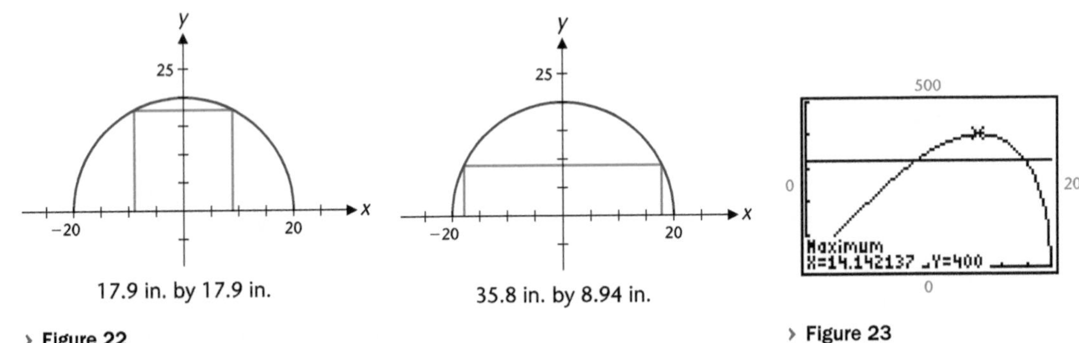

17.9 in. by 17.9 in. 35.8 in. by 8.94 in.

› **Figure 22**

› **Figure 23**

MATCHED PROBLEM 7

A window in the shape of a semicircle with radius 25 inches contains a rectangular pane of glass as shown in Figure 16 in Example 7.

(A) Find a mathematical model for the area of the rectangle. Use one-half the length of the base of the rectangle for the independent variable in your model.

(B) Find the dimensions of the pane if the area of the pane is 500 square inches.

(C) Find the dimensions and the area of the largest possible rectangular pane of glass.

Round all answers to three significant digits.

ANSWERS TO MATCHED PROBLEMS

1. $x = 1 - i$ **2.** $x = 2$ **3.** $x = 16, 81$ **4.** $x = 1, -\frac{243}{32}$ **5.** $x = \pm 1, \pm 2i$
6. 1,273 feet **7.** (A) $A(x) = 2x\sqrt{625 - x^2}, 0 \le x \le 25$
(B) 22.4 inches by 22.4 inches or 44.8 inches by 11.2 inches
(C) 35.4 inches by 17.7 inches, area = 625 square inches

2-6 Exercises

In Problems 1–8, determine the validity of each statement. If a statement is false, explain why.

1. If $x^2 = 5$, then $x = \pm\sqrt{5}$

2. $\sqrt{25} = \pm 5$

3. $(x + 5)^2 = x^2 + 25$

4. $(2x - 1)^2 = 4x^2 - 1$

5. $(\sqrt{x - 1} + 1)^2 = x$

6. $(\sqrt{x - 1})^2 + 1 = x$

7. If $x^3 = 2$, then $x = 8$

8. If $x^{1/3} = 2$, then $x = 8$

In Problems 9–14, transform each equation of quadratic type into a quadratic equation in u and state the substitution used in the transformation. If the equation is not an equation of quadratic type, say so.

9. $2x^{-6} - 4x^{-3} = 0$

10. $\frac{4}{7} - \frac{3}{x} + \frac{6}{x^2} = 0$

11. $3x^3 - 4x + 9 = 0$

12. $7x^{-1} + 3x^{-1/2} + 2 = 0$

13. $\frac{10}{9} + \frac{4}{x^2} - \frac{7}{x^4} = 0$

14. $3x^{3/2} - 5x^{1/2} + 12 = 0$

15. Explain why squaring both sides of an equation sometimes introduces extraneous solutions.

16. Would raising both sides of an equation to the third power ever introduce extraneous solutions? Why or why not?

17. Write an example of a false statement that becomes true when you square both sides. What would every possible example have in common?

18. How can you recognize when an equation is of quadratic type?

In Problems 19–32, solve algebraically and confirm graphically, if possible.

19. $\sqrt{4x - 7} = 5$

20. $\sqrt{4 - x} = 4$

21. $\sqrt{5x + 6} + 6 = 0$

22. $\sqrt{10x + 1} + 8 = 0$

23. $\sqrt[3]{x + 5} = 3$

24. $\sqrt[4]{x - 3} = 2$

25. $\sqrt{x + 5} + 7 = 0$

26. $3 + \sqrt{2x - 1} = 0$

27. $y^4 - 2y^2 - 8 = 0$

28. $x^4 - 7x^2 - 18 = 0$

29. $3x = \sqrt{x^2 - 2}$

30. $x = \sqrt{5x^2 + 9}$

31. $\sqrt{x^2 - 5x} = \sqrt{x - 8}$

32. $\sqrt{2x + 3} = \sqrt{x^2 - 12}$

In Problems 33–56, solve algebraically and confirm graphically, if possible.

33. $\sqrt{5n + 9} = n - 1$

34. $m - 13 = \sqrt{m + 7}$

35. $\sqrt{3x + 4} = 2 + \sqrt{x}$

36. $\sqrt{3w - 2} - \sqrt{w} = 2$

37. $2x^{2/3} + 3x^{1/3} - 2 = 0$

38. $x^{2/3} - 3x^{1/3} - 10 = 0$

39. $(m^2 - m)^2 - 4(m^2 - m) = 12$

40. $(x^2 + 2x)^2 - (x^2 + 2x) = 6$

41. $\sqrt{u - 2} = 2 + \sqrt{2u + 3}$

42. $\sqrt{3t + 4} + \sqrt{t} = -3$

43. $\sqrt{3y - 2} = 3 - \sqrt{3y + 1}$

44. $\sqrt{2x - 1} - \sqrt{x - 4} = 2$

45. $\sqrt{7x - 2} - \sqrt{x + 1} = \sqrt{3}$

46. $\sqrt{3x + 6} - \sqrt{x + 4} = \sqrt{2}$

47. $\sqrt{4x^2 + 12x + 1} - 6x = 9$

48. $6x - \sqrt{4x^2 - 20x + 17} = 15$

49. $3n^{-2} - 11n^{-1} - 20 = 0$

50. $6x^{-2} - 5x^{-1} - 6 = 0$

51. $9y^{-4} - 10y^{-2} + 1 = 0$

52. $4x^{-4} - 17x^{-2} + 4 = 0$

53. $y^{1/2} - 3y^{1/4} + 2 = 0$

54. $4x^{-1} - 9x^{-1/2} + 2 = 0$

55. $(m - 5)^4 + 36 = 13(m - 5)^2$

56. $(x - 3)^4 + 3(x - 3)^2 = 4$

57. Explain why the following "solution" is incorrect:

$$\sqrt{x + 3} + 5 = 12$$
$$x + 3 + 25 = 144$$
$$x = 116$$

58. Explain why the following "solution" is incorrect.

$$\sqrt{x^2 - 16} = 2x + 3$$
$$x - 4 = 2x + 3$$
$$-7 = x$$

In Problems 59–62, solve algebraically and confirm graphically, if possible.

59. $\sqrt{5 - 2x} - \sqrt{x + 6} = \sqrt{x + 3}$

60. $\sqrt{2x + 3} - \sqrt{x - 2} = \sqrt{x + 1}$

61. $2 + 3y^{-4} = 6y^{-2}$

62. $4m^{-2} = 2 + m^{-4}$

In Problems 63–66, solve two ways: by isolating the radical and squaring, and by substitution. Confirm graphically, if possible.

63. $m - 7\sqrt{m} + 12 = 0$

64. $y - 6 + \sqrt{y} = 0$

65. $t - 11\sqrt{t} + 18 = 0$

66. $x = 15 - 2\sqrt{x}$

In Problems 67–70, solve algebraically and graphically. Discuss the advantages and disadvantages of each method.

67. $2\sqrt{x+5} = 0.01x + 2.04$ **68.** $3\sqrt{x-1} = 0.05x + 2.9$

69. $2x^{-2/5} - 5x^{-1/5} + 1 = 0$ **70.** $x^{-2/5} - 3x^{-1/5} + 1 = 0$

APPLICATIONS

71. GEOMETRY The diagonal of a rectangle is 10 inches and the area is 45 square inches. Find the dimensions of the rectangle, correct to one decimal place.

72. GEOMETRY The hypotenuse of a right triangle is 12 inches and the area is 24 square inches. Find the dimensions of the triangle, correct to one decimal place.

73. PHYSICS–WELL DEPTH If the splash of a stone dropped into a well is heard 14 seconds after the stone is released, how deep (to the nearest foot) is the well? Use 1,100 feet per second for the speed of sound.

74. PHYSICS–WELL DEPTH If the splash of a stone dropped into a well is heard 2 seconds after the stone is released, how deep (to the nearest foot) is the well? Use 1,100 feet per second for the speed of sound.

75. MANUFACTURING A lumber mill cuts rectangular beams from circular logs that are 16 inches in diameter (see the figure).

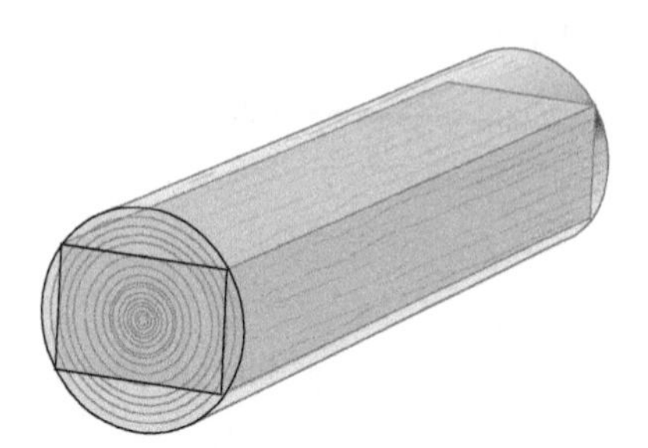

(A) Find a model for the cross-sectional area of the beam. Use the width of the beam as the independent variable.
(B) If the cross-sectional area of the beam is 120 square inches, find the dimensions correct to one decimal place.
(C) Find the dimensions of the beam that has the largest cross-sectional area and find this area. Round answers to one decimal place.

76. DESIGN A food-processing company packages an assortment of their products in circular metal tins 12 inches in diameter. Four identically sized rectangular boxes are used to divide the tin into six compartments (see the figure).

(A) Find a model for the cross-sectional area of one of these boxes. Use the width of the box as the independent variable.
(B) If the cross-sectional area of the box is 15 square inches, find the dimensions correct to one decimal place.
(C) Find the dimensions of the box that has the largest cross-sectional area and find this area. Round answers to one decimal place.

77. CONSTRUCTION A water trough is constructed by bending a 4- by 6-foot rectangular sheet of metal down the middle and attaching triangular ends (see the figure). If the volume of the trough is 9 cubic feet, find the width correct to two decimal places.

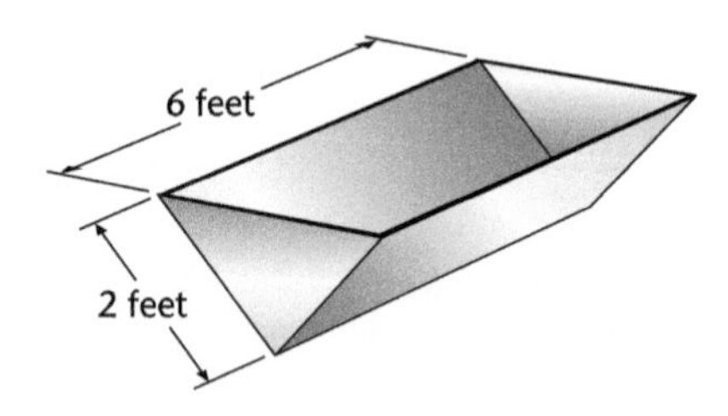

78. DESIGN A paper drinking cup in the shape of a right circular cone is constructed from 125 square centimeters of paper (see the figure). If the height of the cone is 10 centimeters, find the radius correct to two decimal places.

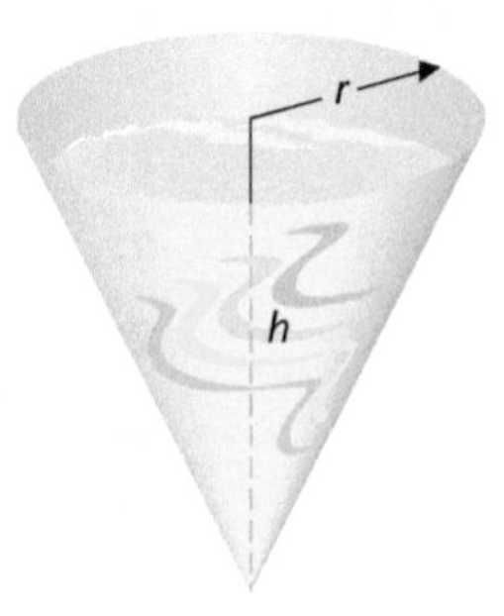

Lateral surface area:

$S = \pi r\sqrt{r^2 + h^2}$

2-7 Solving Inequalities

Now that we have sharpened our equation-solving skills, we turn our attention to solving various types of inequalities and several applications that involve inequalities.

Solving Linear Inequalities

Any inequality that can be written in one of the four forms in (1) is called a **linear inequality in one variable.**

$$\begin{aligned} mx + b &> 0 \\ mx + b &\geq 0 \\ mx + b &< 0 \\ mx + b &\leq 0 \end{aligned} \qquad \text{Linear inequalities} \qquad (1)$$

As was the case with equations, the **solution set of an inequality** is the set of all values of the variable that make the inequality a true statement. Each element of the solution set is called a **solution.** Two inequalities are said to be **equivalent** if they have the same solution set.

EXPLORE-DISCUSS 1

Associated with the linear equation and inequalities

$$3x - 12 = 0 \qquad 3x - 12 < 0 \qquad 3x - 12 > 0$$

is the linear function

$$f(x) = 3x - 12$$

(A) Graph the function f.

(B) From the graph of f describe verbally the values of x for which

$$f(x) = 0 \qquad f(x) < 0 \qquad f(x) > 0$$

(C) How are the answers to part B related to the solutions of

$$3x - 12 = 0 \qquad 3x - 12 < 0 \qquad 3x - 12 > 0$$

As you discovered in Explore-Discuss 1, solving inequalities graphically is both intuitive and efficient. When an inequality has zero on one side, it is a statement about when the nonzero side is positive or negative. When looking at the graph, this corresponds to x values for which the graph is above or below the x axis.

Our study of solving equations is based on an understanding of the algebraic steps that can be performed to produce an equivalent equation. The same is true for solving inequalities. The necessary facts are summarized in Theorem 1. If you need a refresher on inequalities and interval notation, see Appendix B, Section B-1.

> **THEOREM 1 Inequality Properties**
>
> An equivalent inequality will result and the **sense (or direction) will remain the same** if each side of the original inequality
>
> - Has the same real number added to or subtracted from it
> - Is multiplied or divided by the same positive number
>
> An equivalent inequality will result and the **sense (or direction) will reverse** if each side of the original inequality
>
> - Is multiplied or divided by the same negative number
>
> *Note:* Multiplication by 0 and division by 0 are not permitted.

Theorem 1 tells us that we can perform essentially the same operations on inequalities that we perform on equations, with the exception that *the sense (or direction) of the inequality reverses if we multiply or divide both sides by a negative number.* Otherwise the sense of the inequality does not change.

EXAMPLE 1 Solving a Linear Inequality

Solve $0.5x + 1 \le 0$.

SOLUTION

Algebraic Solution

$0.5x + 1 \le 0$ Subtract 1 from both sides.

$0.5x + 1 - 1 \le 0 - 1$

$0.5x \le -1$ Divide both sides by 0.5.

$$\frac{0.5x}{0.5} \le \frac{-1}{0.5}$$

$x \le -2$ or $(-\infty, -2]$

Graphical Solution

The graph of $f(x) = 0.5x + 1$ is shown in Figure 1. We see from the graph that $f(x)$ is negative to the left of -2 and positive to the right.

The inequality requires that $0.5x + 1$ be zero or negative, so the solution set of $0.5x + 1 \le 0$ is $x \le -2$ or, in interval notation, $(-\infty, -2]$.

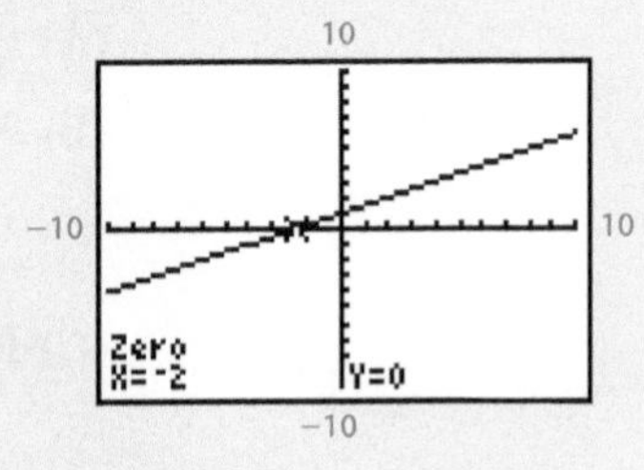

Figure 1

MATCHED PROBLEM 1

Solve $2x - 6 \geq 0$.

Think for a moment about the inequality $-2 < x < 3$. This is another way to describe the interval $(-2, 3)$. In fact, any inequality with three members is a statement about when an expression is between two values. We call these **combined inequalities.** We can solve linear combined inequalities by performing the same operations on all three members.

EXAMPLE 2 Solving a Combined Inequality

Solve $-3 \leq 4 - 7x < 18$.

SOLUTION

Algebraic Solution

To solve algebraically, we perform operations on the combined inequality until we have isolated x in the middle with a coefficient of 1.

$$-3 \leq 4 - 7x < 18 \quad \text{Subtract 4 from each member.}$$

$$-3 - 4 \leq 4 - 7x - 4 < 18 - 4$$

$$-7 \leq -7x < 14 \quad \text{Divide each member by } -7 \text{ and reverse each inequality.}$$

$$\frac{-7}{-7} \geq \frac{-7x}{-7} > \frac{14}{-7}$$

The solution is $1 \geq x > -2$. which can also be written as

$$-2 < x \leq 1 \quad \text{or} \quad (-2, 1] \qquad (2)$$

Graphical Solution

The inequality is a statement about where $4 - 7x$ is between -3 and 18, so we enter $y_1 = -3$, $y_2 = 4 - 7x$, $y_3 = 18$, and find the intersection points (Fig. 2 and Fig. 3). It is clear from the graph that y_2 is between y_1 and y_3 for x between -2 and 1. Because $y_2 = -3$ at $x = 1$, we include 1 in the solution set, obtaining the same solution as shown in (2).

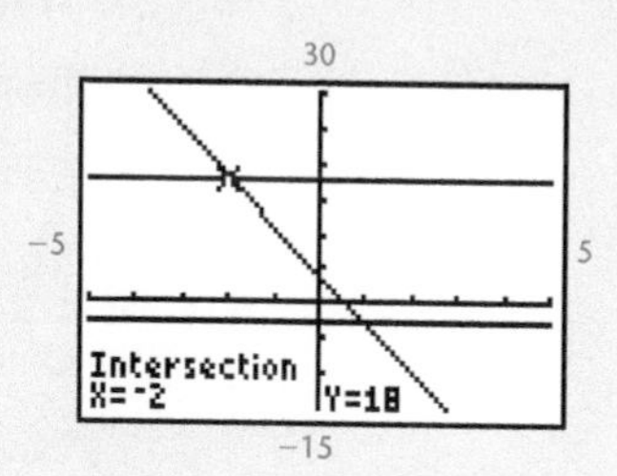

› Figure 2

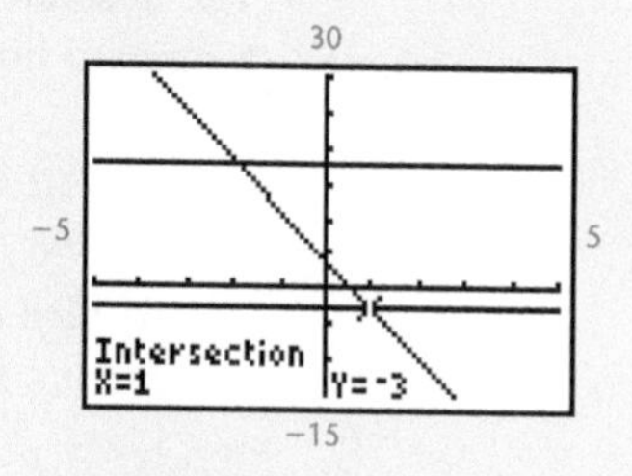

› Figure 3

››› CAUTION ›››

When multiplying or dividing both sides of an inequality by a negative number, don't forget to change the direction of each inequality.

MATCHED PROBLEM 2

Solve $-3 < 7 - 2x \leq 7$.

› Solving Inequalities Involving Absolute Value

››› EXPLORE-DISCUSS 2

Recall the definition of the absolute value function (see Section 1-3)

$$f(x) = |x| = \begin{cases} -x & \text{if } x < 0 \\ x & \text{if } x \geq 0 \end{cases}$$

(A) Graph the absolute value function $f(x) = |x|$ and the constant function $g(x) = 3$ in the same viewing window.

(B) From the graph in part A, determine the values of x for which:

$$|x| < 3 \qquad |x| = 3 \qquad |x| > 3$$

(C) Find all the points with coordinates $(x, 0)$ that are

Less than three units from the origin

Exactly three units from the origin

More than three units from the origin

(D) Compare the solutions found in parts B and C.

The absolute value of a number x is simply the distance between x and the origin on a number line.

$|x| = p$ describes the set of all points that are exactly p units from zero. That is, $x = p$ or $x = -p$.

$|x| < p$ describes the set of all points that are less than p units from zero. That is, $-p < x < p$.

$|x| > p$ describes the set of all points that are more than p units from zero. That is, $x < -p$ or $x > p$.

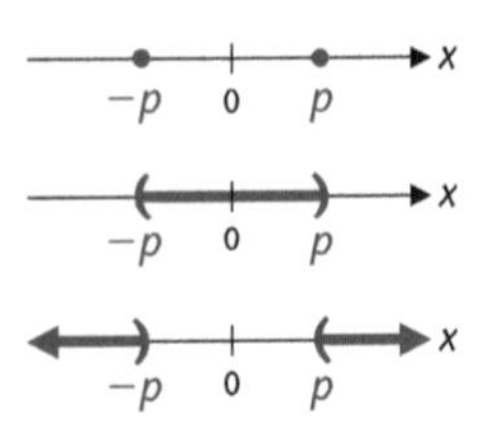

Theorem 2 describes how to apply this to solving inequalities.

› **THEOREM 2 Geometric Interpretation of Absolute Value**

For $p > 0$

1. $|ax + b| < p$ is equivalent to $-p < ax + b < p$.
2. $|ax + b| = p$ is equivalent to $ax + b = p$ or $ax + b = -p$.
3. $|ax + b| > p$ is equivalent to $ax + b < -p$ or $ax + b > p$.

››› **CAUTION** ›››

Don't try to memorize Theorem 2. Instead, think about each part as a statement about distance from zero on a number line.

EXAMPLE 3 Solving Inequalities Involving Absolute Value

Solve and write the solution in both inequality and interval notation for $|2x - 1| < 3$.

SOLUTION

Geometric Solution

The solution is the set of points x for which $2x - 1$ is less than three units from the origin. This means that $2x - 1$ must be between -3 and 3.

$$-3 < 2x - 1 < 3 \quad \text{Add 1 to each member.}$$

$$-3 + 1 < 2x - 1 + 1 < 3 + 1$$

$$-2 < 2x < 4 \quad \text{Divide each member by 2.}$$

$$\frac{-2}{2} < \frac{2x}{2} < \frac{4}{2}$$

$$-1 < x < 2 \quad \text{or} \quad (-1, 2)$$

Graphical Solution

Enter $y_1 = |2x - 1|$ and $y_2 = 3$ and use INTERSECT to find the intersection points (Fig. 4 and Fig. 5).

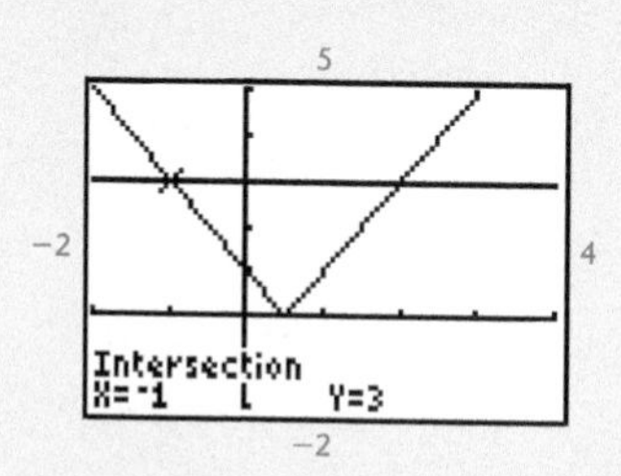

› Figure 4

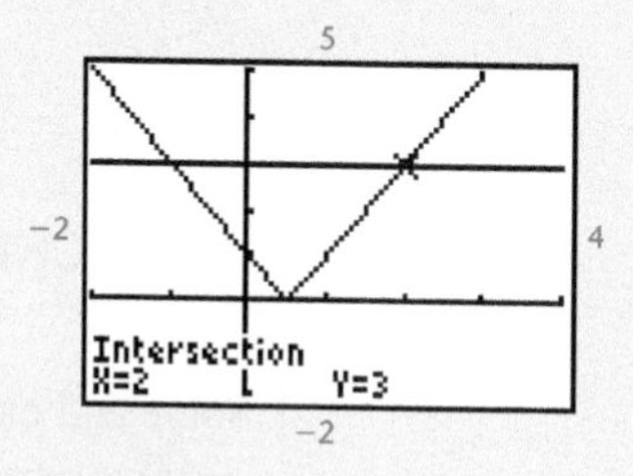

› Figure 5

Examining these graphs, we see that the graph of y_1 is below the graph of y_2 for $-1 < x < 2$.

MATCHED PROBLEM 3

Solve and write the solution in both inequality and interval notation for $|2x + 1| < 5$.

EXAMPLE 4 **Solving an Inequality Involving Absolute Value**

Solve and express the answer in both inequality and interval notation for $|4x - 5| \geq 2$.

SOLUTION

Geometric Solution
The solution is the set of points x for which $4x - 5$ is two or more units from the origin. This occurs when $4x - 5 \leq -2$ or $4x - 5 \geq 2$:

$$4x - 5 \leq -2 \quad \text{or} \quad 4x - 5 \geq 2$$

$$4x \leq 3 \quad \text{or} \quad 4x \geq 7$$

$$x \leq \frac{3}{4} = 0.75 \quad \text{or} \quad x \geq \frac{7}{4} = 1.75$$

In interval notation, the solution set is

$$(-\infty, 0.75] \cup [1.75, \infty)^* \qquad (3)$$

Graphical Solution
Enter $y_1 = |4x - 5|$ and $y_2 = 2$ and use INTERSECT to find the intersection points (Fig. 6 and Fig. 7).

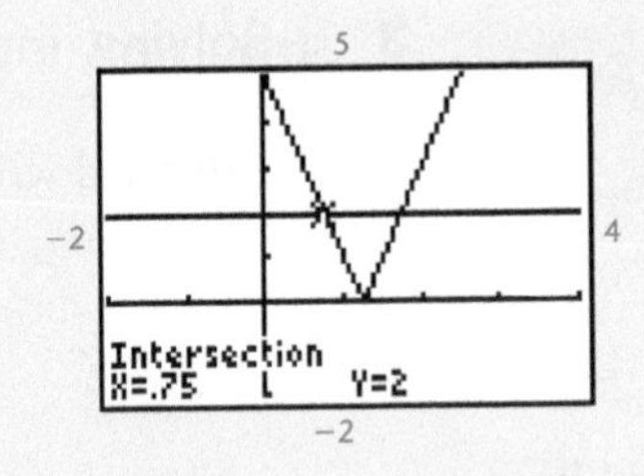

› **Figure 6**

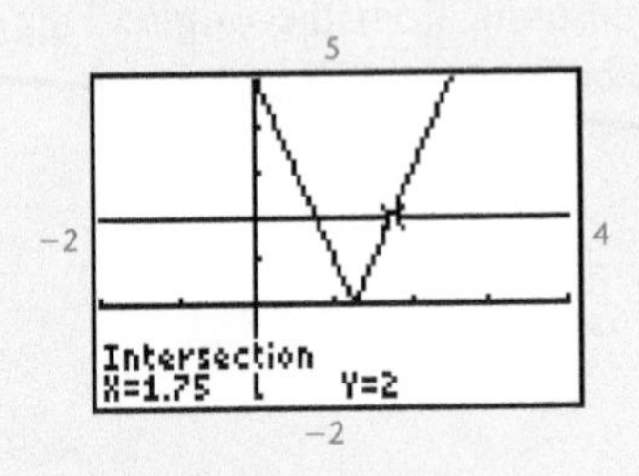

› **Figure 7**

Examining these graphs, we see that if $x \leq 0.75$ or $x \geq 1.75$, then the graph of y_1 is on or above the graph of y_2. This is the same solution given in (3).

MATCHED PROBLEM 4

Solve and express the answer in both inequality and interval notation for $|\frac{2}{3}x + 1| \geq 2$.

*The symbol $\cup$ denotes the union operation for sets. See Appendix B, Section B-1, for a discussion of interval notation and set operations.

Solving Quadratic Inequalities

Solving linear inequalities is very similar to solving linear equations. As we will see, however, the methods we use for solving quadratic equations will not work for quadratic inequalities. This is largely due to the fact that the zero product property does not carry over to inequalities.

EXPLORE-DISCUSS 3

The zero product property tells us that if $a \cdot b = 0$, then one or both of a and b must be zero.

(A) If $a \cdot b > 0$, is it true that $a > 0$ or $b > 0$? Can they both be positive?

(B) If $a \cdot b < 0$, is it true that $a < 0$ or $b < 0$? Can they both be negative?

Consider the following attempt at solving the inequality $(x + 2)(x - 3) > 0$, which is based on the solution of the equation $(x + 2)(x - 3) = 0$.

Equation	**Inequality**
$(x + 2)(x - 3) = 0$	$(x + 2)(x - 3) > 0$
$x + 2 = 0$ or $x - 3 = 0$	$x + 2 > 0$ or $x - 3 > 0$
$x = -2$ or $x = 3$	$x > -2$ or $x > 3$

(C) Graph the alleged solution to the inequality on a number line.

(D) Check this solution by graphing $f(x) = (x + 2)(x - 3)$ on a graphing calculator. Is the alleged solution incorrect? What do you think went wrong?

Now we know that we cannot solve quadratic inequalities just like quadratic equations. But all is not lost. We can use what we know about solving quadratic equations because of the following important fact.

THEOREM 3 The Location Theorem

If $f(x)$ is a continuous function and $f(a)$ and $f(b)$ have opposite signs, then there must be a zero of f somewhere between $x = a$ and $x = b$.*

Why is this helpful? When an inequality has zero on one side, it is a statement about where an expression is positive or negative. Theorem 3 will enable us to identify the x values that make an expression positive or negative by first identifying all of the x values where it can change sign.

*Theorem 3 is actually a special case of a theorem that is very important in calculus called the Intermediate Value Theorem.

EXAMPLE 5 Solving a Quadratic Inequality

Solve the inequality $x^2 - x - 12 > 0$ and write your answer in interval notation.

SOLUTION

Algebraic Solution

Solving the inequality requires finding all x values for which the function $f(x) = x^2 - x - 12$ is positive. This is a continuous function, so Theorem 3 applies.

First, find the zeros of f:

$$x^2 - x - 12 = 0$$
$$(x - 4)(x + 3) = 0$$
$$x = 4, -3$$

These are the only zeros of f, so Theorem 3 implies that f can change sign only at $x = 4$ and $x = -3$. So if f is positive for *any* x values less than -3, it must be positive for *all of them.* Choose a **test number** $x = -5$ (any x value less than -3 will do).

$$x = -5: \quad (-5)^2 - (-5) - 12 = 18 > 0$$ $x^2 - x - 12$ is positive for $x < -3$.

We choose a test number for the intervals $-3 < x < 4$ and $x > 4$, and summarize the information with a table.

Interval	Test Number	Result
$x < -3$	-5	$(-5)^2 - (-5) - 12 = 18$; positive
$-3 < x < 4$	0	$(0)^2 - (0) - 12 = -12$; negative
$x > 4$	10	$(10)^2 - (10) - 12 = 78$; positive

The expression $x^2 - x - 12$ is positive on $x < -3$ or $x > 4$, so the solution to the inequality $x^2 - x - 12 > 0$ in interval notation is $(-\infty, -3) \cup (4, \infty)$.

Graphical Solution

Enter $y_1 = x^2 - x - 12$. Using the ZERO command we see that $y_1 = 0$ at $x = -3$ (Fig. 8) and at $x = 4$ (Fig. 9).

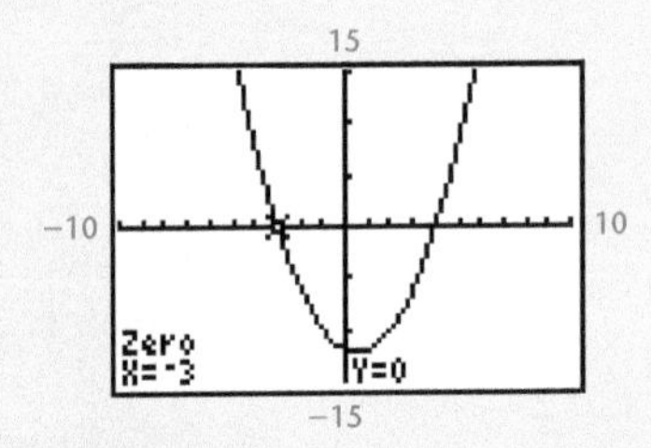

› Figure 8

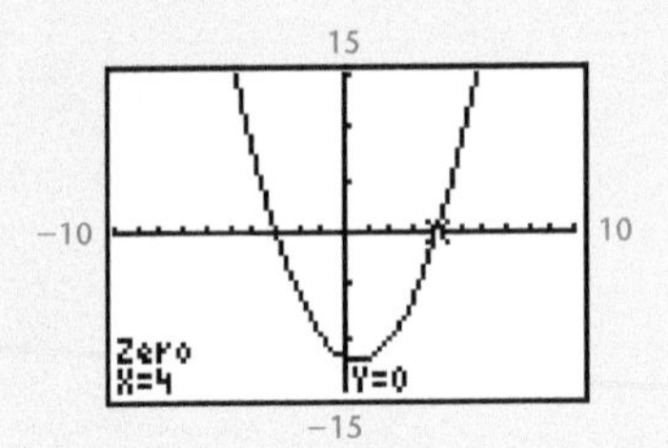

› Figure 9

The graph of y_1 is above the x axis for $x < -3$ and also for $x > 4$. Thus, the solution to the inequality $y_1 > 0$ is

$$(-\infty, -3) \cup (4, \infty)$$

MATCHED PROBLEM 5

Solve the inequality $x^2 - x - 6 > 0$ and write your answer in interval notation.

Note that both the algebraic and graphical solutions accomplished the same thing. First, we identify the x values where $x^2 - x - 12$ is zero, then decide on which intervals bounded by these x values are positive.

EXAMPLE 6 Solving a Quadratic Inequality

Solve the inequality $2x^2 - 5x + 1 \leq 0$. Write your answer in interval notation. Round to two decimal places.

SOLUTION

Algebraic Solution

1. Find the zeros of $f(x) = 2x^2 - 5x + 1$ using the quadratic formula.

$$x = \frac{5 \pm \sqrt{(-5)^2 - 4(2)(1)}}{2(2)}$$

$$= \frac{5 \pm \sqrt{17}}{4} \approx 0.22, 2.28$$

2. Make a table, check test values.

Interval	Test Number	Result
$x < 0.22$	-2	$2(-2)^2 - 5(-2) + 1 = 19$; positive
$0.22 < x < 2.28$	1	$2(1)^2 - 5(1) + 1 = -2$; negative
$x > 2.28$	5	$2(5)^2 - 5(5) + 1 = 26$; positive

We choose the interval where $2x^2 - 5x + 1$ is negative, and include the values for which it is zero. The solution is $[0.22, 2.28]$ to two decimal places.

Graphical Solution

Enter $y_1 = 2x^2 - 5x + 1$. Using the ZERO command, we see that $y_1 = 0$ at approximately $x = 0.22$ and 2.28 (Figs. 10 and 11).

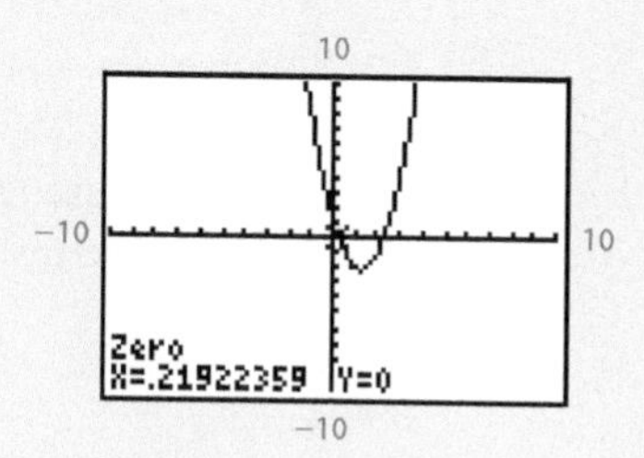

› Figure 10

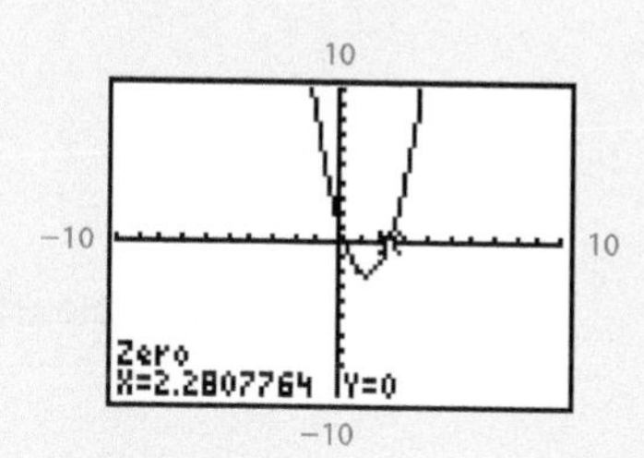

› Figure 11

The graph of y_1 is below the x axis for $0.22 < x < 2.28$. We include the zeros in our solution and get $[0.22, 2.28]$.

››› CAUTION ›››

Always think carefully about whether to include the endpoints of intervals when solving quadratic inequalities. If the inequality sign is $\leq$ or $\geq$, you will need to include the endpoints.

MATCHED PROBLEM 6

Solve the inequality $-x^2 + 7x - 9 \leq 0$. Write your answer in interval notation. Round to two decimal places.

› Mathematical Modeling

EXAMPLE 7 **Projectile Motion**

An artillery shell propelled upward from the ground reaches a maximum height of 576 feet above ground level after 6 seconds. Let the quadratic function $d(t)$ represent the distance above ground level (in feet) t seconds after the shell is released.

(A) Find $d(t)$.

(B) At what times will the shell be more than 320 feet above the ground?

SOLUTIONS

(A) Because the quadratic distance function d has a maximum value of 576 at $t = 6$, the vertex form for $d(t)$ is

$$d(t) = a(t - 6)^2 + 576$$

All that remains is to find a. We use the fact that $d(0) = 0$.

$$\begin{aligned} d(0) = a(-6)^2 + 576 &= 0 \\ 36a &= -576 \\ a &= -16 \end{aligned}$$

The model for the height of this artillery shell is

$$\begin{aligned} d(t) &= -16(t - 6)^2 + 576 \\ &= -16t^2 + 192t \end{aligned}$$

(B) To determine the times when the shell is higher than 320 feet, we solve the inequality

$$d(t) = -16t^2 + 192t > 320$$

Algebraic Solution

$$-16t^2 + 192t > 320$$ Subtract 320 from both sides.

$$-16t^2 + 192t - 320 > 0$$ Divide each side by −16 and reverse the direction of the inequality.

$$\frac{-16t^2}{-16} + \frac{192t}{-16} - \frac{320}{-16} < 0$$

$$t^2 - 12t + 20 < 0$$ Factor.

$$(t - 2)(t - 10) < 0$$

Graphical Solution

Graph $y_1 = -16x^2 + 192x$ and $y_2 = 320$ and find the intersection points (Fig. 12 and Fig. 13).

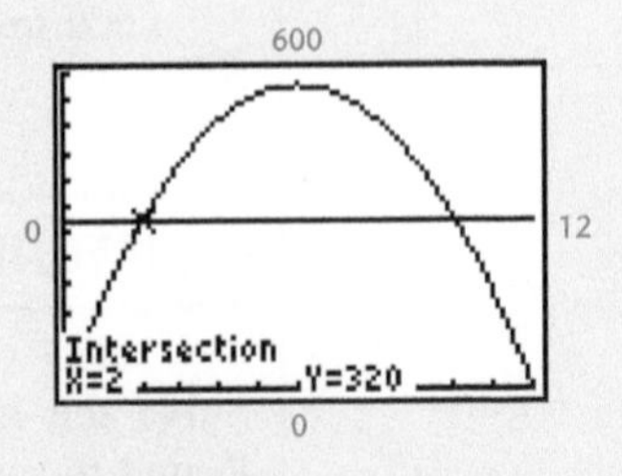

› **Figure 12**

The zeros of $t^2 - 12t + 20$ are 2 and 10.

Interval	Test Number	Result
$0 < t < 2$	1	$(1)^2 - 12(1) + 20 = 9$; positive
$2 < t < 10$	5	$(5)^2 - 12(5) + 20 = -15$; negative
$t > 10$	12	$(12)^2 - 12(12) + 20 = 20$; positive

The solution to $-16t^2 + 192t > 320$ is $2 < t < 10$, so the shell is above 320 feet between 2 and 10 seconds after it is launched.

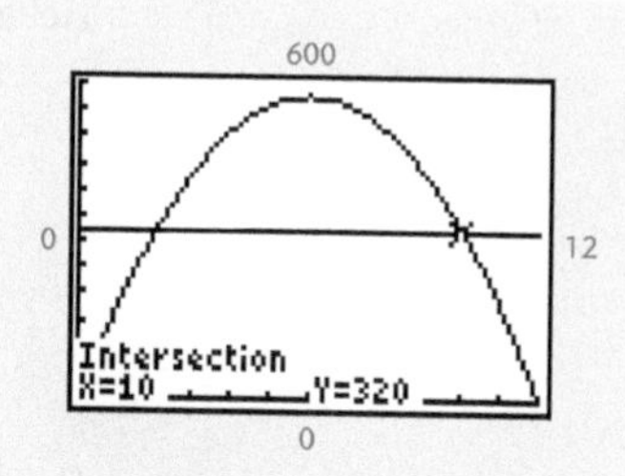

› Figure 13

From these graphs we see that the shell will be above 320 feet between 2 and 10 seconds after it is launched.

MATCHED PROBLEM 7

Refer to the shell equation in Example 7. At what times during its flight will the shell be less than 432 feet above the ground?

› Data Analysis and Regression

EXAMPLE 8

Break-Even, Profit, and Loss

Table 1 Price–Demand Data

Weekly Sales	Price per Gallon
5,610	\$20.50
5,810	\$18.70
5,990	\$17.90
6,180	\$16.20
6,460	\$15.40
6,730	\$13.80
6,940	\$12.90

A paint manufacturer has weekly fixed costs of \$40,000 and variable costs of \$6.75 per gallon produced. Examining past records produces the price–demand data in Table 1. Round all numbers to three significant digits.

(A) Use linear regression to find the price–demand equation $p = d(x)$ for the data in Table 1. What is the domain of $d(x)$?

(B) Find the revenue and cost functions as functions of the sales x. What is the domain of each function?

(C) Find the level of sales for which the company will break even. Describe verbally and graphically the sales levels that result in a profit and those that result in a loss.

(D) Find the sales and the price that will produce the maximum profit. Find the maximum profit.

SOLUTIONS

(A) Enter the data in Table 1 and select the LINREG $(ax + b)$ option (Fig. 14). After rounding, the price–demand equation is

$$p = d(x) = 51.0 - 0.00553x$$

```
LinReg
 y=ax+b
 a=-.0055269853
 b=51.00568555
 r²=.9823555916
 r=-.991138533
```

› Figure 14

Because negative prices don't make sense, x must satisfy

$$51.0 - 0.00553x \geq 0 \quad \text{Add } 0.00553x \text{ to both sides.}$$

$$51 \geq 0.00553x \quad \text{Divide both sides by } 0.00553.$$

$$x \leq \frac{51}{0.00553} = 9{,}220 \quad \text{To three significant digits}$$

Because sales can't be negative, the domain of the price–demand equation is $0 \leq x \leq 9{,}220$.

(B) The revenue function is

$$R(x) = xp \quad \text{Revenue is price} \cdot \text{quantity sold.}$$

$$= x(51 - 0.00553x)$$

$$= 51x - 0.00553x^2 \qquad 0 \leq x \leq 9{,}220$$

Note that the domain of R is the same as the domain of d. The cost function is

$$C(x) = 40{,}000 + 6.75x \qquad x \geq 0 \quad \$40{,}000 \text{ fixed costs} + \$6.75 \text{ per gallon}$$

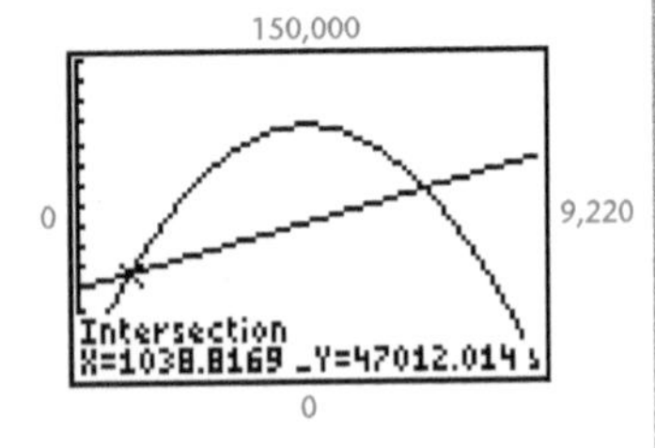

› **Figure 15**

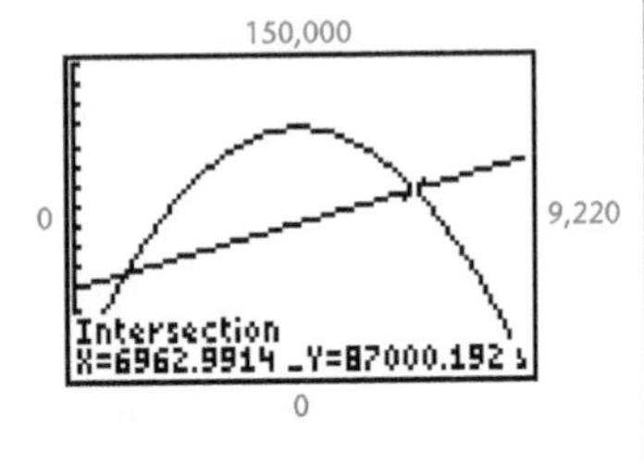

› **Figure 16**

(C) The company will break even when revenue = cost, that is, when $R(x) = C(x)$. An intersection point on the graphs of R and C is often referred to as a **break-even point.** Graphs of both functions and their intersection points are shown in Figures 15 and 16.

Examining these graphs, we see that the company will break even if they sell 1,040 or 6,960 gallons of paint. If they sell between 1,040 and 6,960 gallons, then revenue is greater than cost and the company will make a profit. If they sell fewer than 1,040 or more than 6,960 gallons, then cost is greater than revenue and the company will lose money. These sales levels are illustrated in Figure 17.

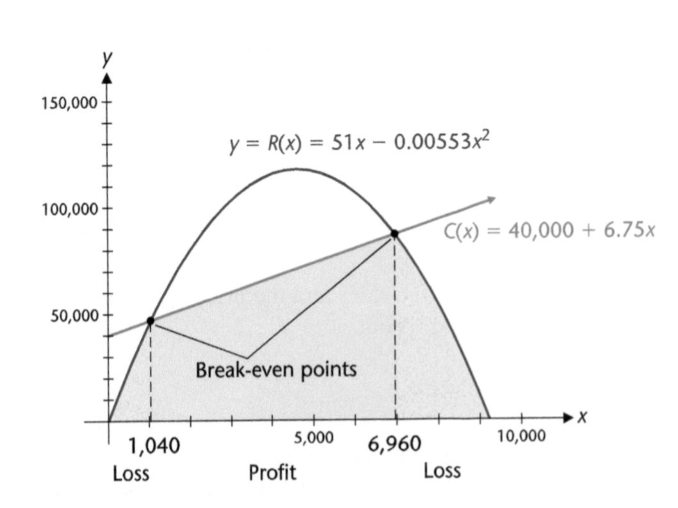

› **Figure 17**

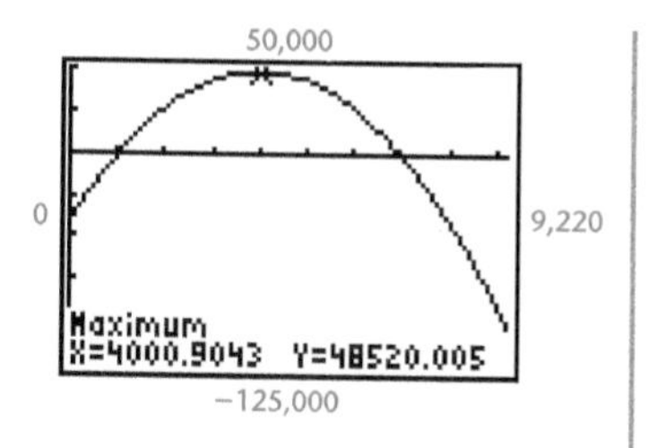

› **Figure 18**

(D) The profit function for this manufacturer is

$$
\begin{aligned}
P(x) &= R(x) - C(x) \\
&= (51x - 0.00553x^2) - (40{,}000 + 6.75x) \\
&= 44.25x - 0.00553x^2 - 40{,}000
\end{aligned}
$$

Profit is revenue − cost.

To find the largest profit, enter $y_1 = P(x)$ and use the MAXIMUM command (Fig. 18).

The maximum profit of \$48,500 occurs when 4,000 gallons of paint are sold. The price is

$$
\begin{aligned}
p = d(4{,}000) &= 51 - 0.00553(4{,}000) \\
&= \$28.90
\end{aligned}
$$

MATCHED PROBLEM 8

Table 2 Price–Demand Data

Weekly Sales	Price per Gallon
5,470	\$18.80
5,640	\$17.30
5,910	\$15.90
6,150	\$14.10
6,380	\$13.30
6,530	\$12.40
6,820	\$10.80

A paint manufacturer has weekly fixed costs of \$50,000 and variable costs of \$7.50 per gallon produced. Examining past records produces the price–demand data in Table 2. Round all numbers to three significant digits.

(A) Use linear regression to find the price–demand equation $p = d(x)$ for the data in Table 2. What is the domain of $d(x)$?

(B) Find the revenue and cost functions as functions of the sales x. What is the domain of each function?

(C) Find the level of sales for which the company will break even. Describe verbally and graphically the sales levels that result in a profit and those that result in a loss.

(D) Find the sales and the price that will produce the maximum profit. Find the maximum profit.

ANSWERS TO MATCHED PROBLEMS

1. $x \geq 3$ or $[3, \infty)$ **2.** $0 \leq x < 5$ or $[0, 5)$ **3.** $-3 < x < 2$ or $(-3, 2)$
4. $x \leq -4.5$ or $x \geq 1.5$; $(-\infty, -4.5] \cup [1.5, \infty)$ **5.** $(-\infty, -2) \cup (3, \infty)$
6. $(-\infty, 1.70] \cup [5.30, \infty)$ **7.** Before 3 seconds and between 9 and 12 seconds after it was launched.
8. (A) $p = d(x) = 50.0 - 0.00577x$, $0 \leq x \leq 8{,}670$
(B) $R(x) = 50x - 0.00577x^2$, $0 \leq x \leq 8{,}670$, $C(x) = 50{,}000 + 7.5x$, $x \geq 0$
(C) The company will break even if they sell 1,470 or 5,900 gallons of paint. If they sell between 1,470 and 5,900 gallons, then revenue is greater than cost and the company will make a profit. If they sell fewer than 1,470 or more than 5,900 gallons, then cost is greater than revenue and the company will lose money.

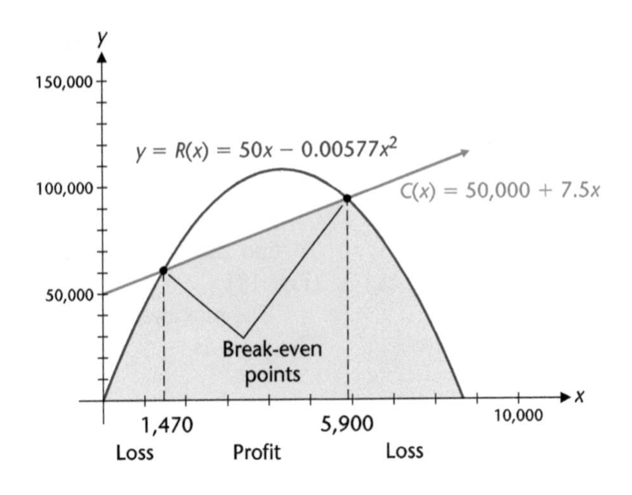

(D) The company will make a maximum profit of $28,300 when they sell 3,680 gallons at $28.80 per gallon.

2-7 Exercises

1. Explain in your own words what it means to solve an inequality.

2. What is the main difference between the procedures for solving linear equations and linear inequalities?

3. Why does any inequality of the form $|f(x)| < 0$ have no solution?

4. Explain why it is not true that $a \cdot b > 0$ implies $a > 0$ or $b > 0$.

Use the graphs of functions u and v in the figure to solve the inequalities in Problems 5–12. Express solutions in interval notation.

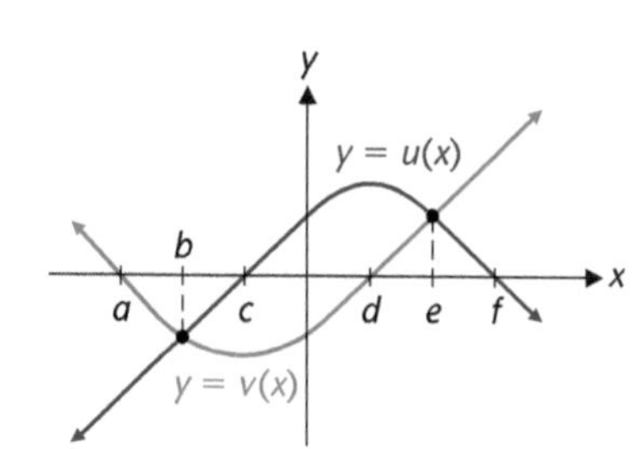

5. $u(x) > 0$ **6.** $v(x) \geq 0$

7. $v(x) \geq u(x)$ **8.** $v(x) < 0$

9. $u(x) \leq 0$ **10.** $u(x) - v(x) \geq 0$

11. $v(x) - u(x) > 0$ **12.** $v(x) < u(x)$

In Problems 13–20, write each statement as an absolute value inequality.

13. x is less than five units from 3.

14. w is more than four units from 2.

15. y is more than six units from -1.

16. z is less than eight units from -2.

17. a is no more than five units from 3.

18. c is no less than seven units from -4.

19. d is no less than four units from -2.

20. m is no more than six units from 1.

In Problems 21–24, write each inequality as a verbal statement about distance.

21. $|y| \leq 7$ **22.** $|t| \leq 5$ **23.** $|w| > 7$ **24.** $|r| > 5$

In Problems 25–38, solve and write answers in both interval and inequality notation.

25. $7x - 8 < 4x + 7$ **26.** $4x + 8 \geq x - 1$

27. $-5t < -10$ **28.** $-7n \geq 21$

29. $3 - m < 4(m - 3)$

30. $2(1 - u) \geq 5u$

31. $(x - 3)(x + 4) < 0$

32. $(x + 10)(x - 15) < 0$

33. $x(2x - 7) \geq 0$

34. $x(5 - 3x) \geq 0$

35. $|s - 5| < 3$

36. $|t - 3| < 4$

37. $|s - 5| > 3$

38. $|t - 3| > 4$

In Problems 39–64, solve and write answers in both interval and inequality notation.

39. $-4 < 5t + 6 \leq 21$

40. $2 \leq 3m - 7 < 14$

41. $-12 < \frac{3}{4}(2 - x) \leq 24$

42. $24 \leq \frac{2}{3}(x - 5) < 36$

43. $\frac{q}{7} - 3 > \frac{q - 4}{3} + 1$

44. $\frac{p}{3} - \frac{p - 2}{2} \leq \frac{p}{4} - 4$

45. $x^2 < 10 - 3x$

46. $x^2 + x < 12$

47. $x^2 + 21 > 10x$

48. $x^2 + 7x + 10 > 0$

49. $x^2 \leq 8x$

50. $x^2 \leq 4x$

51. $x^2 + 1 < 2x$

52. $x^2 + 25 < 10x$

53. $x^2 - 21 \geq 4x$

54. $x^2 + 13x + 40 \leq 0$

55. $x^2 - 5x + 3 > 0$

56. $x^2 + 3x - 8 > 0$

57. $x + 7 \geq 2x^2$

58. $-10x - 1 \geq 3x^2$

59. $|3x - 7| \leq 4$

60. $|5y + 2| \geq 8$

61. $|4 - 2t| > 6$

62. $|10 + 4s| < 6$

63. $|0.2u + 1.7| \geq 0.5$

64. $|0.5v - 2.5| > 1.6$

In Problems 65–68, replace each question mark with $<$ or $>$ and explain why your choice makes the statement true.

65. If $a - b = 1$, then $a ? b$.

66. If $u - v = -2$, then $u ? v$.

67. If $a < 0, b < 0$, and $\frac{b}{a} > 1$, then $a ? b$.

68. If $a > 0, b > 0$, and $\frac{b}{a} > 1$, then $a ? b$.

When studying the concept of limits in calculus, it is very important to specify small distances with inequalities. For Problems 69–72, first write a verbal description of the inequality using distances. Then solve and write your answer in interval notation.

69. $0 < |x - 3| < 0.1$

70. $0 < |x - 5| < 0.01$

71. $0 < |x - c| < 2c, c > 0$

72. $0 < |x - 2c| < c, c > 0$

Finding where certain functions are positive and negative plays a very important role in calculus. In Problems 73–76, find the intervals where each function is positive and the intervals where each is negative. Write your answers in interval notation.

73. $f(x) = 2x^2 - 5x - 12$

74. $g(x) = -3x^2 - 7x + 10$

75. $h(x) = x^2 + 9x + 2$

76. $k(x) = 4 - 5x - 6x^2$

77. Give an example of a quadratic inequality whose solution set is the entire real line.

78. Give an example of a quadratic inequality whose solution set is the empty set.

APPLICATIONS

79. APPROXIMATION The area A of a region is approximately equal to 12.436. The error in this approximation is less than 0.001. Describe the possible values of this area both with an absolute value inequality and with interval notation.

80. APPROXIMATION The volume V of a solid is approximately equal to 6.94. The error in this approximation is less than 0.02. Describe the possible values of this volume both with an absolute value inequality and with interval notation.

81. BREAK-EVEN ANALYSIS An electronics firm is planning to market a new graphing calculator. The fixed costs are \$650,000 and the variable costs are \$47 per calculator. The wholesale price of the calculator will be \$63. For the company to make a profit, revenues must be greater than costs.
(A) How many calculators must be sold for the company to make a profit?
(B) How many calculators must be sold for the company to break even?
(C) Discuss the relationship between the results in parts A and B.

82. BREAK-EVEN ANALYSIS A video game manufacturer is planning to market a handheld version of its game machine. The fixed costs are \$550,000 and the variable costs are \$120 per machine. The wholesale price of the machine will be \$140.
(A) How many game machines must be sold for the company to make a profit?
(B) How many game machines must be sold for the company to break even?
(C) Discuss the relationship between the results in parts A and B.

83. BREAK-EVEN ANALYSIS The electronics firm in Problem 81 finds that rising prices for parts increase the variable costs to \$50.50 per calculator.
(A) Discuss possible strategies the company might use to deal with this increase in costs.
(B) If the company continues to sell the calculators for \$63, how many must they sell now to make a profit?

(C) If the company wants to start making a profit at the same production level as before the cost increase, how much should they increase the wholesale price?

84. BREAK-EVEN ANALYSIS The video game manufacturer in Problem 82 finds that unexpected programming problems increase the fixed costs to $660,000.
(A) Discuss possible strategies the company might use to deal with this increase in costs.
(B) If the company continues to sell the game machines for $140, how many must they sell now to make a profit?
(C) If the company wants to start making a profit at the same production level as before the cost increase, how much should they increase the wholesale price?

85. PROFIT ANALYSIS A screen printer produces custom silk-screen apparel. The cost $C(x)$ of printing x custom T-shirts and the revenue $R(x)$ from the sale of x T-shirts (both in dollars) are given by

$$C(x) = 200 + 2.25x$$
$$R(x) = 10x - 0.05x^2$$

Determine the production levels x (to the nearest integer) that will result in the printer showing a profit.

86. PROFIT ANALYSIS Refer to Problem 85. Determine the production levels x (to the nearest integer) that will result in the printer showing a profit of at least $60.

87. CELSIUS/FAHRENHEIT A formula for converting Celsius degrees to Fahrenheit degrees is given by the linear function

$$F = \frac{9}{5}C + 32$$

Determine to the nearest degree the Celsius range in temperature that corresponds to the Fahrenheit range of 60°F to 80°F.

88. CELSIUS/FAHRENHEIT A formula for converting Fahrenheit degrees to Celsius degrees is given by the linear function

$$C = \frac{5}{9}(F - 32)$$

Determine to the nearest degree the Fahrenheit range in temperature that corresponds to a Celsius range of 20°C to 30°C.

89. PROJECTILE MOTION A projectile propelled straight upward from the ground reaches a maximum height of 256 feet above ground level after 4 seconds. Let the quadratic function $d(t)$ represent the distance above ground level (in feet) t seconds after the projectile is released.
(A) Find $d(t)$.
(B) At what times will the projectile be more than 240 feet above the ground? Write and solve an inequality to find the times. Express the answer in inequality notation.

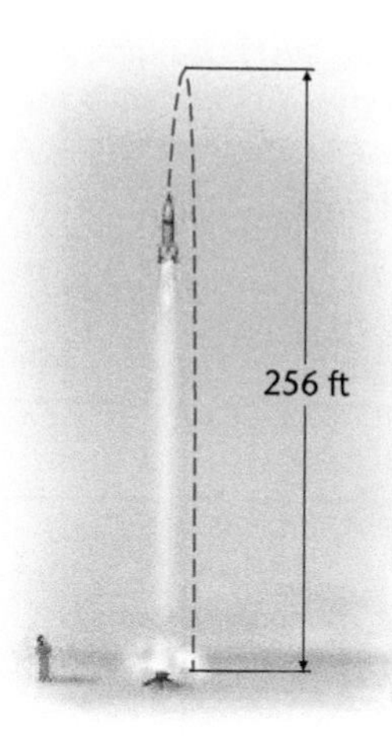

90. PROJECTILE MOTION A projectile propelled straight upward from the ground reaches a maximum height of 784 feet above ground level after 7 seconds. Let the quadratic function $d(t)$ represent the distance above ground level (in feet) t seconds after the projectile is released.
(A) Find $d(t)$.
(B) At what times will the projectile be less than 640 feet above the ground? Write and solve an inequality to find the times. Express the answer in inequality notation.

91. EARTH SCIENCE Deeper and deeper holes are being bored into the Earth's surface every year in search of energy in the form of oil, gas, or heat. A bore at Windischeschenbach in the North German basin has reached a depth of more than 8 kilometers. The temperature in the bore is 30°C at a depth of 1 kilometer and increases 2.8°C for each additional 100 meters of depth. Find a mathematical model for the temperature T at a depth of x kilometers. At what interval of depths will the temperature be between 150°C and 200°C? Round answers to three decimal places.

92. EARTH SCIENCE A bore at Basel, Switzerland, has reached a depth of more than 5 kilometers. The temperature is 35°C at a depth of 1 kilometer and increases 3.6°C for each additional 100 meters of depth. Find a mathematical model for the temperature T at a depth of x kilometers. At what interval of depths will the temperature be between 100°C and 150°C? Round answers to three decimal places.

DATA ANALYSIS AND REGRESSION

Twice each day 70 weather stations in the United States release high-altitude balloons containing instruments that send various data back to the station. Eventually, the balloons burst and the instruments parachute back to Earth to be reclaimed. The air *pressure (in hectopascals*), the altitude (in meters), and the temperature (in degrees Celsius) collected on the same day at two midwestern stations are given in Table 3. Round all numbers to three significant digits.*

Table 3 Upper-Air Weather Data

North Platte, NE			Minneapolis, MN		
PRES	HGT	TEMP	PRES	HGT	TEMP
745	2,574	8	756	2,438	2
700	3,087	5	728	2,743	0
627	3,962	−1	648	3,658	−4
559	4,877	−8	555	4,877	−10
551	4,992	−8	500	5,680	−17
476	6,096	−16	400	7,330	−28
404	7,315	−24	367	7,944	−32
387	7,620	−27	300	9,330	−45
300	9,410	−43	250	10,520	−55
259	10,363	−49	241	10,751	−57

Source: NOAA Air Resources Laboratory

93. WEATHER Let x be the altitude of the balloon released from North Platte and let y be the corresponding temperature. Use linear regression to find a linear function $y = ax + b$ that fits these data. For what altitudes will the temperature be between $-10°C$ and $-30°C$?

94. WEATHER Let x be the altitude of the balloon released from Minneapolis and let y be the corresponding temperature. Use linear regression to find a linear function $y = ax + b$ that fits these data. For what altitudes will the temperature be between $-20°C$ and $-40°C$?

95. WEATHER Let x be the altitude of the balloon released from North Platte and let y be the corresponding air pressure. Use linear regression to find a linear function $y = ax + b$ that fits these data. For what altitudes will the air pressure be between 350 hectopascals and 650 hectopascals?

96. WEATHER Let x be the altitude of the balloon released from Minneapolis and let y be the corresponding air pressure. Use linear regression to find a linear function $y = ax + b$ that fits these data. For what altitudes will the air pressure be between 350 hectopascals and 650 hectopascals?

*A unit of pressure equivalent to 1 millibar.

97. BREAK-EVEN ANALYSIS Table 4 contains weekly price–demand data for orange juice and grapefruit juice for a fruit juice producer. The producer has weekly fixed costs of $20,000 and variable costs of $0.50 per gallon of orange juice produced.
(A) Use linear regression to find the price–demand equation $p = d(x)$ for the orange juice data in Table 4. What is the domain of $d(x)$?
(B) Find the revenue and cost functions as functions of the sales x. What is the domain of each function?
(C) Find the level of sales for which the company will break even. Describe verbally and graphically the sales levels that result in a profit and those that result in a loss.
(D) Find the sales and the price that will produce the maximum profit. Find the maximum profit.

Table 4 Fruit Juice Production

Orange Juice Demand (gal.)	Price	Grapefruit Juice Demand (gal.)	Price
21,800	$1.95	2,130	$2.32
24,300	$1.81	2,480	$2.21
26,700	$1.43	2,610	$2.07
28,900	$1.37	2,890	$1.87
29,700	$1.28	3,170	$1.81
33,700	$1.14	3,640	$1.68
34,800	$0.96	4,350	$1.56

98. BREAK-EVEN ANALYSIS The juice producer in Problem 97 has weekly fixed costs of $3,000 and variable costs of $0.40 per gallon of grapefruit juice produced.
(A) Use linear regression to find the price–demand equation $p = d(x)$ for the grapefruit juice data in Table 4. What is the domain of $d(x)$?
(B) Find the revenue and cost functions as functions of the sales x. What is the domain of each function?
(C) Find the level of sales for which the company will break even. Describe verbally and graphically the sales levels that result in a profit and those that result in a loss.
(D) Find the sales and the price that will produce the maximum profit. Find the maximum profit.

CHAPTER 2 Review

2-1 Linear Functions

A function f is a **linear function** if $f(x) = mx + b$, $m \neq 0$, where m and b are real numbers. The **domain** is the set of all real numbers and the **range** is the set of all real numbers. If $m = 0$, then f is called a **constant function,** $f(x) = b$, which has the set of all real numbers as its **domain** and the constant b as its **range.** The **standard form** for the equation of a line is $Ax + By = C$, where A, B, and C are real constants, and A and B are not both 0. Every straight line in a Cartesian coordinate system is the graph of an equation of this type. The **slope** of a line is a number that measures how steep a line is. The slope of the line through the points (x_1, y_1) and (x_2, y_2) is

$$m = \frac{y_2 - y_1}{x_2 - x_1} \qquad x_1 \neq x_2$$

The slope is not defined for a vertical line where $x_1 = x_2$.

Equations of a Line

Standard Form	$Ax + By = C$	A and B not both 0
Slope–Intercept Form	$y = mx + b$	Slope: m; y intercept: b
Point–Slope Form	$y - y_1 = m(x - x_1)$	Slope: m; Point: (x_1, y_1)
Horizontal Line	$y = b$	Slope: 0
Vertical Line	$x = a$	Slope: Undefined

To graph a linear function, it is sufficient to plot two points and connect them with a line. But it is a good idea to plot three points to check for possible errors.

Two nonvertical lines with slopes m_1 and m_2 are **parallel** if and only if $m_1 = m_2$ and **perpendicular** if and only if $m_1 m_2 = -1$.

The slope of a linear function describes the rate at which the output of the function changes as the input changes. In short, slope can be interpreted as a **rate of change.** The y intercept of a linear cost function is called the **fixed cost** and the slope is called the **variable cost.**

2-2 Linear Equations and Models

Solving an equation is the process of finding all values of the variable that make the equation a true statement. An equation that is true for some values of the variable is called a **conditional equation.** An equation that is true for all permissible values of the variable is called an **identity,** and the solution is all real numbers. An equation that is false for all permissible values of the variable is called a **contradiction,** and has no solution.

Linear equations are solved by performing algebraic steps that result in equivalent equations until the result is an equation whose solution is obvious. When an equation has fractions, begin by multiplying both sides by the least common denominator of all the fractions. The formula distance = rate · time is useful in modeling problems that involve motion.

Linear regression is used to fit a curve to a data set. A **scatter diagram** is a graph of a data set. **Diagnostics** indicate how well a curve fits a data set. Supply and demand curves intersect at the **equilibrium point,** which consists of the **equilibrium price** and **equilibrium quantity.**

2-3 Quadratic Functions

If a, b, and c are real numbers with $a \neq 0$, then the function $f(x) = ax^2 + bx + c$ is a **quadratic function** (in **general form**) and its graph is a **parabola. Completing the square** of the quadratic expression $x^2 + bx$ produces a perfect square:

$$x^2 + bx + \left(\frac{b}{2}\right)^2 = \left(x + \frac{b}{2}\right)^2$$

Completing the square for $f(x) = ax^2 + bx + c$ produces the **vertex form** $f(x) = a(x - h)^2 + k$ and gives the following properties:

1. The graph of f is a parabola:

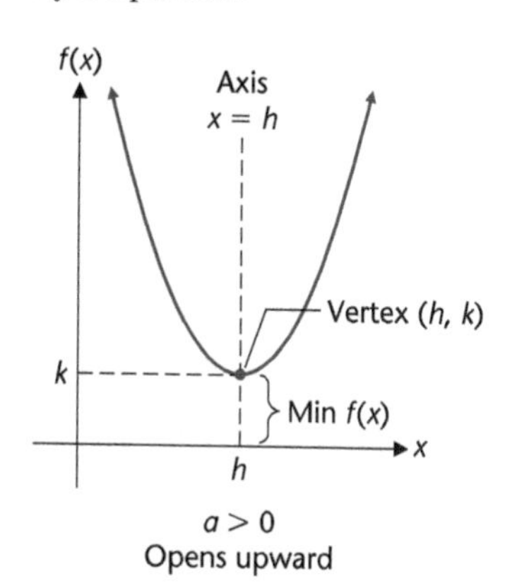

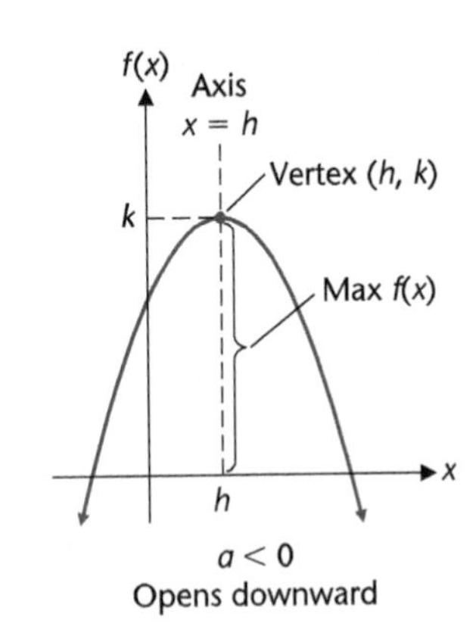

2. **Vertex:** (h, k) (Parabola increases on one side of the vertex and decreases on the other.)

3. **Axis (of symmetry):** $x = h$ (parallel to y axis)

4. $f(h) = k$ is the minimum if $a > 0$ and the maximum if $a < 0$.

5. Domain: All real numbers
   Range: $(-\infty, k]$ if $a < 0$ or $[k, \infty)$ if $a > 0$

6. The graph of f is the graph of $g(x) = ax^2$ translated horizontally h units and vertically k units.

The first coordinate of the vertex of a parabola in standard form can be located using the formula $x = -b/2a$. This can then be substituted into the function to find the second coordinate. The vertex form of a parabola can be used to find the equation when the vertex and one other point on the graph are known.

2-4 Complex Numbers

A **complex number** in **standard form** is a number in the form $a + bi$ where a and b are real numbers and i denotes a square root of -1. The number i is known as the **imaginary unit.** For a complex number $a + bi$, a is the **real part** and bi is the **imaginary part.**

If $b \neq 0$ then $a + bi$ is also called an **imaginary number.** If $a = 0$ then $0 + bi = bi$ is also called a **pure imaginary number.** If $b = 0$ then $a + 0i = a$ is a **real number.** The complex **zero** is $0 + 0i = 0$. The **conjugate** of $a + bi$ is $a - bi$. **Equality, addition,** and **multiplication** are defined as follows:

1. $a + bi = c + di$ if and only if $a = c$ and $b = d$

2. $(a + bi) + (c + di) = (a + c) + (b + d)i$

3. $(a + bi)(c + di) = (ac - bd) + (ad + bc)i$

Because complex numbers obey the same commutative, associative, and distributive properties as real numbers, most operations with complex numbers are performed by using these properties in the same way that algebraic operations are performed on the expression $a + bx$. Keep in mind that $i^2 = -1$.

The **property of conjugates,**

$$(a + bi)(a - bi) = a^2 + b^2$$

can be used to find **reciprocals** and **quotients.** To divide by a complex number, we multiply the numerator and denominator by the conjugate of the denominator. This enables us to write the result in $a + bi$ form. If $a > 0$, then the **principal square root of the negative real number** $-a$ is $\sqrt{-a} = i\sqrt{a}$.

To solve equations involving complex numbers, set the real and imaginary parts equal to each other and solve.

2-5 Quadratic Equations and Models

A **quadratic equation** is an equation that can be written in the form

$$ax^2 + bx + c = 0 \qquad a \neq 0$$

where x is a variable and a, b, and c are real numbers. This is known as the **general form** for a quadratic equation.

Algebraic methods of solution include:

1. **Factoring** and using the **zero product property:** $m \cdot n = 0$ if and only if $m = 0$ or $n = 0$ (or both).

2. **Completing the square** and using the **square root property:**
   If A is a complex number, C is a real number, and $A^2 = C$, then $A = \pm\sqrt{C}$.

3. Using the **quadratic formula:**

$$x = \frac{-b \pm \sqrt{b^2 - 4ac}}{2a}$$

If the **discriminant** $b^2 - 4ac$ is positive, the equation has two distinct **real roots;** if the discriminant is 0, the equation has one real **double root;** and if the discriminant is negative, the equation has two **imaginary roots,** each the conjugate of the other.

2-6 Additional Equation-Solving Techniques

A **radical** can be eliminated from an equation by isolating the radical on one side of the equation and raising both sides of the equation to the same natural number power to produce a new equation. The solution set of the original equation is a subset of the solution set of the new equation. The new equation may have **extraneous solutions** that are not solutions of the original equation. Consequently, **every solution of the new equation must be checked in the original equation to eliminate extraneous solutions.** If an equation contains more than one radical, then the process of isolating a radical and raising both sides to the same natural number power can be repeated until all radicals are eliminated. If a substitution transforms an equation into the form $au^2 + bu + c = 0$, where u is an expression in some other variable, then the equation is an **equation of quadratic type,** which can be solved by quadratic methods.

2-7 Solving Inequalities

Linear inequalities in one variable are expressed using the inequality symbols $<$, $>$, $\leq$, $\geq$. The **solution set of an inequality** is the set of all values of the variable that make the inequality a true statement. Each element of the solution set is called a **solution.** Two inequalities are **equivalent** if they have the same solution set. An equivalent inequality will result and the **sense (or direction) will remain the same** if each side of the original inequality:

- Has the same real number added to or subtracted from it.
- Is multiplied or divided by the same positive number.

An equivalent inequality will result and the **sense (or direction) will reverse** if each side of the original inequality:

- Is multiplied or divided by the same negative number.

Note that multiplication by 0 and division by 0 are not permitted.

A linear **combined inequality** (one that has three members) can be solved by performing the same operations on all three members until the variable is isolated in the center.

The **absolute value function** $|x|$ can also be interpreted as the **distance** between x and the origin. More generally, for $p > 0$:

1. $|ax + b| < p$ is equivalent to $-p < ax + b < p$.
2. $|ax + b| = p$ is equivalent to $ax + b = p$ or $ax + b = -p$.
3. $|ax + b| > p$ is equivalent to $ax + b < -p$ or $ax + b > p$.

Quadratic inequalities can be solved with the following process:

1. Rearrange so that zero is on one side, and a quadratic expression is on the other.
2. Find the roots of that expression.
3. Choose a test number in each interval determined by the roots and substitute into the quadratic expression, noting whether the result is positive or negative.
4. Write the solution based on where the quadratic expression is positive, negative, or zero.

A **break-even point** is an intersection point for the graphs of a cost and a revenue equation.

CHAPTER 2 Review Exercises

Work through all the problems in this chapter review and check answers in the back of the book. Answers to most review problems are there, and following each answer is a number in italics indicating the section in which that type of problem is discussed. Where weaknesses show up, review appropriate sections in the text.

1. Use the graph of the linear function in the figure to find the rise, run, and slope. Write the equation of the line in the form $Ax + By = C$, where A, B, and C are integers with $A > 0$. (The horizontal and vertical line segments have integer lengths.)

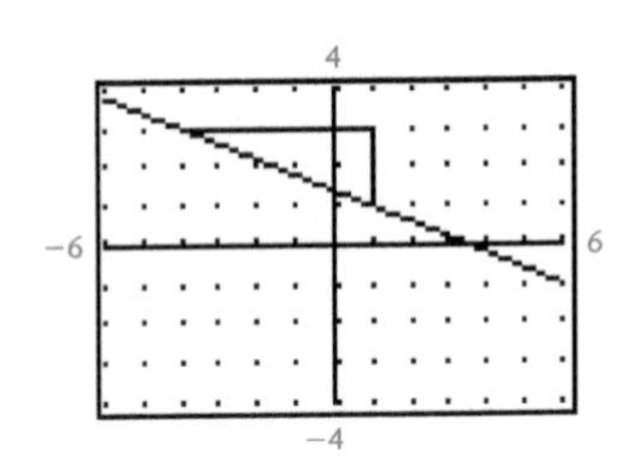

2. Graph $3x + 2y = 9$ and indicate its slope.

3. Write an equation of a line with x intercept 6 and y intercept 4. Write the final answer in the form $Ax + By = C$, where A, B, and C are integers with $A > 0$.

4. Write the slope–intercept form of the equation of the line with slope $-\frac{2}{3}$ and y intercept 2.

5. Write the equations of the vertical and horizontal lines passing through the point $(-3, 4)$. What is the slope of each?

6. Solve algebraically and confirm graphically:

(A) $0.05x + 0.25(30 - x) = 3.3$

(B) $\frac{5x}{3} - \frac{4 + x}{2} = \frac{x - 2}{4} + 1$

In Problems 7 and 8,

(A) *Complete the square and find the vertex form of the function.*

(B) *Write a brief verbal description of the relationship between the graph of the function and the graph of $y = x^2$.*

(C) *Find the x intercepts algebraically and confirm graphically.*

7. $f(x) = -x^2 - 2x + 3$ **8.** $f(x) = x^2 - 3x - 2$

9. Find the vertex of the function $f(x) = -3x^2 + 9x - 4$. Is it a maximum or a minimum?

10. Perform the indicated operations and write the answers in standard form:

(A) $(-3 + 2i) + (6 - 8i)$ (B) $(3 - 3i)(2 + 3i)$

(C) $\dfrac{13 - i}{5 - 3i}$ (D) $(7 + 6i) - (8 + 9i)$

In Problems 11–21, solve algebraically and confirm graphically, if possible.

11. $4 - 3(2x + 7) = 5(4 - x) + 11x - 3$

12. $(2x + 5)^2 = 23$ **13.** $x^2 - 2x + 3 = x^2 + 3x - 7$

14. $2x^2 - 7 = 0$ **15.** $2x^2 = 4x$

16. $2x^2 = 7x - 3$ **17.** $m^2 + m + 1 = 0$

18. $y^2 = \frac{3}{2}(y + 1)$ **19.** $\sqrt{4 + 7x} = 5$

20. $\sqrt{5x - 6} - x = 0$ **21.** $\sqrt{x^2 + 2} = \sqrt{4x + 14}$

In Problems 22–24, solve and express answers in inequality and interval notation.

22. $3(2 - x) - 2 \le 2x - 1$ **23.** $x^2 + x < 20$

24. $x^2 > 4x + 12$

25. Discuss the use of the terms *rising, falling, increasing,* and *decreasing* as they apply to the descriptions of the following:

(A) A line with positive slope

(B) A line with negative slope

(C) A parabola that opens upward

(D) A parabola that opens downward

26. Find an equation of the line through the points $(-4, 3)$ and $(0, -3)$. Write the final answer in the form $Ax + By = C$, where A, B, and C are integers with $A > 0$.

27. Write the slope–intercept form of the equation of the line that passes through the point $(-2, 1)$ and is

(A) parallel to the line $6x + 3y = 5$

(B) perpendicular to the line $6x + 3y = 5$

In Problems 28–30, solve each inequality. Write answers in inequality notation.

28. $|y + 9| < 5$ **29.** $|2x - 8| \ge 3$ **30.** $2x^2 \ge 7x - 1$

In Problems 31 and 32, write each inequality verbally as a statement about distance, then solve. Write answers in both interval and inequality notation.

31. $|y - 5| \le 2$ **32.** $|t + 6| > 9$

For each equation in Problems 33–35, use the discriminant to determine the number and type of zeros and confirm graphically.

33. $0.1x^2 + x + 1.5 = 0$ **34.** $0.1x^2 + x + 2.5 = 0$

35. $0.1x^2 + x + 3.5 = 0$

36. Let $f(x) = 0.5x^2 - 4x + 5$.

(A) Sketch the graph of f and label the axis and the vertex.

(B) Where is f increasing? Decreasing? What is the range? (Express answers in interval notation.)

(C) Find the maximum or minimum.

37. Find the equations of the linear function g and the quadratic function f whose graphs are shown in the figure. This line is called the tangent line to the graph of f at the point $(-1, 0)$.

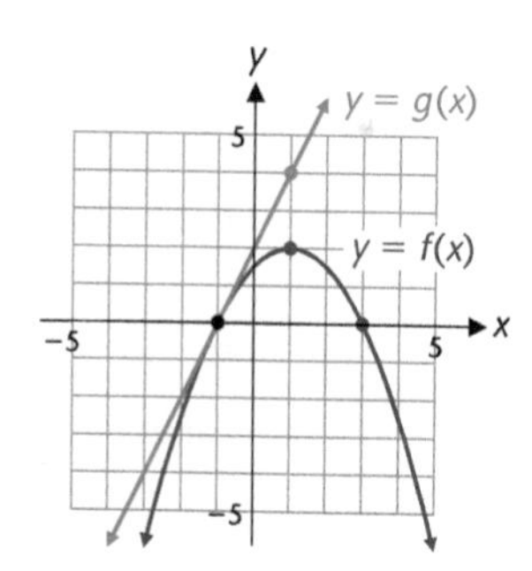

38. Perform the indicated operations and write the final answers in standard form:

(A) $(3 + i)^2 - 2(3 + i) + 3$ (B) i^{27}

39. Convert to $a + bi$ forms, perform the indicated operations, and write the final answers in standard form:

(A) $(2 - \sqrt{-4}) - (3 - \sqrt{-9})$ (B) $\dfrac{2 - \sqrt{-1}}{3 + \sqrt{-4}}$

(C) $\dfrac{4 + \sqrt{-25}}{\sqrt{-4}}$ (D) $\sqrt{-16}\sqrt{-25}$

Solve Problems 40–45 algebraically and confirm graphically, if possible.

40. $(x + \frac{5}{2})^2 = \frac{5}{4}$ **41.** $1 + \dfrac{3}{u^2} = \dfrac{2}{u}$

42. $2x + 3\sqrt{4x^2 - 4x + 9} = 1$

43. $2x^{2/3} - 5x^{1/3} - 12 = 0$

44. $m^4 + 5m^2 - 36 = 0$ **45.** $\sqrt{y - 2} - \sqrt{5y + 1} = -3$

46. Use linear regression to fit a line to each of the following data sets. How are the graphs of the two functions related? How are the two functions related?

(A)

x	y
2	-1
3	1
4	3

(B)

x	y
-1	2
1	3
3	4

47. Can a quadratic function have only imaginary zeros? If not, explain why. If so, give an example and discuss any special relationship between the zeros.

48. If a quadratic function has only imaginary zeros, can the function be graphed? If not, explain why. If so, what is the graph's relationship to the x axis?

49. Consider the quadratic equation

$$x^2 - 6x + c = 0$$

where c is a real number. Discuss the relationship between the values of c and the three types of roots listed in Table 1 in Section 2-5.

Solve Problems 50 and 51 for the indicated variable in terms of the other variables.

50. $P = M - Mdt$ for M (mathematics of finance)

51. $P = EI - RI^2$ for I (electrical engineering)

52. For what values of a and b is the following inequality true?

$$a + b < b - a$$

53. If a and b are negative numbers and $a > b$, then is a/b greater than 1 or less than 1?

54. Solve and graph. Write the answer using interval notation: $0 < |x - 6| < d$

55. Evaluate: $(a + bi)\left(\frac{a}{a^2 + b^2} - \frac{b}{a^2 + b^2}i\right)$; $a, b, \neq 0$

56. Are the graphs of $mx - y = b$ and $x + my = b$ parallel, perpendicular, or neither? Justify your answer.

57. Show by substituting for x that $2 + 3i$ is one of the zeros of $f(x) = 2x^2 - 8x + 26$. Without solving an equation, what is the other one?

58. If $5 + 2i$ is one root of $x^2 - bx + c = 0$, find b and c.

59. Solve $3x^{-2/5} - 4x^{-1/5} + 1 = 0$ algebraically and graphically.

60. Find all solutions of $x^3 + 1 = 0$.

61. Find three consecutive integers whose sum is 144.

62. Find three consecutive even integers so that the first plus twice the second is twice the third.

Problems 63 and 64 refer to a triangle with base b and height h (see the figure). Write a mathematical expression in terms of b and h for each of the verbal statements in Problems 63 and 64.

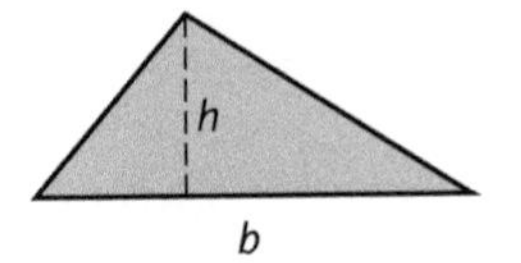

63. The base is five times the height.

64. The height is one-fourth of the base.

APPLICATONS

65. METEOROLOGY The number of inches of snow on the ground during a blizzard in upstate New York on one February day can be modeled by $S(x) = 3.4x + 11.1$, where x is hours after it started snowing.

(A) At what rate is the snow falling? Include units.

(B) How much snow was on the ground before it started to snow that day?

66. INTERNET GROWTH According to the British newspaper the *Telegraph,* on August 1, 2006, there were 60 million online blogs worldwide, and that number was growing at the rate of 75,000 per day.

(A) Write a linear function describing the number of blogs worldwide in terms of months after August 1, 2006. (Note the difference in units of time.)

(B) When does your function predict that the number of blogs would hit 100 million?

67. TIME SPENT STUDYING As part of a group project for a statistics class, several students at a Midwestern university found that the score students could expect on the final exam in a history class could be predicted by the function $G(x) = -0.23x^2 + 8.54x + 15$, where x is the total number of hours spent studying for the final. If this model is accurate, how many hours should a student in this course study to maximize their score?

68. GEOMETRY The diagonal of a rectangle is 32.5 inches and the area is 375 square inches. Find the dimensions of the rectangle, correct to one decimal place.

69. FALLING OBJECT A worker at the top of a radio tower drops a hammer to the ground. If the hammer hits the ground 3.5 seconds after it is dropped, how high is the tower?

70. COST ANALYSIS Cost equations for manufacturing companies are often quadratic—costs are high at very low and very high production levels. The weekly cost $C(x)$ (in dollars) for manufacturing x inexpensive calculators is

$$C(x) = 0.001x^2 - 9.5x + 30{,}000$$

Find the production level(s) (to the nearest integer) that

(A) Produces the minimum weekly cost. What is the minimum weekly cost (to the nearest cent)?

(B) Produces a weekly cost of $12,000.

(C) Produces a weekly cost of $6,000.

71. BREAK-EVEN ANALYSIS The manufacturing company in Problem 70 sells its calculators to wholesalers for $3 each. How many calculators (to the nearest integer) must the company sell to break even?

72. PROFIT ANALYSIS Refer to Problems 70 and 71. Find the production levels that produce a profit and the production levels that produce a loss.

73. LINEAR DEPRECIATION A computer system was purchased by a small company for $12,000 and is assumed to have a depreciated value of $2,000 after 8 years. If the value depreciates linearly from $12,000 to $2,000:

(A) Find the linear equation that relates value V (in dollars) to time t (in years).

(B) What would be the depreciated value of the system after 5 years?

74. BUSINESS–PRICING A sporting goods store carries a brand of tennis shorts that costs them $30 per pair and a brand of sunglasses that costs them $20 per pair. They sell the shorts for $48 and the glasses for $32.

(A) If the markup policy of the store for items that cost over $10 is assumed to be linear and is reflected in the pricing of these two items, write an equation that expresses retail price R as a function of cost C.

(B) What should be the retail price of a pair of skis that cost $105?

75. INCOME A salesperson receives a base salary of $400 per week and a commission of 10% on all sales over $3,000 during the week. If x represents the salesperson's weekly sales, express the total weekly earnings $E(x)$ as a function of x. Find $E(2{,}000)$ and $E(5{,}000)$.

76. CONSTRUCTION A farmer has 120 feet of fencing to be used in the construction of two identical rectangular pens sharing a common side (see the figure).

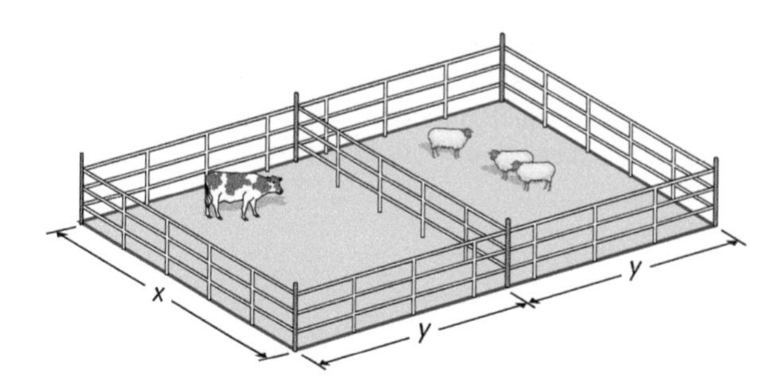

(A) Express the total area $A(x)$ enclosed by both pens as a function of the width x.

(B) From physical considerations, what is the domain of the function A?

(C) Find the dimensions of the pens that will make the total enclosed area maximum.

77. SPORTS MEDICINE The following quotation was found in a sports medicine handout: "The idea is to raise and sustain your heart rate to 70% of its maximum safe rate for your age. One way to determine this is to subtract your age from 220 and multiply by 0.7."

(A) If H is the maximum safe sustained heart rate (in beats per minute) for a person of age A (in years), write a formula relating H and A.

(B) What is the maximum safe sustained heart rate for a 20-year-old?

(C) If the maximum safe sustained heart rate for a person is 126 beats per minute, how old is the person?

78. DESIGN The pages of a textbook have uniform margins of 2 centimeters on all four sides (see the figure). If the area of the entire page is 480 square centimeters and the area of the printed portion is 320 square centimeters, find the dimensions of the page.

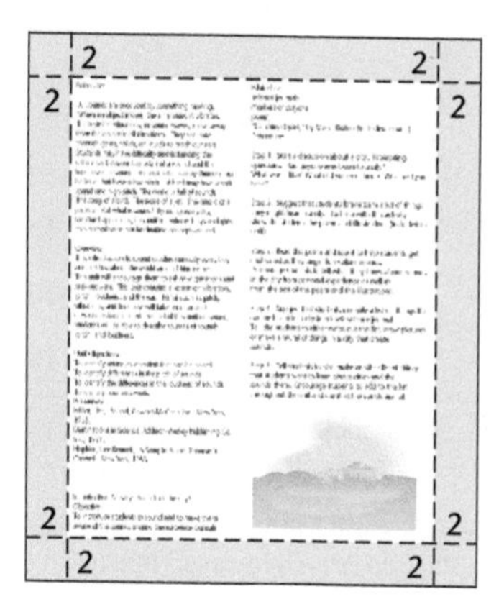

79. DESIGN A landscape designer uses 8-foot timbers to form a pattern of three identical isosceles triangles along the wall of a building (see the figure). If the area of each triangle is 24 square feet, find the base correct to two decimal places.

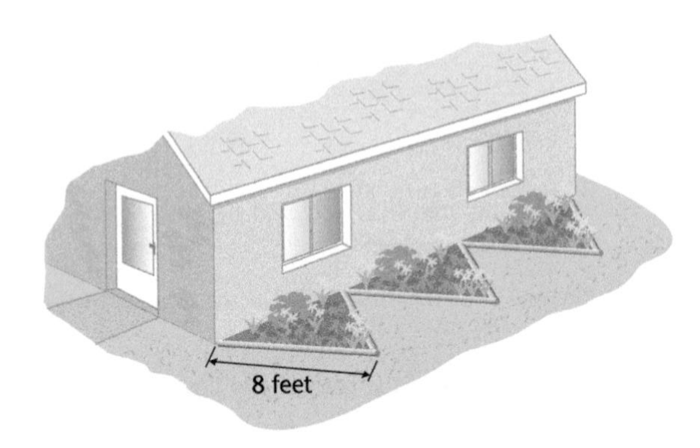

80. ARCHITECTURE An entranceway in the shape of a parabola 12 feet wide and 12 feet high must enclose a rectangular door that is 8.4 feet high. What is the widest doorway (to the nearest tenth of a foot) that can be installed in the entranceway?

DATA ANALYSIS AND REGRESSION

In Problems 81–84, unless directed otherwise, round all numbers to three significant digits.

81. DRUG USE The use of marijuana by teenagers declined throughout the 1980s, but began to increase during the 1990s. Table 1 gives the percentage of 12- to 17-year-olds who have ever used marijuana for selected years from 1979 to 2003.

Table 1 Marijuana Use: 12 to 17 Years Old

Year	Ever Used [%]
1979	26.7
1985	20.1
1990	12.7
1994	13.6
1995	16.2
2003	19.6

Source: National Household Survey on Drug Abuse

(A) Find a quadratic regression model for the percentage of 12- to 17-year-olds who have ever used marijuana, using years since 1970 for the independent variable.

(B) Use your model to predict the year during which the percentage of marijuana users will return to the 1979 level.

82. POLITICAL SCIENCE Association of economic class and party affiliation did not start with Roosevelt's New Deal; it goes back to the time of Andrew Jackson (1767–1845). Paul Lazarsfeld of Columbia University published an article in the November 1950 issue of *Scientific American* in which he discusses statistical investigations of the relationships between economic class and party affiliation. The data in Table 2 are taken from this article.

Table 2 Political Affiliations in 1836

Ward	Average Assessed Value per Person [in $100]	Democratic Votes [%]
12	1.7	51
3	2.1	49
1	2.3	53
5	2.4	36
2	3.6	65
11	3.7	35
10	4.7	29
4	6.2	40
6	7.1	34
9	7.4	29
8	8.7	20
7	11.9	23

(A) Find a linear regression model for the data in the second and third columns of the table, using the average assessed value as the independent variable.

(B) Use the linear regression model to predict (to two decimal places) the percentage of votes for democrats in a ward with an average assessed value of $300.

83. SUPPLY AND DEMAND Table 3 contains price–supply data and price–demand data for a broccoli grower. Find a linear model for the price–supply data where x is supply (in pounds) and y is price (in dollars). Do the same for the price–demand data. Find the equilibrium price for broccoli.

Table 3 Supply and Demand for Broccoli

Price $/lb	Supply (lb)	Demand (lb)
0.71	25,800	41,500
0.77	27,400	38,700
0.84	30,200	36,200
0.91	33,500	32,800
0.96	34,900	29,800
1.01	37,800	27,900
1.08	39,210	25,100

84. BREAK-EVEN ANALYSIS The broccoli grower in Problem 83 has fixed costs of $15,000 and variable costs of $0.20 per pound of broccoli produced.

(A) Find the revenue and cost functions as functions of the sales x. What is the domain of each function?

(B) Find the level of sales for which the company will break even. Describe verbally and graphically the sales levels that result in a profit and those that result in a loss.

(C) Find the sales and the price that will produce the maximum profit. Find the maximum profit.

85. OPTIMAL SPEED Table 4 contains performance data for a speedboat powered by a Yamaha outboard motor.

(A) Let x be the speed of the boat in miles per hour (mph) and y the associated mileage in miles per gallon (mpg). Use the data in Table 4 to find a quadratic regression function $y = ax^2 + bx + c$ for this boat.

(B) A marina rents this boat for $15 per hour plus the cost of the gasoline used. If gasoline costs $2.55 per gallon and you take a 100-mile trip in this boat, construct a mathematical model and use it to answer the following questions:

What speed should you travel to minimize the rental charges?

What mileage will the boat get?

How long does the trip take?

How much gasoline will you use?

How much will the trip cost you?

Table 4 Performance Data

mph	mpg
9.5	1.67
21.1	1.92
28.3	2.16
33.7	1.88
37.9	1.77
42.6	1.49

Source: www.yamaha-motor.com

CHAPTER 2

››› GROUP ACTIVITY Mathematical Modeling in Population Studies

In a study on population growth in California, Tulane University demographer Leon Bouvier recorded the past population totals for every 10 years starting at 1900. Then, using sophisticated demographic techniques, he made high, low, and medium projections to the year 2040. Table 1 shows actual populations up to 1990 and medium projections (to the nearest million) to 2040.

Table 1 California Population 1900–2040

Years after 1900	Date	Population [millions]	
0	1900	2	Actual
10	1910	3	
20	1920	4	
30	1930	5	
40	1940	5	
50	1950	10	
60	1960	15	
70	1970	20	
80	1980	23	
90	1990	30	
100	2000	35	Projected
110	2010	45	
120	2020	53	
130	2030	61	
140	2040	70	

1. Building a Mathematical Model.
   (A) Plot the first and last columns in Table 1 up to 1990 (actual populations). Would a linear or a quadratic function be the better model for these data? Why?
   (B) Use a graphing utility to compute both a linear and a quadratic regression function to model the data you plotted in part A.
   (C) Graph both functions and the data from part A for $0 \le x \le 150$.
   (D) Based on the graph, which model appears to be more realistic? Explain your reasoning.
2. Using the Mathematical Models for Projections.
   For each regression model, answer the following questions.
   (A) Calculate projected populations for California at 10-year intervals, starting at 2000 and ending at 2040. Compare your projections with Professor Bouvier's projections, both numerically and graphically.
   (B) During what year would each model project that the population will reach 40 million? 50 million?
   (C) For what years would each model project the population to be between 34 million and 68 million, inclusive?
   (D) Use a library or the Internet to look up the 2000 population of California. Which model predicted it most accurately: linear, quadratic, or Professor Bouvier?

CHAPTERS 1–2 Cumulative Review

Work through all the problems in this cumulative review and check answers in the back of the book. Answers to most review problems are there, and following each answer is a number in italics indicating the section in which that type of problem is discussed. Where weaknesses show up, review appropriate sections in the text.

1. (A) Plot the points in the table below in a rectangular coordinate system.

(B) Find the smallest viewing window that will contain all of these points. State your answer in terms of the window variables.

(C) Does this set of points define a function? Explain.

x	-3	1	-2	1	3
y	4	-2	4	-4	4

2. Given points $A = (3, 2)$ and $B = (5, 6)$,

(A) Find the slope–intercept form of the equation of the line through A and B.

(B) Find the slope–intercept form of the equation of the line through B and perpendicular to the line through A and B.

(C) Graph the lines from parts B and C on the same coordinate system.

3. Graph $2x - 3y = 6$ and indicate its slope and intercepts.

4. For $f(x) = x^2 - 2x + 5$ and $g(x) = 3x - 2$, find

(A) $f(-2) + g(-3)$ (B) $f(1) \cdot g(1)$ (C) $\dfrac{g(0)}{f(0)}$

5. How are the graphs of the following related to the graph of $y = |x|$?

(A) $y = 2|x|$ (B) $y = |x - 2|$ (C) $y = |x| - 2$

Problems 6–8 refer to the function f given by the graph:

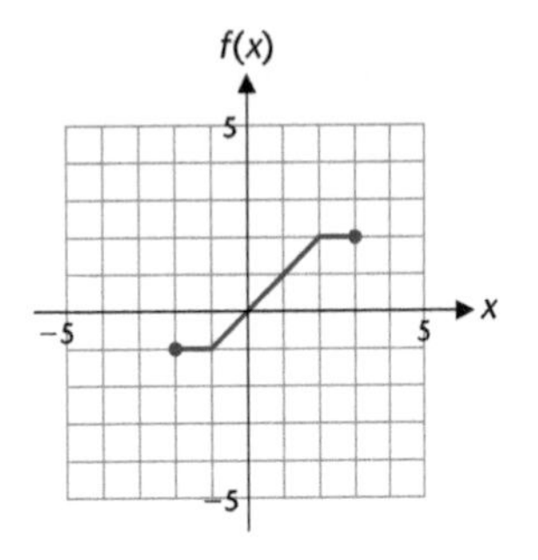

6. Find the domain and range of f. Express answers in interval notation.

7. Is f an even function, an odd function, or neither? Explain.

8. Use the graph of f to sketch a graph of the following:

(A) $y = -f(x + 1)$ (B) $y = 2f(x) - 2$

In Problems 9–15, solve algebraically and confirm graphically.

9. $5 - 3(x + 4) = x + 2(11 - 2x)$ **10.** $(4x + 15)^2 = 9$

11. $\dfrac{7x}{5} - \dfrac{3 + 2x}{2} = \dfrac{x - 10}{3} + 2$ **12.** $3x^2 = -12x$

13. $4x^2 - 20 = 0$ **14.** $x^2 - 6x + 2 = 0$

15. $x - \sqrt{12 - x} = 0$

In Problems 16–19, solve and express answers in inequality and interval notation.

16. $2(3 - y) + 4 \le 5 - y$ **17.** $-3 \le 2 - 3x < 11$

18. $|x - 2| < 7$ **19.** $x^2 + 3x \ge 10$

20. Let $f(x) = x^2 - 4x - 1$.

(A) Find the vertex form of f.

(B) How is the graph of f related to the graph of $y = x^2$?

(C) Find the x intercepts algebraically and confirm graphically.

21. Perform the indicated operations and write the answer in standard form:

(A) $(2 - 3i) - (-5 + 7i)$ (B) $(1 + 4i)(3 - 5i)$

(C) $\dfrac{5 + i}{2 + 3i}$

22. Find each of the following for the function f given by the graph shown.

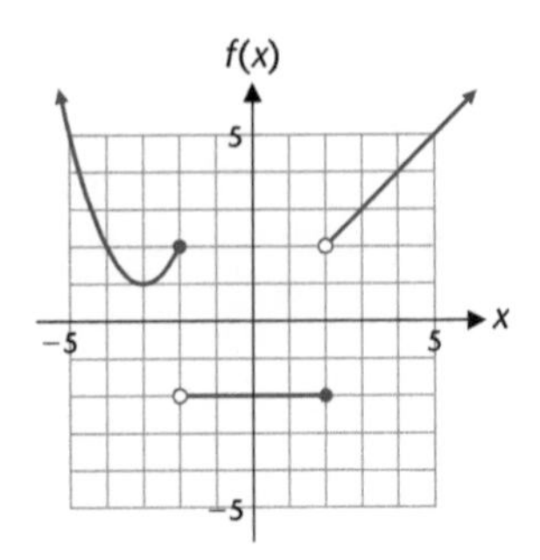

(A) The domain of f

(B) The range of f

(C) $f(-3) + f(-2) + f(2)$

(D) The intervals over which f is increasing.

(E) The x coordinates of any points of discontinuity.

23. Given $f(x) = 1/(x - 2)$ and $g(x) = (x + 3)/x$, find $f \circ g$. What is the domain of $f \circ g$?

24. Find $f^{-1}(x)$ for $f(x) = 2x + 5$.

25. Let $f(x) = \sqrt{x + 4}$

(A) Find $f^{-1}(x)$.

(B) Find the domain and range of f and f^{-1}.

(C) Graph f, f^{-1}, and $y = x$ on the same coordinate system and identify each graph.

26. Which of the following functions is one-to-one?

(A) $f(x) = x^3 + x$ (B) $g(x) = x^3 + x^2$

27. Write the slope–intercept form of the equation of the line passing through the point $(-6, 1)$ that is

(A) parallel to the line $3x + 2y = 12$.

(B) perpendicular to the line $3x + 2y = 12$.

28. Graph $f(x) = x^2 - 2x - 8$. Label the axis of symmetry and the coordinates of the vertex, and find the range, intercepts, and maximum or minimum value of $f(x)$.

In Problems 29 and 30, solve and express answers in inequality and interval notation.

29. $|4x - 9| > 3$ **30.** $\frac{1}{2}x^2 - x - 8 > 0$

31. Perform the indicated operations and write the final answers in standard form.

(A) $(2 - 3i)^2 - (4 - 5i)(2 - 3i) - (2 + 10i)$

(B) $\frac{3}{5} + \frac{4}{5}i + \frac{1}{\frac{3}{5} + \frac{4}{5}i}$ (C) i^{35}

32. Convert to $a + bi$ form, perform the indicated operations, and write the final answers in standard form.

(A) $(5 + 2\sqrt{-9}) - (2 - 3\sqrt{-16})$

(B) $\frac{2 + 7\sqrt{-25}}{3 - \sqrt{-1}}$ (C) $\frac{12 - \sqrt{-64}}{\sqrt{-4}}$

33. Graph, finding the domain, range, and any points of discontinuity.

$$f(x) = \begin{cases} x - 1 & \text{if } x < 0 \\ x^2 + 1 & \text{if } x \geq 0 \end{cases}$$

34. The graph in the figure is the result of applying a sequence of transformations to the graph of $y = |x|$. Describe the transformations verbally and write an equation for the graph in the figure.

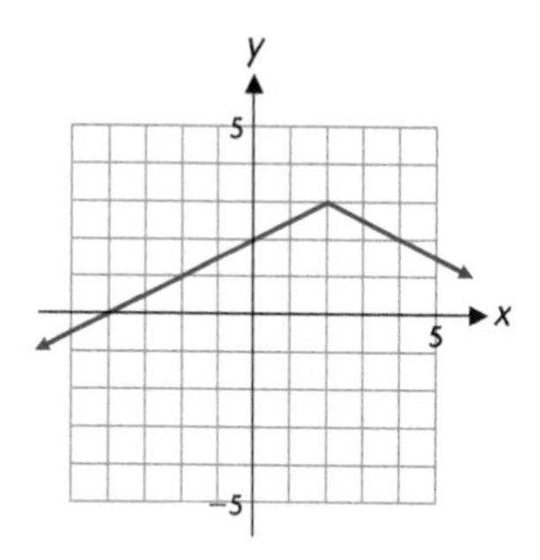

35. Find the standard form of the quadratic function whose graph is shown in the figure.

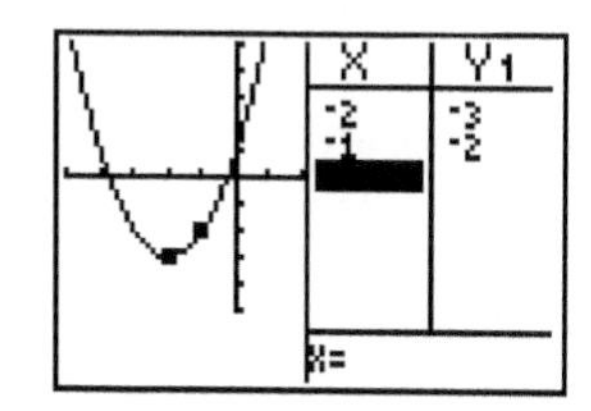

In Problems 36–40, solve algebraically and confirm graphically, if possible.

36. $1 + \frac{14}{y^2} = \frac{6}{y}$ **37.** $4x^{2/3} - 4x^{1/3} - 3 = 0$

38. $u^4 + u^2 - 12 = 0$ **39.** $\sqrt{8t - 2} - 2\sqrt{t} = 1$

40. $6x = \sqrt{9x^2 - 48}$

41. Consider the quadratic equation

$$x^2 + bx + 1 = 0$$

where b is a real number. Discuss the relationship between the values of b and the three types of roots listed in Table 1 in Section 2-5.

42. Give an example of an odd function. Of an even function. Can a function be both even and odd? Explain.

43. Can a quadratic equation with real coefficients have one imaginary root and one real root? One double imaginary root? Explain.

44. If $g(x) = -2x^2 + 3x - 1$, find $\frac{g(2 + h) - g(2)}{h}$.

45. The graph is the result of applying one or more transformations to the graph of one of the six basic functions in Figure 1, Section 1-4. Find an equation for the graph.

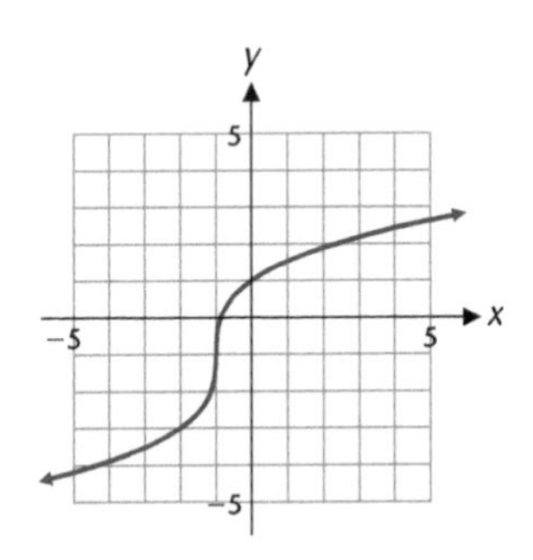

46. The total surface area of a right circular cylinder with radius r and height h is given by

$$A = 2\pi r(r + h) \qquad r > 0, h > 0$$

(A) Solve for h in terms of the other variables.

(B) Solve for r in terms of the other variables. Why is there only one solution?

47. Given $f(x) = x^2$ and $g(x) = \sqrt{4 - x^2}$, find

(A) Domain of g (B) f/g and its domain

(C) $f \circ g$ and its domain

48. Let $f(x) = x^2 - 2x - 3, x \geq 1$.

(A) Find $f^{-1}(x)$. (B) Find the domain and range of f^{-1}.

(C) Graph f, f^{-1}, and $y = x$ on the same coordinate system.

49. Evaluate $x^2 - x + 2$ for $x = \frac{1}{2} - \frac{i}{2}\sqrt{7}$.

50. For what values of a and b is the inequality $a - b < b - a$ true?

51. Write in standard form: $\frac{a + bi}{a - bi}$; $a, b \neq 0$

In Problems 52–55, solve algebraically and confirm graphically, if possible.

52. $3x^2 = 2\sqrt{2x} - 1$ **53.** $1 + 13x^{-2} + 36x^{-4} = 0$

54. $\sqrt{16x^2 + 48x + 39} - 2x = 3$

55. $3x^{-2/5} - x^{-1/5} - 1 = 0$

56. Show that $5 + i$ and $-5 - i$ are the square roots of $24 + 10i$. Describe how you could find these square roots algebraically.

57. For $f(x) = 0.5x^2 - 3x - 7$, find

(A) $\frac{f(x + h) - f(x)}{h}$ (B) $\frac{f(x) - f(a)}{x - a}$

58. The function f is continuous for all real numbers and its graph passes through the points $(0, 4)$, $(5, -3)$, $(10, 2)$. Discuss the minimum and maximum number of x intercepts for f.

59. Let $f(x) = |x + 2| + |x - 2|$. Find a piecewise definition of f that does not involve the absolute value function. Graph f and find the domain and range.

60. Let $f(x) = 2x - [\![2x]\!]$. Write a piecewise definition for f and sketch the graph of f. Include sufficient intervals to clearly illustrate both the definition and the graph. Find the domain, range, and any points of discontinuity.

61. Find all solutions of $x^3 - 8 = 0$.

APPLICATIONS

62. CONSTRUCTION After a water main breakage, the underground level of a building under construction is flooded with 400,000 gallons of water. The construction manager rents three pumps, each of which can remove water at the rate of 4,400 gallons per hour.

(A) Write a linear function that describes the amount of water remaining to be pumped out x hours after the three pumps are started.

(B) Use your function to determine how long it will take for all the water to be pumped out.

(C) Write and solve an inequality that describes the times when the amount of water remaining is between 100,000 and 200,000 gallons.

63. BREAK-EVEN ANALYSIS The publisher's fixed costs for the production of a new cookbook are \$41,800. Variable costs are \$4.90 per book. If the book is sold to bookstores for \$9.65, how many must be sold for the publisher to break even?

64. FINANCE An investor instructs a broker to purchase a certain stock whenever the price per share p of the stock is within \$10 of \$200. Express this instruction as an absolute value inequality.

65. PROFIT AND LOSS ANALYSIS At a price of \$$p$ per unit, the marketing department in a company estimates that the weekly cost C and the weekly revenue R, in thousands of dollars, will be given by the equations

$$C = 88 - 12p \qquad \text{Cost equation}$$
$$R = 15p - 2p^2 \qquad \text{Revenue equation}$$

Find the prices for which the company has

(A) A profit (B) A loss

66. DEPRECIATION Office equipment was purchased for \$20,000 and is assumed to depreciate linearly to a scrap value of \$4,000 after 8 years.

(A) Find a linear function $v = d(t)$ that relates value v in dollars to time t in years.

(B) Find $t = d^{-1}(v)$. What information does $d^{-1}(v)$ provide?

67. SHIPPING A ship leaves Port A, sails east to Port B, and then north to Port C, a total distance of 115 miles. The next day the ship sails directly from Port C back to Port A, a distance of 85 miles. Find the distance between Ports A and B and between Ports B and C.

68. PRICE AND DEMAND The weekly demand for mouthwash in a chain of drugstores is 1,160 bottles at a price of \$3.79 each. If the price is lowered to \$3.59, the weekly demand increases to 1,340 bottles. Assuming the relationship between the weekly demand x and the price per bottle p is linear, express x as a function of p. How many bottles would the store sell each week if the price were lowered to \$3.29?

69. BUSINESS-PRICING A telephone company begins a new pricing plan that charges customers for local calls as follows: The first 60 calls each month are 6 cents each, the next 90 are 5 cents each, the next 150 are 4 cents each, and any additional calls are 3 cents each. If C is the cost, in dollars, of placing x calls per month, write a piecewise definition of C as a function of x and graph.

70. CONSTRUCTION A home owner has 80 feet of chain-link fencing to be used to construct a dog pen adjacent to a house (see the figure).

(A) Express the area $A(x)$ enclosed by the pen as a function of the width x.

(B) From physical considerations, what is the domain of the function A?

(C) Graph A and determine the dimensions of the pen that will make the area maximum.

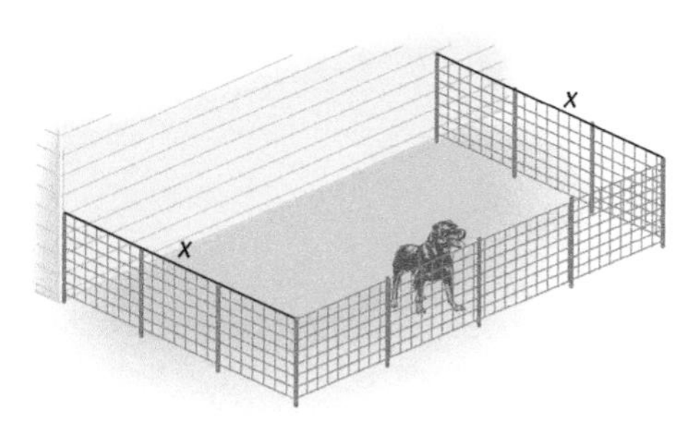

71. COMPUTER SCIENCE Let $f(x) = x - 2[\![x/2]\!]$. This function can be used to determine if an integer is odd or even.

(A) Find $f(1)$, $f(2)$, $f(3)$, $f(4)$.

(B) Find $f(n)$ for any integer n. [*Hint:* Consider two cases, $n = 2k$ and $n = 2k + 1$, k is an integer.]

72. PRICE AND DEMAND The demand for barley q (in thousands of bushels) and the corresponding price p (in cents) at a midwestern grain exchange are shown in the figure.

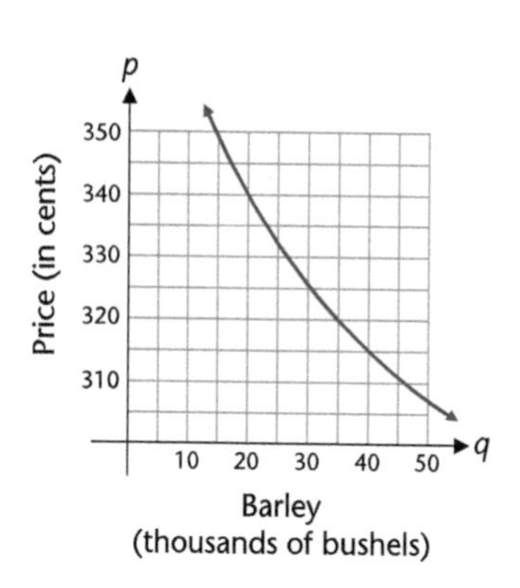

(A) What is the demand (to the nearest thousand bushels) when the price is 325 cents per bushel?

(B) Does the demand increase or decrease if the price is increased to 340 cents per bushel? By how much?

(C) Does the demand increase or decrease if the price is decreased to 315 cents per bushel? By how much?

(D) Write a brief description of the relationship between price and demand illustrated by this graph.

(E) Use the graph to estimate the price (to the nearest cent) when the demand is 20, 25, 30, 35, and 40 thousand bushels. Use these data to find a quadratic regression model for the price of barley using the demand as the independent variable.

DATA ANALYSIS AND REGRESSION

In Problems 73–75 round all values to three significant digits, unless directed otherwise.

73. DEMAND Egg consumption per capita decreased from a high of about 400 per capita in 1945 to a low of about 230 in 1991, then it began to increase. Table 1 lists the annual per capita consumption of eggs in the United States since 1970.

Table 1 Per Capita Egg Consumption

1970	1975	1980	1985	1990	1995	2000	2005
309	276	271	255	233	234	252	255

Source: Department of Agriculture.

(A) Find a quadratic regression equation $y = f(x)$ for the data in Table 1, where x is the number of years since 1970.

(B) Use the quadratic regression equation to project the year in which the per capita consumption will return to the 1970 level; to the 1945 level.

(C) Write a brief description of egg consumption from 1970 to 2005.

74. STOPPING DISTANCE Table 2 contains data related to the length of the skid marks left by an automobile when making an emergency stop.

(A) Let x be the speed of the vehicle in miles per hour. Find a quadratic regression model for the braking distance.

(B) An insurance investigator finds skid marks 220 feet long at the scene of an accident involving this automobile. How fast (to the nearest mile per hour) was the automobile traveling when it made these skid marks?

Table 2 Skid Marks

Speed (mph)	Length of Skid Marks (in feet)
20	24
30	48
40	81
50	118
60	187
70	246
80	312

75. OPTIMAL SPEED Table 3 contains performance data for a speedboat powered by a Yamaha outboard motor.

(A) Let x be the speed of the boat in miles per hour (mph) and y the associated mileage in miles per gallon (mpg). Use the data in Table 3 to find a quadratic regression function $y = ax^2 + bx + c$ for this boat.

(B) A marina rents this boat for $10 per hour plus the cost of the gasoline used. If gasoline costs $2.60 per gallon and you take a 200-mile trip in this boat, construct a mathematical model and use it to answer the following questions:

What speed should you travel to minimize the rental charges?

What mileage will the boat get?

How long does the trip take?

How much gasoline will you use?

How much will the trip cost you?

Table 3 Performance Data

mph	mpg
4.8	1.41
8.6	1.65
11.9	1.85
26.7	1.78
35.9	1.51
44.5	1.08

Source: www.yamaha-motor.com

Polynomial and Rational Functions

Polynomial and Rational Functions

IN Chapter 2, we were able to model a wide variety of situations with linear and quadratic functions. But both types of functions have relatively simple graphs: At most, the graph can change direction once. What if we want to model more complicated phenomena? We can use a more general class of functions known as *polynomials.* They are relatively easy to work with since they're based on the basic operations of addition, subtraction, multiplication, and division, and their graphs are smooth, continuous curves. Depending on the type of polynomial, the graph can change direction any number of times. This enables us to model data that linear and quadratic functions can't. We can then use polynomials to define *rational functions,* which further expands the number of functions in our library, enabling us to model even more situations.

CHAPTER 3

OUTLINE

3-1 Polynomial Functions and Models

- Recognizing Polynomial Functions
- Analyzing Graphs of Polynomials
- Left and Right Behavior of Polynomials
- Mathematical Modeling and Data Analysis

In this section, we will build upon the work we did with linear and quadratic functions in Chapter 2 by defining polynomial functions. After defining this class of functions, we will study their graphs, which show a much wider variety than the graphs we studied in Chapter 2. Finally, we will have a look at how polynomials can be used to model situations that might not be modeled as well with linear or quadratic functions.

Recognizing Polynomial Functions

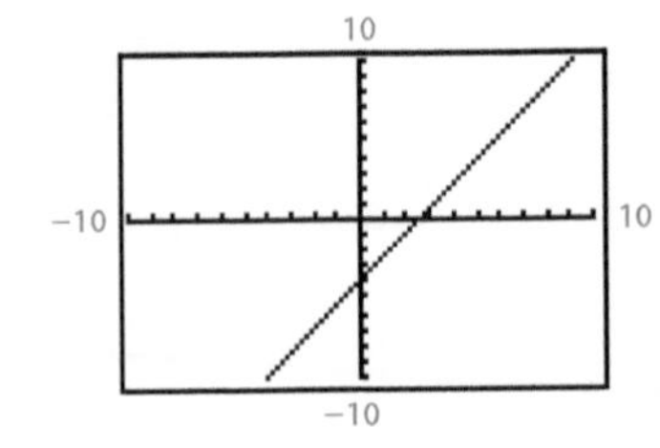

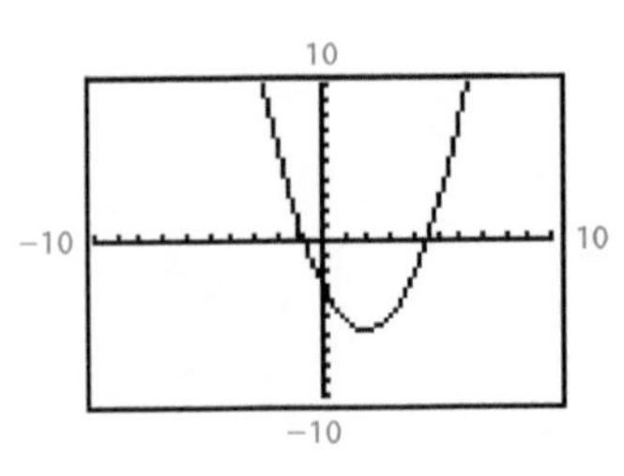

Figure 1 Graphs of linear and quadratic functions.

In Chapter 2 you were introduced to linear and quadratic functions and their graphs (Fig. 1):

$$f(x) = ax + b, \qquad a \neq 0 \qquad \text{Linear function}$$

$$f(x) = ax^2 + bx + c, \qquad a \neq 0 \qquad \text{Quadratic function}$$

In this chapter we will study functions like

$$g(x) = 7x^4 - 5x^3 + 2x^2 + 3x - 1.95$$

Notice that g is the sum of a finite number of terms, each of the form ax^k, where a is a number and k is a nonnegative integer. A function that can be written in this form is called a *polynomial function*. The polynomial function $g(x)$ is said to have *degree* 4 because x^4 is the highest power of x that appears among the terms of $g(x)$. Therefore, linear and quadratic functions are polynomial functions of degrees 1 and 2, respectively. The two functions $h(x) = x^{-1}$ and $k(x) = x^{1/2}$, however, are not polynomial functions (the exponents -1 and $\frac{1}{2}$ are not nonnegative integers).

> **DEFINITION 1 Polynomial Function**
>
> If n is a nonnegative integer, a function that can be written in the form
>
> $$P(x) = a_n x^n + a_{n-1}x^{n-1} + \cdots + a_1 x + a_0, \qquad a_n \neq 0$$
>
> is called a **polynomial function of degree n.** This is called the **general form** for a polynomial. The numbers $a_n, a_{n-1}, \ldots, a_1, a_0$ are called the **coefficients** of $P(x)$.

Note that the order of the terms is not important, but we will usually write the terms in order from largest power to smallest.

EXAMPLE 1 Recognizing Polynomial Functions

Determine whether each function is a polynomial. Write the degree of any polynomials.

(A) $f(x) = 5 - 3x + \frac{1}{2}x^2 - (2 + i)x^4$

(B) $g(x) = 3\sqrt{x} + 7x^5 - 1$

(C) $k(x) = 2x(x - 4)(x + 3)$

SOLUTIONS

(A) The function $f(x)$ in part A is a polynomial since every term is of the form ax^k, where a is a number and k is a nonnegative integer. (You can think of the constant term as $5x^0$.) The degree of f is 4.

(B) The function $g(x)$ in part B is not a polynomial since the term $3\sqrt{x}$ in exponent form is $3x^{1/2}$ and $\frac{1}{2}$ is not an integer.

(C) While the function $k(x)$ in part C is not in the general form for a polynomial, it could be written in that form by multiplying the three factors:

$$\begin{aligned} k(x) = 2x(x - 4)(x + 3) &= (2x^2 - 8x)(x + 3) \\ &= 2x^3 + 6x^2 - 8x^2 - 24x \\ &= 2x^3 - 2x^2 - 24x \end{aligned}$$

So $k(x)$ is a polynomial of degree 3.

MATCHED PROBLEM 1

Determine whether each function is a polynomial. Write the degree of any polynomials.

(A) $y(x) = 4x^2 - \sqrt{5}x^3 + \frac{x^5}{2} - ix^6$

(B) $z(x) = (2x^2 - 3)(x^2 + 4)$

(C) $w(x) = 7x^3 + \frac{5}{x^2} - 8$

Most of the polynomial functions we will study have real-number coefficients, but on occasion we will see complex number coefficients. In some cases, we will restrict our attention to integer or rational number coefficients. Similarly, the domain of a polynomial function can be the set of complex numbers, the set of real numbers, or a subset of either, depending on the situation.

Notice that a constant function like $f(x) = 5$ fits the definition of polynomial with degree zero [it can be written as $f(x) = 5x^0$]. The one exception to this is $f(x) = 0$, which violates the condition that a_n is not zero. This particular function is considered to be a polynomial with no degree.

› Analyzing Graphs of Polynomials

We will be working with zeros of polynomials throughout much of this chapter, so a review of the definition of a zero of a function is timely.

> **› DEFINITION 2 Zeros or Roots**
>
> A number r is said to be a **zero** or **root** of a function $P(x)$ if $P(r) = 0$.

The zeros of $P(x)$ are the solutions of the equation $P(x) = 0$. So if the coefficients of a polynomial $P(x)$ are real numbers, then the real zeros of $P(x)$ are just the x intercepts of the graph of $P(x)$. For example, the real zeros of the polynomial $P(x) = x^2 - 4$ are 2 and -2, the x intercepts of the graph of $P(x)$ [Fig. 2(a)]. However, a polynomial may have zeros that are not x intercepts. $Q(x) = x^2 + 4$, for example, has zeros $2i$ and $-2i$, but its graph has no x intercepts [Fig. 2(b)].

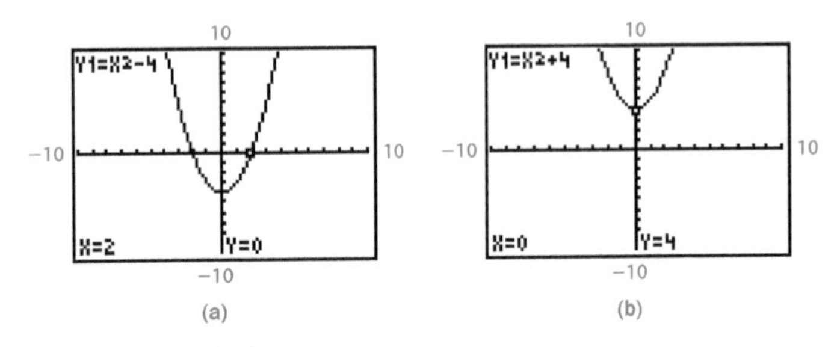

› **Figure 2** Real zeros are x intercepts.

EXAMPLE 2 Zeros and x Intercepts

(A) Figure 3 shows the graph of a polynomial function of degree 5. List its real zeros to the nearest integer.

(B) List all zeros of the polynomial function

$$P(x) = (x - 4)(x + 7)^3(x^2 + 9)(x^2 - 2x + 2)$$

Which zeros of $P(x)$ are x intercepts?

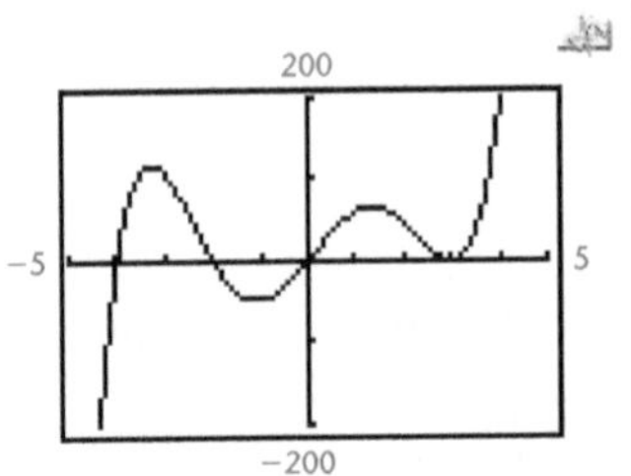

› **Figure 3**

SOLUTIONS

(A) The real zeros are the x intercepts: $-4, -2, 0$, and 3.

(B) Note first that $P(x)$ is a polynomial because it can be written in the form of Definition 1 if multiplied out. The zeros of $P(x)$ are the solutions to the equation $P(x) = 0$. Because a product equals 0 if and only if one of the factors is zero (the zero product property), we can find the zeros by solving each of the following equations. (The last was solved using the quadratic formula with the details omitted.)

$x - 4 = 0$	$(x + 7)^3 = 0$	$x^2 + 9 = 0$	$x^2 - 2x + 2 = 0$
$x = 4$	$x = -7$	$x = \pm 3i$	$x = 1 \pm i$

Therefore, the zeros of $P(x)$, are $4, -7, 3i, -3i, 1 + i$, and $1 - i$. Only two of the six zeros are real numbers and thus x intercepts: 4 and -7.

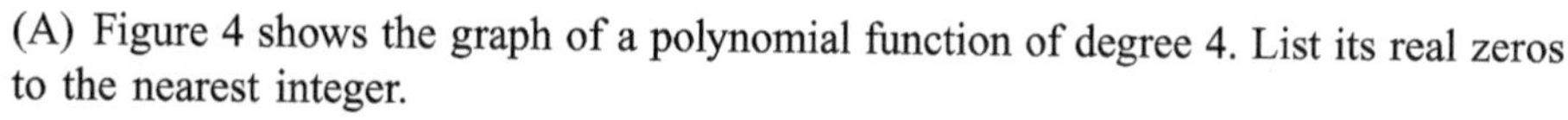

(A) Figure 4 shows the graph of a polynomial function of degree 4. List its real zeros to the nearest integer.

(B) List all zeros of the polynomial function

$$P(x) = (x + 5)(x^2 - 4)(x^2 + 4)(x^2 + 2x + 5)$$

Which zeros of $P(x)$ are x intercepts?

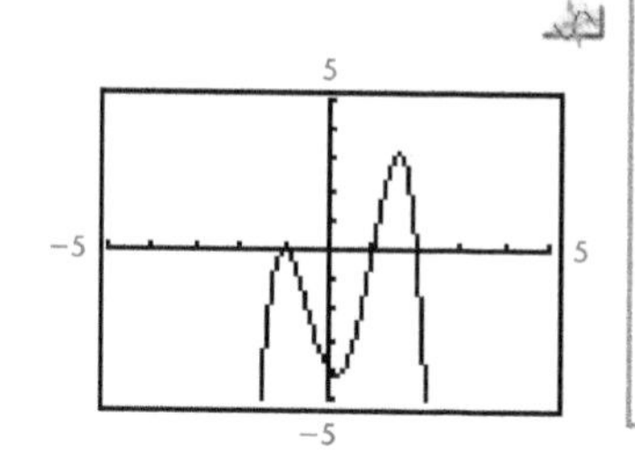

› Figure 4

››› CAUTION ›››

When a polynomial is written in factored form like the function in Example 2 part B, you may be tempted to multiply out the parentheses and write it in general form. In this case, that would be a really bad idea! Not only would it be very difficult, it is far easier to find the zeros when a polynomial is in factored form.

A point on a continuous graph where the direction changes from increasing to decreasing, or vice versa, is called a **turning point.** The vertex of a parabola, for example, is a turning point. The graph of a linear function with real coefficients is a line, so it must have exactly one real zero and no turning points. The graph of a quadratic function with real coefficients is a parabola. It must have exactly one turning point, and either two, one, or no real zeros, depending on the location of the vertex.

By definition, the y coordinate of any turning point is either a maximum or minimum. It is possible, however, that $f(c)$ is a local extremum for a continuous function f even though $(c, f(c))$ is not a turning point. See Problems 79 and 80 in Exercises 3-1.

››› EXPLORE-DISCUSS 1

(A) Graph the polynomials

$$f(x) = 0.1x^4 - 0.5x^3 - 0.7x^2 + 4.5x - 3.1$$
$$g(x) = -1.1x^5 + 6.3x^3 - 8.2x - 0.1$$
$$h(x) = 0.01x^8 + x^6 - 7x^4 + 11x^2 - 3$$

in the standard viewing window.

(B) Assuming that all real zeros of $f(x)$, $g(x)$, and $h(x)$ appear in the standard viewing window, how do you think the number of real zeros of a polynomial is related to its degree?

(C) Assuming that all turning points of $f(x)$, $g(x)$, and $h(x)$ appear in the standard viewing window, how do you think the number of turning points of a polynomial is related to its degree?

Explore-Discuss 1 suggests that the graphs of polynomial functions with real coefficients have the properties listed in Theorem 1, which we will accept now without proof. Property 3 is proved in the next section. The other properties are established in calculus.

› THEOREM 1 Properties of Graphs of Polynomial Functions

Let $P(x)$ be a polynomial of degree $n > 0$ with real coefficients. Then the graph of $P(x)$:

1. Is continuous for all real numbers
2. Has no sharp corners
3. Has at most n real zeros
4. Has at most $n - 1$ turning points
5. Increases or decreases without bound as x approaches ∞ and as x approaches $-\infty$

Property 5 requires a bit of extra attention. When discussing the behavior of graphs, we will often examine what the graph does "out toward the edges"—that is, for large values of x, both positive and negative. We call this the **left and right behavior** of a graph. We will study left and right behavior in depth later in this section. For now, we notice that when studying the behavior of a graph for large values of x, we use the notation $x \to \infty$ (for increasingly large positive values) and $x \to -\infty$ (for increasingly large negative values).* Keep in mind that ∞ and $-\infty$ are not real numbers, but concepts.

*This notation is used frequently in the study of limits, which is absolutely crucial to calculus.

Figure 5 shows graphs of representative polynomial functions of degrees 1 through 6, illustrating the five properties of Theorem 1.

› **Figure 5** Graphs of polynomial functions.

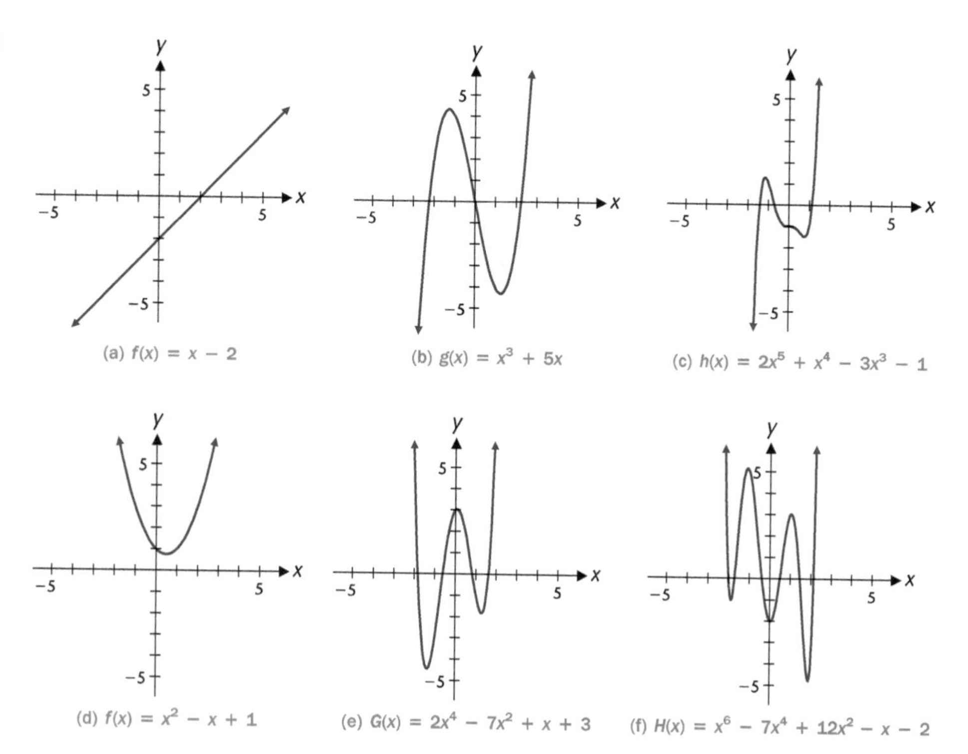

(a) $f(x) = x - 2$ (b) $g(x) = x^3 + 5x$ (c) $h(x) = 2x^5 + x^4 - 3x^3 - 1$

(d) $f(x) = x^2 - x + 1$ (e) $G(x) = 2x^4 - 7x^2 + x + 3$ (f) $H(x) = x^6 - 7x^4 + 12x^2 - x - 2$

Note that in each case, the number of turning points is at least one less than the degree of the polynomial, but not always exactly one less. Likewise, the number of zeros is never more than the degree, but in some cases is less.

EXAMPLE 3 Properties of Graphs of Polynomials

Explain why each graph is *not* the graph of a polynomial function by listing the properties of Theorem 1 that it *fails* to satisfy.

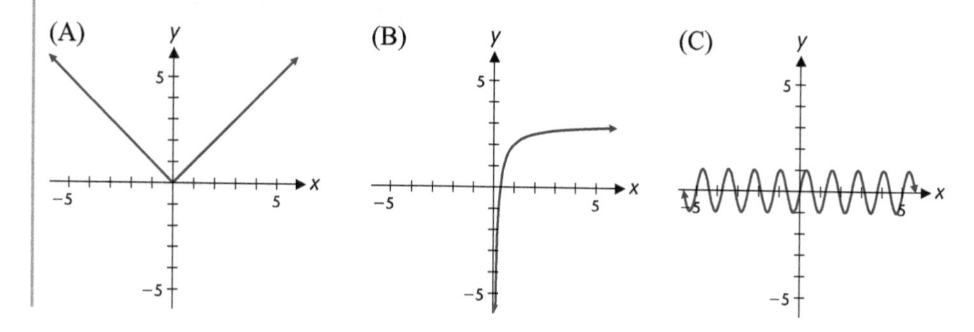

SOLUTIONS

(A) The graph has a sharp corner when $x = 0$. Property 2 fails.

(B) There are no points on the graph with negative x coordinates, so the graph is not continuous for all real numbers (Property 1). Property 5 is also violated. The graph does not increase or decrease without bound as $x \to -\infty$; it does nothing! The graph also levels off at height 3 as $x \to \infty$, which is another violation of Property 5.

(C) There are an infinite number of zeros and an infinite number of turning points, so Properties 3 and 4 fail. Furthermore, the graph is bounded by the horizontal lines $y = \pm 1$ and does not increase or decrease without bound as $x \to \infty$ and $x \to -\infty$. Property 5 fails.

MATCHED PROBLEM 3

Explain why each graph is *not* the graph of a polynomial function by listing the properties of Theorem 1 that it *fails* to satisfy.

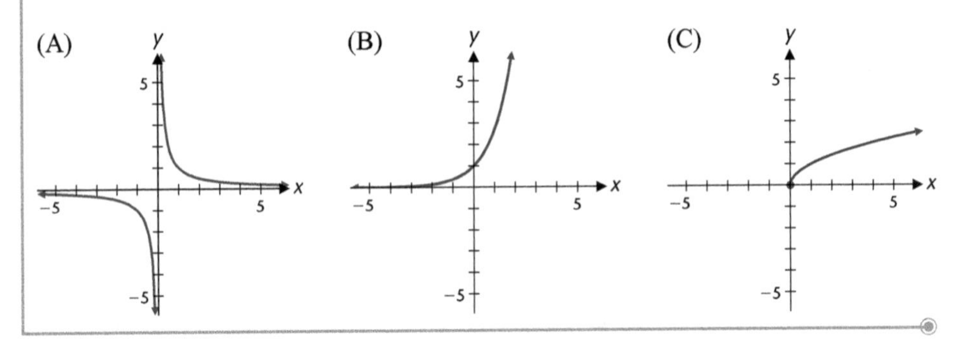

› Left and Right Behavior of Polynomials

››› EXPLORE-DISCUSS 2

If n is a positive integer, then $y_1 = x^n$, $y_2 = x^{n-1}$, and $y_3 = x^n + x^{n-1}$ are all polynomial functions. Is the shape of y_3 more similar to the shape of y_1 or to the shape of y_2? Obtain evidence for your answer by graphing all three functions for several values of n.

Explore-Discuss 2 suggests that the shape of the graph of a polynomial function with real coefficients is similar to the shape of the graph of the **leading term,** that is, the term of highest degree. The coefficient of the leading term is called the **leading**

coefficient. Figure 6 compares the graph of the polynomial $h(x) = x^5 - 6x^3 + 8x + 1$ with the graph of its leading term $p(x) = x^5$. The graphs are dissimilar near the origin, but as we zoom out, the shapes of the two graphs become quite similar.

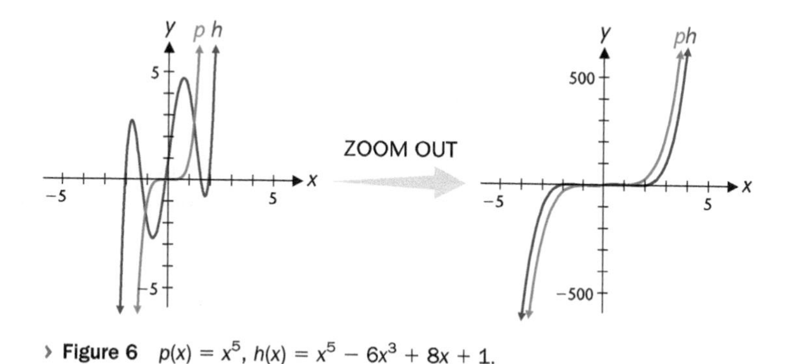

› **Figure 6** $p(x) = x^5$, $h(x) = x^5 - 6x^3 + 8x + 1$.

››› EXPLORE-DISCUSS 3

Consider the polynomial $h(x) = x^5 - 6x^3 + 8x + 1$. Make a table of values for $h(x)$, using $x = 0, 2, 4, 6, 8$, and 10. Make a separate column for each individual term of h, and put the output of the entire function in the last column. What do you notice about the relative sizes of each term as x gets larger?

Explore-Discuss 3 illustrates why the graphs of $h(x) = x^5 - 6x^3 + 8x + 1$ and $p(x) = x^5$ are very different near the origin, but very similar as x gets larger. The leading term in the polynomial dominates all other terms combined. Because the graph of $p(x)$ increases without bound as $x \to \infty$, the same is true of the graph of $h(x)$. And because the graph of $p(x)$ decreases without bound as $x \to -\infty$, the same is true of the graph of $h(x)$.

Because of this domination by the highest power, *the left and right behavior of a polynomial function with real coefficients is determined by the left and right behavior of its leading term.* Based on this principle, we can make Property 5 of Theorem 1 much more specific.

When the graph of a function $p(x)$ increases without bound, we can informally describe this as the value of $p(x)$ approaching ∞, and use the symbol $p(x) \to \infty$. When the graph decreases without bound, we write $p(x) \to -\infty$. Using these symbols to describe $p(x) = x^5$ in Figure 6, we would write $p(x) \to \infty$ as $x \to \infty$ and $p(x) \to -\infty$ as $x \to -\infty$. We will use this notation to describe the left and right behavior of polynomial functions.

› THEOREM 2 Left and Right Behavior of Polynomial Functions

Let $P(x) = a_nx^n + a_{n-1}x^{n-1} + \cdots + a_1x + a_0$ be a polynomial function with real coefficients, $a_n \neq 0$, $n > 0$. If P has:

1. Positive leading coefficient, even degree: $P(x) \to \infty$ as $x \to \infty$ and $P(x) \to \infty$ as $x \to -\infty$ (like the graph of $y = x^2$).
2. Positive leading coefficient, odd degree: $P(x) \to \infty$ as $x \to \infty$ and $P(x) \to -\infty$ as $x \to -\infty$ (like the graph of $y = x^3$).
3. Negative leading coefficient, even degree: $P(x) \to -\infty$ as $x \to \infty$ and $P(x) \to -\infty$ as $x \to -\infty$ (like the graph of $y = -x^2$).
4. Negative leading coefficient, odd degree: $P(x) \to -\infty$ as $x \to \infty$ and $P(x) \to \infty$ as $x \to -\infty$ (like the graph of $y = -x^3$).

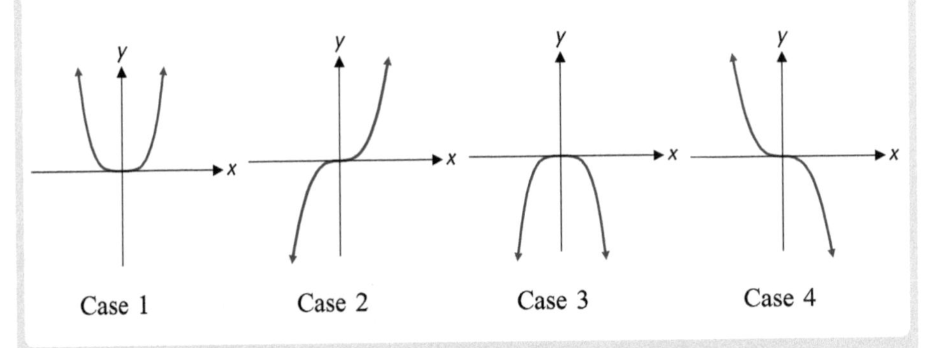

Case 1 Case 2 Case 3 Case 4

The key to remembering the results of Theorem 2 is not trying to memorize each rule, but rather being familiar with the graphs of $y = x^2, -x^2, x^3$, and $-x^3$.

EXAMPLE 4 Left and Right Behavior of Polynomials

Determine the left and right behavior of each polynomial. Use the notation from Theorem 2.

(A) $P(x) = 3 - x^2 + 4x^3 - x^4 - 2x^6$

(B) $Q(x) = 4x^5 + 8x^3 + 5x - 1$

SOLUTIONS

(A) The degree of $P(x)$ is 6 (even) and the coefficient a_6 is -2 (negative), so the left and right behavior is the same as that of $-x^6$, and also $-x^2$ (Case 3 of Theorem 2): $P(x) \to -\infty$ as $x \to \infty$ and $P(x) \to -\infty$ as $x \to -\infty$.

(B) The degree of $Q(x)$ is 5 (odd) and the coefficient a_5 is 4 (positive), so the left and right behavior is the same as that of x^5, and also x^3 (Case 2 of Theorem 2): $P(x) \to \infty$ as $x \to \infty$ and $P(x) \to -\infty$ as $x \to -\infty$.

MATCHED PROBLEM 4

Determine the left and right behavior of each polynomial.

(A) $P(x) = 4x^9 - 3x^{11} + 5$
(B) $Q(x) = 1 - 2x^{50} + x^{100}$

››› EXPLORE-DISCUSS 4

(A) What is the least number of turning points that a polynomial function of degree 5, with real coefficients, can have? The greatest number? Explain.

(B) What is the least number of x intercepts that a polynomial function of degree 5, with real coefficients, can have? The greatest number? Explain.

(C) What is the least number of turning points that a polynomial function of degree 6, with real coefficients, can have? The greatest number? Explain.

(D) What is the least number of x intercepts that a polynomial function of degree 6, with real coefficients, can have? The greatest number? Explain.

EXAMPLE 5 Sketching the Graph of a Polynomial

Sketch the graph of a polynomial with odd degree, a positive leading coefficient, and zeros -4, 1, and $\frac{5}{2}$.

SOLUTION

The zeros will all be x intercepts of the graph, so we plot those points first (Fig. 7). A polynomial with odd degree and a positive leading coefficient increases without bound to the right and decreases without bound to the left, giving us the graph in Figure 7. Note that we were given no information about the heights of any points not on the x axis, so we did not include a scale on the y axis.

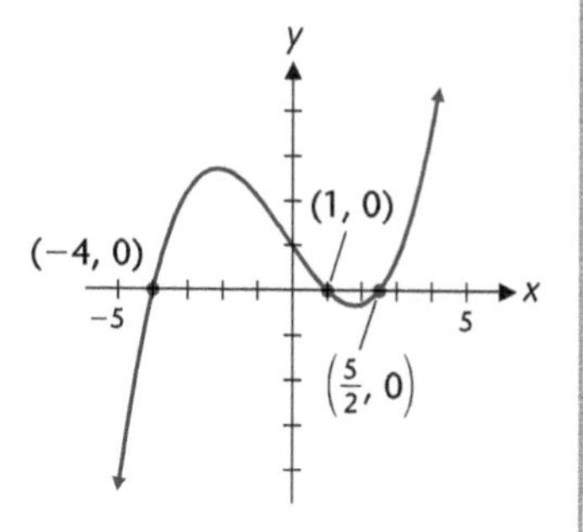

› Figure 7

MATCHED PROBLEM 5

Sketch the graph of a polynomial with even degree, positive leading coefficient, and zeros -3, 0, 1, and 4.

EXAMPLE 6 Analyzing the Graph of a Polynomial

Approximate to two decimal places the zeros and local extrema for

$$P(x) = x^3 - 14x^2 + 27x - 12$$

SOLUTION

Examining the graph of P in a standard viewing window [Fig. 8(a)], we see two zeros, and a local maximum near $x = 1$. Zooming in shows these points more clearly [Fig. 8(b)]. Using the ZERO and MAXIMUM commands (details omitted), we find that $P(x) = 0$ for $x \approx 0.66$ and $x \approx 1.54$, and that $P(1.09) \approx 2.09$ is a local maximum value.

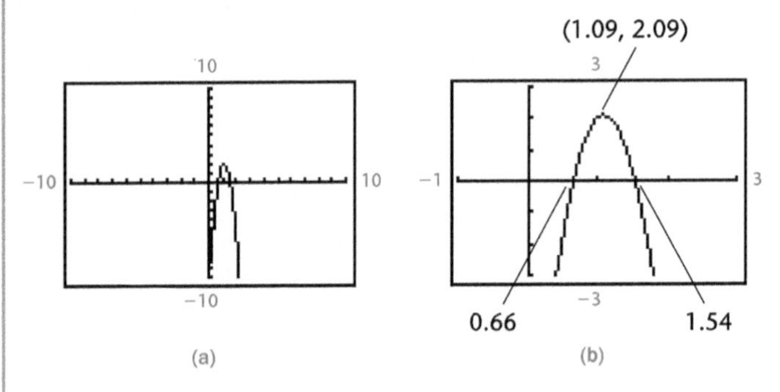

› **Figure 8** $P(x) = x^3 - 14x^2 + 27x - 12.$

But have we found all the zeros and local extrema? The graph in Figure 8(a) seems to indicate that $P(x) \to -\infty$ as $x \to \infty$ and $P(x) \to -\infty$ as $x \to -\infty$. But $P(x)$ has an odd degree and a positive leading coefficient, so in fact, it must be true that $P(x) \to \infty$ as $x \to \infty$. This tells us that $P(x)$ has to change direction somewhere outside the standard viewing window. In other words, there must be a local minimum and another zero that are not visible in the viewing window. Examining a table of values [Fig. 9(a)], it looks like there is a turning point near $x = 8$, and a zero near $x = 12$. Adjusting the window variables produces the graph in Figure 9(b). Using the ZERO and MAXIMUM commands again, we find that $P(x) = 0$ for $x \approx 11.80$ and that $P(8.24) \approx -180.61$ is a local minimum.

Now are we finished? Because a third-degree polynomial can have at most three zeros and two turning points, we have found all the zeros and local extrema for this polynomial.

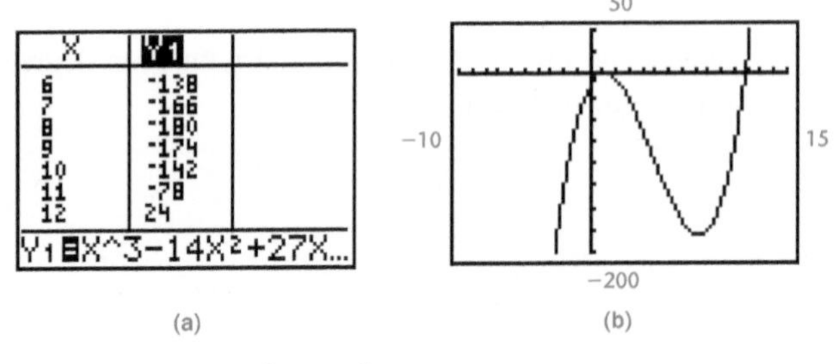

X	Y1
6	-138
7	-166
8	-180
9	-174
10	-142
11	-78
12	24

Y1=X^3-14X²+27X...

› **Figure 9** $P(x) = x^3 - 14x^2 + 27x - 12.$

MATCHED PROBLEM 6

Approximate to two decimal places the zeros and the coordinates of the local extrema for

$$P(x) = -x^3 - 14x^2 - 15x + 5$$

Mathematical Modeling and Data Analysis

In Chapter 2 we saw that regression techniques can be used to construct a linear or quadratic model for a set of data. This was useful in modeling a wide variety of situations. But it's unreasonable to assume that every set of data can be modeled well with either a line or a parabola. Fortunately, most graphing calculators have the ability to use a variety of functions other than linear and quadratic for modeling data. We will discuss polynomial regression models in this section and other types of regression models in later sections.

EXAMPLE 7

Estimating the Weight of Fish

Table 1 Sturgeon

Length (in.) x	Weight (oz.) y
18	13
22	26
26	46
30	75
34	115
38	166
44	282
52	492
60	796

Source: www.thefishernet.com

Using the length of a fish to estimate its weight is of interest to both scientists and sport anglers. The data in Table 1 give the average weight of North American sturgeon for certain lengths. Use these data and regression techniques to find a cubic polynomial model that can be used to estimate the weight of a sturgeon for any length. Estimate (to the nearest ounce) the weights of sturgeon of lengths 45, 46, 47, 48, 49, and 50 inches, respectively.

SOLUTION

We begin by entering the data in Table 1 and examining a scatter plot of the data [Fig. 10(a)]. This makes it clear that linear regression would be a poor choice. And, in fact, we would not expect a linear relationship between length and weight. Instead, because weight is associated with volume, which involves three dimensions, it is more likely that the weight would be related to the cube of the length. We use a cubic (third-degree) regression polynomial to model these data [Fig. 10(b)]. Figure 10(c) adds the graph of the polynomial model to the graph of the data. The graph in Figure 10(c) shows that this cubic polynomial does provide a good fit for the data. (We will have more to say about the choice of functions and the accuracy of the fit provided by regression analysis later in the text.) Figure 10(d) shows the estimated weights for the requested lengths.

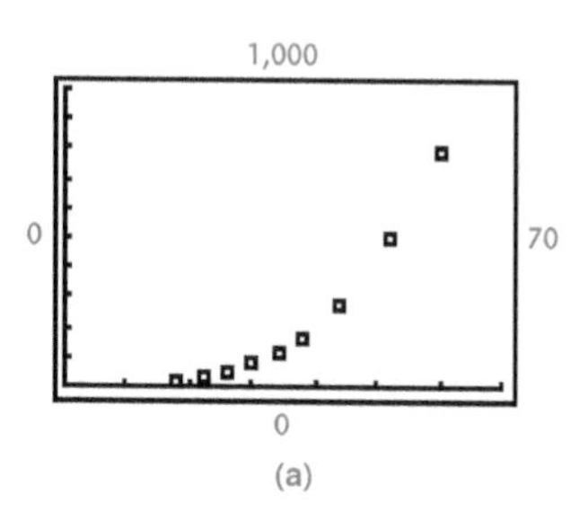

(a)

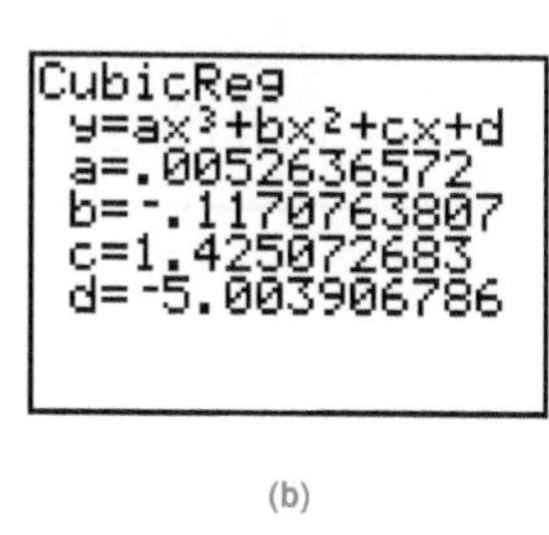

(b)

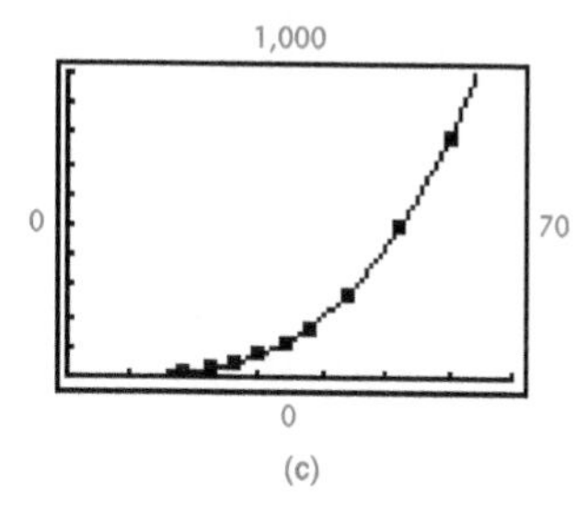

(c)

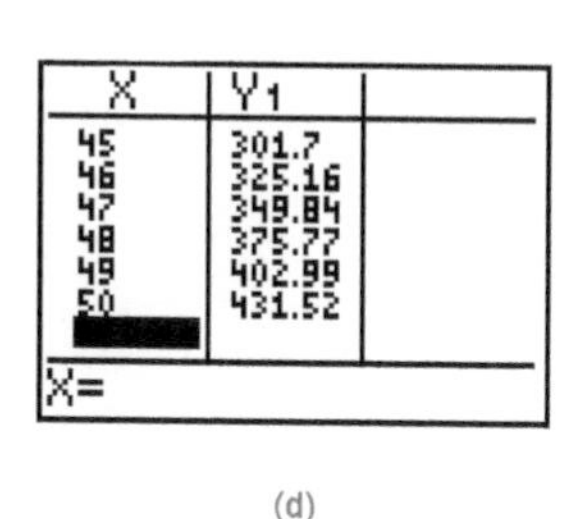

(d)

Figure 10

MATCHED PROBLEM 7

Find a quadratic regression model for the data in Table 1 and compare it with the cubic regression model found in Example 7. Which model appears to provide a better fit for these data? Use numerical and/or graphical comparisons to support your choice.

EXAMPLE 8 Hydroelectric Power

Table 2

Year	U.S. Consumption of Hydroelectric Power (quadrillion BTU)
1983	3.90
1985	3.40
1987	3.12
1989	2.99
1991	3.14
1993	3.13
1995	3.48
1997	3.88
1999	3.47
2001	2.38
2003	2.53
2005	2.61

Source: U.S. Department of Energy

The data in Table 2 give the annual consumption of hydroelectric power (in quadrillion BTU) in the United States for selected years since 1983. Use regression techniques to find an appropriate polynomial model for the data. Discuss how well the model is likely to predict annual hydroelectric power consumption in the second decade of the twenty-first century.

SOLUTION

From Table 2 it appears that a polynomial model of the data would have three turning points—near 1989, 1997, and 2001. Because a polynomial with three turning points must have degree at least 4, we use quartic (fourth-degree) regression to find the polynomial of the form

$$y = ax^4 + bx^3 + cx^2 + dx + e$$

that best fits the data. Using $x = 0$ to represent the year 1983, we enter the data [Fig. 11(a)] and find the quartic regression model

$$y = 0.00013x^4 - 0.0067x^3 + 0.107x^2 - 0.59x + 4.03$$

[Fig. 11(b)]. We then plot both the data points and the model [Fig. 11(c)]. The model is not likely to be a good predictor of consumption of hydroelectric power in the second decade of the twenty-first century. In fact, it predicts a sudden dramatic increase to unprecedented levels after 2008. This brings up an important point: A model that fits a set of data points well is not automatically a good model for predicting future trends.

L1	L2	L3 3
0	3.9	
2	3.4	
4	3.12	
6	2.99	
8	3.14	
10	3.13	
12	3.48	

L3(1)=

(a)

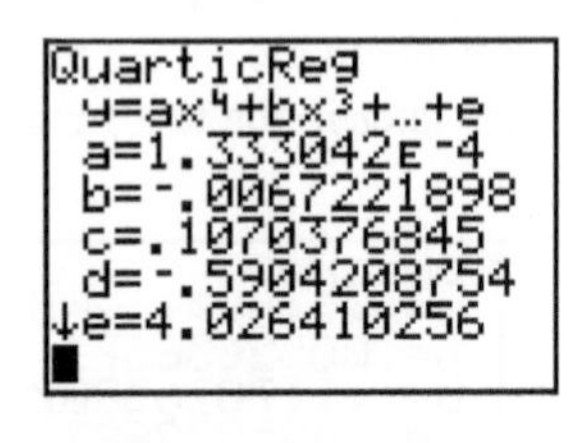

(b)

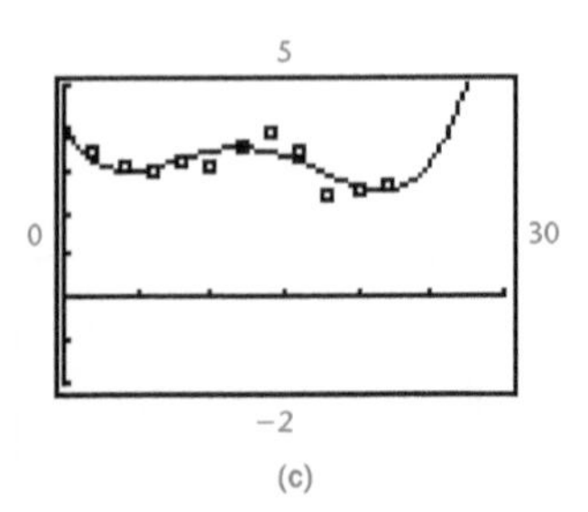

(c)

› **Figure 11**

MATCHED PROBLEM 8

Find the cubic regression model for the data of Table 2. Discuss which model is a better fit of the data—the cubic model or the quartic model of Example 8.

ANSWERS TO MATCHED PROBLEMS

1. (A) Polynomial, degree 6 (B) Polynomial, degree 4 (C) Not a polynomial
2. (A) $-1, 1, 2$ (B) The zeros are $-5, -2, 2, 2i, -2i, -1 + 2i$, and $-1 - 2i$; the x intercepts are $-5, -2$, and 2. **3.** (A) Properties 1 and 5 (B) Property 5
(C) Properties 1 and 5 **4.** (A) $P(x) \to -\infty$ as $x \to \infty$ and $P(x) \to \infty$ as $x \to -\infty$.
(B) $P(x) \to \infty$ as $x \to \infty$ and $P(x) \to \infty$ as $x \to -\infty$.
5.

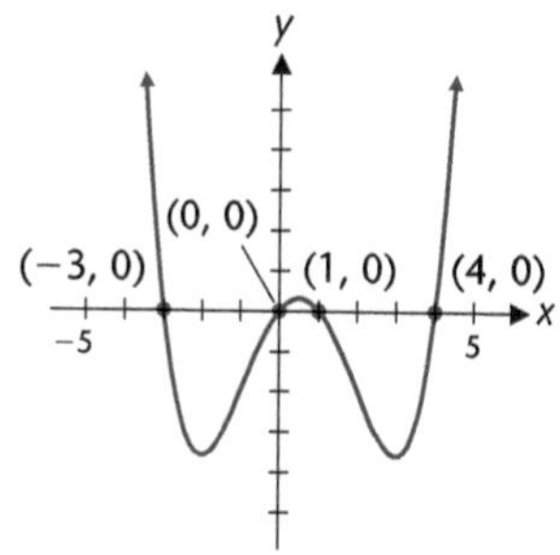

6. Zeros: $-12.80, -1.47, 0.27$; local maximum: $P(-0.57) \approx 9.19$; local minimum: $P(-8.76) \approx -265.71$ **7.** The quadratic regression model is $y = 0.49x^2 - 20.48x + 234.57$. The cubic regression model provides a better model for these data, especially for $18 \le x \le 26$. **8.** The cubic regression model is $y = -0.00086x^3 + 0.026x^2 - 0.23x + 3.79$. The quartic regression model is a better fit.

3-1 Exercises

1. Explain what a polynomial is in your own words.

2. What is the connection between the zeros of a polynomial and its factors? Explain.

3. Explain in your own words what is meant by the statement $P(x) \to \infty$ as $x \to \infty$.

4. Explain in your own words what is meant by the statement $P(x) \to -\infty$ as $x \to -\infty$.

In Problems 5–10, decide if the statement is true or false, then explain your choice.

5. Every quadratic function is a polynomial.

6. There exists a polynomial with degree $\frac{5}{2}$.

7. The coefficients of a polynomial must be real numbers.

8. A polynomial with only imaginary zeros has no x intercepts.

9. A polynomial with no x intercepts has no zeros.

10. The graph of a polynomial can level off at a finite height as x increases without bound.

In Problems 11–14, a is a positive real number. Match each function with one of graphs (a)–(d).

11. $f(x) = ax^3$ **12.** $g(x) = -ax^4$

13. $h(x) = ax^6$ **14.** $k(x) = -ax^5$

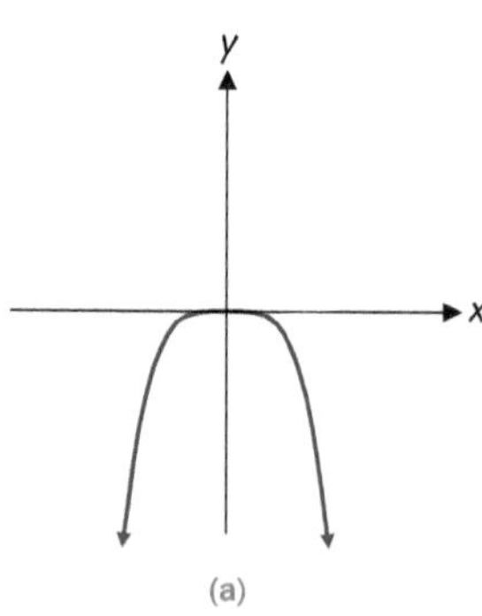
(a)

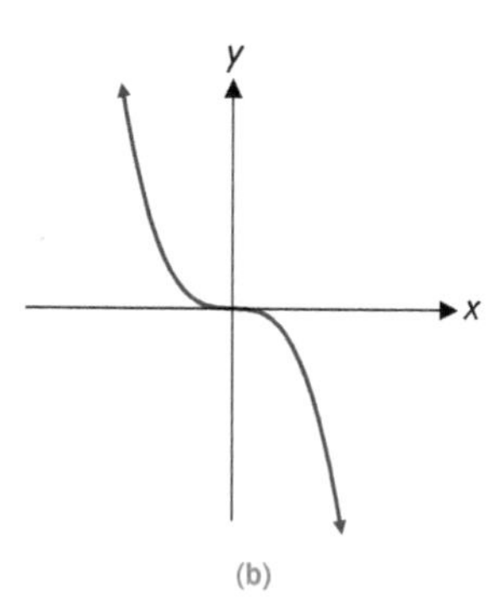
(b)

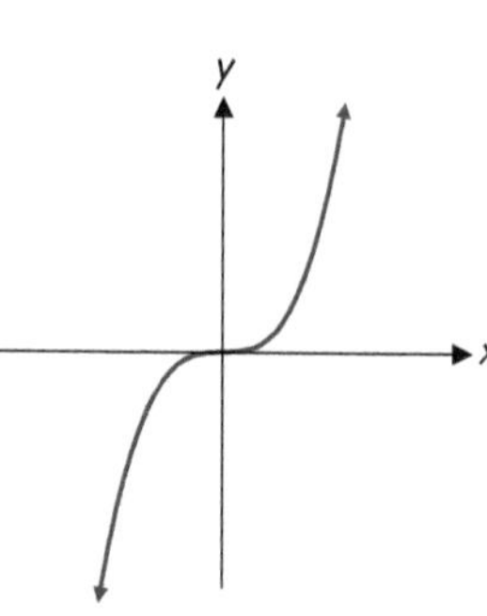
(c)

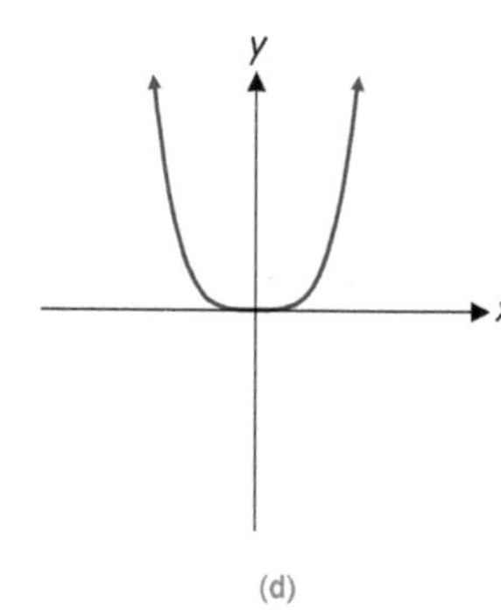
(d)

In Problems 15–18, list the real zeros and turning points, and state the left and right behavior, of the polynomial function P(x) that has the indicated graph.

15.

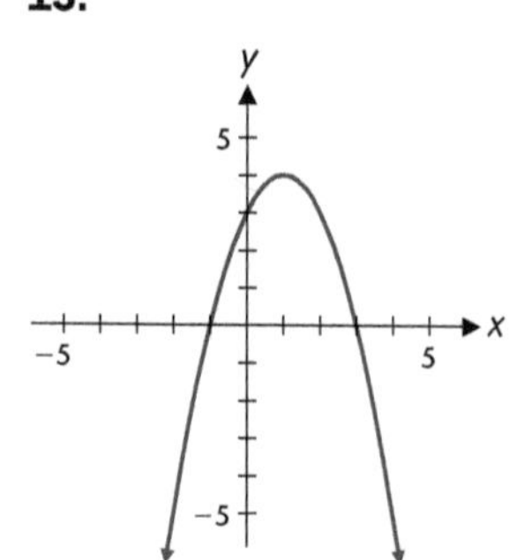

16.

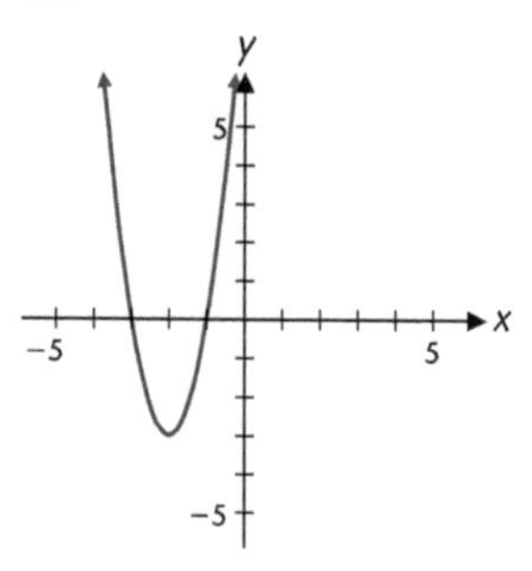

17.

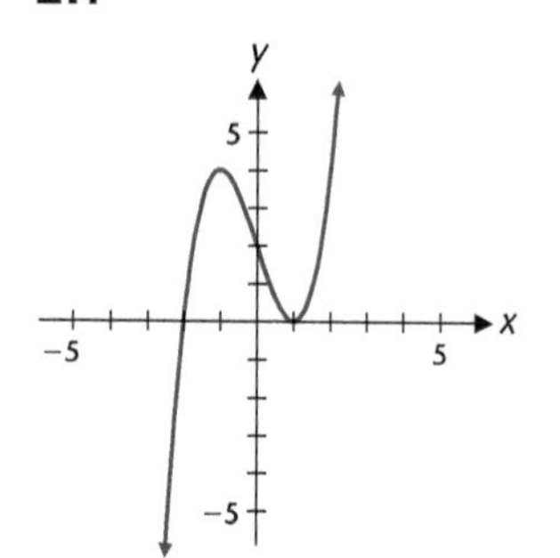

18.

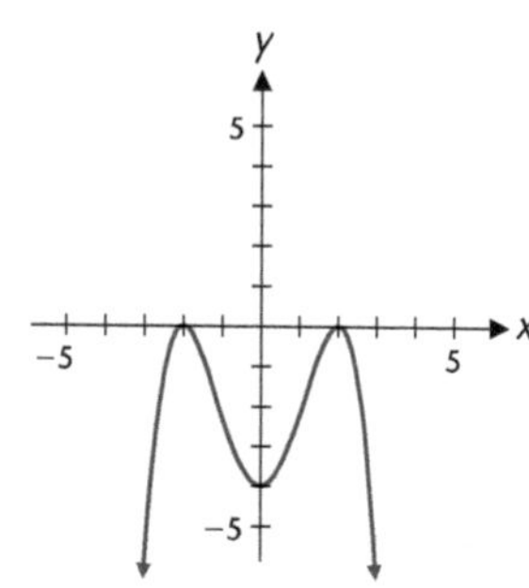

In Problems 19–22, explain why each graph is not the graph of a polynomial function.

19.

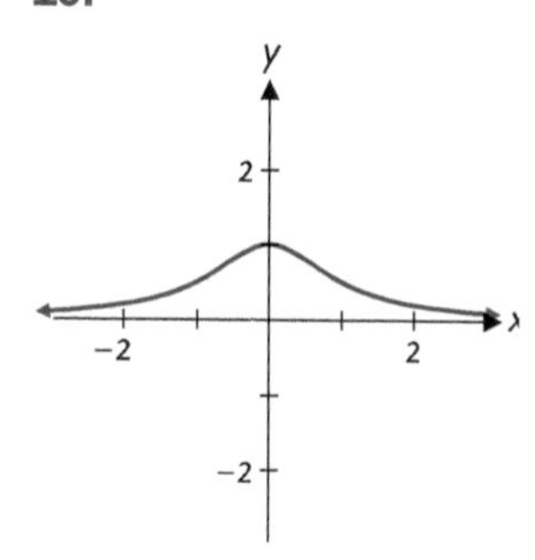

20.

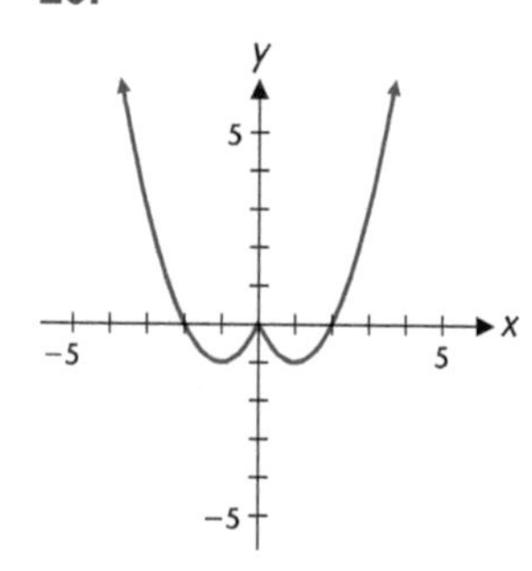

21.

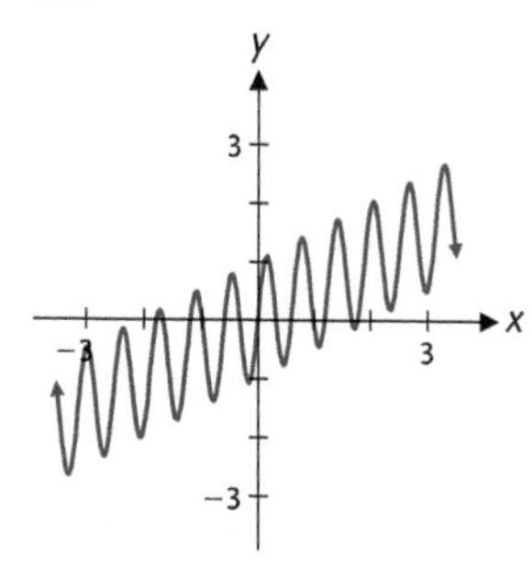

22.

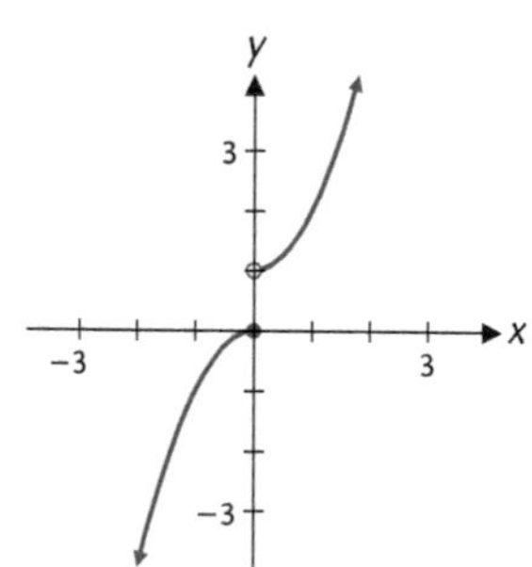

In Problems 23–30, determine whether the function is a polynomial. If it is, state the degree.

23. $f(x) = 4x + 7x^2 - \sqrt{8}x^3$

24. $g(x) = 2 - \sqrt{5}x^2 + x^5$

25. $h(x) = 4x^2 + 3x - 5 + \dfrac{2}{x}$

26. $k(x) = \dfrac{1}{3}x^3 + x - \dfrac{7}{x^2}$

27. $f(x) = 4\sqrt{x} + 7$ **28.** $g(x) = 8x - \sqrt[3]{x}$

29. $h(x) = 4(2x - 7)(x + 1)(3 + i - x)$

30. $k(x) = 2i(4 - x)(5 - x)(6 - x)$

In Problems 31–34, list all zeros of each polynomial function, and specify those zeros that are x intercepts.

31. $P(x) = x(x^2 - 9)(x^2 + 4)$ **32.** $P(x) = (x^2 - 4)(x^4 - 1)$

33. $P(x) = (x + 5)(x^2 + 9)(x^2 + 16)$

34. $P(x) = (x^2 - 5x + 6)(x^2 - 5x + 7)$

For each polynomial function in Problems 35–40:

(A) State the left and right behavior, the maximum number of x intercepts, and the maximum number of local extrema.

(B) Write the intervals where P is increasing, and intervals where P is decreasing.

(C) Approximate (to two decimal places) the x intercepts and the local extrema.

35. $P(x) = x^3 - 5x^2 + 2x + 6$

36. $P(x) = x^3 + 2x^2 - 5x - 3$

37. $P(x) = -x^3 + 4x^2 + x + 5$

38. $P(x) = -x^3 - 3x^2 + 4x - 4$

39. $P(x) = x^4 + x^3 - 5x^2 - 3x + 12$

40. $P(x) = -x^4 + 6x^2 - 3x - 16$

In Problems 41–46, sketch the graph of a polynomial fitting each description.

41. Zeros $x = -4, 3$; even degree, positive leading coefficient

42. Zeros $x = 1, 5$; even degree, negative leading coefficient

43. Zeros $x = -10, 0, 10$; odd degree, negative leading coefficient

44. Zeros $x = -7, 1, 11$; odd degree, positive leading coefficient

45. Zeros $x = -\frac{5}{2}, 0, 3, \frac{11}{2}$; even degree, negative leading coefficient

46. Zeros $x = -3, -\frac{1}{2}, \frac{1}{2}, 2$; even degree, positive leading coefficient

In Problems 47–54, find a polynomial of least degree with integer coefficients that has the given zeros. Write your answer in both factored form and general form.

47. $x = 0, 2, -3$ **48.** $x = 0, -4, 1$

49. $x = -\frac{1}{2}, 4, 0$ **50.** $x = \frac{5}{2}, -1, 0$

51. $x = 2, 3, 4$ **52.** $x = -2, -3, -4$

53. $x = 0, i, -i$ **54.** $x = 0, 2i, -2i$

In Problems 55–58, either give an example of a polynomial with real coefficients that satisfies the given conditions or explain why such a polynomial cannot exist.

55. $P(x)$ is a third-degree polynomial with one x intercept.

56. $P(x)$ is a fourth-degree polynomial with no x intercepts.

57. $P(x)$ is a third-degree polynomial with no x intercepts.

58. $P(x)$ is a fourth-degree polynomial with no turning points.

In calculus, the limit concept is very important. We have used the symbols $x \to \infty$, $x \to -\infty$, $P(x) \to \infty$, and $P(x) \to -\infty$ to describe right and left behavior of polynomials. In calculus, the right behavior of a function f(x) is symbolized as $\lim_{x\to\infty} f(x)$ and read "the limit as x approaches infinity of f(x)." Similarly, the left behavior is symbolized as $\lim_{x\to-\infty} f(x)$. In Problems 59–66, use our study of left and right behavior to find each limit.

59. $\lim_{x\to\infty} x^2$ **60.** $\lim_{x\to-\infty} x^2$

61. $\lim_{x\to-\infty} (x^3 - x^2 + x)$ **62.** $\lim_{x\to\infty} (x^3 - x^2 + x)$

63. $\lim_{x\to\infty} (4 - x - 3x^4)$ **64.** $\lim_{x\to-\infty} (4 - x - 3x^4)$

65. $\lim_{x\to-\infty} (-x^4 + x^3 + 5x^2)$ **66.** $\lim_{x\to\infty} (-x^4 + x^3 + 5x^2)$

In Problems 67–74, approximate (to two decimal places) the x intercepts and the local extrema.

67. $P(x) = 40 + 50x - 9x^2 - x^3$

68. $P(x) = 40 + 70x + 18x^2 + x^3$

69. $P(x) = 0.04x^3 - 10x + 5$

70. $P(x) = -0.01x^3 + 2.8x - 3$

71. $P(x) = 0.1x^4 + 0.3x^3 - 23x^2 - 23x + 90$

72. $P(x) = 0.1x^4 + 0.2x^3 - 19x^2 + 17x + 100$

73. $P(x) = x^4 - 24x^3 + 167x^2 - 275x + 131$

74. $P(x) = x^4 + 20x^3 + 118x^2 + 178x + 79$

75. (A) What is the least number of turning points that a polynomial function of degree 4, with real coefficients, can have? The greatest number? Explain and give examples.

(B) What is the least number of x intercepts that a polynomial function of degree 4, with real coefficients, can have? The greatest number? Explain and give examples.

76. (A) What is the least number of turning points that a polynomial function of degree 3, with real coefficients, can have? The greatest number? Explain and give examples.

(B) What is the least number of x intercepts that a polynomial function of degree 3, with real coefficients, can have? The greatest number? Explain and give examples.

77. Is every polynomial of even degree an even function? Explain.

78. Is every polynomial of odd degree an odd function? Explain.

79. Let $f(x) = \begin{cases} x^2 & \text{if } |x| \geq 2 \\ 4 & \text{if } |x| < 2 \end{cases}$

(A) Graph f and observe that f is continuous.
(B) Find all numbers c such that $f(c)$ is a local extremum although $(c, f(c))$ is not a turning point.

80. Explain why the y coordinate of any turning point on the graph of a continuous function is a local extremum.

81. Is it possible for a third-degree polynomial to have real zeros $x = 0$ and $x = 2$ and no other real zeros? Explain, illustrating with graphs if necessary.

82. Is it possible for a fourth-degree polynomial to have real zeros $x = -5$, 1, and 4 and no other real zeros? Explain, illustrating with graphs if necessary.

APPLICATIONS

83. REVENUE The price–demand equation for 8,000-BTU window air conditioners is given by

$$p = 0.0004x^2 - x + 569 \qquad 0 \leq x \leq 800$$

where x is the number of air conditioners that can be sold at a price of p dollars each.
(A) Find the revenue function.
(B) Find the number of air conditioners that must be sold to maximize the revenue, the corresponding price to the nearest dollar, and the maximum revenue to the nearest dollar.

84. PROFIT Refer to Problem 83. The cost of manufacturing 8,000-BTU window air conditioners is given by

$$C(x) = 10{,}000 + 90x$$

where $C(x)$ is the total cost in dollars of producing x air conditioners.
(A) Find the profit function.
(B) Find the number of air conditioners that must be sold to maximize the profit, the corresponding price to the nearest dollar, and the maximum profit to the nearest dollar.

85. CONSTRUCTION A rectangular container measuring 1 foot by 2 feet by 4 feet is covered with a layer of lead shielding of uniform thickness (see the figure below and at the top of the next column).
(A) Find the volume of lead shielding V as a function of the thickness x (in feet) of the shielding.
(B) Find the thickness of the lead shielding to three decimal places if the volume of the shielding is 3 cubic feet.

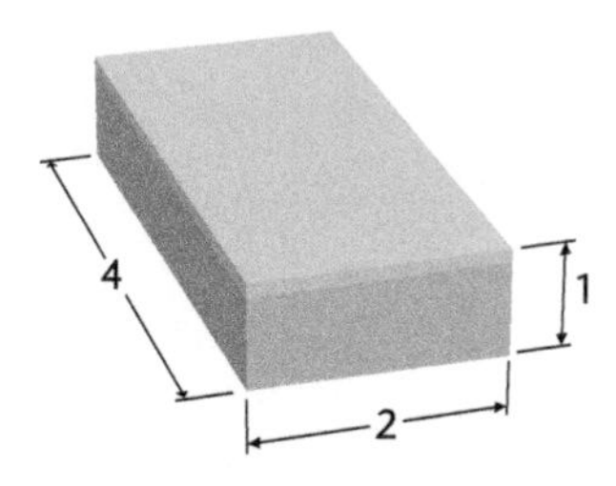

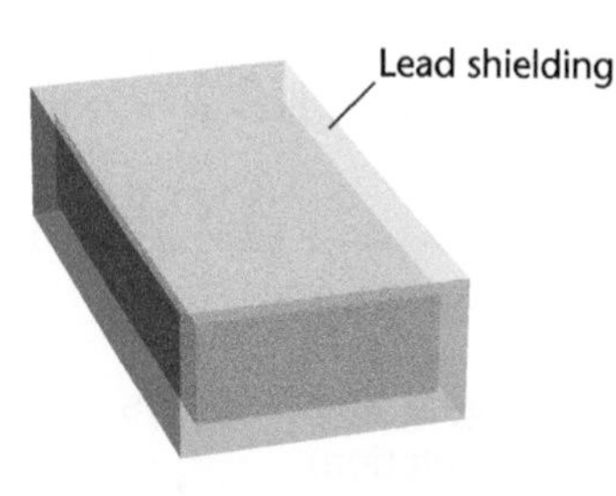

86. MANUFACTURING A rectangular storage container measuring 2 feet by 2 feet by 3 feet is coated with a protective coating of plastic of uniform thickness.
(A) Find the volume of plastic V as a function of the thickness x (in feet) of the coating.
(B) Find the thickness of the plastic coating to four decimal places if the volume of the shielding is 0.1 cubic feet.

MODELING AND DATA ANALYSIS

87. HEALTH CARE Table 3 shows the total national expenditures (in billion dollars) and the per capita expenditures (in dollars) for selected years since 1960.

Table 3 National Health Expenditures

Year	Total Expenditures (billion \$)	Per Capita Expenditures (\$)
1960	27.5	143
1970	74.9	348
1980	253.9	1,067
1990	714.0	2,737
1995	1,016.5	3,686
2000	1,353.3	4,790
2005	1,987.7	6,697

Source: U.S. Dept. of Health and Human Services

(A) Let x represent the number of years since 1960 and find a cubic regression polynomial for the total national expenditures. Round coefficients to three significant digits.
(B) Use the polynomial model from part A to estimate the total national expenditures (to the nearest tenth of a billion) for 2010.
(C) Find a quadratic regression model for the total national expenditures. Which model predicts more rapid long-term increase?

88. HEALTH CARE Refer to Table 3.
(A) Let x represent the number of years since 1960 and find a cubic regression polynomial for the per capita expenditures. Round coefficients to three significant digits.
(B) Use the polynomial model from part A to estimate the per capita expenditures (to the nearest dollar) for 2010.

(C) Find a quadratic regression model for the per capita expenditures. Which model predicts more rapid long-term increase?

89. MARRIAGE Table 4 shows the marriage and divorce rates per 1,000 population for selected years since 1950.

Table 4 Marriages and Divorces (per 1,000 Population)

Year	Marriages	Divorces
1950	11.1	2.6
1960	8.5	2.2
1970	10.6	3.5
1980	10.6	5.2
1990	9.8	4.7
2000	8.5	4.2
2005	7.5	3.6

Source: U.S. Census Bureau

(A) Let x represent the number of years since 1950 and find a cubic and a quartic regression polynomial for the marriage rate. Round coefficients to three significant digits.
(B) Use the polynomial models from part A to estimate the marriage rate (to one decimal place) for 2008.
(C) Which model fits the actual data points better, cubic or quartic? Which provides a more realistic prediction for the marriage rate in 2008? Why?
(D) Based on the data in Table 4, why would a quadratic function do a poor job of modeling the data?

90. DIVORCE Refer to Table 4.
(A) Let x represent the number of years since 1950 and find a cubic and a quartic regression polynomial for the divorce rate. Round coefficients to three significant digits.
(B) Use the polynomial models from part A to estimate the divorce rate (to one decimal place) for 2008.
(C) Which model fits the actual data points better, cubic or quartic? Which provides a more realistic prediction for the divorce rate in 2008? Why?
(D) Based on the data in Table 4, why would a quadratic function do a poor job of modeling the data?

3-2 Polynomial Division

- Dividing Polynomials Using Long Division
- Dividing Polynomials Using Synthetic Division
- The Remainder and Factor Theorems

In the last section, we introduced the main properties of graphs of polynomials with real coefficients and saw the usefulness of these properties in analyzing graphs. But to understand why, for example, a polynomial function of degree n can have at most n real zeros, we will need to look at polynomials from an algebraic perspective. The first steps in doing so take place in this section. Two of the key algebraic procedures in studying polynomials from this perspective are division and factorization.

Dividing Polynomials Using Long Division

One method of dividing polynomials is long division, a process similar to long division of numbers in arithmetic. The terminology is very important in being able to understand our description of the process, so we begin with a simple division problem to illustrate the necessary vocabulary.

$$\frac{11}{2} = 5 + \frac{1}{2}$$

Dividend 11, Divisor 2, Quotient 5, Remainder 1

The process of polynomial long division is illustrated in Example 1.

EXAMPLE 1 Dividing Polynomials Using Long Division

Divide $P(x) = 2x^3 + 5x^2 - 3x + 1$ by $x + 2$.

SOLUTION

We begin by setting up the division:

$$\text{Divisor} \quad x + 2\overline{)2x^3 + 5x^2 - 3x + 1} \quad \text{Dividend}$$

The first term of the quotient is found by dividing the first term of the dividend by the first term of the divisor; in this case,

$$\frac{2x^3}{x} = 2x^2$$

We write this result above the division sign:

$$\begin{array}{r} 2x^2 \\ x + 2\overline{)2x^3 + 5x^2 - 3x + 1} \end{array}$$

Now we multiply $2x^2$ by the divisor, writing the result under the first two terms of the dividend. Then we subtract these two pairs of terms.

$$\begin{array}{rl} 2x^2 & \\ x + 2\overline{)2x^3 + 5x^2 - 3x + 1} & \quad 2x^2(x + 2) = 2x^3 + 4x^2 \\ -(2x^3 + 4x^2) & \quad \text{Subtract.} \\ \hline 0x^3 + x^2 & \end{array}$$

Next, we bring down the next term of the dividend and repeat the above process.

$$\begin{array}{rl} 2x^2 + x - 5 & \\ x + 2\overline{)2x^3 + 5x^2 - 3x + 1} & \\ -(2x^3 + 4x^2) & \\ \hline x^2 - 3x & \quad \frac{x^2}{x} = x;\ x(x + 2) = x^2 + 2x \\ -(x^2 + 2x) & \quad \text{Subtract; bring down last term of dividend.} \\ \hline -5x + 1 & \quad -\frac{5x}{x} = -5;\ -5(x + 2) = -5x - 10 \\ -(-5x - 10) & \quad \text{Subtract.} \\ \hline 11 & \end{array}$$

The quotient is $2x^2 + x - 5$ and the remainder is 11, so

$$\frac{2x^3 + 5x^2 - 3x + 1}{x + 2} = 2x^2 + x - 5 + \frac{11}{x + 2}$$

Check: You can always check division using multiplication.

$$\begin{aligned}(x + 2)\left(2x^2 + x - 5 + \frac{11}{x + 2}\right)& \\ &= (x + 2)(2x^2 + x - 5) + 11 \\ &= 2x^3 + x^2 - 5x + 4x^2 + 2x - 10 + 11 \\ &= 2x^3 + 5x^2 - 3x + 1\end{aligned}$$

MATCHED PROBLEM 1

Divide $P(x) = x^3 - 6x^2 + 8x - 2$ by $x + 3$.

››› CAUTION ›››

When subtracting during the long-division process, make sure that you subtract every term. It may help to include parentheses and think of it as distributing the negative sign.

The procedure illustrated in Example 1 is called the **division algorithm.** The concluding equation of Example 1 (before the check) may be multiplied by the divisor $x + 2$ to give the following form:

$$\underbrace{2x^3 + 5x^2 - 3x + 1}_{\text{Dividend}} = \underbrace{(x + 2)}_{\text{Divisor}} \cdot \underbrace{(2x^2 + x - 5)}_{\text{Quotient}} + \underbrace{11}_{\text{Remainder}}$$

This last equation is an *identity:* it is true for all replacements of x by real or complex numbers including $x = -2$. Theorem 1, which we state without proof, gives the general result of applying the division algorithm.

› THEOREM 1 The Division Algorithm

For any two polynomials $P(x)$ and $D(x)$ with $D(x) \neq 0$, there are unique polynomials $Q(x)$ and $R(x)$ so that

$$P(x) = D(x)\,Q(x) + R(x)$$

and the degree of $R(x)$ is less than the degree of $D(x)$. The polynomial $P(x)$ is called the **dividend,** $D(x)$ is the **divisor,** $Q(x)$ is the **quotient,** and $R(x)$ is the **remainder.** Note that $R(x)$ may be zero.

In essence, Theorem 1 tells us that any two polynomials can be divided (as long as the divisor is not zero), and it also tells us what the result will look like.

When dividing polynomials that have "missing" powers of x, like $x^2 - 2$ (which lacks a first-power term), the missing term must be restored with a zero coefficient for the process to work correctly. This is illustrated in Example 2.

EXAMPLE 2 Dividing Polynomials Using Long Division

Divide $x^4 - 5x^2 + 2x + 1$ by $x^2 - 2$.

SOLUTION

We set up the division, putting in zero coefficients for the missing terms, and proceed as in Example 1.

$$\begin{array}{r l}
x^2 - 3 & \\
x^2 + 0x - 2\overline{)x^4 + 0x^3 - 5x^2 + 2x + 1} & \frac{x^4}{x^2} = x^2;\ x^2(x^2 + 0x - 2) = x^4 + 0x^3 - 2x^2 \\
\underline{-(x^4 + 0x^3 - 2x^2)} & \text{Subtract; bring down next two terms of dividend.} \\
-3x^2 + 2x + 1 & -\frac{3x^2}{x^2} = -3;\ -3(x^2 + 0x - 2) = -3x^2 + 0x + 6 \\
\underline{-(-3x^2 + 0x + 6)} & \text{Subtract.} \\
2x - 5 &
\end{array}$$

Result: $\dfrac{x^4 - 5x^2 + 2x + 1}{x^2 - 2} = x^2 - 3 + \dfrac{2x - 5}{x^2 - 2}$

Note that we had to bring down the next two terms after the first subtraction since there was only one nonzero term remaining, and the divisor has three terms.

MATCHED PROBLEM 2

Divide $3x^5 - x^3 + 5x + 6$ by $x^2 + 3$.

› Dividing Polynomials Using Synthetic Division

Let's take another look at the long division from Example 1. It turns out that it can be carried out by a shortcut called **synthetic division.** The coefficients that represent the essential elements of the long-division process are indicated in color.

$$\begin{array}{r}
2x^2 + 1x - 5 \\
x + 2\overline{)2x^3 + 5x^2 - 3x + 1} \\
\underline{-(2x^3 + 4x^2)} \\
1x^2 - 3x \\
\underline{-(x^2 + 2x)} \\
-5x + 1 \\
\underline{-(-5x - 10)} \\
11
\end{array}$$

The coefficients printed in color can be arranged more conveniently as follows:

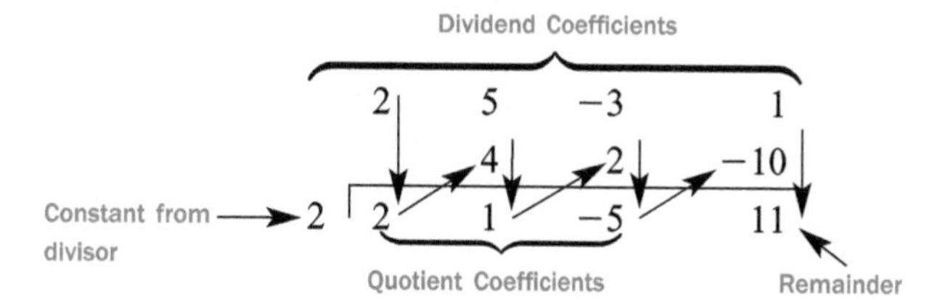

This probably looks confusing at first, but the arrows indicate how the middle and bottom rows can be found without having to do the long division. The first coefficient from the dividend is simply brought down to be the first digit of the quotient. This is then multiplied by the 2 from the divisor, resulting in 4 placed in the middle row. As in long division, we then subtract downward to get 1. This process is then repeated: Multiply 1 by 2 (the constant term from the divisor), to get the next digit in the middle row, then subtract down. When all the rows are filled in, the bottom row represents the coefficients of the quotient and remainder.

There is a way to make the process of synthetic division a bit quicker and less prone to arithmetic mistakes. We will change the $+2$ from the divisor to a -2. This enables us to add down, rather than subtract.

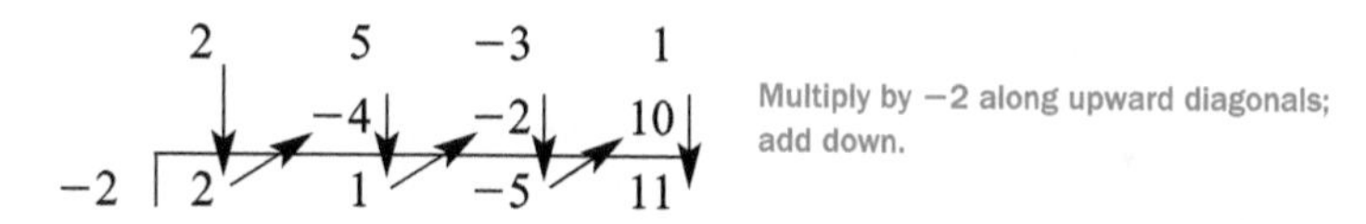

The quotient is $2x^2 + x - 5$, and the remainder is 11.

Clearly, this is much simpler than long division. But there is a catch: Synthetic division only works when the divisor is of the form $x - r$. If the divisor has any other form, long division is the only choice.

We will now summarize the steps in performing synthetic division.

KEY STEPS IN THE SYNTHETIC DIVISION PROCESS

To divide the polynomial $P(x)$ by $x - r$:

1. Write the coefficients of $P(x)$ in order of descending powers of x. Write 0 as the coefficient for any missing powers. Draw a horizontal line below, leaving space for the middle row. Draw a short vertical line downward from the left edge of the horizontal line, and write r to the left of it.
2. Bring down the first coefficient from the dividend and write it in the third row, below the horizontal line. Then multiply that coefficient by r, and put the result in the middle row below the second coefficient of the dividend. Add the two numbers in this second column, writing the result in the bottom row.
3. Repeat this "multiply, then add down" process until all columns have been filled in.
4. The last number to the right in the third row of numbers is the remainder. The other numbers in the third row are the coefficients of the quotient, which is of degree 1 less than $P(x)$.

EXAMPLE 3 Synthetic Division

Use synthetic division to divide $P(x) = 4x^5 - 30x^3 - 50x - 2$ by $x + 3$. Find the quotient and remainder. Write the conclusion in the form $P(x) = (x - r)Q(x) + R$.

SOLUTION

Because $x + 3 = x - (-3)$, we have $r = -3$, and

	4	0	−30	0	−50	−2
		−12	36	−18	54	−12
−3	4	−12	6	−18	4	−14

The quotient is $4x^4 - 12x^3 + 6x^2 - 18x + 4$ with a remainder of -14. This means that $4x^5 - 30x^3 - 50x - 2 = (x + 3)(4x^4 - 12x^3 + 6x^2 - 18x + 4) - 14$.

MATCHED PROBLEM 3

Repeat Example 3 with $P(x) = 3x^4 - 11x^3 - 18x + 8$ and divisor $x - 4$.

››› CAUTION ›››

1. Remember that synthetic division only works if the divisor is linear with leading coefficient 1.
2. Don't forget to write the divisor in the form $x - r$ before setting up the division. In Example 3, the divisor $x + 3$ had to be written as $x - (-3)$ to see that $r = -3$.

A calculator is a convenient tool for performing synthetic division. Any type of calculator can be used, although one with a memory will save some keystrokes. The flowchart in Figure 1 shows the repetitive steps in the synthetic division process, and Figure 2 illustrates the results of applying this process to Example 3 on a graphing calculator.

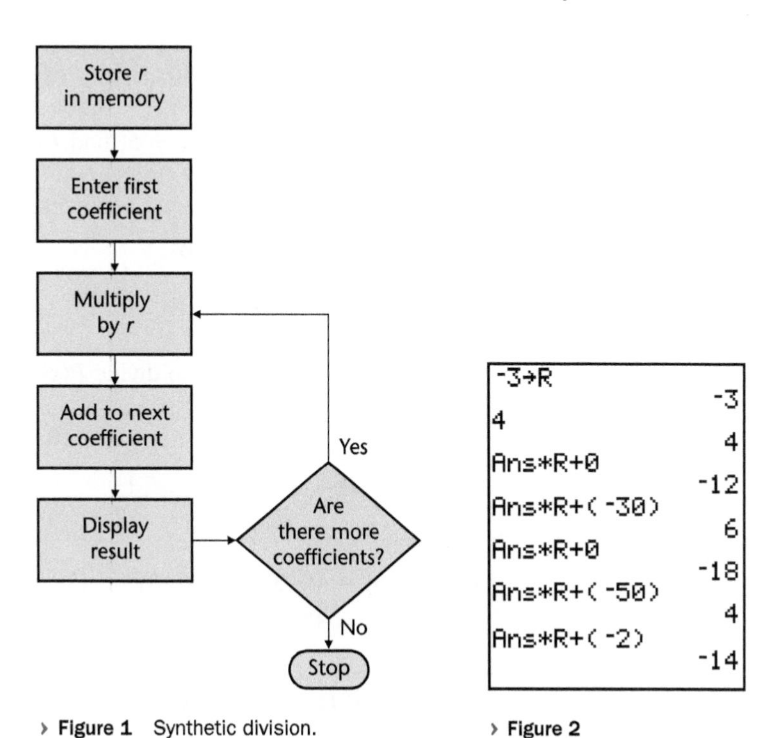

› **Figure 1** Synthetic division.

› **Figure 2**

› The Remainder and Factor Theorems

››› EXPLORE-DISCUSS 1

Let $P(x) = x^3 - 3x^2 - 2x + 8$.

(A) Find $P(-2)$, $P(1)$, and $P(3)$.

(B) Use synthetic division to find the remainder when $P(x)$ is divided by

$$x + 2, x - 1, \text{ and } x - 3.$$

What conclusion does a comparison of the results in parts A and B suggest?

Explore-Discuss 1 suggests that when a polynomial $P(x)$ is divided by $x - r$, the remainder is equal to $P(r)$, the value of the polynomial $P(x)$ at $x = r$. In Problem 81 in Exercises 3-2, you will be asked to complete a proof of this fact, which we call the *remainder theorem*.

› THEOREM 2 The Remainder Theorem

If R is the remainder after dividing the polynomial $P(x)$ by $x - r$, then

$$P(r) = R$$

EXAMPLE 4 Two Methods for Evaluating Polynomials

If $P(x) = 4x^4 + 10x^3 + 19x + 5$, find $P(-3)$ two different ways:

(A) Use the remainder theorem and synthetic division.
(B) Evaluate $P(-3)$ directly.

SOLUTIONS

(A) Use synthetic division to divide $P(x)$ by $x - (-3)$.

$$\begin{array}{r|rrrrr} & 4 & 10 & 0 & 19 & 5 \\ & & -12 & 6 & -18 & -3 \\ \hline -3 & 4 & -2 & 6 & 1 & 2 = R = P(-3) \end{array}$$

(B) $P(-3) = 4(-3)^4 + 10(-3)^3 + 19(-3) + 5$
$= 324 - 270 - 57 + 5 = 2$

MATCHED PROBLEM 4

Repeat Example 4 for $P(x) = 3x^4 - 16x^2 - 3x + 7$ and $x = -2$.

You might think the remainder theorem is not a very effective tool for evaluating polynomials. But let's consider the number of operations performed in parts A and B of Example 4. Synthetic division requires only four multiplications and four additions to find $P(-3)$, whereas the direct evaluation requires ten multiplications and four additions. [Note that evaluating $4(-3)^4$ actually requires five multiplications.] The difference becomes even larger as the degree of the polynomial increases. Computer programs that involve numerous polynomial evaluations often use synthetic division because of its efficiency. We will find synthetic division and the remainder theorem to be useful tools later in this chapter.

One useful consequence of the remainder theorem is that if synthetic division of a polynomial $P(x)$ by $x - r$ results in a zero remainder, then r is actually a zero of $P(x)$. This result can be applied to factoring polynomials.

Suppose that $x - r$ is a factor of a polynomial $P(x)$. This means that $P(x)$ can be written as $P(x) = (x - r)\,Q(x)$, where $Q(x)$ is some other polynomial with degree one less than $P(x)$. If we are trying to find the zeros of $P(x)$, we set up the equation

$$P(x) = 0 \qquad \text{or} \qquad (x - r)Q(x) = 0$$

The zero product property tells us that $x = r$ is a zero of $P(x)$. Conclusion: If $x - r$ is a factor of $P(x)$, then $x = r$ is a zero.

The remainder theorem can be used to show that the reverse is also true. If $x = r$ is a zero, then division by $x - r$ results in a remainder of zero. The division algorithm then gives us

$$P(x) = (x - r)Q(x) + 0$$

In other words, $x - r$ is a factor of $P(x)$. We have proved the *factor theorem.*

> **THEOREM 3 The Factor Theorem**
>
> If r is a zero of the polynomial $P(x)$, then $x - r$ is a factor of $P(x)$. Conversely, if $x - r$ is a factor of $P(x)$, then r is a zero of $P(x)$.

The factor theorem shows that there is a perfect correlation between the zeros of a polynomial and its linear factors. Find all the linear factors, and you know all the zeros. Find all the zeros, and you know all the linear factors.

EXAMPLE 5 Factors of Polynomials

Use the factor theorem to show that $x + 1$ is a factor of $P(x) = x^{25} + 1$ but is not a factor of $Q(x) = x^{25} - 1$.

SOLUTION

Because

$$P(-1) = (-1)^{25} + 1 = -1 + 1 = 0$$

$x - (-1) = x + 1$ is a factor of $x^{25} + 1$. On the other hand,

$$Q(-1) = (-1)^{25} - 1 = -1 - 1 = -2$$

so -1 is not a zero, and $x + 1$ is not a factor of $x^{25} - 1$.

MATCHED PROBLEM 5

Use the factor theorem to show that $x - i$ is a factor of $P(x) = x^8 - 1$ but is not a factor of $Q(x) = x^8 + 1$.

One consequence of the factor theorem is Theorem 4, which will be proved in Problem 82 in Exercises 3-2.

> **THEOREM 4 Zeros of Polynomials**
>
> A polynomial of degree n has at most n zeros.

Theorem 4 implies that the graph of a polynomial of degree n with real coefficients has at most n real zeros (Property 3 of Theorem 1 in the last section). The polynomial

$$H(x) = x^6 - 7x^4 + 12x^2 - x - 2$$

for example, has degree 6 and the maximum number, namely six, of real zeros [see Fig. 5(f) on page 279]. Of course polynomials of degree 6 may have fewer than six real zeros. In fact, $p(x) = x^6 + 1$ has no real zeros. However, it can be shown that the polynomial $p(x) = x^6 + 1$ has exactly six complex zeros.

The remainder and factor theorems can work together to help find the zeros of a polynomial. Example 6 illustrates this process, which we will use repeatedly in the section after next.

EXAMPLE 6

Finding the Zeros of a Polynomial

(A) Use synthetic division to show that $x = 3$ is a zero of $P(x) = x^3 - 8x^2 + 9x + 18$.

(B) Use the result of part A to find any other zeros.

SOLUTIONS

(A) We divide by $x - 3$ using synthetic division.

$$\begin{array}{r|rrrr} & 1 & -8 & 9 & 18 \\ & & 3 & -15 & -18 \\ \hline 3 & 1 & -5 & -6 & 0 \end{array}$$

The zero remainder confirms that $x = 3$ is a zero.

(B) The division in part A tells us that

$$\frac{x^3 - 8x^2 + 9x + 18}{x - 3} = x^2 - 5x - 6$$

or, applying the division algorithm,

$$P(x) = x^3 - 8x^2 + 9x + 18 = (x - 3)(x^2 - 5x - 6)$$

To find the remaining zeros, we need to solve $P(x) = 0$.

$$\begin{aligned} P(x) = (x - 3)(x^2 - 5x - 6) &= 0 \\ x - 3 = 0 \quad \text{or} \quad x^2 - 5x - 6 &= 0 \\ x = 3 \quad\quad (x - 6)(x + 1) &= 0 \\ x - 6 = 0 \quad \text{or} \quad x + 1 &= 0 \\ x = 6 \quad\quad x &= -1 \end{aligned}$$

The remaining zeros are $x = 6$ and $x = -1$.

MATCHED PROBLEM 6

(A) Use synthetic division to show that $x = -2$ is a zero of $P(x) = x^3 + 2x^2 - 9x - 18$.

(B) Use the result of part A to find any other zeros.

ANSWERS TO MATCHED PROBLEMS

1. $x^2 - 9x + 35 - \frac{107}{x + 3}$ **2.** $3x^3 - 10x + \frac{35x + 6}{x^2 + 3}$ **3.** $3x^4 - 11x^3 - 18x + 8 = (x - 4)(3x^3 + x^2 + 4x - 2)$ **4.** $P(-2) = -3$ for both parts, as it should **5.** $P(i) = 0$, so $x - i$ is a factor of $x^8 - 1$; $Q(i) - 2$, so $x - i$ is not a factor of $x^8 + 1$
6. (B) $x = -3, 3$

3-2 Exercises

1. Write this division problem in the form of the division algorithm, then label the dividend, divisor, quotient, and remainder.

$$\frac{x^2 - 5x + 12}{x - 3} = x - 2 + \frac{6}{x - 3}$$

2. Describe the type of division problem for which synthetic division can be applied.

3. What is wrong with the following setup for dividing $x^4 + 3x^2 - 8x + 1$ by $x - 3$ using synthetic division?

$$\begin{array}{r|rrrr} & 1 & 3 & -8 & 1 \\ 3 & & & & \\ \hline \end{array}$$

4. What is wrong with the following setup for dividing $2x^3 + 5x^2 - x - 3$ by $x + 6$?

$$\begin{array}{r|rrrr} & 2 & 5 & -1 & -3 \\ 6 & & & & \\ \hline \end{array}$$

5. Describe what the remainder theorem says in your own words.

6. What is the relationship between the factors of a polynomial and its zeros?

In Problems 7–14, divide, using algebraic long division.

7. $(4m^2 - 1) \div (2m - 1)$ **8.** $(y^2 - 9) \div (y + 3)$

9. $(6 - 6x + 8x^2) \div (2x + 1)$

10. $(11x - 2 + 12x^2) \div (3x + 2)$

11. $(x^3 - 1) \div (x - 1)$ **12.** $(a^3 + 27) \div (a + 3)$

13. $(3y - y^2 + 2y^3 - 1) \div (y + 2)$

14. $(3 + x^3 - x) \div (x - 3)$

In Problems 15–20, divide using synthetic division.

15. $(x^2 + 3x - 7) \div (x - 2)$

16. $(x^2 + 3x - 3) \div (x - 3)$

17. $(4x^2 + 10x - 9) \div (x + 3)$

18. $(2x^2 + 7x - 5) \div (x + 4)$

19. $(2x^3 - 3x + 1) \div (x - 2)$

20. $(x^3 + 2x^2 - 3x - 4) \div (x + 2)$

In Problems 21–26, evaluate the polynomial two ways: by substituting in the given value of x, and by using synthetic division.

21. Find $P(-2)$ for $P(x) = 3x^2 - x - 10$.

22. Find $P(-3)$ for $P(x) = 4x^2 + 10x - 8$.

23. Find $P(2)$ for $P(x) = 2x^3 - 5x^2 + 7x - 7$.

24. Find $P(5)$ for $P(x) = 2x^3 - 12x^2 - x + 30$.

25. Find $P(-4)$ for $P(x) = x^4 - 10x^2 + 25x - 2$.

26. Find $P(-7)$ for $P(x) = x^4 + 5x^3 - 13x^2 - 30$.

In Problems 27–30, determine whether the second polynomial is a factor of the first polynomial without dividing or using synthetic division. [Hint: Evaluate directly and use the factor theorem.]

27. $x^{18} - 1; x - 1$

28. $x^{18} - 1; x + 1$

29. $3x^3 - 7x^2 - 8x + 2; x + 1$

30. $3x^4 - 2x^3 + 5x - 6; x - 1$

In Problems 31–38, divide using long division.

31. $(-6x^3 + 5x^2 - 5x + 12) \div (-3x + 4)$

32. $(4x^3 - 7x^2 - 14x - 3) \div (4x + 1)$

33. $(2x^3 - 5x^2 - 8x + 1) \div (2x - 1)$

34. $(3x^3 + 8x^2 + 16x - 5) \div (3x + 2)$

35. $(x^3 - 4x^2 - 7x + 1) \div (x^2 - 2)$

36. $(x^4 - x^2 - 3) \div (x^2 + 4)$

37. $(3x^4 - 2x^2 - 3x + 5) \div (x^2 + x + 2)$

38. $(-2x^4 + x^3 + 5x + 2) \div (x^2 + 2x + 3)$

In Problems 39–54, divide, using synthetic division. As coefficients get more involved, a calculator should prove helpful. Do not round off—all quantities are exact.

39. $(3x^4 - x - 4) \div (x + 1)$

40. $(5x^4 - 2x^2 - 3) \div (x - 1)$

41. $(x^5 + 1) \div (x + 1)$

42. $(x^4 - 16) \div (x - 2)$

43. $(3x^4 + 2x^3 - 4x - 1) \div (x + 3)$

44. $(x^4 - 3x^3 - 5x^2 + 6x - 3) \div (x - 4)$

45. $(2x^6 - 13x^5 + 75x^3 + 2x^2 - 50) \div (x - 5)$

46. $(4x^6 + 20x^5 - 24x^4 - 3x^2 - 13x + 30) \div (x + 6)$

47. $(4x^4 + 2x^3 - 6x^2 - 5x + 1) \div (x + \frac{1}{2})$

48. $(2x^3 - 5x^2 + 6x + 3) \div (x - \frac{1}{2})$

49. $(4x^3 + 4x^2 - 7x - 6) \div (x + \frac{3}{2})$

50. $(3x^3 - x^2 + x + 2) \div (x + \frac{2}{3})$

51. $(3x^4 - 2x^3 + 2x^2 - 3x + 1) \div (x - 0.4)$

52. $(4x^4 - 3x^3 + 5x^2 + 7x - 6) \div (x - 0.7)$

53. $(3x^5 + 2x^4 + 5x^3 - 7x - 3) \div (x + 0.8)$

54. $(7x^5 - x^4 + 3x^3 - 2x^2 - 5) \div (x + 0.9)$

In Problems 55–60, evaluate the polynomial two ways: by substituting in the given value of x, and by using synthetic division.

55. Find $P(\frac{5}{2})$ for $P(x) = 4x^3 - 12x^2 - 7x + 10$.

56. Find $P(\frac{1}{3})$ for $P(x) = 3x^3 - 13x^2 + 10x + 3$.

57. Find $P(\frac{1}{2})$ for $P(x) = 3x^3 + 5x^2 - x + 2$.

58. Find $P(\frac{1}{2})$ for $P(x) = -5x^3 - 2x^2 + 3x + 4$.

59. Find $P(2i)$ for $P(x) = x^3 + 1$.

60. Find $P(-i)$ for $P(x) = 2x^3 - 8$.

In Problems 61–68, use synthetic division to show that the given x value is a zero of the polynomial. Then find all other zeros.

61. $P(x) = x^3 - 7x + 6;\quad x = 1$

62. $P(x) = x^3 - 2x^2 - 5x + 6;\quad x = 1$

63. $P(x) = 3x^3 - 8x^2 - 5x + 6;\quad x = 3$

64. $P(x) = 2x^3 - 8x^2 + 2x + 12;\quad x = 3$

65. $P(x) = x^3 - 5x^2 + 4x - 20;\quad x = 5$

66. $P(x) = x^3 - 4x^2 + 9x - 36;\quad x = 4$

67. $P(x) = x^3 - 2x^2 - 3x + 10;\quad x = -2$

68. $P(x) = x^3 - x^2 + 8x + 10;\quad x = -1$

In Problems 69 and 70, divide, using synthetic division. Do not use a calculator.

69. $(x^3 - 3x^2 + x - 3) \div (x - i)$

70. $(x^3 - 2x^2 + x - 2) \div (x + i)$

71. Let $P(x) = x^2 + 2ix - 10$. Find
(A) $P(2 - i)$ (B) $P(5 - 5i)$
(C) $P(3 - i)$ (D) $P(-3 - i)$

72. Let $P(x) = x^2 - 4ix - 13$. Find
(A) $P(5 + 6i)$ (B) $P(1 + 2i)$
(C) $P(3 + 2i)$ (D) $P(-3 + 2i)$

73. Use synthetic division to find the value of k so that $x = 2$ is a zero of $P(x) = x^3 - 3x^2 + 4x + k$.

74. Use synthetic division to find the value of k so that $x = -2$ is a zero of $P(x) = 2x^3 + 5x^2 - x + k$.

75. Use synthetic division to find the value of k so that $x = -3$ is a zero of $P(x) = -4x^3 - 6x^2 + kx - 6$.

76. Use synthetic division to find the value of k so that $x = 4$ is a zero of $P(x) = 3x^3 - 14x^2 + kx + 64$.

77. (A) Divide $P(x) = a_2x^2 + a_1x + a_0$ by $x - r$, using both synthetic division and the long-division process, and compare the coefficients of the quotient and the remainder produced by each method.
(B) Expand the expression representing the remainder. What do you observe?

78. Repeat Problem 77 for

$$P(x) = a_3x^3 + a_2x^2 + a_1x + a_0$$

79. Polynomials also can be evaluated using a "nested factoring" scheme. For example, the polynomial $P(x) = 2x^4 - 3x^3 + 2x^2 - 5x + 7$ can be written in a nested factored form as follows:

$$\begin{aligned} P(x) &= 2x^4 - 3x^3 + 2x^2 - 5x + 7 \\ &= (2x - 3)x^3 + 2x^2 - 5x + 7 \\ &= [(2x - 3)x + 2]x^2 - 5x + 7 \\ &= \{[(2x - 3)x + 2]x - 5\}x + 7 \end{aligned}$$

Use the nested factored form to find $P(-2)$ and $P(1.7)$. [*Hint:* To evaluate $P(-2)$, store -2 in your calculator's memory and proceed from left to right recalling -2 as needed.]

80. Let $P(x) = 3x^4 + x^3 - 10x^2 + 5x - 2$. Find $P(-2)$ and $P(1.3)$ using the nested factoring scheme presented in Problem 79.

81. Prove the remainder theorem:

(A) Write the result of the division algorithm if a polynomial $P(x)$ is divided by $x - r$.

(B) Evaluate both sides of the result for $x = r$. What can you conclude?

82. In this problem we will prove Theorem 4. Write the reason that justifies each step. Let $P(x)$ be a polynomial of degree n, and suppose that P has n distinct zeros $r_1, r_2, \ldots, r_n$.

Step 1: We can write $P(x)$ as $P(x) = (x - r_1)Q_1(x)$, where the degree of $Q_1(x)$ is $n - 1$.

Step 2: Since r_2 is a zero of P, $Q_1(r_2) = 0$.

Step 3: $Q_1(x) = (x - r_2)Q_2(x)$, where the degree of $Q_2(x)$ is $n - 2$.

Step 4: We can now write $P(x)$ as $P(x) = (x - r_1)(x - r_2)Q_2(x)$

Step 5: Continuing, we will get $P(x) = (x - r_1)(x - r_2) \cdots (x - r_n)Q_n(x)$, where the degree of $Q_n(x)$ is zero.

Step 6: $Q_n(x)$ has no zeros, so the only zeros of P are $r_1, r_2, \ldots, r_n$.

83. If you are given one zero for a cubic polynomial, is it *always* possible to find two more real zeros? Explain.

84. If you are given one zero for a cubic polynomial, is it *always* possible to find two more complex zeros? Explain.

3-3 Real Zeros and Polynomial Inequalities

- Finding Upper and Lower Bounds for Real Zeros
- Using the Bisection Method to Locate Zeros
- Approximating Real Zeros at Turning Points
- Solving Polynomial Inequalities
- Mathematical Modeling

We have seen that the real zeros of a polynomial $P(x)$ with real coefficients are just the x intercepts of the graph of $P(x)$. So an obvious strategy for finding the real zeros consists of two steps:

1. Graph $P(x)$ on a graphing calculator.

2. Use the ZERO command to approximate each x intercept.

In this section, we develop two important tools for carrying out this strategy: the *upper and lower bound theorem,* which determines appropriate window variables for step 1, and a simple approximation technique called the *bisection method* that underpins step 2. We also investigate some potential difficulties when the strategy is applied to polynomials that have a zero at a turning point, and we apply the strategy to solve polynomial inequalities.

In this section we will restrict our attention to the real zeros of polynomials with real coefficients.

Finding Upper and Lower Bounds for Real Zeros

In this section, we will make use of the fact that a polynomial of degree n has at most n zeros. When relying on graphs to find the zeros of a function, we always have to wonder whether the viewing window is showing all of the zeros, or if there may be more that we can't see. When the function is a polynomial, this may not be an issue. For example, if the calculator's viewing window is showing three x intercepts of a cubic polynomial, then we know for a fact that the zero command will find all of the zeros.

EXAMPLE 1 Approximating Real Zeros

Approximate the zeros of $P(x) = x^3 - 6x^2 + 9x - 3$ to three decimal places.

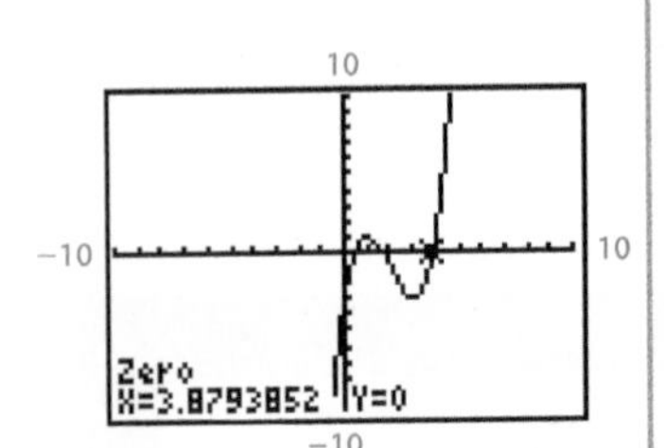

Figure 1 A zero of $P(x) = x^3 - 6x^2 + 9x - 3$.

SOLUTION

A graph of $P(x)$ in the standard viewing window shows three x intercepts (Fig. 1). We can find each of them by applying the ZERO command: rounded to three decimal places they are 0.468, 1.653, and 3.879. Because a polynomial of degree 3 can have at most three zeros, we can be sure that we have found all of the zeros of $P(x)$.

MATCHED PROBLEM 1

Approximate the zeros of $P(x) = 21 + 10x - 3x^2 - x^3$ to three decimal places.

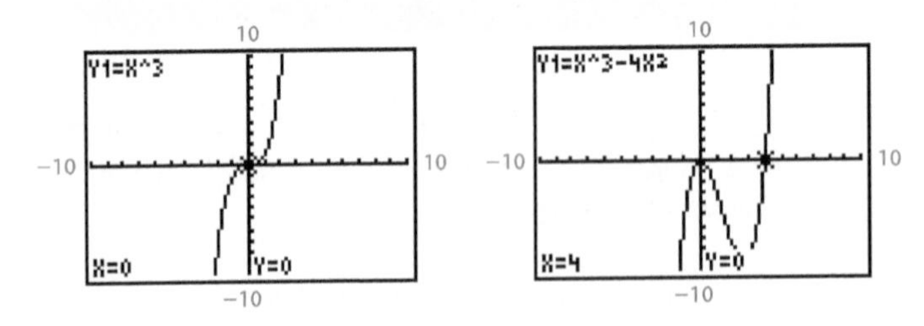

Figure 2 Cubic polynomials having one or two zeros.

Unfortunately, there is a problem with this approach. A polynomial of degree 3 has at most three real zeros, but it may have exactly one or exactly two (Fig. 2). If we can't find a viewing window that displays more than one zero for a particular cubic polynomial, how long do we have to search before we can decide whether the polynomial has one, two, or three real zeros?

››› EXPLORE-DISCUSS 1

For $P(x) = x^3 - 2x^2 + 2x + 3$,

(A) Use synthetic division to divide $P(x)$ by $x - 3$; note the sign of all coefficients in the quotient row.

(B) Evaluate $P(x)$ for five different values of x greater than 3. What do all of the results have in common?

(C) Write the result of the division in the form $P(x) = (x - 3)Q(x) + R$. Explain why the right side of the equation will always be positive for any x values greater than 3.

Explore-Discuss 1 hints at a result that will enable us to know for sure when a given viewing window contains all of the x intercepts for a polynomial. The result is known as the *upper and lower bound theorem*. This theorem indicates how to find two numbers, a **lower bound** that is less than or equal to all real zeros of the polynomial, and an **upper bound** that is greater than or equal to all real zeros of the polynomial. All of the real zeros are guaranteed to lie between the lower bound and the upper bound. So if we graph the polynomial with these two numbers as our least and greatest x values, we'll know for sure that the graph will display all of the real zeros.

› THEOREM 1 Upper and Lower Bound Theorem

Let $P(x)$ be a polynomial of degree $n > 0$ with real coefficients, $a_n > 0$:

1. Upper bound: A number $r > 0$ is an upper bound for the real zeros of $P(x)$ if, when $P(x)$ is divided by $x - r$ using synthetic division, all numbers in the quotient row, including the remainder, are nonnegative.
2. Lower bound: A number $r < 0$ is a lower bound for the real zeros of $P(x)$ if, when $P(x)$ is divided by $x - r$ using synthetic division, all numbers in the quotient row, including the remainder, alternate in sign.

[*Note:* In the lower-bound test, if 0 appears in one or more places in the quotient row, including the remainder, the sign in front of it can be considered either positive or negative, but not both. For example, the numbers 1, 0, 1 can be considered to alternate in sign, whereas 1, 0, -1 cannot.]

Note: The upper and lower bound theorem works only if the leading coefficient of a polynomial is positive. See Problems 71 and 72 in Exercises 3-3 for a look at what to do if the leading coefficient is negative, and Problems 85 and 86 for a sketch of a proof of Theorem 1.

EXAMPLE 2 Bounding Real Zeros

Let $P(x) = x^4 - 2x^3 - 10x^2 + 40x - 90$. Use the upper and lower bound theorem to find the smallest positive integer and the largest negative integer that are upper and lower bounds, respectively, for the real zeros of $P(x)$.

SOLUTION

The idea is to perform synthetic division repeatedly until we find the patterns from Theorem 1. We begin with $r = 1$.

$$\begin{array}{r|rrrrr} & 1 & -2 & -10 & 40 & -90 \\ & & 1 & -1 & -11 & 29 \\ \hline 1 & 1 & -1 & -11 & 29 & -61 \end{array}$$

The resulting coefficients are not all positive, so $x = 1$ is not an upper bound for the zeros of P. We should next try $r = 2, 3, \ldots$ until we find all positive coefficients. We should then repeat the process using $r = -1, -2, -3, \ldots$ until the quotient row alternates in sign. But it quickly becomes apparent that it will be cumbersome to keep doing synthetic divisions individually, so instead we will make a *synthetic division table*. We will write only the result of each division, doing the arithmetic that usually generates the middle row mentally.

		1	−2	−10	40	−90	
	1	1	−1	−11	29	−61	
	2	1	0	−10	20	−50	
	3	1	1	−7	19	−33	
	4	1	2	−2	32	38	
UB	5	1	3	5	65	235	← This quotient row is nonnegative, so 5 is an upper bound (UB).
	−1	1	−3	−7	47	−137	
	−2	1	−4	−2	44	−178	
	−3	1	−5	5	25	−165	
	−4	1	−6	14	−16	−26	
LB	−5	1	−7	25	−85	335	← This quotient row alternates in sign, so −5 is a lower bound (LB).

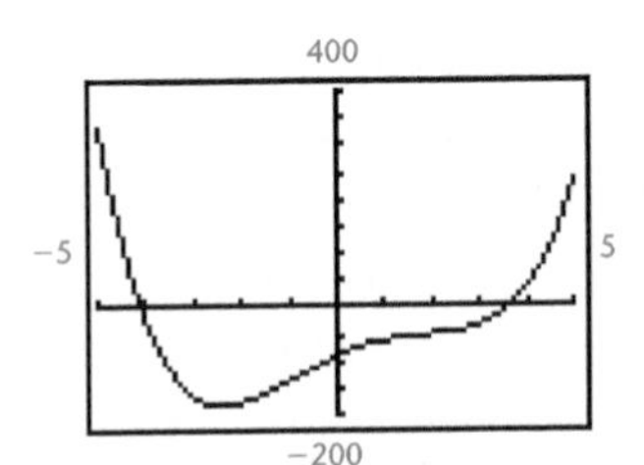

› **Figure 3** $P(x) = x^4 - 2x^3 - 10x^2 + 40x - 90$.

The graph of $P(x) = x^4 - 2x^3 - 10x^2 + 40x - 90$ for $-5 \le x \le 5$ is shown in Figure 3. Since Theorem 1 guarantees that all the real zeros of $P(x)$ are between -5 and 5, we can be certain that the graph does not change direction and cross the x axis somewhere outside the viewing window in Figure 3.

MATCHED PROBLEM 2

Let $P(x) = x^4 - 5x^3 - x^2 + 40x - 70$. Use the upper and lower bound theorem to find the smallest positive integer and the largest negative integer that are upper and lower bounds, respectively, for the real zeros of $P(x)$.

```
{1,-6,9,-3}→L1
        {1 -6 9 -3}
prgmSYNDIV
R=?0
     {1 -6 9 -3}
R=?1
      {1 -5 4 1}
R=?2
     {1 -4 1 -1}
R=?3
     {1 -3 0 -3}
R=?4
      {1 -2 1 1}
R=?5
     {1 -1 4 17}
R=?6
      {1 0 9 51}
R=?-1
   {1 -7 16 -19}
```

› **Figure 4** Synthetic division on a graphing calculator.

Theorem 1 requires performing synthetic division repeatedly until the desired pattern occurs in the quotient row. This is not terribly difficult, but it can be tedious. SYNDIV* is a program for some TI-model graphing calculators that makes this process routine. Figure 4 shows the results of dividing the polynomial $P(x) = x^3 - 6x^2 + 9x - 3$ from Example 1 by $x - r$ for integer values of r from -1 through 6 using SYNDIV. (When $r = 2$, for example, the quotient is $x^2 - 4x + 1$ and the remainder is -1.)

From Figure 4 we see that the positive number 6 is an upper bound for the real zeros of $P(x)$ because all numbers in the quotient row, including the remainder, are nonnegative. Furthermore, the negative number -1 is a lower bound for the real zeros of $P(x)$ because all numbers in the quotient row, including the remainder, alternate in sign. We can then conclude that all zeros of $P(x)$ are between -1 and 6.

One of the biggest issues in using a graphing calculator is determining the correct viewing window. The upper and lower bound theorem provides some very helpful guidance in dealing with this issue for polynomial functions. Example 3 illustrates how the upper and lower bound theorem and the ZERO command on a graphing calculator work together to analyze the graph of a polynomial.

EXAMPLE 3 Approximating Real Zeros

Let $P(x) = x^3 - 30x^2 + 275x - 720$.

(A) Use the upper and lower bound theorem to find the smallest positive integer multiple of 10 and the largest negative integer multiple of 10 that are upper and lower bounds, respectively, for the real zeros of $P(x)$.

(B) Approximate all real zeros of $P(x)$ to two decimal places.

SOLUTIONS

(A) We construct a synthetic division table to search for bounds for the zeros of $P(x)$. The size of the coefficients in $P(x)$ suggests that we can speed up this search by choosing larger increments between test values.

		1	−30	275	−720
	10	1	−20	75	30
	20	1	−10	75	780
UB	30	1	0	275	7,530
LB	−10	1	−40	675	−7,470

Because all real zeros of $P(x) = x^3 - 30x^2 + 275x - 720$ must be between -10 and 30, we should choose Xmin $= -10$ and Xmax $= 30$.

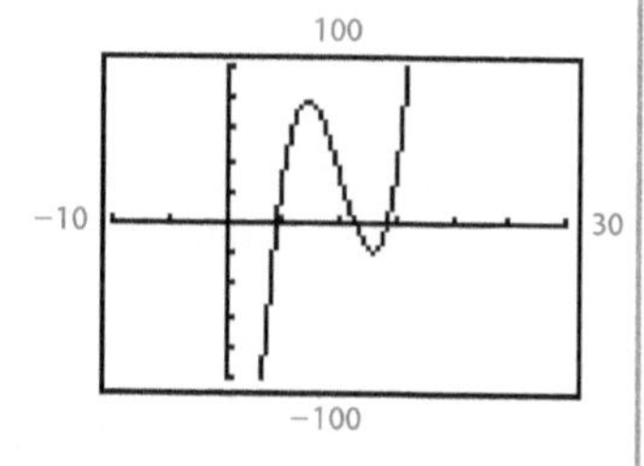

› **Figure 5** $P(x) = x^3 - 30x^2 + 275x - 720$.

(B) Graphing $P(x)$ for $-10 \le x \le 30$ (Fig. 5) shows that $P(x)$ has three zeros. The approximate values of these zeros (details omitted) are 4.48, 11.28, and 14.23.

*Programs for TI-83, TI-84, and TI-86 graphing calculators can be found at the website for this book (see Preface).

MATCHED PROBLEM 3

Let $P(x) = x^3 - 25x^2 + 170x - 170$.

(A) Use the upper and lower bound theorem to find the smallest positive integer multiple of 10 and the largest negative integer multiple of 10 that are upper and lower bounds, respectively, for the real zeros of $P(x)$.

(B) Approximate all real zeros of $P(x)$ to two decimal places.

››› CAUTION ›››

The upper and lower bound theorem does not tell us the exact location of any zeros, nor how many to expect. It simply gives a range of values that must include all of the real zeros.

› Using the Bisection Method to Locate Zeros

We begin this topic with a review of the location theorem from Section 2-7. Since it is relevant to two topics in this section, we will restate it as Theorem 2.

› THEOREM 2 The Location Theorem

If $f(x)$ is a continuous function on some interval containing a and b, and $f(a)$ and $f(b)$ have opposite signs, then there must be a zero of f somewhere between $x = a$ and $x = b$.

The graph of every polynomial is continuous for all x, so the location theorem can be applied. Consider the polynomial $P(x) = x^5 + 3x - 1$, shown in Figure 6. Note that P is negative at $x = 0$ $[P(0) = -1]$ and positive at $x = 1$ $[P(1) = 3]$. According to the location theorem, the graph of P has to cross the x axis at least once between $x = 0$ and $x = 1$.

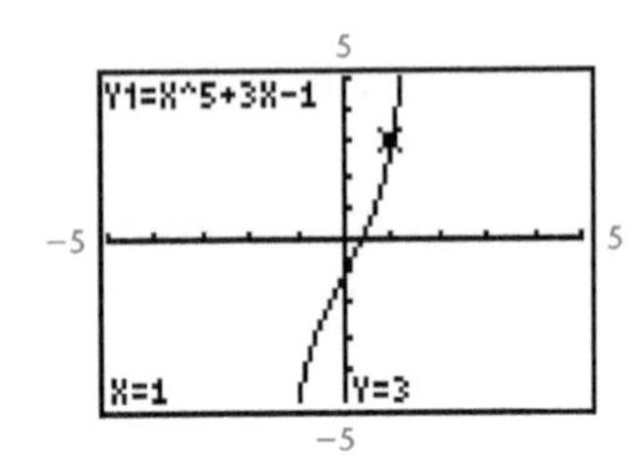

› **Figure 6** $P(x) = x^5 + 3x - 1$.

On the other hand, the conclusion of the location theorem doesn't tell us that there is only one zero between a and b; for example, if $g(x) = x^3 + x^2 - 2x - 1$, then $g(-2)$ and $g(2)$ have opposite signs, and there are actually three real zeros between $x = -2$ and $x = 2$ [Fig. 7(a)].

What if we change the direction of the implication in Theorem 2? If $f(x)$ has a zero between $x = a$ and $x = b$, must $f(a)$ and $f(b)$ have opposite signs? (This is known as the *converse* of Theorem 2.) In fact, this is not true: $h(x) = x^2$ has a zero at $x = 0$, but does not change sign [Fig. 7(b)].

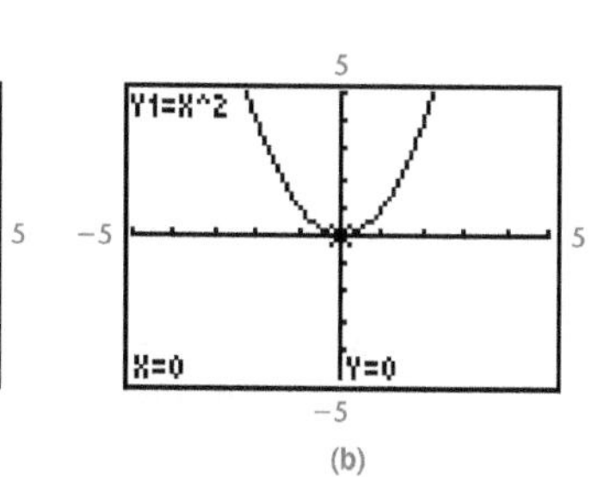

(a) (b)

› **Figure 7** Polynomials may or may not change sign at a zero.

››› EXPLORE-DISCUSS 2

When synthetic division is used to divide a polynomial $P(x)$ by $x - 3$ the remainder is -33. When the same polynomial is divided by $x - 4$ the remainder is 38. Must $P(x)$ have a zero between 3 and 4? Explain.

Explore-Discuss 3 will provide an introduction to a repeated systematic application of the location theorem called the *bisection method*. This method forms the basis for the method that many graphing calculators use to find zeros.

››› EXPLORE-DISCUSS 3

Let $P(x) = x^5 + 3x - 1$. Because $P(0)$ is negative and $P(1)$ is positive, the location theorem implies that $P(x)$ must have at least one zero in the interval $(0, 1)$.

(A) Is $P(0.5)$ positive or negative? Does the location theorem guarantee a zero of $P(x)$ in the interval $(0, 0.5)$ or in $(0.5, 1)$?

(B) Let m be the midpoint of the interval from part A that contains a zero of $P(x)$. Is $P(m)$ positive or negative? What does this tell you about the location of the zero?

(C) Explain how this process could be used repeatedly to approximate a zero to any desired accuracy.

(D) Check your answers to parts A and B by using the ZERO command on a graphing calculator.

The **bisection method** is a systematic application of the procedure suggested in Explore-Discuss 3: Let $P(x)$ be a polynomial with real coefficients. If $P(x)$ has opposite signs at the endpoints of an interval (a, b), then by the location theorem $P(x)$ has a zero in (a, b). Bisect this interval (that is, find the midpoint $m = \frac{a+b}{2}$), and find $P(m)$. If $P(m) = 0$, you've found the zero. If not, $P(m)$ has to be either positive or negative, and, in turn, it has to be opposite in sign with either $P(a)$ or $P(b)$. The location theorem then implies that there is a zero in either (a, m) or (m, b)—whichever has opposite signs at the endpoints.

We repeat this bisection procedure (producing a set of intervals, each contained in and half the length of the previous interval, and each containing the zero) until we either find the zero exactly, or the two endpoints agree to the desired accuracy. Example 4 illustrates the procedure, and clarifies when the procedure is finished.

EXAMPLE 4 The Bisection Method

The polynomial $P(x) = x^4 - 2x^3 - 10x^2 + 40x - 90$ from Example 2 has a zero between 3 and 4. Use the bisection method to approximate it to one-decimal-place accuracy.

SOLUTION

We organize the results of our calculations in Table 1.

Table 1 Bisection Approximation

Sign Change Interval (a, b)	Midpoint m	Sign of P: $P(a)$	$P(m)$	$P(b)$	
(3, 4)	3.5	−	−	+	Choose (3.5, 4)
(3.5, 4)	3.75	−	+	+	Choose (3.5, 3.75)
(3.5, 3.75)	3.625	−	+	+	Choose (3.5, 3.625)
(3.5, 3.625)	3.5625	−	−	+	Choose (3.5625, 3.625)
(3.5625, 3.625)	We stop here	−		+	

Because the sign of $P(x)$ changes at the endpoints of the interval (3.5625, 3.625), we conclude that a real zero lies in this interval. But notice that each endpoint of that interval rounds to 3.6. So any number in between will round to 3.6 as well, and we can conclude that the zero is 3.6 to one-decimal-place accuracy.

MATCHED PROBLEM 4

The polynomial $P(x) = x^4 - 2x^3 - 10x^2 + 40x - 90$ from Example 2 has a zero between −5 and −4. Use the bisection method to approximate it to one-decimal-place accuracy.

Figure 8 illustrates the nested intervals produced by the bisection method in Table 1. Match each step in Table 1 with an interval in Figure 8. Note how each interval that contains a zero gets smaller and smaller and is contained in the preceding interval that contained the zero. In short, the intervals keep "closing in" on the zero.

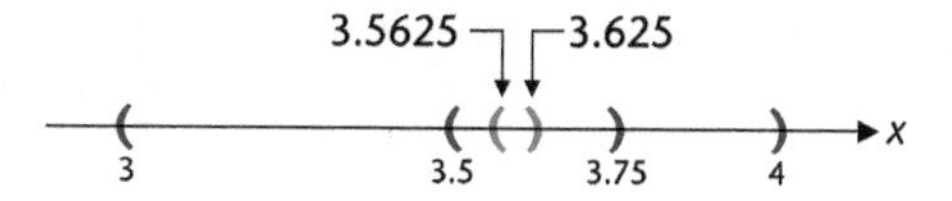

› **Figure 8** Nested intervals produced by the bisection method in Table 1.

If we had wanted two-decimal-place accuracy, we would have continued the process in Table 1 until the endpoints of a sign change interval rounded to the same two-decimal-place number.

› Approximating Real Zeros at Turning Points

The bisection method for approximating zeros fails if a polynomial has a turning point at a zero, because the polynomial does not change sign at such a zero. Most graphing calculators use methods that are more sophisticated than the bisection method. Nevertheless, it is not unusual to get an error message when using the ZERO command to approximate a zero that is also a turning point. In this case, we can use the MAXIMUM or MINIMUM command, as appropriate, to approximate the turning point, and thus the zero.

EXAMPLE 5 Approximating Zeros at Turning Points

Let $P(x) = x^5 + 6x^4 + 4x^3 - 24x^2 - 16x + 32$. Use the upper and lower bound theorem to find the smallest positive integer and the largest negative integer that are upper and lower bounds, respectively, for the real zeros of $P(x)$. Approximate the zeros to two decimal places, using MAXIMUM or MINIMUM commands to approximate any zeros at turning points.

SOLUTION

The relevant rows of a synthetic division table show that 2 is an upper bound and -6 is a lower bound:

	1	6	4	−24	−16	32	
1	1	7	11	−13	−29	3	
2	1	8	20	16	16	64	← All positive coefficients
−5	1	1	−1	−19	79	−363	
−6	1	0	4	−48	272	−1600	← Coefficients alternate signs

Examining the graph of $P(x)$ on the next page, we find three zeros: the zero -3.24, found using the MAXIMUM command [Fig. 9(a)]; the zero -2, found using the ZERO command [Fig. 9(b)]; and the zero 1.24, found using the MINIMUM command [Fig. 9(c)].

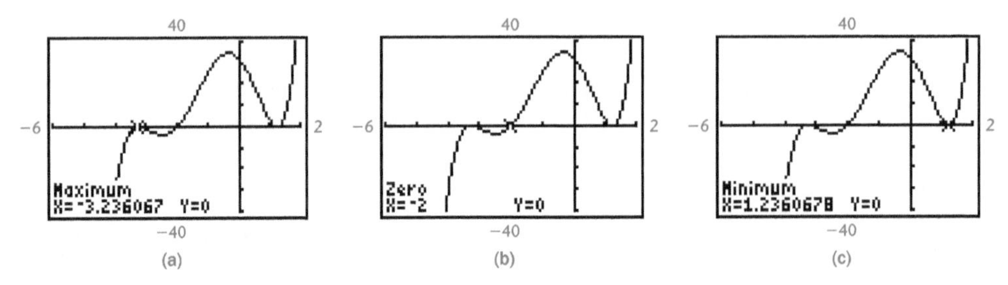

› **Figure 9** Zeros of $P(x) = x^5 + 6x^4 + 4x^3 - 24x^2 - 16x + 32$.

MATCHED PROBLEM 5

Let $P(x) = x^5 - 6x^4 + 40x^2 - 12x - 72$. Use the upper and lower bound theorem to find the smallest positive integer and the largest negative integer that are upper and lower bounds, respectively, for the real zeros of $P(x)$. Approximate the zeros to two decimal places, using MAXIMUM or MINIMUM commands to approximate any zeros at turning points.

››› EXPLORE-DISCUSS 4

(A) Graph the polynomial $P(x) = x^3 - 8.1x^2 + 16.4x$ in a standard viewing window. How many zeros are apparent?

(B) Try to find the zero near $x = 4$ using the MINIMUM command. What does the result indicate?

(C) How many zeros actually exist in the standard viewing window?

(D) Repeat for $P(x) = x^3 - 8.1x^2 + 16.4x + 0.1$

The point of Explore-Discuss 4 is that you have to be careful about zeros at turning points. When it looks like a maximum or minimum occurs at height zero, it's possible that it may be a bit above or below the x axis. When this happens, there might actually be two zeros there, or none at all.

› Solving Polynomial Inequalities

In Section 2-7, we developed a procedure for solving quadratic inequalities. It was based on two things: finding the zeros of a quadratic function, and applying the location theorem. Since we now know that the location theorem applies to polynomials, we can use the same "test number" procedure to solve polynomial inequalities. Of course, we can still rely on graphical methods as well, but once again an understanding of both methods will lead to a better overall grasp of the concepts.

EXAMPLE 6 Solving Polynomial Inequalities

Solve the inequality $x^3 - x^2 - 6x > 0$.

SOLUTION

Algebraic Solution

Let $P(x) = x^3 - x^2 - 6x$. Then $P(x)$ can be factored:

$$x^3 - x^2 - 6x = x(x^2 - x - 6) = x(x + 2)(x - 3)$$

The zeros are $x = 0, -2$, and 3. This divides the x axis into four intervals, which we put in the following table. We then choose a test number in each interval and record the sign of the result.

Interval	Test number	Result
$(-\infty, -2)$	-3	$-3(-3 + 2)(-3 - 3) = -18$; negative
$(-2, 0)$	-1	$-1(-1 + 2)(-1 - 3) = 4$; positive
$(0, 3)$	1	$1(1 + 2)(1 - 3) = -6$; negative
$(3, \infty)$	4	$9(4 + 2)(4 - 3) = 54$; positive

Notice that it's simpler to substitute test numbers into the factored form of $P(x)$ than the original form.

The solution of the inequality is $(-2, 0) \cup (3, \infty)$.

Graphical Solution

We graph P [Fig. 10] and use the ZERO command to find that -2, 0, and 3 are the zeros of P (details omitted). They partition the x axis into four intervals

$$(-\infty, -2), (-2, 0), (0, 3), \text{ and } (3, \infty)$$

By inspecting the graph of P we see that P is above the x axis on the intervals $(-2, 0)$ and $(3, \infty)$. Thus, the solution set of the inequality is

$$(-2, 0) \cup (3, \infty)$$

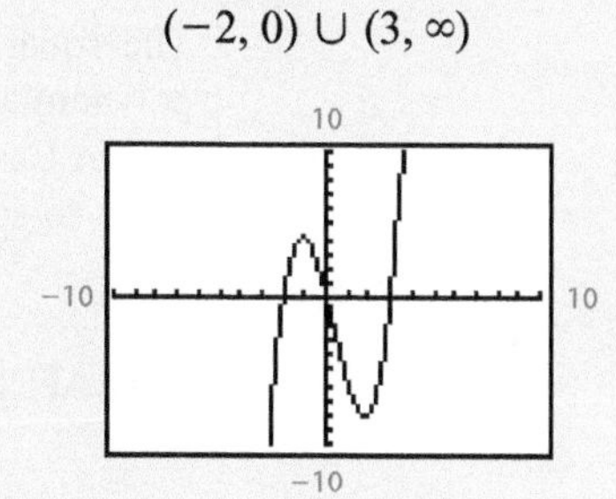

› **Figure 10** $P(x) = x^3 - x^2 - 6x$.

MATCHED PROBLEM 6

Solve the inequality $x^3 + 2x^2 - 8x < 0$.

››› EXPLORE-DISCUSS 5

For the function $P(x) = x^3 - x^2 - 6x$ from Example 6, let $f(x) = \frac{P(x)}{|P(x)|}$.

(A) Graph f in a standard viewing window.

(B) Write the intervals where f takes on value 1, and the intervals where f takes on value -1. Compare the results to the solution of Example 6.

(C) Use the graph of f to write solutions for the following inequalities:

$$x^3 - x^2 - 6x < 0$$
$$x^3 - x^2 - 6x \geq 0$$
$$x^3 - x^2 - 6x \leq 0$$

(D) Discuss this procedure for solving inequalities graphically. Do you prefer this method over the graphical solution in Example 6?

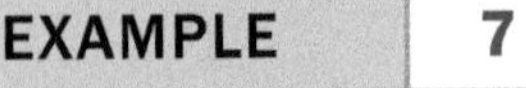

EXAMPLE 7

Solving Polynomial Inequalities

Solve $3x^2 + 12x - 4 \geq 2x^3 - 5x^2 + 7$ accurate to three decimal places.

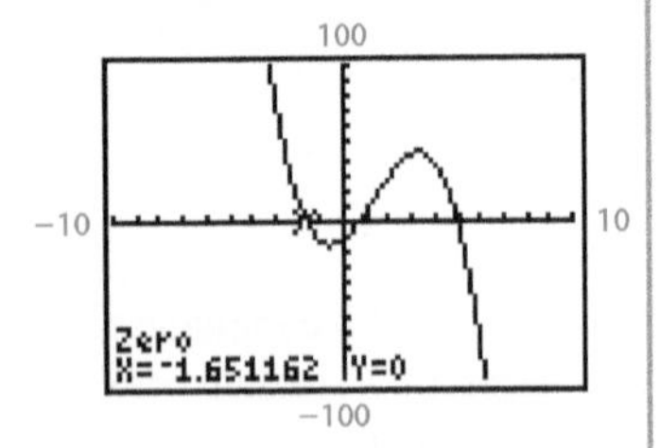

› Figure 11

SOLUTION

Subtracting the right side gives the equivalent inequality

$$P(x) = -2x^3 + 8x^2 + 12x - 11 \geq 0$$

The zeros of $P(x)$, to three decimal places, are found to be -1.651, 0.669, and 4.983 (Fig. 11) using the graph and the ZERO command.

The graph of P is above the x axis on the intervals $(-\infty, -1.651)$ and $(0.669, 4.983)$. The solution set of the inequality is thus

$$(-\infty, -1.651] \cup [0.669, 4.983]$$

The square brackets indicate that the endpoints of the intervals—the zeros of the polynomial—also satisfy the inequality.

In Example 7, because we needed to find the zeros graphically, it naturally made sense to solve the inequality graphically.

MATCHED PROBLEM 7

Solve $5x^3 - 13x < 4x^2 + 10x - 5$ accurate to three decimal places.

› Mathematical Modeling

EXAMPLE 8

Construction

An oil tank is in the shape of a right circular cylinder with a hemisphere (half sphere) at each end (Fig. 12). The cylinder is 55 inches long. Let x denote the common radius of the hemispheres and the cylinder.

› Figure 12

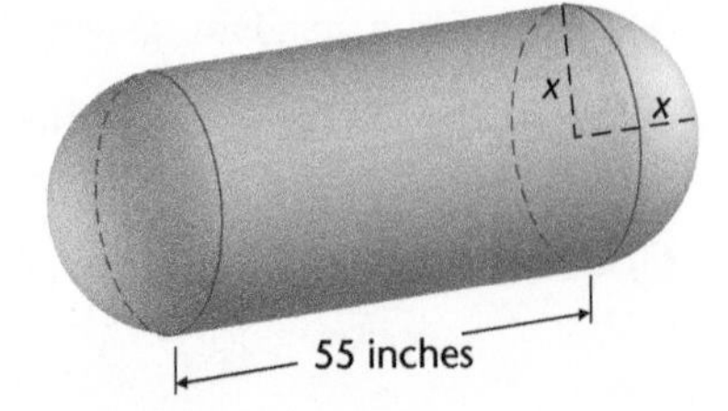

(A) Find a polynomial model for the volume of the tank.

(B) If the volume of the tank is required by a distributor to be $11{,}000\pi$ cubic inches (about 20 cubic feet), find x. Round to one decimal place.

SOLUTIONS

(A) The tank is made from a cylinder and a sphere (the two hemispheres). The volume of a cylinder is given by $V = \pi r^2 h$, where r is radius and h is height, so the volume of the cylindrical part of the tank has volume $\pi x^2(55)$. The volume of a sphere is $V = \frac{4}{3}\pi r^3$, which in this case is $V = \frac{4}{3}\pi x^3$. So the total volume can be modeled by

$$\begin{pmatrix}\text{Volume}\\ \text{of}\\ \text{tank}\end{pmatrix} = \begin{pmatrix}\text{Volume}\\ \text{of two}\\ \text{hemispheres}\end{pmatrix} + \begin{pmatrix}\text{Volume}\\ \text{of}\\ \text{cylinder}\end{pmatrix}$$

$$V = \frac{4}{3}\pi x^3 + 55\pi x^2$$

(B) We substitute $11{,}000\pi$ for V and solve for x.

$$11{,}000\pi = \tfrac{4}{3}\pi x^3 + 55\pi x^2 \qquad \text{Multiply by 3 and divide by } \pi.$$
$$33{,}000 = 4x^3 + 165x^2 \qquad \text{Subtract 33,000 from both sides.}$$
$$0 = 4x^3 + 165x^2 - 33{,}000$$

The desired value of x must be a positive zero of

$$P(x) = 4x^3 + 165x^2 - 33{,}000$$

Because the coefficients of $P(x)$ are large, we use large increments in a synthetic division table:

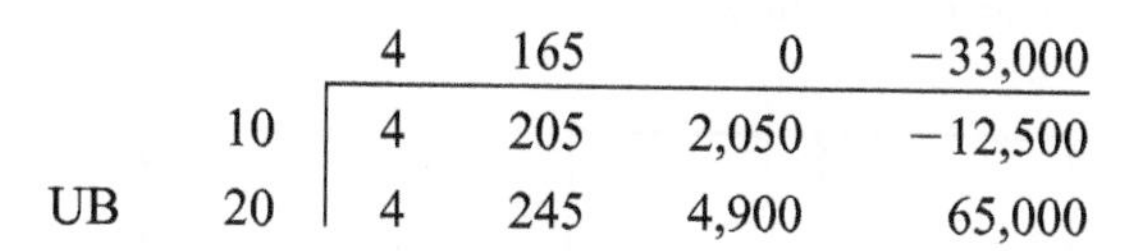

		4	165	0	−33,000
	10	4	205	2,050	−12,500
UB	20	4	245	4,900	65,000

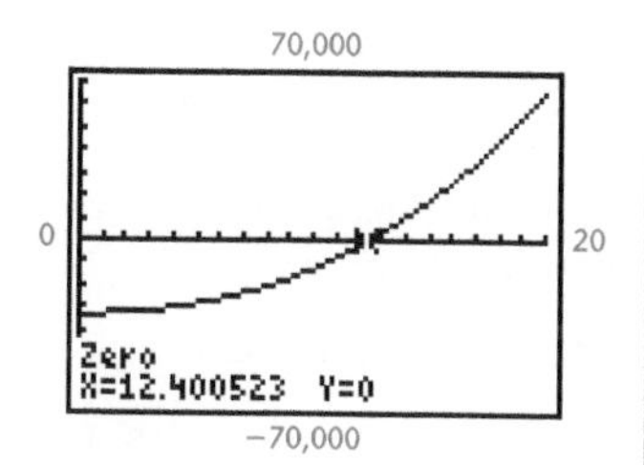

› **Figure 13**
$P(x) = 4x^3 + 165x^2 - 33{,}000$.

We know x can't be negative, so no lower bound is needed. Graphing $y = P(x)$ for $0 \le x \le 20$ (Fig. 13), we see that $x = 12.4$ inches (to one decimal place).

MATCHED PROBLEM 8

Repeat Example 8 if the length of the cylinder is 80 inches, and the volume of the tank is $44{,}000\pi$ cubic inches.

ANSWERS TO MATCHED PROBLEMS

1. $-4.190, -1.721, 2.912$ **2.** Lower bound: -3; upper bound: 6
3. (A) Lower bound: -10; upper bound: 30 (B) Real zeros: 1.20, 11.46, 12.34
4. $x = -4.1$ **5.** Lower bound: -2; upper bound: 6; $-1.65, 2, 3.65$
6. $(-\infty, -4) \cup (0, 2)$ **7.** $(-\infty, -1.899) \cup (0.212, 2.488)$
8. (A) $V = \frac{4}{3}\pi x^3 + 80\pi x^2$ (B) 20.3 inches

3-3 Exercises

In Problems 1–6, use the upper and lower bound theorem to decide if the given positive number is an upper bound for the real zeros of P(x), and if the given negative number is a lower bound.

1. $P(x) = 2x^3 - 4x^2 - 18x + 1; x = 4; x = -3$

2. $P(x) = 3x^3 - 2x^2 - 10x + 2; x = 2; x = -2$

3. $P(x) = x^3 + 4x^2 - 3x - 10; x = 2; x = -4$

4. $P(x) = x^3 - 3x^2 + 4x + 10; x = 3; x = -1$

5. $P(x) = x^4 + 2x^3 - 3x^2 + 4x - 5; x = 1; x = -3$

6. $P(x) = x^4 - 4x^3 + 8x^2 + 2x + 1; x = 5; x = -2$

In Problems 7–10, approximate the real zeros of each polynomial to three decimal places.

7. $P(x) = x^2 + 5x - 2$

8. $P(x) = 3x^2 - 7x + 1$

9. $P(x) = 2x^3 - 5x + 2$

10. $P(x) = x^3 - 4x^2 - 8x + 3$

11. The graph of $f(x) = x^3 + 4x^2 - 4x - 16$ is shown here in a standard viewing window. Can you be sure that all of the real zeros can be found using this window? Explain.

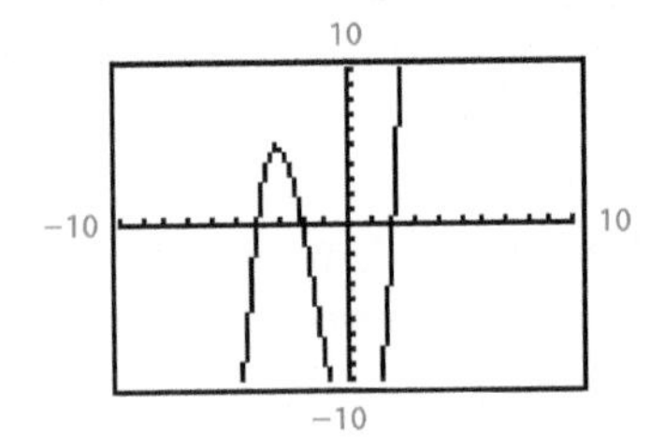

12. The graph of $g(x) = x^3 - 3x^2 + 4x - 12$ is shown here in a standard viewing window. Can you be sure that all of the real zeros can be found using this window? Explain.

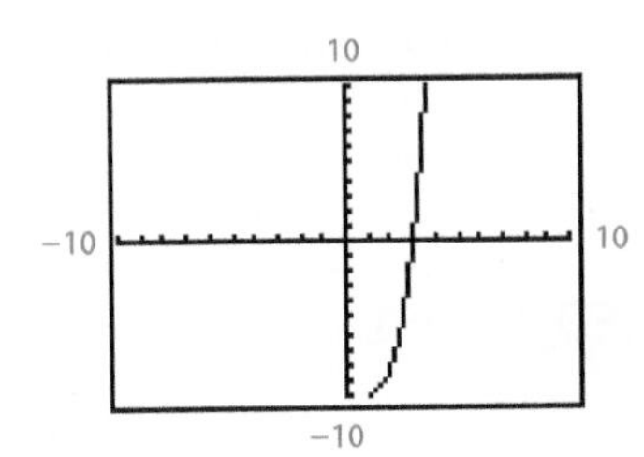

13. Suppose that synthetic division of a polynomial P by $x - 4$ results in all positive numbers in the quotient row. Is $x = 10$ an upper bound for the real zeros of P? Explain.

14. Suppose that synthetic division of a polynomial P by $x + 5$ results in a quotient row with alternating signs. Is $x = -10$ a lower bound for the real zeros of P? Explain.

15. State the location theorem in your own words.

16. Describe the connection between the location theorem and the bisection method.

In Problems 17–20, use the graph of P(x) to write the solution set for each inequality.

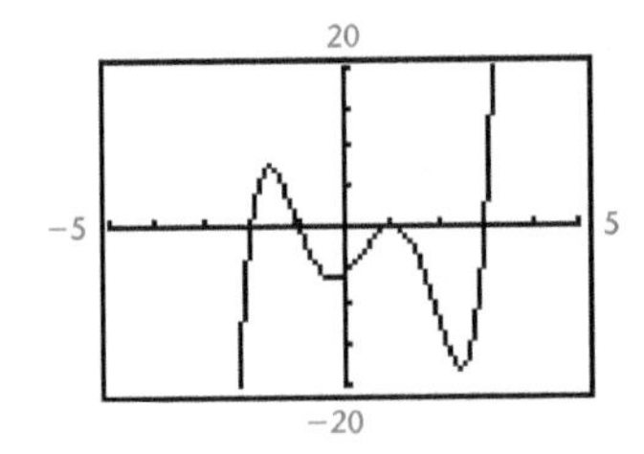

17. $P(x) \geq 0$

18. $P(x) < 0$

19. $P(x) > 0$

20. $P(x) \leq 0$

In Problems 21–24, solve each polynomial inequality to three decimal places (note the connection with Problems 7–10).

21. $x^2 + 5x - 2 > 0$

22. $3x^2 - 7x + 1 \geq 0$

23. $2x^3 - 5x + 2 \leq 0$

24. $x^3 - 4x^2 - 8x + 3 < 0$

Use the upper and lower bound theorem to find the smallest positive integer and largest negative integer that are upper and lower bounds, respectively, for the real zeros of each of the polynomials given in Problems 25–30.

25. $P(x) = x^3 - 3x + 1$

26. $P(x) = x^3 - 4x^2 + 4$

27. $P(x) = x^4 - 3x^3 + 4x^2 + 2x - 9$

28. $P(x) = x^4 - 4x^3 + 6x^2 - 4x - 7$

29. $P(x) = x^5 - 3x^3 + 3x^2 + 2x - 2$

30. $P(x) = x^5 - 3x^4 + 3x^2 + 2x - 1$

In Problems 31–38,

(A) Use the upper and lower bound theorem to find the smallest positive integer and largest negative integer that are upper and lower bounds, respectively, for the real zeros of P(x).

(B) Approximate the real zeros of each polynomial to two decimal places.

31. $P(x) = x^3 - 2x^2 + 3x - 8$

32. $P(x) = x^3 + 3x^2 + 4x + 5$

33. $P(x) = x^4 + x^3 - 5x^2 + 7x - 22$

34. $P(x) = x^4 - x^3 - 8x^2 - 12x - 25$

35. $P(x) = x^5 - 3x^3 - 4x + 4$

36. $P(x) = x^5 - x^4 - 2x^2 - 4x - 5$

37. $P(x) = x^5 + x^4 + 3x^3 + x^2 + 2x - 5$

38. $P(x) = x^5 - 2x^4 - 6x^2 - 9x + 10$

In Problems 39–46,

(A) Use the location theorem to explain why the polynomial function has a zero in the indicated interval.

(B) Determine the number of additional intervals required by the bisection method to obtain a one-decimal-place approximation to the zero and state the approximate value of the zero.

39. $P(x) = x^3 - 2x^2 - 5x + 4; (3, 4)$

40. $P(x) = x^3 + x^2 - 4x - 1; (1, 2)$

41. $P(x) = x^3 - 2x^2 - x + 5; (-2, -1)$

42. $P(x) = x^3 - 3x^2 - x - 2; (3, 4)$

43. $P(x) = x^4 - 2x^3 - 7x^2 + 9x + 7; (3, 4)$

44. $P(x) = x^4 - x^3 - 9x^2 + 9x + 4; (2, 3)$

45. $P(x) = x^4 - x^3 - 4x^2 + 4x + 3; (-1, 0)$

46. $P(x) = x^4 - 3x^3 - x^2 + 3x + 3; (2, 3)$

Problems 47–50 refer to the polynomial

$$P(x) = (x - 1)^2(x - 2)(x - 3)^4$$

47. Can the zero at $x = 1$ be approximated by the bisection method? Explain.

48. Can the zero at $x = 2$ be approximated by the bisection method? Explain.

49. Can the zero at $x = 3$ be approximated by the bisection method? Explain.

50. Which of the zeros can be approximated using the MAXIMUM command? Using the MINIMUM command? Using the ZERO command?

In Problems 51–56, approximate the zeros of each polynomial function to two decimal places, using MAXIMUM or MINIMUM commands to approximate any zeros at turning points.

51. $P(x) = x^4 - 4x^3 - 10x^2 + 28x + 49$

52. $P(x) = x^4 + 4x^3 - 4x^2 - 16x + 16$

53. $P(x) = x^5 - 6x^4 + 4x^3 + 24x^2 - 16x - 32$

54. $P(x) = x^5 - 6x^4 + 2x^3 + 28x^2 - 15x + 2$

55. $P(x) = x^5 - 6x^4 + 11x^3 - 4x^2 - 3.75x - 0.5$

56. $P(x) = x^5 + 12x^4 + 47x^3 + 56x^2 - 15.75x + 1$

In Problems 57–70, solve each polynomial inequality. Approximate to three decimal places if necessary.

57. $(2x - 5)(x + 3)(x + 7) > 0$

58. $(x + 4)(3x - 9)(x - 1) < 0$

59. $x^2 > 2$

60. $2x^2 \le 38$

61. $x^3 \le 9x$

62. $25x > x^3$

63. $x^3 + 5x^2 \le -6x$

64. $7x^2 > 8x - x^3$

65. $x^2 + 7x - 3 \le x^3 + x + 4$

66. $x^4 + 1 > 3x^2$

67. $x^4 < 8x^3 - 17x^2 + 9x - 2$

68. $x^3 + 5x \ge 2x^3 - 4x^2 + 6$

69. $(x^2 + 2x - 2)^2 \ge 2$

70. $5 + 2x < (x^2 - 4)^2$

71. The statement of the upper and lower bound theorem requires that the leading coefficient of a polynomial be positive. What if the leading coefficient is negative?

(A) Graph $P(x) = -x^3 - x^2 + 6x$ in a standard viewing window. How many real zeros do you see? Are these all of the real zeros? How can you tell?

(B) Based on the graph, is $x = 3$ an upper bound for the real zeros?

(C) Use synthetic division to divide $P(x)$ by $x - 3$. What do you notice about the quotient row? What can you conclude about upper bounds for polynomials with negative leading coefficients?

72. Refer to Problem 71.

(A) Based on the graph, is $x = -4$ a lower bound for the real zeros?

(B) Use synthetic division to divide $P(x)$ by $x + 4$. What do you notice about the quotient row? What can you conclude about lower bounds for polynomials with negative leading coefficients?

In Problems 73–82,

(A) Use the upper and lower bound theorem to find the smallest positive integer multiple of 10 and largest negative integer multiple of 10 that are upper and lower bounds, respectively, for the real zeros of each polynomial.

(B) Approximate the real zeros of each polynomial to two decimal places.

73. $P(x) = x^3 - 24x^2 - 25x + 10$

74. $P(x) = x^3 - 37x^2 + 70x - 20$

75. $P(x) = x^4 + 12x^3 - 900x^2 + 5,000$

76. $P(x) = x^4 - 12x^3 - 425x^2 + 7,000$

77. $P(x) = x^4 - 100x^2 - 1{,}000x - 5{,}000$

78. $P(x) = x^4 - 5x^3 - 50x^2 - 500x + 7{,}000$

79. $P(x) = 4x^4 - 40x^3 - 1{,}475x^2 + 7{,}875x - 10{,}000$

80. $P(x) = 9x^4 + 120x^3 - 3{,}083x^2 - 25{,}674x - 48{,}400$

81. $P(x) = 0.01x^5 - 0.1x^4 - 12x^3 + 9{,}000$

82. $P(x) = 0.1x^5 + 0.7x^4 - 18.775x^3 - 340x^2 - 1{,}645x - 2{,}450$

83. When synthetic division is used to divide a polynomial $P(x)$ by $x + 4$ the remainder is 10. When the same polynomial is divided by $x + 5$ the remainder is -8. Must $P(x)$ have a zero between -5 and -4? Explain.

84. When synthetic division is used to divide a polynomial $Q(x)$ by $x + 4$ the remainder is 10. When the same polynomial is divided by $x + 5$ the remainder is 8. Could $Q(x)$ have a zero between -5 and -4? Explain.

85. In this problem, we sketch a proof of the upper bound theorem. We suppose that a polynomial $P(x)$ is divided by $x - r$ $(r > 0)$ using synthetic division, and all numbers in the quotient row are nonnegative.

(A) Write the result of the division algorithm for this division. What can we say about the coefficients of $Q(x)$ and the remainder R?

(B) Suppose that x is a number greater than r. What is the sign of $x - r$? Why can we say that the sign of $Q(x)$ must be positive?

(C) Is it possible for $P(x)$ to be zero? Why not?

(D) How does this prove the upper bound theorem?

86. In this problem, we sketch a proof of one case of the lower bound theorem. Suppose that a polynomial $P(x)$ is divided by $x - r(r < 0)$ using synthetic division, and the quotient row alternates in sign.

(A) If we use the division algorithm to write $P(x) = Q(x)(x - r) + R$, where R is positive, what is the sign of the constant term of $Q(x)$? What is the sign of all even-powered terms? What about all odd-powered terms? (Remember: alternating signs!)

(B) Suppose that x is a negative number less than r. What will be the sign of the result when substituting x into all of the even-powered terms? What about all of the odd-powered terms?

(C) Is it possible for $P(x)$ to be zero? Why not?

(D) How does this prove the lower bound theorem?

APPLICATIONS

87. PROFIT A small manufacturing company produces toasters for a national chain of discount stores. An economic consultant estimates that the company's weekly profit can be modeled by the function $P(x) = -0.000\,068x^3 + 0.0041x^2 + 15.18x - 1{,}225$, where P is profit in dollars and x is number of toasters produced. The company can produce at most 500 toasters per week.

(A) How many toasters does the company need to produce in order to break even (that is, have profit zero)?

(B) How many toasters should the company produce to make a profit of at least \$1,200 per week?

88. PROFIT An independent home builder's annual profit in thousands of dollars can be modeled by the polynomial $P(x) = 5.152x^3 - 143.0x^2 + 1{,}102x - 1{,}673$ where x is the number of houses built in a year. His company can build at most 13 houses in a year.

(A) How many houses must he build to break even (that is, have profit zero)?

(B) How many houses should he build to have a profit of at least \$400,000?

Express the solutions to Problems 89–94 as the roots of a polynomial equation of the form $P(x) = 0$ and approximate these solutions to three decimal places.

89. GEOMETRY Find all points on the graph of $y = x^2$ that are one unit away from the point (1, 2). [*Hint:* Use the distance-between-two-points formula from Appendix B, Section B-3.]

90. GEOMETRY Find all points on the graph of $y = x^2$ that are one unit away from the point (2, 1).

91. MANUFACTURING A box is to be made out of a piece of cardboard that measures 18 by 24 inches. Squares, x inches on a side, will be cut from each corner, and then the ends and sides will be folded up (see the figure). Find the value of x that would result in a box with a volume of 600 cubic inches.

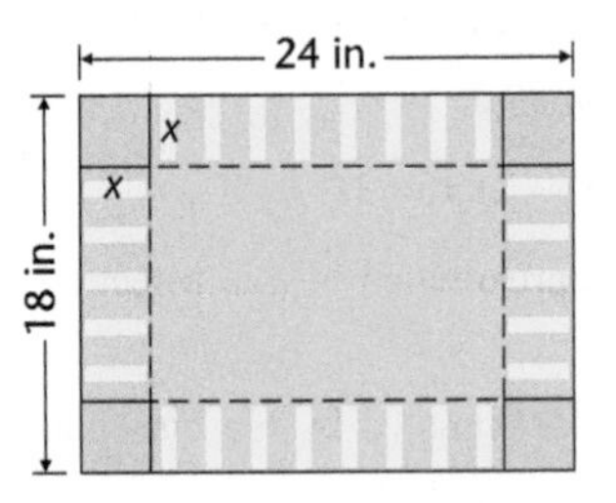

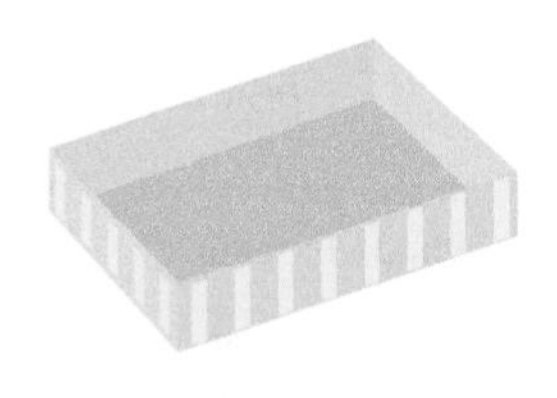

92. MANUFACTURING A box with a hinged lid is to be made out of a piece of cardboard that measures 20 by 40 inches. Six squares, x inches on a side, will be cut from each corner and the middle, and then the ends and sides will be folded up to form the box and its lid (see the figure). Find the value of x that would result in a box with a volume of 500 cubic inches.

40 in.
x
x
20 in.

93. CONSTRUCTION A propane gas tank is in the shape of a right circular cylinder with a hemisphere at each end (see the figure). If the overall length of the tank is 10 feet and the volume is 20π cubic feet, find the common radius of the hemispheres and the cylinder.

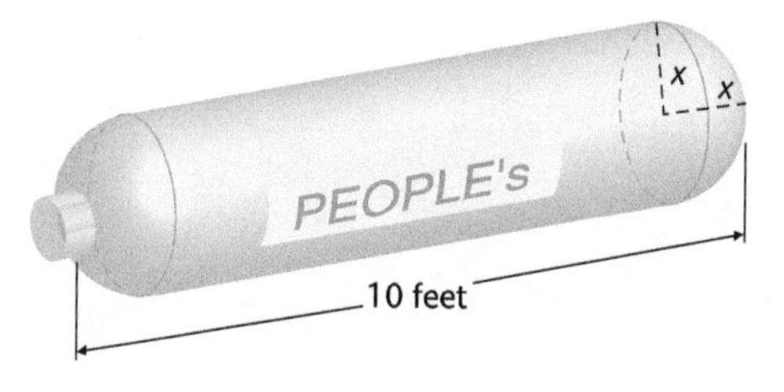

94. SHIPPING A shipping box is reinforced with steel bands in all three directions (see the figure). A total of 20.5 feet of steel tape is to be used, with 6 inches of waste because of a 2-inch overlap in each direction. If the box has a square base and a volume of 2 cubic feet, find its dimensions.

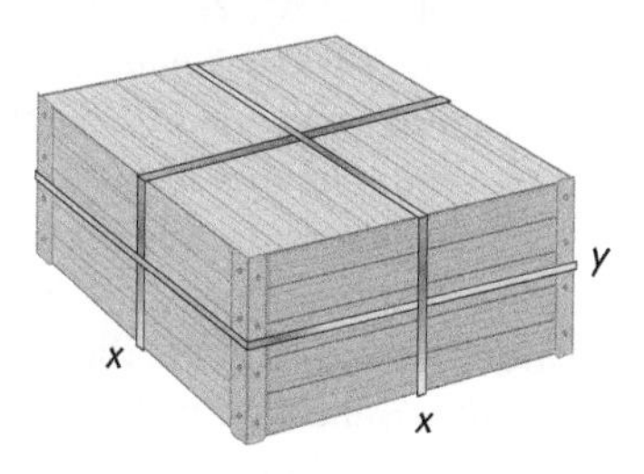

MATHEMATICAL MODELING AND REGRESSION ANALYSIS

Problems 95–98 refer to Table 2, which shows homeownership rates for households of various races and ethnicities from 1996 to 2005. For each problem, use $x = 0$ for 1996, and round all coefficients to 3 significant digits.

Table 2 Homeownership Rates by Race and Ethnicity

	Hispanic	Asian	White
1996	42.8%	50.8%	69.1%
1998	44.7%	52.6%	70.0%
2000	46.3%	52.8%	71.1%
2002	48.2%	54.7%	71.8%
2003	46.7%	56.3%	72.1%
2004	48.1%	59.8%	72.8%
2005	49.5%	60.1%	72.7%

Source: U.S. Census Bureau

95. Find a cubic regression model for the homeownership rates for Hispanic households. Then set up and solve an inequality that predicts years in which the homeownership for Hispanic households will exceed 60%.

96. Find a cubic regression model for the homeownership rates for Asian households. Then set up and solve an inequality that predicts the years in which the homeownership for Asian households will exceed 70%.

97. Refer to Problem 95. Find a linear regression model for the homeownership rates for white households. Then set up and solve an inequality that predicts the years in which the homeownership for Hispanic households will exceed the percentage for white households.

98. Refer to Problems 95 and 96. Set up and solve an inequality that predicts the years in which the homeownership for Hispanic households will exceed the percentage for Asian households.

Problems 99 and 100 refer to Table 3, which provides the percentage of males and females in the United States who have completed four or more years of college from 1970 to 2005. In each problem, use $x = 0$ for 1970, and round coefficients to three significant digits.

Table 3 Percentage of People in the United States Who Have Completed 4 or More Years of College

Year	Males	Females
1970	14.1	8.2
1980	20.9	13.6
1990	24.4	18.4
1995	26.0	20.2
2000	27.8	23.6
2005	28.9	26.5

Source: www.infoplease.com

99. Find a cubic regression model for the percentage of males having completed 4 or more years of college. Then set up and solve an inequality that predicts the first year in which this percentage will exceed 40%.

100. Refer to Problem 99. Find a cubic regression model for the percentage of females having completed 4 or more years of college. Then set up and solve an inequality that predicts the years in which this percentage will exceed the percentage for males.

3-4 Complex Zeros and Rational Zeros of Polynomials

- The Fundamental Theorem of Algebra
- Finding Factors of Polynomials with Real Coefficients
- Graphs of Polynomials with Real Coefficients
- Finding Rational Zeros

In this section, we will attempt to answer a question that may have occurred to you earlier in this chapter when looking for zeros of polynomials: How do you know exactly how many zeros to look for?

The graph of the polynomial function $P(x) = x^2 + 4$ does not cross the x axis, so $P(x)$ has no real zeros. It does, however, have complex zeros, $2i$ and $-2i$. This tells us that $P(x)$ can be factored as $x^2 + 4 = (x - 2i)(x + 2i)$. The *fundamental theorem of algebra* guarantees that *every* nonconstant polynomial with real or complex coefficients has at least one complex zero. We will use it to show that any such polynomial can be factored completely as a product of linear factors. In this section, we will study the fundamental theorem of algebra and its implications. This will help us improve our understanding of the graphs of polynomials with real coefficients. Finally, we will consider a problem that has led to important advances in mathematics and its applications: When can the zeros of a polynomial be found *exactly*?

The Fundamental Theorem of Algebra

The fundamental theorem of algebra was proved by Karl Friedrich Gauss (1777–1855), one of the greatest mathematicians of all time, in his doctoral thesis. A proof of the theorem is beyond the scope of this book, so we will state and use it without proof.

THEOREM 1 The Fundamental Theorem of Algebra

Every polynomial of degree $n > 0$ with complex coefficients has a complex zero.

CAUTION

Remember that real numbers are complex numbers, too! The fundamental theorem does not say that every polynomial has a complex zero of the form $a + bi$, where b is not zero. It also does not require that any of the coefficients are of that form. It simply guarantees that every nonconstant polynomial has at least one zero, which may or may not be real.

The fundamental theorem of algebra certainly has an important-sounding name for a pretty simple fact. While it may not seem terribly important that every polynomial has a zero, the main value of the fundamental theorem in this course is that it can be used to develop other results that tell us a lot more about polynomials.

If $P(x)$ is any polynomial of degree $n > 0$, then by Theorem 1 it has a zero, which we'll call r_1. So the factor theorem tells us that $x - r_1$ is a factor of $P(x)$. In other words,

$$P(x) = (x - r_1)Q(x)$$

where $Q(x)$ has degree $n - 1$. Now $Q(x)$ is a polynomial also, so by Theorem 1, it has a zero r_2 (which may or may not be equal to r_1). So

$$Q(x) = (x - r_2)Q_2(x) \quad \text{and}$$
$$P(x) = (x - r_1)(x - r_2)Q_2(x)$$

where $Q_2(x)$ has degree $n - 2$. Do you see where this is headed? If we continue this process n times (recall that n is the degree of P), we develop Theorem 2.

› THEOREM 2 The n Linear Factors Theorem

Every polynomial of degree $n > 0$ with complex coefficients can be factored completely as a product of n linear factors.

Theorem 2 guarantees n linear factors for a polynomial of degree n, but it doesn't guarantee n *distinct* linear factors. For example, the polynomial

$$P(x) = (x - 5)^3(x + 1)^2(x - 6i)(x + 2 + 3i) \quad (1)$$

can also be written as

$$P(x) = (x - 5)(x - 5)(x - 5)(x + 1)(x + 1)(x - 6i)(x + 2 + 3i)$$

In this form, we see that there are, in fact, seven linear factors of this seventh-degree polynomial. But because some factors are repeated, there are only four distinct zeros: $5, -1, 6i$, and $-2 - 3i$. Because the factor $x - 5$ appears to the power 3, we say that the corresponding zero $x = 5$ has **multiplicity** 3. Similarly, -1 has multiplicity 2, and $6i$ and $-2 - 3i$ have multiplicity 1. A zero of multiplicity 2 is called a **double zero.** *Note that the sum of multiplicities is always equal to the degree of the polynomial:* For $P(x)$ in equation (1), $3 + 2 + 1 + 1 = 7$. This fact answers our question about the number of zeros for a polynomial:

Every polynomial of degree n has n zeros, if you count a zero of multiplicity m as m zeros.

EXAMPLE 1 Multiplicities of Zeros

Find all zeros and write their multiplicities:

(A) $P(x) = (x + 2)^7(x - 4)^8(x^2 + 1)$ (B) $Q(x) = (x + 1)^3(x^2 - 1)(x + 1 - i)$

SOLUTIONS

(A) Note that $x^2 + 1 = 0$ has the solutions i and $-i$. The zeros of $P(x)$ are -2 (multiplicity 7), 4 (multiplicity 8), i and $-i$ (each multiplicity 1).

(B) Note that $x^2 - 1 = (x - 1)(x + 1)$, so $Q(x)$ can be written as $Q(x) = (x + 1)^3 (x + 1)(x - 1)(x + 1 - i)$, and $x + 1$ appears four times as a factor of $Q(x)$. The zeros of $Q(x)$ are -1 (multiplicity 4), 1 (multiplicity 1), and $-1 + i$ (multiplicity 1). [The factor $x + 1 - i$ can be written as $x - (-1 + i)$.]

MATCHED PROBLEM 1

Find all zeros and write their multiplicities:

(A) $P(x) = (x - 5)^3(x + 3)^2(x^2 + 16)$ (B) $Q(x) = (x^2 - 25)^3(x + 5)(x - i)$

› Finding Factors of Polynomials with Real Coefficients

We saw in Section 2-5 that if a quadratic function has an imaginary zero $a + bi$, then its conjugate $a - bi$ is a zero as well. (See Problem 94 in Exercises 2-5.) It turns out that this is actually true for any polynomial of positive degree with real coefficients.

› THEOREM 3 Imaginary Zeros of Polynomials with Real Coefficients

Imaginary zeros of polynomials with real coefficients, if they exist, occur in conjugate pairs: If $a + bi$ is a zero, then its conjugate $a - bi$ is a zero as well.

››› EXPLORE-DISCUSS 1

(A) Suppose that a polynomial has an imaginary zero $a + bi$, and the only other zero is a real number c. Then $x - (a + bi)$ and $x - c$ are factors of P. Multiply these two factors, then simplify. What type of coefficients must P have in this case?

(B) What if $a - bi$ is also a zero? Multiply $x - (a + bi)$ and $x - (a - bi)$, then simplify. Are all the coefficients real now?

Explore-Discuss 1 gives a rough indication of why imaginary zeros of a polynomial with real coefficients must occur in pairs. If they didn't, when multiplying all the factors out, you would always get at least one imaginary coefficient.

But Explore-Discuss 1 actually does much more: It provides a road map for factoring any polynomial with real coefficients. We already know that any such polynomial of degree n can be factored into n linear factors (Theorem 2). If any zeros are imaginary, some of the factors will have imaginary coefficients. But now we know that these factors will occur in pairs, and when we multiply those pairs, the result is a quadratic factor with real coefficients. This result is summarized in Theorem 4.

› THEOREM 4 The Linear and Quadratic Factors Theorem

If $P(x)$ is a polynomial of degree $n > 0$ with real coefficients, then $P(x)$ can be factored as a product of linear factors (with real coefficients) and quadratic factors (with real coefficients and imaginary zeros).

EXAMPLE 2

Factors of Polynomials

Given that $x = -1$ is a zero of $P(x) = x^3 + x^2 + 4x + 4$, factor $P(x)$ in two ways:

(A) As a product of linear factors (with real coefficients) and quadratic factors (with real coefficients and imaginary zeros);

(B) As a product of linear factors with complex coefficients.

SOLUTIONS

We first need to find all of the zeros of $P(x)$. (You may want to refer back to Example 6 in Section 3-2.)

First, divide by $x + 1$ using synthetic division:

$$\begin{array}{r|rrrr} & 1 & 1 & 4 & 4 \\ & & -1 & 0 & -4 \\ \hline -1 & 1 & 0 & 4 & 0 \end{array}$$

Now we know that $P(x) = (x + 1)(x^2 + 4)$. Next, we find the zeros of the remaining factor:

$$\begin{aligned} x^2 + 4 &= 0 \\ x^2 &= -4 \\ x &= 2i, -2i \end{aligned}$$

(A) We've already solved part A: $P(x) = (x + 1)(x^2 + 4)$.

(B) The zeros of $P(x)$ are -1, $2i$, and $-2i$, so $P(x) = (x + 1)(x - 2i)(x + 2i)$.

MATCHED PROBLEM 2

Factor $P(x) = x^5 - x^4 - x + 1$ in two ways:

(A) As a product of linear factors (with real coefficients) and quadratic factors (with real coefficients and imaginary zeros);

(B) As a product of linear factors with complex coefficients.

Example 2 may have made you wonder how we would know to start with $x = -1$. We'll address this important question at the end of this section.

Graphs of Polynomials with Real Coefficients

The factorization described in Theorem 4 gives additional information about the graphs of polynomial functions with real coefficients. For certain polynomials the factorization of Theorem 4 will involve only linear factors; for others, only quadratic factors. Of course, if only quadratic factors are present, then the degree of the polynomial $P(x)$ must be a multiple of 2; that is, even. On the other hand, a polynomial $P(x)$ of odd degree with real coefficients must have at least one linear factor with real coefficients. This proves Theorem 5.

THEOREM 5 Real Zeros and Polynomials of Odd Degree

Every polynomial of odd degree with real coefficients has at least one real zero, and consequently at least one x intercept.

EXPLORE-DISCUSS 2

The graph of the polynomial $P(x) = x(x - 1)^2(x + 1)^4(x - 2)^3$ is shown in Figure 1. Find the real zeros of $P(x)$ and their multiplicities. How can a real zero of even multiplicity be distinguished from a real zero of odd multiplicity using only the graph?

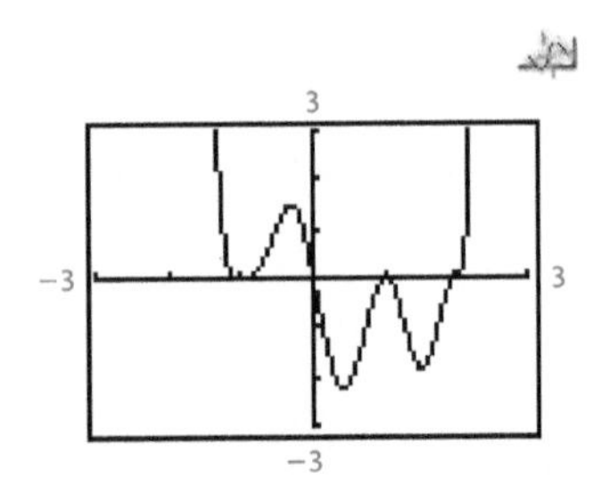

Figure 1 Graph of $P(x) = x(x - 1)^2(x + 1)^4(x - 2)^3$.

For polynomials with real coefficients, as suggested by Explore-Discuss 2, you can easily distinguish real zeros of even multiplicity from those of odd multiplicity using only the graph. Theorem 6, which we state without proof, tells us how to do that.

› **THEOREM 6 Zeros of Even or Odd Multiplicity**

Let $P(x)$ be a polynomial with real coefficients:

1. If r is a real zero of $P(x)$ of even multiplicity, then $P(x)$ has a turning point at r and does not change sign at r. (The graph just touches the x axis, then changes direction.)
2. If r is a real zero of $P(x)$ of odd multiplicity, then $P(x)$ does not have a turning point at r and changes sign at r. (The graph continues through to the opposite side of the x axis.)

EXAMPLE 3 Multiplicities from Graphs

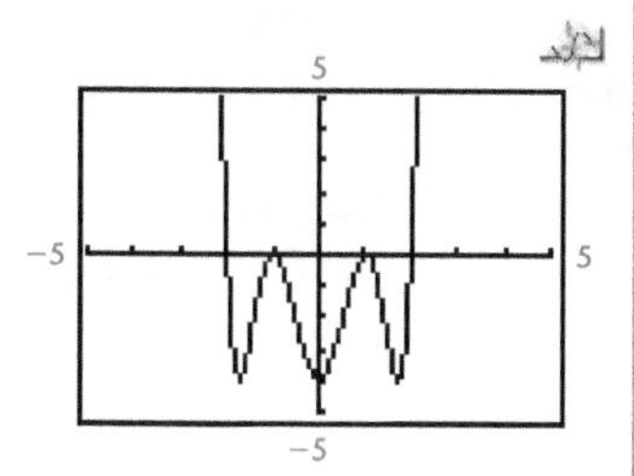

› **Figure 2**

Figure 2 shows the graph of a polynomial function of degree 6. Find the real zeros and their multiplicities.

SOLUTION

The numbers $-2, -1, 1$, and 2 are real zeros (x intercepts). The graph has turning points at $x = \pm 1$ but not at $x = \pm 2$. Therefore, by Theorem 6, the zeros -1 and 1 have even multiplicity, and -2 and 2 have odd multiplicity. Because the sum of the multiplicities must equal 6 (the degree), the zeros -1 and 1 each have multiplicity 2, and the zeros -2 and 2 each have multiplicity 1. Any multiplicities greater than 1 or 2 would result in a degree greater than 6.

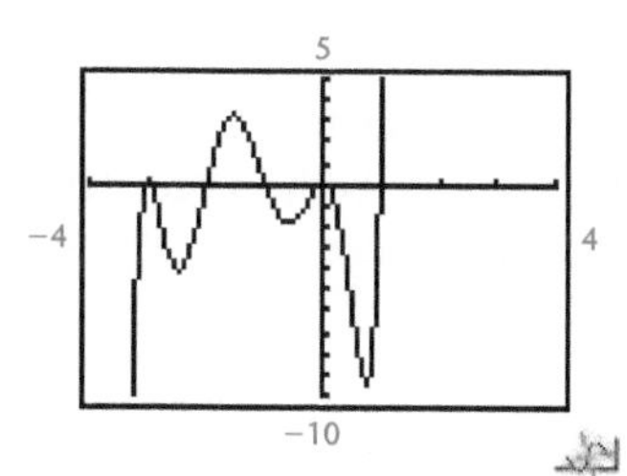

› **Figure 3**

MATCHED PROBLEM 3

Figure 3 shows the graph of a polynomial function of degree 7. Find the real zeros and their multiplicities.

› Finding Rational Zeros

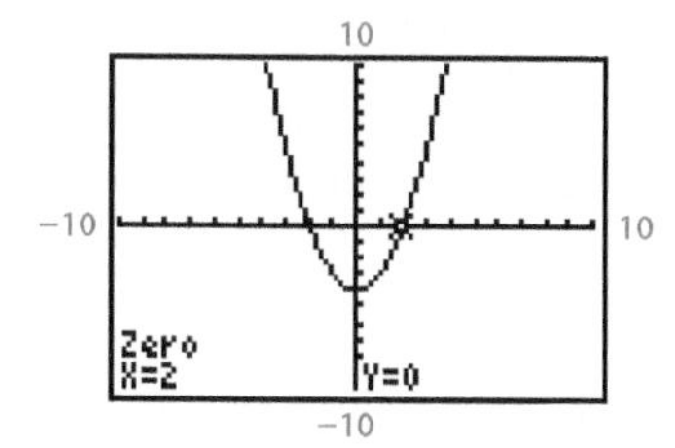

› **Figure 4** $P(x) = x^2 - (4 + 10^{-9})$.

From a graphical perspective, finding a zero of a polynomial means finding a good approximation to an actual zero. A graphing calculator, for example, might give 2 as a zero of $P(x) = x^2 - (4 + 10^{-9})$ even though $P(2)$ is equal to -10^{-9}, not 0 (Fig. 4).

It is natural, however, to want to find zeros *exactly*. Although this is impossible in general, we will adopt an algebraic strategy to find exact zeros in a special case: when a polynomial with rational coefficients has at least some zeros that are rational numbers. We will find a graphing calculator to be very helpful in carrying out our algebraic strategy.

EXPLORE-DISCUSS 3

(A) Use a graphing calculator to find the zeros of $P_1(x) = \frac{1}{9}x^3 - \frac{1}{9}x^2 - x + 1$.

(B) Use a graphing calculator to find the zeros of $P_2(x) = x^3 - x^2 - 9x + 9$.

(C) Explain why the two equations $\frac{1}{9}x^3 - \frac{1}{9}x^2 - x + 1 = 0$ and $x^3 - x^2 - 9x + 9 = 0$ have the same solution.

Using the idea behind Explore-Discuss 3, we can reduce our work in finding zeros of polynomials with rational coefficients. If we multiply a function $P(x)$ by the least common denominator of any fractions in $P(x)$, we will get a new polynomial with integer coefficients, and the exact same zeros as $P(x)$. (The new polynomial will have a different graph, different maximums and minimums, etc., but it will have the same zeros.)

The point is that we can study zeros of polynomials with rational coefficients by studying just the polynomials with integer coefficients.

We will introduce a method for identifying potential rational zeros by examining the following quadratic polynomial whose zeros can be found easily by factoring:

$$P(x) = 6x^2 - 13x - 5 = (2x - 5)(3x + 1)$$

$$\text{Zeros of } P(x)\text{: } \frac{5}{2} \quad \text{and} \quad -\frac{1}{3} = \frac{-1}{3}$$

Notice that the numerators, 5 and -1, of the zeros are both integer factors of -5, the constant term in $P(x)$. The denominators 2 and 3 of the zeros are both integer factors of 6, the leading coefficient of $P(x)$. This is not a coincidence. These observations are generalized in Theorem 7.

THEOREM 7 The Rational Zero Theorem

If the rational number b/c, in lowest terms, is a zero of the polynomial

$$P(x) = a_nx^n + a_{n-1}x^{n-1} + \cdots + a_1x + a_0 \qquad a_n \neq 0$$

with integer coefficients, then b must be an integer factor of a_0 (the constant term) and c must be an integer factor of a_n (the leading coefficient).

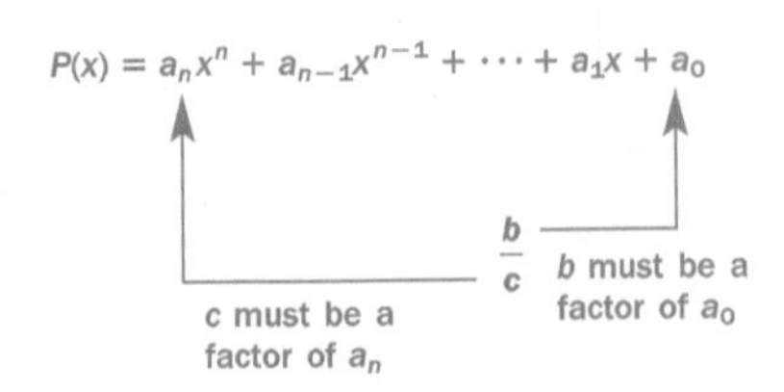

The rational zero theorem is a bit hard to understand until it is illustrated with an example.

EXAMPLE 4 Identifying Possible Rational Zeros

Make a list of all possible rational zeros of $P(x) = 4x^3 - x^2 + 2x + 6$.

SOLUTION

1. Make a list of all factors of the constant term, 6: $\pm 1, \pm 2, \pm 3, \pm 6$
2. Make a list of all possible factors of the leading coefficient, 4: $\pm 1, \pm 2, \pm 4$
3. Write all possible fractions with numerator from the first list and denominator from the second:

$$\pm\frac{1}{1}, \pm\frac{1}{2}, \pm\frac{1}{4}, \pm\frac{2}{1}, \pm\frac{2}{2}, \pm\frac{2}{4}, \pm\frac{3}{1}, \pm\frac{3}{2}, \pm\frac{3}{4}, \pm\frac{6}{1}, \pm\frac{6}{2}, \pm\frac{6}{4}$$

4. Reduce and eliminate all repeats from the list:

$$\pm 1, \pm\frac{1}{2}, \pm\frac{1}{4}, \pm 2, \pm 3, \pm\frac{3}{2}, \pm\frac{3}{4}, \pm 6$$

MATCHED PROBLEM 4

Make a list of all possible rational zeros of $P(x) = 3x^4 - 7x^2 + 12$.

››› EXPLORE-DISCUSS 4

Let $P(x) = a_3x^3 + a_2x^2 + a_1x + a_0$, where a_3, a_2, a_1, and a_0 are integers.

1. If $P(2) = 0$, there is one coefficient that must be an even integer. Identify this coefficient and explain why it must be even.
2. If $P(\frac{1}{2}) = 0$, there is one coefficient that must be an even integer. Identify this coefficient and explain why it must be even.
3. If $a_3 = a_0 = 1$, $P(-1) \neq 0$, and $P(1) \neq 0$, does $P(x)$ have any rational zeros? Support your conclusion with verbal arguments and/or examples.

>>> CAUTION >>>

The rational zero theorem does *not* say that any of the rational numbers it lists actually are zeros! It's entirely possible that none of them are. But if there are any rational zeros for a given polynomial, they will be on the list. In short, the theorem identifies *potential* zeros, which can then be checked.

Once we have used the rational zero theorem to build a list of potential rational zeros, we can find any that actually are zeros using a process of elimination illustrated in Example 5.

EXAMPLE 5

Finding Rational Zeros

Find all the rational zeros for $P(x) = 2x^3 + 9x^2 + 7x - 6$.

SOLUTION

We begin by making lists, as in Example 4.

Factors of constant term, -6: $\pm 1, \pm 2, \pm 3, \pm 6$
Factors of leading coefficient, 2: $\pm 1, \pm 2$

All possible fractions with numerator from the first list and denominator from the second:

$$\pm\frac{1}{1}, \pm\frac{1}{2}, \pm\frac{2}{1}, \pm\frac{2}{2}, \pm\frac{3}{1}, \pm\frac{3}{2}, \pm\frac{6}{1}, \pm\frac{6}{2}$$

Reduce and eliminate repeats to find a list of potential rational zeros:

$$\pm 1, \pm\frac{1}{2}, \pm 2, \pm 3, \pm\frac{3}{2}, \pm 6 \qquad (2)$$

If $P(x)$ has any rational zeros, they must be in list (2). We could test each number r in this list by evaluating $P(r)$, either directly or using synthetic division. However, exploring the graph of $y = P(x)$ first will usually indicate which numbers in the list are the most likely candidates for zeros. Examining a graph of $P(x)$, we see that there are zeros near -3, near -2, and between 0 and 1. So the most likely candidates from our list are -3, -2, and $\frac{1}{2}$. We next use a graphing calculator to evaluate $P(x)$ for these three values (Fig. 5).

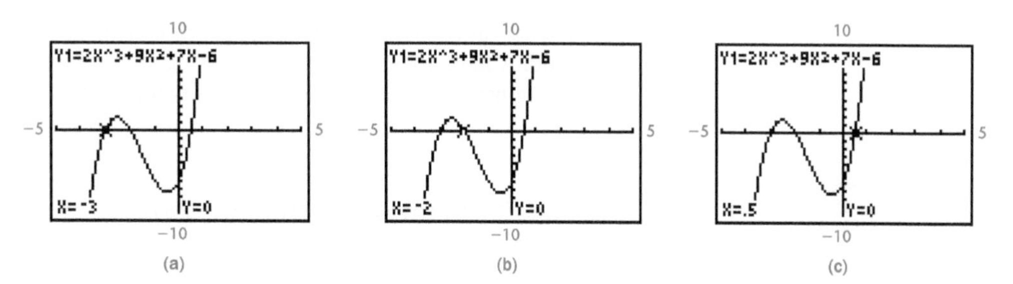

› **Figure 5**

It turns out that -3, -2, and $\frac{1}{2}$ are rational zeros of $P(x)$. Because a third-degree polynomial can have at most three zeros, we have found all the rational zeros. There is no need to test the remaining candidates in list (2).

MATCHED PROBLEM 5

Find all rational zeros for $P(x) = 2x^3 + x^2 - 11x - 10$.

As we saw in the solution of Example 5, rational zeros can be located by simply evaluating the polynomial. However, if we want to find multiple zeros, imaginary zeros, or exact values of irrational zeros, we need to consider *reduced polynomials*. If r is a zero of a polynomial $P(x)$, then we know that we can write

$$P(x) = (x - r)Q(x)$$

where $Q(x)$ is a polynomial of degree one less than the degree of $P(x)$. We will call the quotient polynomial $Q(x)$ the **reduced polynomial** for $P(x)$. In Example 5, we could have checked if $x = -3$ is a zero of $P(x)$ using synthetic division.

$$\begin{array}{r|rrrr} & 2 & 9 & 7 & -6 \\ & & -6 & -9 & 6 \\ \hline -3 & 2 & 3 & -2 & 0 \end{array}$$

This would not only show that $x = -3$ is, in fact, a zero, but also that $P(x) = (x + 3)(2x^2 + 3x - 2)$.

Because the reduced polynomial $Q(x) = 2x^2 + 3x - 2$ is a quadratic, we can find its zeros by factoring or the quadratic formula. Thus,

$$P(x) = (x + 3)(2x^2 + 3x - 2) = (x + 3)(x + 2)(2x - 1)$$

and we see that the zeros of $P(x)$ are -3, -2, and $\frac{1}{2}$, as before.

The advantage to this second approach is that if some of the zeros were irrational, we couldn't have found them exactly using a graphing calculator. Worse still, if any were imaginary, we couldn't have found them at all.

EXAMPLE 6 Finding Rational and Irrational Zeros

Find all zeros exactly for $P(x) = 2x^3 - 7x^2 + 4x + 3$.

SOLUTION

First, list the possible rational zeros as in Example 4:

$$\pm 1, \pm 3, \pm \tfrac{1}{2}, \pm \tfrac{3}{2}$$

Examining the graph of $y = P(x)$ (Fig. 6), we see that there is a zero between -1 and 0, another between 1 and 2, and a third between 2 and 3. We test the only likely candidates on our list, $-\frac{1}{2}$ and $\frac{3}{2}$, using synthetic division:

$$\begin{array}{r|rrrr} & 2 & -7 & 4 & 3 \\ & & -1 & 4 & -4 \\ \hline -\frac{1}{2} & 2 & -8 & 8 & -1 \end{array} \qquad \begin{array}{r|rrrr} & 2 & -7 & 4 & 3 \\ & & 3 & -6 & -3 \\ \hline \frac{3}{2} & 2 & -4 & -2 & 0 \end{array}$$

› Figure 6

So $-\frac{1}{2}$ is not a zero, but that's okay; $\frac{3}{2}$ is one zero, and the reduced polynomial is $2x^2 - 4x - 2$. Because the reduced polynomial is quadratic, we can use the quadratic formula to find the exact values of the remaining zeros:

$$2x^2 - 4x - 2 = 0 \quad \text{Divide both sides by 2.}$$

$$x^2 - 2x - 1 = 0 \quad \text{Use the quadratic formula with } a = 1, b = -2, c = -1.$$

$$x = \frac{2 \pm \sqrt{4 - 4(1)(-1)}}{2}$$

$$= \frac{2 \pm 2\sqrt{2}}{2} = 1 \pm \sqrt{2}$$

The exact zeros of $P(x)$ are $\frac{3}{2}$ and $1 \pm \sqrt{2}$.

MATCHED PROBLEM 6

Find all zeros exactly for $P(x) = 3x^3 - 10x^2 + 5x + 4$.

EXAMPLE 7 Finding Rational and Imaginary Zeros

Find all zeros exactly for $P(x) = x^4 - 6x^3 + 14x^2 - 14x + 5$.

SOLUTION

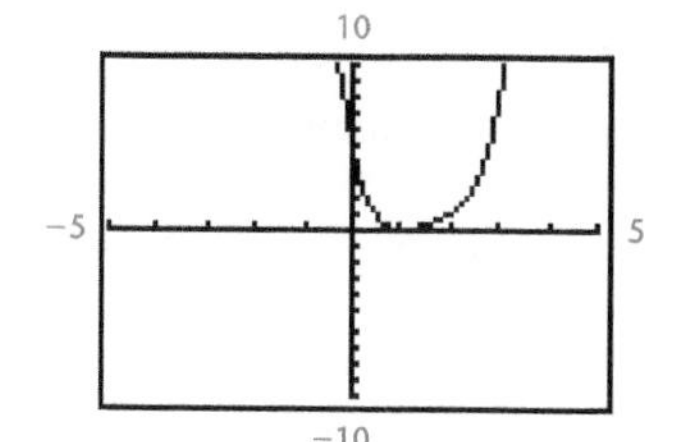

› Figure 7

Using the rational zero theorem, the only possible rational zeros are ± 1 and ± 5. The graph of $P(x)$ indicates that $x = 1$ is the only likely candidate (Fig. 7).

$$\begin{array}{r|rrrrr} & 1 & -6 & 14 & -14 & 5 \\ & & 1 & -5 & 9 & -5 \\ \hline 1 & 1 & -5 & 9 & -5 & 0 \end{array}$$

The reduced polynomial is $x^3 - 5x^2 + 9x - 5$.

So $x = 1$ is a zero. Note that it looks like there is a turning point at $x = 1$, so the zero may have even multiplicity. To check, we try synthetic division again, this time with the reduced polynomial.

$$\begin{array}{r|rrrr} & 1 & -5 & 9 & -5 \\ & & 1 & -4 & 5 \\ \hline 1 & 1 & -4 & 5 & 0 \end{array}$$

The new reduced polynomial is $x^2 - 4x + 5$.

This tells us that $x = 1$ is a zero of multiplicity 2, and that $P(x) = (x - 1)^2(x^2 - 4x + 5)$.

We use the quadratic formula to find the zeros of $x^2 - 4x + 5$:

$$x^2 - 4x + 5 = 0 \quad \text{Use the quadratic formula with } a = 1, b = -4, c = 5.$$

$$x = \frac{4 \pm \sqrt{16 - 4(1)(5)}}{2}$$

$$= \frac{4 \pm \sqrt{-4}}{2} = 2 \pm i$$

The exact zeros of $P(x)$ are 1 (multiplicity 2), $2 - i$, and $2 + i$.

MATCHED PROBLEM 7

Find all zeros exactly for $P(x) = x^4 + 4x^3 + 10x^2 + 12x + 5$.

REMARK: We were successful in finding all the zeros of the polynomials in Examples 6 and 7 because we could find sufficient rational zeros to reduce the original polynomial to a quadratic. This is not always possible. For example, the polynomial

$$P(x) = x^3 + 6x - 2$$

has no rational zeros, but does have an irrational zero at $x \approx 0.32748$ (Fig. 8). The other two zeros are imaginary. The techniques we have developed will not find the exact value of these roots.

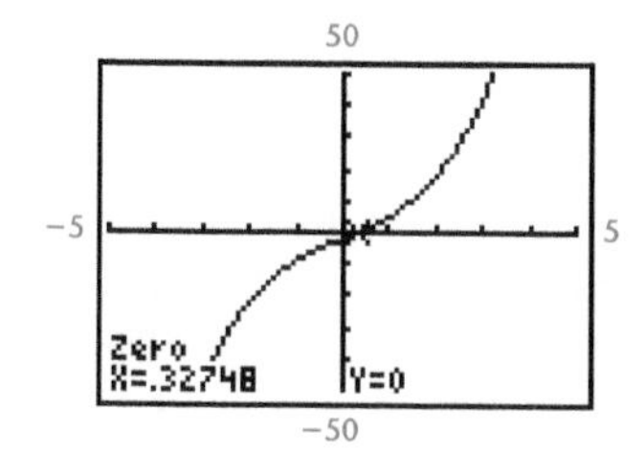

› Figure 8 $P(x) = x^3 + 6x - 2$.

››› EXPLORE-DISCUSS 5

There is a technique for finding the exact zeros of cubic polynomials, usually referred to as Cardano's formula.* This formula shows that the exact value of the irrational zero of $P(x) = x^3 + 6x - 2$ (see Fig. 8) is

$$x = \sqrt[3]{4} - \sqrt[3]{2}$$

(A) Verify that this is correct by expanding and simplifying

$$P(\sqrt[3]{4} - \sqrt[3]{2})$$

(B) Cardano's formula also shows that the two imaginary zeros are

$$-\tfrac{1}{2}(\sqrt[3]{4} - \sqrt[3]{2}) \pm \tfrac{1}{2}i\sqrt{3}(\sqrt[3]{4} - \sqrt[3]{2})$$

If you like algebraic manipulation, you can also verify that these are correct. (But you'd have to like it an awful lot.)

(C) Find a reference for Cardano's formula in a library or on the Internet. Use this formula to find the exact value of the irrational zero of

$$P(x) = x^3 + 9x - 6$$

Check your answer by comparing it with the approximate value obtained on a graphing calculator.

ANSWERS TO MATCHED PROBLEMS

1. (A) 5 (multiplicity 3), -3 (multiplicity 2), $4i$ and $-4i$ (each multiplicity 1)
(B) -5 (multiplicity 4), 5 (multiplicity 3), i (multiplicity 1)
2. (A) $(x + 1)(x - 1)^2(x^2 + 1)$ (B) $(x + 1)(x - 1)^2(x + i)(x - i)$
3. -3 (multiplicity 2), -2 (multiplicity 1), -1 (multiplicity 1), 0 (multiplicity 2), 1 (multiplicity 1) **4.** $\pm 1, \pm\frac{1}{3}, \pm 2, \pm\frac{2}{3}, \pm 3, \pm 4, \pm\frac{4}{3}, \pm 6, \pm 12$ **5.** $-2, -1, \frac{5}{2}$
6. $\frac{4}{3}, 1 - \sqrt{2}, 1 + \sqrt{2}$ **7.** -1 (multiplicity 2), $-1 - 2i, -1 + 2i$

*Girolamo Cardano (1501–1576), an Italian mathematician and physician, was the first to publish a formula for the solution to cubic equations of the form $x^3 + ax + b = 0$ and the first to realize that this technique could be used to solve other cubic equations. Having predicted that he would live to the age of 75, Cardano committed suicide in 1576.

3-4 Exercises

Write the zeros of each polynomial in Problems 1–8, and indicate the multiplicity of each if more than 1. What is the degree of each polynomial?

1. $P(x) = (x + 8)^3(x - 6)^2$ **2.** $P(x) = (x - 5)(x + 7)^2$

3. $P(x) = 3(x + 4)^3(x - 3)^2(x + 1)$

4. $P(x) = 5(x - 2)^3(x + 3)^2(x - 1)$

5. $P(x) = (x^2 + 4)^3(x^2 - 4)^5(x + 2i)$

6. $P(x) = (x^2 + 7x + 10)^2(x^2 + 6x + 10)^3$

7. $P(x) = (x^3 - 9x)(x^2 + 9)(x + 9)^2$

8. $P(x) = (x^3 - 3x^2 + 3x - 1)(x^2 - 1)(x - i)$

9. Explain in your own words what the fundamental theorem of algebra says. Does it guarantee that every polynomial has a nonreal zero?

10. Do you agree or disagree with the following statement: Every polynomial of degree n has n zeros? Explain.

11. Explain the connection between the zeros of a polynomial, and its linear factors.

12. What is the least degree that a polynomial with zeros 3, i, and $4 + i$ can have if its coefficients are real? Why?

13. True or false: The rational zero test indicates that every polynomial has some rational zeros. Explain.

14. True or false: Every real zero of a polynomial will appear on the list of numbers provided by the rational zero test. Explain.

In Problems 15–20, find a polynomial $P(x)$ of lowest degree, with leading coefficient 1, that has the indicated set of zeros. Leave the answer in a factored form. Indicate the degree of the polynomial.

15. 3 (multiplicity 2) and -4

16. -2 (multiplicity 3) and 1 (multiplicity 2)

17. -7 (multiplicity 3), $-3 + \sqrt{2}$, $-3 - \sqrt{2}$

18. $\frac{1}{3}$ (multiplicity 2), $5 + \sqrt{7}$, $5 - \sqrt{7}$

19. $(2 - 3i)$, $(2 + 3i)$, -4 (multiplicity 2)

20. $i\sqrt{3}$ (multiplicity 2), $-i\sqrt{3}$ (multiplicity 2), and 4 (multiplicity 3)

In Problems 21–26, find a polynomial of lowest degree, with leading coefficient 1, that has the indicated graph. Assume all zeros are integers. Leave the answer in a factored form. Indicate the degree of each polynomial.

21.

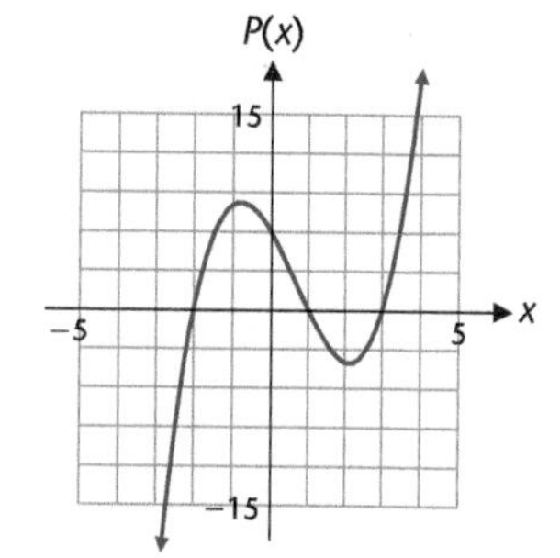

22.

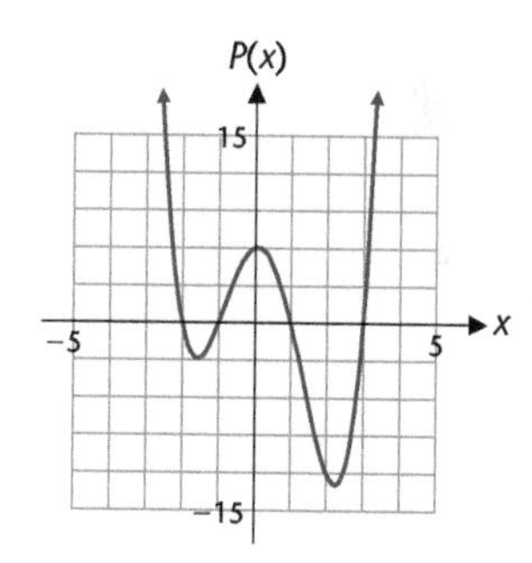

23.

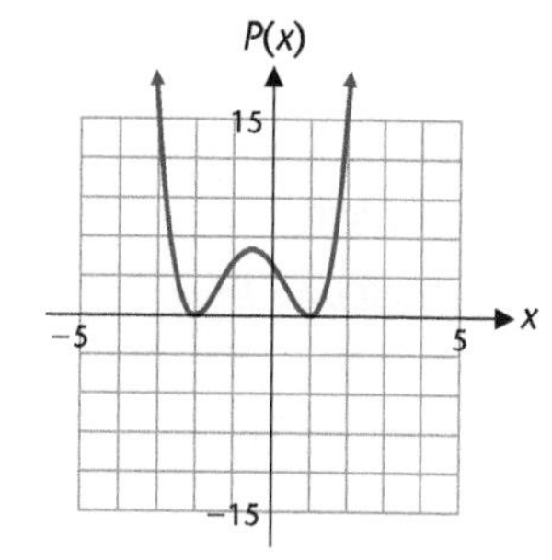

24.

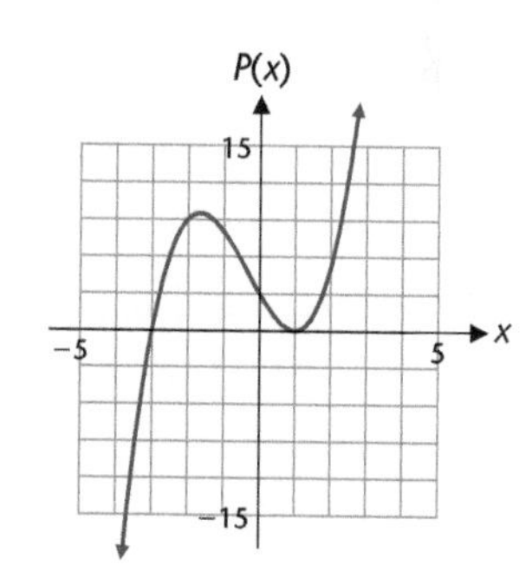

25.

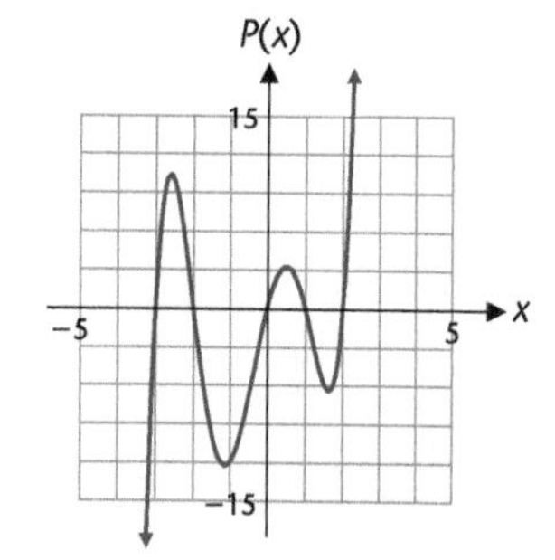

26.

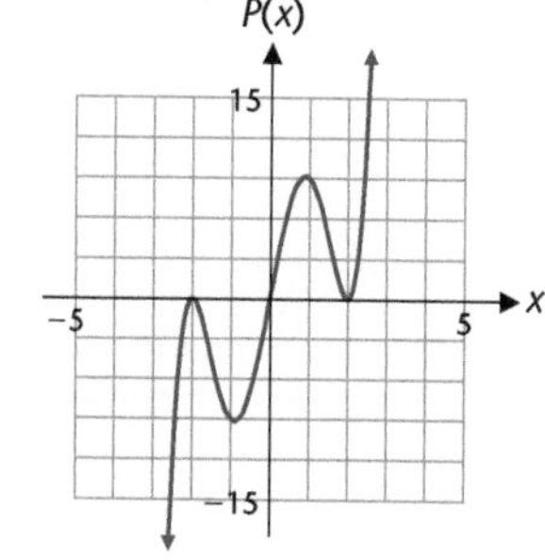

For each polynomial in Problems 27–32, use the rational zero theorem to list all possible rational zeros.

27. $P(x) = x^3 - 2x^2 - 5x + 6$

28. $P(x) = x^3 + 3x^2 - 6x - 8$

29. $P(x) = 3x^3 - 11x^2 + 8x + 4$

30. $P(x) = 2x^3 + x^2 - 4x - 3$

31. $P(x) = 12x^3 - 16x^2 - 5x + 3$

32. $P(x) = 2x^3 - 9x^2 + 14x - 5$

In Problems 33–36, factor each polynomial in two ways:
(A) As a product of linear factors (with real coefficients) and quadratic factors (with real coefficients and imaginary zeros)
(B) As a product of linear factors with complex coefficients

33. $P(x) = x^4 + 5x^2 + 4$ **34.** $P(x) = x^4 + 18x^2 + 81$

35. $P(x) = x^3 - x^2 + 25x - 25$

36. $P(x) = x^5 + x^4 - x - 1$

In Problems 37–42, write P(x) as a product of linear factors.

37. $P(x) = x^3 + 9x^2 + 24x + 16$; -1 is a zero

38. $P(x) = x^3 - 4x^2 - 3x + 18$; 3 is a double zero

39. $P(x) = x^4 - 1$; 1 and -1 are zeros

40. $P(x) = x^4 + 2x^2 + 1$; i is a double zero

41. $P(x) = 2x^3 - 17x^2 + 90x - 41$; $\frac{1}{2}$ is a zero

42. $P(x) = 3x^3 - 10x^2 + 31x + 26$; $-\frac{2}{3}$ is a zero

In Problems 43–52, find all zeros exactly (rational, irrational, and imaginary) for each polynomial.

43. $P(x) = x^3 - 19x + 30$ **44.** $P(x) = x^3 - 7x^2 + 36$

45. $P(x) = x^4 - \frac{21}{10}x^3 + \frac{2}{5}x$

46. $P(x) = x^4 + \frac{7}{6}x^3 - \frac{7}{3}x^2 - \frac{5}{2}x$

47. $P(x) = x^4 - 5x^3 + \frac{15}{2}x^2 - 2x - 2$

48. $P(x) = x^4 - \frac{13}{4}x^2 - \frac{5}{2}x - \frac{1}{4}$ **49.** $P(x) = x^4 + 11x^2 + 30$

50. $P(x) = x^4 + 5x^2 + 6$

51. $P(x) = 3x^5 - 5x^4 - 8x^3 + 16x^2 + 21x + 5$

52. $P(x) = 2x^5 - 3x^4 - 6x^3 + 23x^2 - 26x + 10$

In Problems 53–62, find all zeros exactly (rational, irrational, and imaginary) for each polynomial equation.

53. $2x^3 - 5x^2 + 1 = 0$ **54.** $2x^3 - 10x^2 + 12x - 4 = 0$

55. $x^4 + 4x^3 - x^2 - 20x - 20 = 0$

56. $x^4 - 4x^2 - 4x - 1 = 0$

57. $x^4 - 2x^3 - 5x^2 + 8x + 4 = 0$

58. $x^4 - 2x^2 - 16x - 15 = 0$

59. $x^4 + 10x^2 + 9 = 0$ **60.** $x^4 + 29x^2 + 100 = 0$

61. $2x^5 - 3x^4 - 2x + 3 = 0$

62. $2x^5 + x^4 - 6x^3 - 3x^2 - 8x - 4 = 0$

In Problems 63–68, write each polynomial as a product of linear factors.

63. $P(x) = 6x^3 + 13x^2 - 4$

64. $P(x) = 6x^3 - 17x^2 - 4x + 3$

65. $P(x) = x^3 + 2x^2 - 9x - 4$

66. $P(x) = x^3 - 8x^2 + 17x - 4$

67. $P(x) = 4x^4 - 4x^3 - 9x^2 + x + 2$

68. $P(x) = 2x^4 + 3x^3 - 4x^2 - 3x + 2$

In Problems 69–74, multiply.

69. $[x - (4 - 5i)][x - (4 + 5i)]$

70. $[x - (2 - 3i)][x - (2 + 3i)]$

71. $[x - (3 + 4i)][x - (3 - 4i)]$

72. $[x - (5 + 2i)][x - (5 - 2i)]$

73. $[x - (a + bi)][x - (a - bi)]$ **74.** $(x - bi)(x + bi)$

75. Given that $2 + i$ is a zero of $P(x) = x^3 - 7x^2 + 17x - 15$, find all other zeros by
(A) Writing the conjugate zero.
(B) Writing the two linear factors corresponding to these zeros.
(C) Multiplying these factors to obtain a quadratic factor.
(D) Using long division to divide $P(x)$ by this quadratic factor.

76. See Problem 75. Find all other zeros of $P(x)$ by
(A) Dividing out $2 + i$ using synthetic division.
(B) Dividing out the conjugate zero by synthetic division.
Do you prefer the method of Problem 75 or Problem 76?

In Problems 77–82, find all other zeros of P(x), given the indicated zero. (See Problems 75 and 76.)

77. $P(x) = x^3 - 5x^2 + 4x + 10$; $3 - i$ is one zero

78. $P(x) = x^3 + x^2 - 4x + 6$; $1 + i$ is one zero

79. $P(x) = x^3 - 3x^2 + 25x - 75$; $-5i$ is one zero

80. $P(x) = x^3 + 2x^2 + 16x + 32$; $4i$ is one zero

81. $P(x) = x^4 - 4x^3 + 3x^2 + 8x - 10$; $2 + i$ is one zero

82. $P(x) = x^4 - 2x^3 + 7x^2 - 18x - 18$; $-3i$ is one zero

Prove that each of the real numbers in Problems 83–86 is not rational by writing an appropriate polynomial and making use of the rational zero theorem.

83. $\sqrt{6}$ **84.** $\sqrt{12}$ **85.** $\sqrt[3]{5}$ **86.** $\sqrt[5]{8}$

In Problems 87–90, determine the number of real zeros of each polynomial P(x), and explain why P(x) has no rational zeros.

87. $P(x) = x^4 - 5x^2 - 6$

88. $P(x) = 3x^4 + x^2 + 12$

89. $P(x) = x^3 - 3x - 1$

90. $P(x) = x^3 - 5x + 3$

In Problems 91–96, find all zeros (rational, irrational, and imaginary) exactly.

91. $P(x) = 3x^3 - 37x^2 + 84x - 24$

92. $P(x) = 2x^3 - 9x^2 - 2x + 30$

93. $P(x) = 4x^4 + 4x^3 + 49x^2 + 64x - 240$

94. $P(x) = 6x^4 + 35x^3 + 2x^2 - 233x - 360$

95. $P(x) = 4x^4 - 44x^3 + 145x^2 - 192x + 90$

96. $P(x) = x^5 - 6x^4 + 6x^3 + 28x^2 - 72x + 48$

97. The solutions to the equation $x^3 - 1 = 0$ are all the cube roots of 1.
(A) How many cube roots of 1 are there?
(B) 1 is obviously a cube root of 1; find all others.

98. The solutions to the equation $x^3 - 8 = 0$ are all the cube roots of 8.
(A) How many cube roots of 8 are there?
(B) 2 is obviously a cube root of 8; find all others.

99. If P is a polynomial function with real coefficients of degree n, with n odd, then what is the maximum number of times the graph of $y = P(x)$ can cross the x axis? What is the minimum number of times?

100. Answer the questions in Problem 99 for n even.

101. Given $P(x) = x^2 + 2ix - 5$ with $2 - i$ a zero, show that $2 + i$ is not a zero of $P(x)$. Does this contradict Theorem 3? Explain.

102. If $P(x)$ and $Q(x)$ are two polynomials of degree n, and if $P(x) = Q(x)$ for more than n values of x, then how are $P(x)$ and $Q(x)$ related?

103. Theorem 5 asserts that every polynomial of odd degree with real coefficients has at least one real zero. Use what you learned about right and left behavior of polynomials in Section 3-1 to justify this fact.

104. Use the rational zero theorem to prove that a polynomial with a nonzero constant term cannot have $x = 0$ as one of its zeros. Then confirm this fact using direct substitution of $x = 0$ into a generic polynomial with nonzero constant term.

105. If the constant term of a polynomial is zero, the rational zero theorem fails because the only potential zero on the list will be zero. How can you overcome this? [*Hint:* What do all of the nonzero terms have in common in this case?]

106. In this problem we will sketch a proof of the rational zero theorem. Let $P(x) = a_nx^n + a_{n-1}x^{n-1} + a_{n-2}x^{n-2} + \cdots + a_1x + a_0$ and suppose that p/q is a rational number in lowest terms that is a zero of $P(x)$.
(A) Substitute p/q in for x and set the result equal to zero. Show that the resulting equation can be written as $a_np^n + a_{n-1}p^{n-1}q + a_{n-2}p^{n-2}q^2 + \cdots a_1pq^{n-1} = -a_0q^n$.
(B) Notice that p appears in every term on the left, so is a factor of the left side. Explain why p cannot be a factor of q^n. [*Hint:* What do we know about p/q?]
(C) Since p is a factor of the left side, and *not* a factor of q^n, what is the relationship between p and a_0? How does this prove half of the rational zero theorem?
(D) Rearrange the equation from part A so that the only term on the left is the one with no power of q. Then adapt parts B and C to prove that q must be a factor of a_n.

APPLICATIONS

Find all rational solutions exactly, and find irrational solutions to two decimal places.

107. STORAGE A rectangular storage unit has dimensions 1 by 2 by 3 feet. If each dimension is increased by the same amount, how much should this amount be to create a new storage unit with volume 10 times the old?

108. CONSTRUCTION A rectangular box has dimensions 1 by 1 by 2 feet. If each dimension is increased by the same amount, how much should this amount be to create a new box with volume six times the old?

109. PACKAGING An open box is to be made from a rectangular piece of cardboard that measures 8 by 5 inches, by cutting out squares of the same size from each corner and bending up the sides (see the figure). If the volume of the box is to be 14 cubic inches, how large a square should be cut from each corner? [*Hint:* Determine the domain of x from physical considerations before starting.]

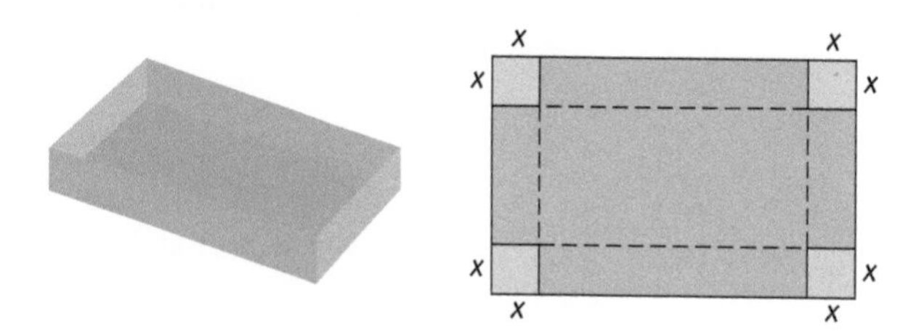

110. FABRICATION An open metal chemical tank is to be made from a rectangular piece of stainless steel that measures 10 by 8 feet, by cutting out squares of the same size from each corner and bending up the sides (see the figure for Problem 109). If the volume of the tank is to be 48 cubic feet, how large a square should be cut from each corner?

3-5 Rational Functions and Inequalities

- Rational Functions and Properties of Their Graphs
- Finding Vertical and Horizontal Asymptotes
- Drawing the Graph of a Rational Function
- Solving Rational Inequalities

In this section, we will apply our knowledge of the graphs and zeros of polynomial functions to study *rational functions,* which are functions that are quotients of polynomials. Now more than ever, it's important to understand the features of these graphs before attempting to use a graphing calculator to draw them. Often, the output that appears on the screen will require a lot of interpretation, and unless you have a good idea of what to expect, you may struggle with this interpretation. Our goal will be to produce hand sketches (with help from a graphing calculator) that clearly show all of the important features of the graph.

Rational Functions and Properties of Their Graphs

The number $\frac{7}{13}$ is called a *rational number* because it is a quotient (or ratio) of integers. The function

$$f(x) = \frac{x + 1}{x^2 - x - 6}$$

is called a *rational function* because it is a quotient of polynomials.

DEFINITION 1 Rational Function

A function f is a **rational function** if it can be written in the form

$$f(x) = \frac{p(x)}{q(x)}$$

where $p(x)$ and $q(x)$ are polynomials.

When working with rational functions, we will assume that the coefficients of $p(x)$ and $q(x)$ are real numbers, and that the domain of f is the set of all real numbers x such that $q(x) \neq 0$.

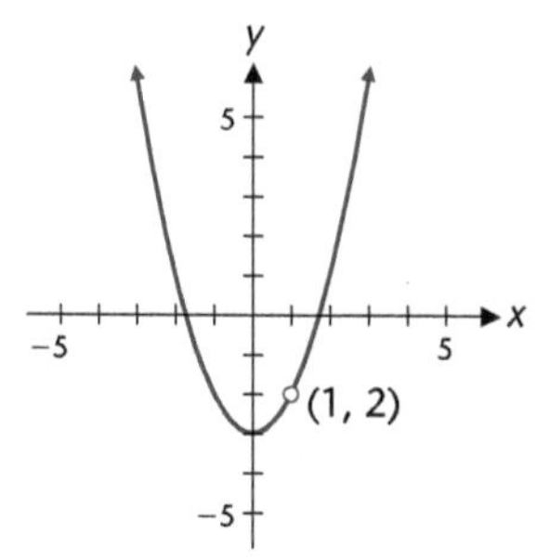

(a) $p(x) = \frac{(x-1)(x^2-3)}{x-1}$

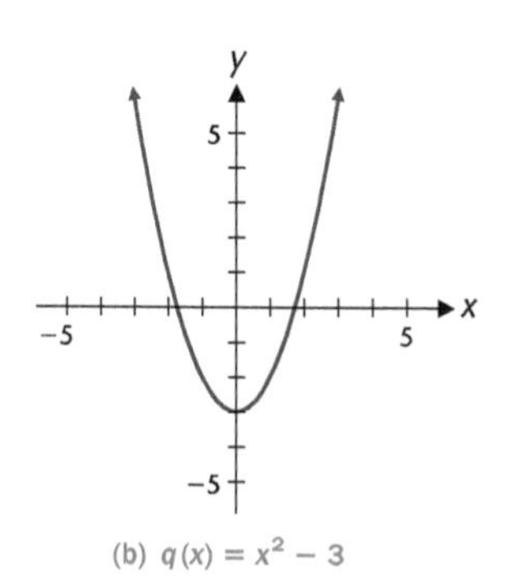

(b) $q(x) = x^2 - 3$

› Figure 1

Consider the rational function

$$p(x) = \frac{(x-1)(x^2-3)}{x-1}$$

and the polynomial $q(x) = x^2 - 3$. Are they actually the same function? If you answered yes, you're almost right. They're not identical because $p(1)$ is undefined, while $q(1) = -2$. For every other x value, they are equal. Their graphs are identical except at $x = 1$, where the graph of $p(x)$ has a hole (Fig. 1).

In general, when a real number c is a zero of both $p(x)$ and $q(x)$, then $x - c$ is a factor of both, and we can write their quotient as

$$f(x) = \frac{p(x)}{q(x)} = \frac{(x-c)p_r(x)}{(x-c)q_r(x)}$$

$p_r(x)$ and $q_r(x)$ are polynomials with degree one less than p and q, respectively.*

Then the graph of $f_r(x) = p_r(x)/q_r(x)$, is identical to the graph of $f(x) = p(x)/q(x)$, except possibly for a hole at $x = c$.

Later in this section we will discuss how to handle the minor complication caused by common real zeros of $p(x)$ and $q(x)$. But to avoid that complication now, **unless stated to the contrary, we will assume that for any rational function f we consider, $p(x)$ and $q(x)$ have no real zero in common.**

For any rational function, the zeros of the numerator and denominator each have significance. A rational function is undefined for any x value that is a zero of its denominator, so those values are not in the domain. If the degree of the denominator is n, there are at most n such values. The real zeros of the numerator, on the other hand, are the zeros (and x intercepts) of a rational function. (This is because a fraction is zero exactly when its numerator is zero.) If the degree of the numerator is m, there are at most m x intercepts.

EXAMPLE 1 Domain and x Intercepts

Find the domain and x intercepts for $f(x) = \frac{2x^2 - 2x - 4}{x^2 - 9}$.

SOLUTION

Since we need the zeros of the numerator and denominator, it's a good idea to begin by factoring both.

$$f(x) = \frac{2x^2 - 2x - 4}{x^2 - 9} = \frac{2(x-2)(x+1)}{(x-3)(x+3)}$$

Because the denominator is zero for $x = 3$ and $x = -3$, the domain of f is

$$x \neq \pm 3 \quad \text{or} \quad (-\infty, -3) \cup (-3, 3) \cup (3, \infty)$$

*We referred to p_r and q_r as reduced polynomials in the last section.

Because the numerator is zero for $x = 2$ and $x = -1$, the zeros of f, and thus the x intercepts of f, are -1 and 2.

MATCHED PROBLEM 1

Find the domain and x intercepts for $f(x) = \dfrac{3x^2 - 12}{x^2 + 2x - 3}$.

The graph of the rational function

$$f(x) = \frac{x^2 - 1.44}{x^3 - x}$$

is shown in Figure 2.

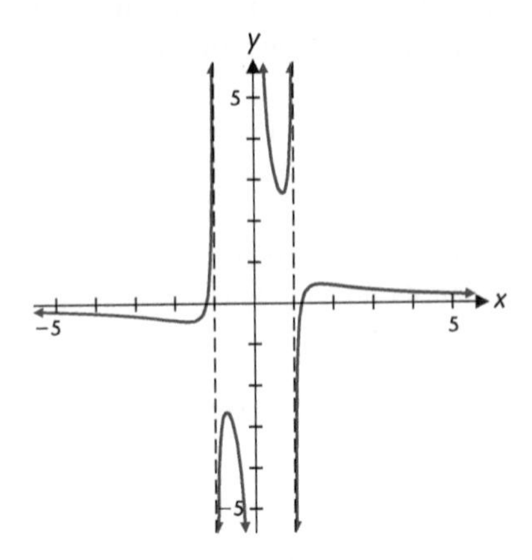

› **Figure 2** $f(x) = \dfrac{x^2 - 1.44}{x^3 - x}$.

The domain of f consists of all real numbers except $x = -1$, $x = 0$, and $x = 1$ (the zeros of the denominator $x^3 - x$). The dotted vertical lines at $x = \pm 1$ indicate that those values of x are excluded from the domain. (Zero is excluded as well, but a dotted vertical line at $x = 0$ would coincide with the y axis and is omitted.) The graph is discontinuous at $x = -1$, $x = 0$, and $x = 1$, but is continuous elsewhere and has no sharp corners. The zeros of f are the zeros of the numerator $x^2 - 1.44$, which are $x = -1.2$ and $x = 1.2$. The graph of f has four turning points. Its left and right behavior is the same as that of the function $g(x) = \frac{1}{x}$, which we learned in Chapter 1. (The graph is close to the x axis for very large positive and negative values of x.) The graph of f illustrates the general properties of rational functions that are listed in Theorem 1. We have already justified Property 3; the other properties are established in calculus.

> **THEOREM 1 Properties of Rational Functions**
>
> Let $f(x) = p(x)/q(x)$ be a rational function where $p(x)$ and $q(x)$ are polynomials of degrees m and n, respectively. Then the graph of $f(x)$:
>
> 1. Is continuous with the exception of at most n real numbers (the zeros of the denominator)
> 2. Has no sharp corners
> 3. Has at most m real zeros
> 4. Has at most $m + n - 1$ turning points
> 5. Has the same left and right behavior as the quotient of the highest-power terms of $p(x)$ and $q(x)$

Figure 3 shows graphs of several rational functions, illustrating the properties of Theorem 1.

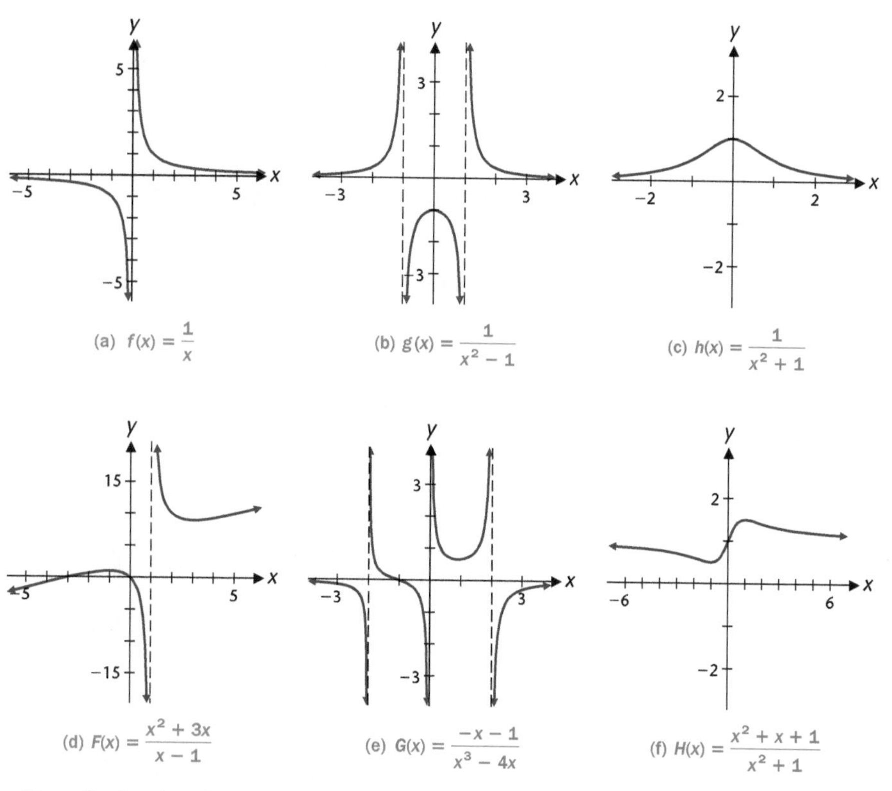

› **Figure 3** Graphs of rational functions.

EXAMPLE 2 Properties of Graphs of Rational Functions

Use Theorem 1 to explain why each graph is not the graph of a rational function.

(A)

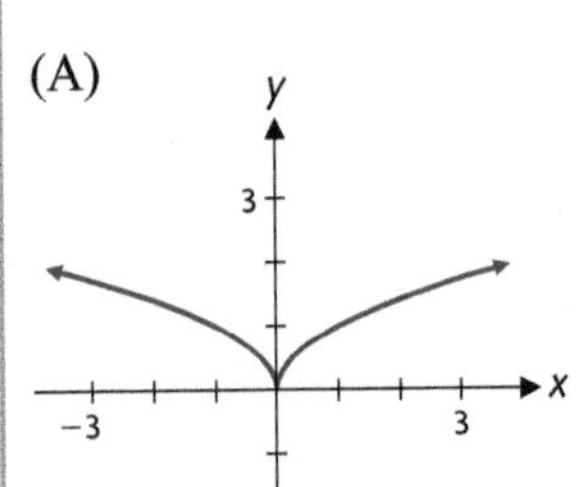

(B)

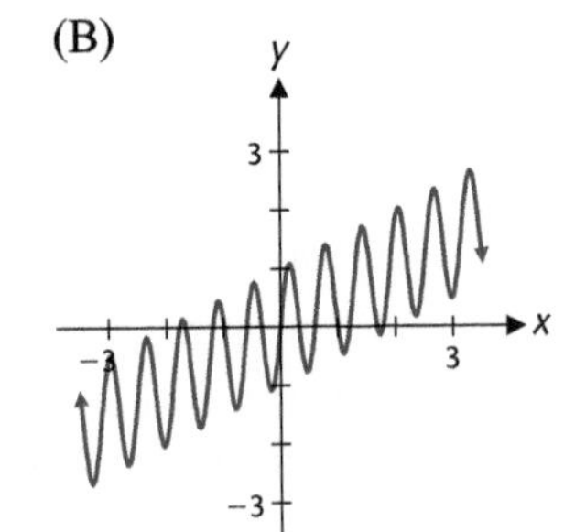

(C)

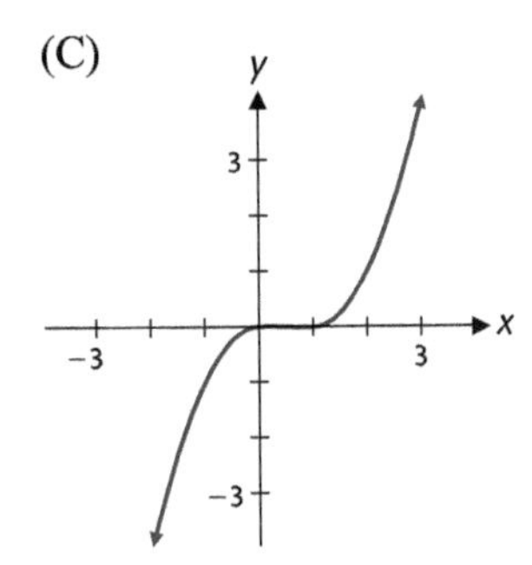

SOLUTIONS

(A) The graph has a sharp corner when $x = 0$, so Property 2 is not satisfied.

(B) The graph has an infinite number of turning points, so Property 4 is not satisfied.

(C) The graph has an infinite number of zeros (all values of x between 0 and 1, inclusive, are zeros), so Property 3 is not satisfied.

MATCHED PROBLEM 2

Use Theorem 1 to explain why each graph is not the graph of a rational function.

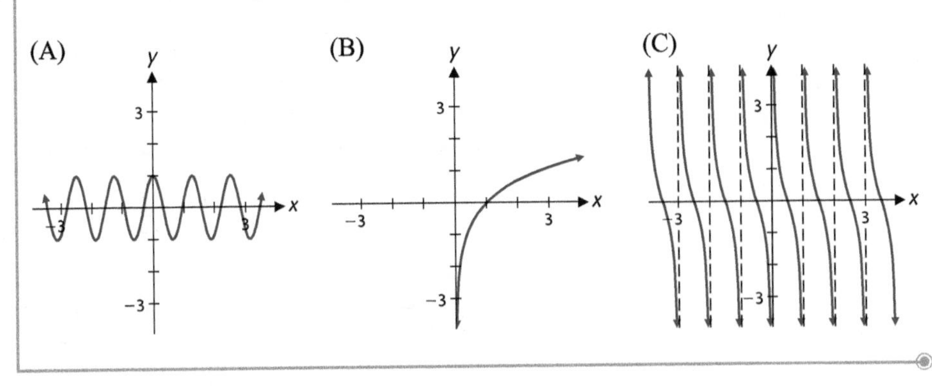

Finding Vertical and Horizontal Asymptotes

All of the graphs in Figure 3 exhibit similar behavior near their points of discontinuity. This behavior can be described using the concept of *vertical asymptote.*

››› EXPLORE-DISCUSS 1

(A) Complete Table 1.

Table 1 Behavior of $\frac{5}{x}$ as x Approaches Zero from the Right

x	1	0.1	0.01	0.001	0.0001	0.000 01
$5/x$						

Describe the outputs as the x values approach zero from the right.

(B) Complete Table 2.

Table 2 Behavior of $\frac{5}{x}$ as x Approaches Zero from the Left

x	−1	−0.1	−0.01	−0.001	−0.0001	−0.000 01
$5/x$						

Describe the outputs as the x values approach zero from the left.

(C) Use parts A and B and a graph of $y = 5/x$ to discuss how the output of $y = 5/x$ for x values close to zero affects the graph near $x = 0$.

In Explore-Discuss 1, we see why most of the graphs in Figure 3 exhibit the behavior they do near the dotted vertical lines. As x approaches a zero of the denominator, the outputs of the function get larger and larger (either positive or negative) and approach ∞ or $-\infty$. For the function $f(x) = 5/x$, we would say that as x approaches zero from the right, $5/x$ approaches ∞, and write this as

$$\frac{5}{x} \to \infty \quad \text{as} \quad x \to 0^+$$

As x approaches zero from the left, $5/x$ approaches $-\infty$; we write

$$\frac{5}{x} \to -\infty \quad \text{as} \quad x \to 0^-$$

In this case, we say that the vertical line $x = 0$ (the y axis) is a *vertical asymptote* for the graph of $f(x)$.

››› EXPLORE-DISCUSS 2

Construct tables similar to Tables 1 and 2 for $g(x) = 1/x^2$ and discuss the behavior of the graph of $g(x)$ near $x = 0$.

› DEFINITION 2 Vertical Asymptote

The vertical line $x = a$ is a **vertical asymptote** for the graph of $y = f(x)$ if

$$f(x) \to \infty \quad \text{or} \quad f(x) \to -\infty \quad \text{as} \quad x \to a^+ \quad \text{or as} \quad x \to a^-$$

(that is, if $f(x)$ either increases or decreases without bound as x approaches a from the right or from the left).

Informally, a vertical asymptote is a vertical line that the graph approaches but never intersects. To find the vertical asymptotes of a rational function, you simply need to find the zeros of the denominator. For example, the denominator of

$$f(x) = \frac{x^2 - 1.44}{x^3 - x} = \frac{x^2 - 1.44}{x(x - 1)(x + 1)}$$

has three zeros (0, 1, and -1), so the graph of $f(x)$ has three vertical asymptotes, $x = 0$, $x = 1$, and $x = -1$ (see Fig. 2 on page 338).

› THEOREM 2 Vertical Asymptotes of Rational Functions

Let $f(x) = p(x)/q(x)$ be a rational function. If a is a zero of $q(x)$, then the line $x = a$ is a vertical asymptote of the graph of f.*

We next turn our attention to the left and right behavior of rational functions. For many (but not all) rational functions, it can be described using the concept of *horizontal asymptotes*.

*Recall that we are assuming that $p(x)$ and $q(x)$ have no real zeros in common. Theorem 2 may not be valid without this assumption.

››› EXPLORE-DISCUSS 3

Refer back to your graph of $y = 5/x$ in part C of Explore-Discuss 1.

(A) Complete Table 3.

Table 3 Behavior of $\frac{5}{x}$ as $x \to \infty$

x	1	10	100	1,000	10,000	100,000
$5/x$						

Describe the outputs as the x values approach ∞.

(B) Complete Table 4.

Table 4 Behavior of $\frac{5}{x}$ as $x \to -\infty$

x	−1	−10	−100	−1,000	−10,000	−100,000
$5/x$						

Describe the outputs as the x values approach $-\infty$.

(C) Use parts A and B and a graph of $y = 5/x$ to discuss how the output of $y = 5/x$ for large values of x affects the graph.

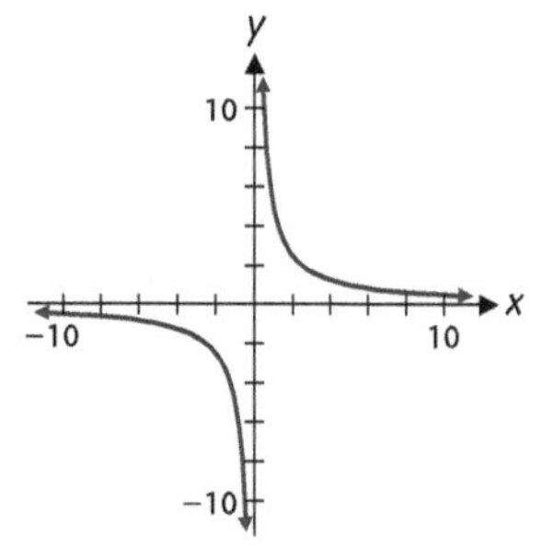

› **Figure 4**

Note that the left and right behavior of the graph of $f(x) = 5/x$ shows the graph approaching the x axis in both directions (Fig. 4).

In symbols, we would write

$$\frac{5}{x} \to 0 \quad \text{as} \quad x \to \infty \quad \text{and as} \quad x \to -\infty$$

In this case, we would say that the line $y = 0$ (the x axis) is a *horizontal asymptote* of the graph of $f(x)$.

››› EXPLORE-DISCUSS 4

Construct tables similar to Tables 3 and 4 for each of the following functions, and discuss the behavior of each as $x \to \infty$ and as $x \to -\infty$:

(A) $f(x) = \dfrac{3x}{x^2 + 1}$ **(B)** $g(x) = \dfrac{3x^2}{x^2 + 1}$ **(C)** $h(x) = \dfrac{3x^3}{x^2 + 1}$

> **DEFINITION 3 Horizontal Asymptote**

The horizontal line $y = b$ is a **horizontal asymptote** for the graph of $f(x)$ if

$$f(x) \rightarrow b \quad \text{as} \quad x \rightarrow -\infty \quad \text{or as} \quad x \rightarrow \infty$$

(that is, if $f(x)$ approaches b as x increases without bound or as x decreases without bound).

Informally, a horizontal asymptote is a horizontal line that the graph gets infinitely close to as x increases or decreases without bound.

While the mathematical behavior of a function near horizontal and vertical asymptotes is quite different, they are very similar graphically—they are lines that a graph gets infinitely close to.

A rational function $f(x) = p(x)/q(x)$ has the same left and right behavior as the quotient of the leading terms of $p(x)$ and $q(x)$ (Property 5 of Theorem 1). Consequently, **a rational function has at most one horizontal asymptote.** Moreover, we can determine easily whether a rational function has a horizontal asymptote, and if it does, find its equation. Theorem 3 gives the details.

> **THEOREM 3 Horizontal Asymptotes of Rational Functions**

Consider the rational function

$$f(x) = \frac{a_m x^m + \cdots + a_1 x + a_0}{b_n x^n + \cdots + b_1 x + b_0}$$

where $a_m \neq 0$, $b_n \neq 0$. Note that m is the degree of the numerator, and n is the degree of the denominator.

1. If $m < n$, the line $y = 0$ (the x axis) is a horizontal asymptote.
2. If $m = n$, the line $y = a_m/b_n$ is a horizontal asymptote.
3. If $m > n$, there is no horizontal asymptote.

In 1 and 2, the graph of f approaches the horizontal asymptote both as $x \rightarrow \infty$ and as $x \rightarrow -\infty$.

EXAMPLE 3 Finding Vertical and Horizontal Asymptotes for a Rational Function

Find all vertical and horizontal asymptotes for

(A) $f(x) = \dfrac{2x^2 - 2x - 4}{x^2 - 9}$ (B) $g(x) = \dfrac{3x}{x^3 + 5x^2}$ (C) $k(x) = \dfrac{x^3 + 2x - 100}{x^2 + 10}$

SOLUTIONS

(A) Because the denominator can be factored as $(x + 3)(x - 3)$, its zeros are 3 and -3, and the graph of $f(x)$ has vertical asymptotes at $x = 3$ and $x = -3$. Because the numerator and denominator have the same degree, according to Theorem 3, part 2, the line

$$y = \frac{a_2}{b_2} = \frac{2}{1} = 2^* \qquad a_2 = 2, b_2 = 1$$

is a horizontal asymptote (Theorem 3, part 2).

(B) The denominator factors as $x^3 + 5x^2 = x^2(x + 5)$, so its zeros are 0 and -5, and the graph of $g(x)$ has vertical asymptotes at $x = 0$ and $x = -5$. The degree of the denominator is greater than that of the numerator, so the line $y = 0$ is a horizontal asymptote (Theorem 3, part 1).

(C) The denominator has no real zeros, so there are no vertical asymptotes. The degree of the numerator is greater than that of the denominator, so there is no horizontal asymptote (Theorem 3, part 3).

MATCHED PROBLEM 3

Find all vertical and horizontal asymptotes for

(A) $f(x) = \dfrac{3x^2 - 12}{x^2 + 2x - 3}$ (B) $g(x) = \dfrac{x^2 - 10}{3x^4 - 3x^2}$ (C) $k(x) = \dfrac{8x^4}{x^2 + x + 5}$

››› CAUTION ›››

The asymptotes of a graph are *lines,* not numbers. You should always write the equation of an asymptote in the form $x = a$ (vertical) or $y = a$ (horizontal).

› Drawing the Graph of a Rational Function

We will now use the techniques for locating asymptotes, along with other graphing aids discussed in the text, to graph several rational functions. First, we outline a step-by-step approach to the problem of graphing rational functions.

*The dashed "think boxes" are used to enclose steps that may be performed mentally.

ANALYZING AND SKETCHING THE GRAPH OF A RATIONAL FUNCTION: $f(x) = p(x)/q(x)$

Step 1. *Intercepts.* Find the real solutions of the equation $p(x) = 0$ and use these solutions to plot any x intercepts of the graph of f. Evaluate $f(0)$, if it exists, and plot the y intercept.

Step 2. *Vertical Asymptotes.* Find the real solutions of the equation $q(x) = 0$ and use these solutions to determine the domain of f, the points of discontinuity, and the vertical asymptotes. Sketch any vertical asymptotes as dashed lines.

Step 3. *Horizontal Asymptotes.* Determine whether there is a horizontal asymptote and if so, sketch it as a dashed line.

Step 4. *Complete the Sketch.* Use the information determined in steps 1–3, and a graphing calculator, to sketch the graph by hand.

EXAMPLE 4 Graphing a Rational Function

Graph $f(x) = \dfrac{2x}{x - 3}$.

SOLUTION

$$f(x) = \frac{2x}{x - 3}$$

Step 1. *Intercepts.* Find real zeros of $2x$ and find $f(0)$:

$$\begin{aligned} 2x &= 0 \\ x &= 0 \quad \text{x intercept} \\ f(0) &= 0 \quad \text{y intercept} \end{aligned}$$

The graph crosses the coordinate axes only at the origin. Plot this intercept, as shown in Figure 5.

Step 2. *Vertical Asymptotes.* Find real zeros of $x - 3$:

$$\begin{aligned} x - 3 &= 0 \\ x &= 3 \end{aligned}$$

The graph has a vertical asymptote at $x = 3$. The domain of f is $x \neq 3$, and f is discontinuous at $x = 3$. Sketch this asymptote, as shown in Figure 5.

Step 3. *Horizontal Asymptote.* The numerator and denominator have the same degree, so we can use part 2 of Theorem 3. The leading coefficients of the numerator and denominator are 2 and 1, respectively, so

$$y = \frac{2}{1} = 2$$

is a horizontal asymptote, as shown in Figure 5.

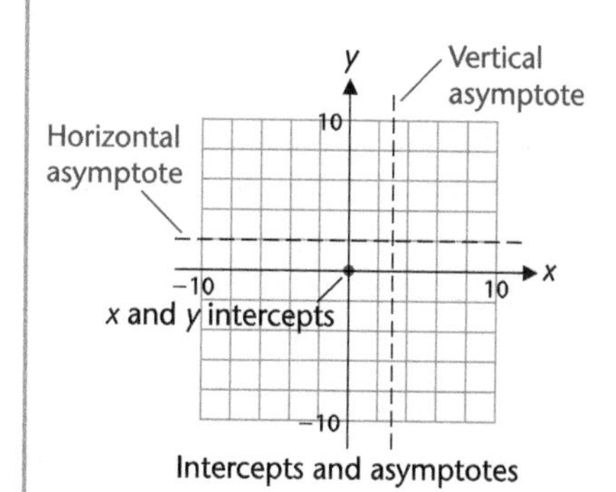

› Figure 5

Step 4. Based on the information we've obtained, it looks like a standard viewing window is likely to show all of the key features of the graph.

Using the graphing calculator graph in Figure 6(a), we obtain the graph in Figure 6(b). Notice that the graph is a smooth continuous curve over the interval $(-\infty, 3)$ and over the interval $(3, \infty)$. As expected, there is a break in the graph at $x = 3$, and the graph levels off at height 2.

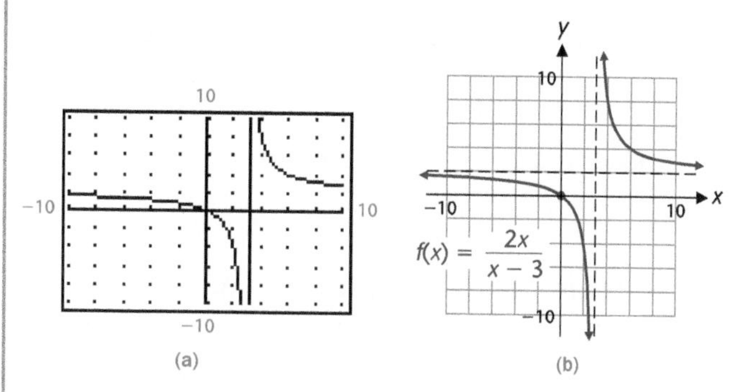

› Figure 6

MATCHED PROBLEM 4

Proceed as in Example 4 and sketch the graph of $f(x) = \dfrac{3x}{x + 2}$.

››› CAUTION ›››

When drawing the graph of a rational function, do not draw asymptotes as part of the graph! See the following remarks.

REMARK: When $f(x) = 2x/(x - 3)$ (see Example 4) is graphed on a graphing calculator [Fig. 6(a)], it appears that the graphing calculator has also drawn the vertical asymptote at $x = 3$, but this is not the case. Many graphing calculators, when set in *connected mode,* calculate points on a graph and connect these points with line segments. The last point plotted to the left of the asymptote and the first plotted to the right of the asymptote will usually have very large y coordinates. If these y coordinates have opposite signs, then the graphing calculator may connect the two points with a nearly vertical line segment, which gives the appearance of an asymptote. If you wish, you can set the calculator in *dot mode* to plot the points without the connecting line segments [Fig. 7(a)].

Depending on the scale, a graph may even appear to be continuous at a vertical asymptote [Fig. 7(b)]. That's why it is important to always locate the vertical asymptotes as we did in step 2 *before* turning to the graphing calculator to complete the sketch. If you already know there's a vertical asymptote at a certain x value, you'll be a lot less likely to misinterpret the calculator's display.

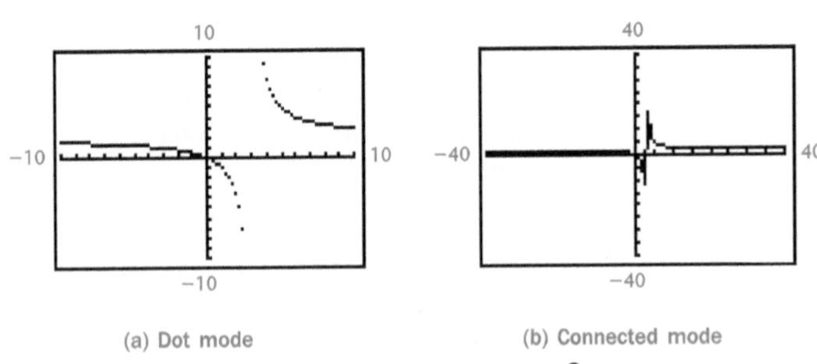

Figure 7 Graphing calculator graphs of $f(x) = \dfrac{2x}{x - 3}$.

EXAMPLE 5 Graphing a Rational Function

Graph $f(x) = \dfrac{x^2 - 6x + 9}{x^2 - 9x - 10}$.

SOLUTION

$$f(x) = \frac{x^2 - 6x + 9}{x^2 - 9x - 10} = \frac{(x - 3)^2}{(x - 10)(x + 1)}$$ Factor numerator and denominator.

Step 1. *Intercepts*

$$(x - 3)^2 = 0$$ Find zeros of numerator.

$$x = 3$$ x intercept

$$f(0) = \frac{0 - 0 + 9}{0 - 0 - 10} = -\frac{9}{10}$$ Evaluate $f(0)$ to find y intercept.

Step 2. *Vertical Asymptotes*

$$(x - 10)(x + 1) = 0 \qquad \text{Find zeros of denominator.}$$
$$x = 10 \qquad x = -1$$

The vertical asymptotes are $x = -1$ and $x = 10$. The domain is $x \neq -1$ or 10, and f is discontinuous at $x = -1$ and $x = 10$.

Step 3. *Horizontal Asymptote.* The numerator and denominator have the same degree, so $y = \frac{1}{1} = 1$ is a horizontal asymptote.

Step 4. *Complete the Sketch.* The vertical asymptote at $x = 10$ suggests that we should look at x values of at least 20; the small y intercept suggests that smaller y values may be appropriate. The resulting graphing calculator graph in Figure 8(a) leads to the graph in Figure 8(b).

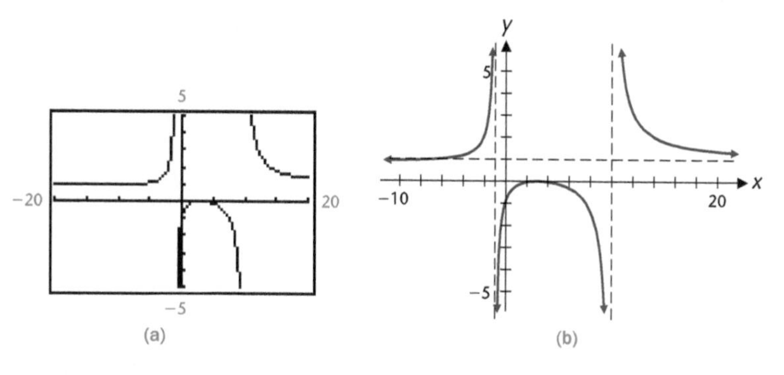

› **Figure 8**

Note: If we had used a standard viewing window, we would have totally missed the right portion of the graph (Fig. 9). This is exactly why it's so important to find the asymptotes and intercepts before using the calculator to draw the graph.

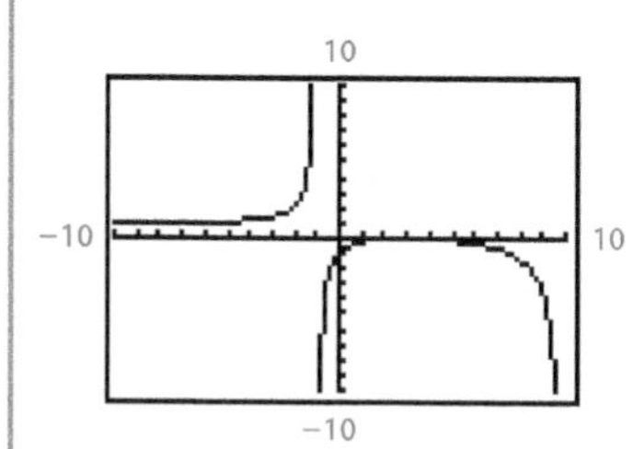

› **Figure 9**

MATCHED PROBLEM 5

Graph $f(x) = \dfrac{x^2}{x^2 - 11x + 18}$.

»» CAUTION »»

The graph of a function cannot cross a vertical asymptote, but the same statement is not true for horizontal asymptotes. The rational function

$$f(x) = \frac{2x^6 + x^5 - 5x^3 + 4x + 2}{x^6 + 1}$$

has the line $y = 2$ as a horizontal asymptote. The graph of f in Figure 10 clearly shows that **the graph of a function can cross a horizontal asymptote.**

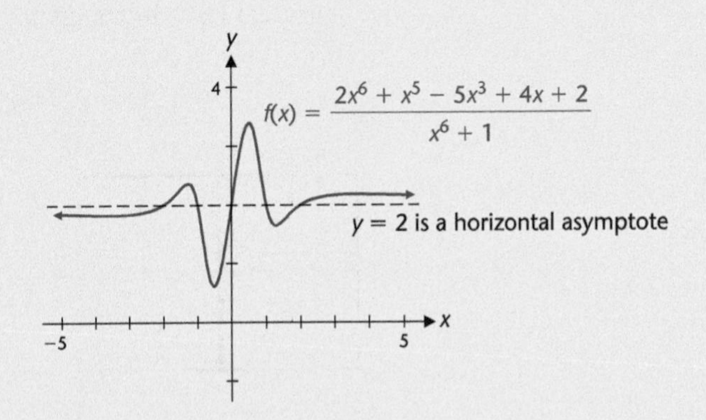

› **Figure 10** Multiple intersections of a graph and a horizontal asymptote.

Remember, horizontal asymptotes are all about what the graph looks like for large values of x. They have no effect on the "middle" of the graph.

EXAMPLE 6 Graphing a Rational Function

Graph $f(x) = \dfrac{x^2 - 3x - 4}{x - 2}$.

SOLUTION

$$f(x) = \frac{x^2 - 3x - 4}{x - 2} = \frac{(x + 1)(x - 4)}{x - 2}$$ Factor numerator and denominator.

Step 1. *Intercepts*

$$(x + 1)(x - 4) = 0$$ Find zeros of the numerator.

$$x = -1, 4$$ Two x intercepts

$$f(0) = \frac{0 - 0 - 4}{0 - 2} = 2$$ Evaluate $f(0)$ to find y intercept.

Step 2. *Vertical Asymptotes*

$$x - 2 = 0 \quad \text{Find zeros of the denominator.}$$
$$x = 2 \quad \text{Vertical asymptote}$$

The domain is $x \neq 2$, and f is discontinuous at $x = 2$.

Step 3. *Horizontal Asymptote.* The degree of the numerator is greater than that of the denominator, so by Theorem 3, part 3, there is no horizontal asymptote. However, we can still gain some useful information about the behavior of the graph as $x \to -\infty$ and as $x \to \infty$ if we first perform a long division (you'll see why in a minute):

$$\begin{array}{r l}
x - 1 & \text{Quotient} \\
x - 2\overline{)x^2 - 3x - 4} & \\
\underline{x^2 - 2x} & \\
-x - 4 & \\
\underline{-x + 2} & \\
-6 & \text{Remainder}
\end{array}$$

So we can rewrite $f(x)$ as

$$f(x) = \frac{x^2 - 3x - 4}{x - 2} = x - 1 - \frac{6}{x - 2}$$

Now notice that as $x \to \infty$ or $x \to -\infty$, $6/(x - 2)$ approaches 0, and the output of f approaches the output of $y = x - 1$. We can conclude that the graph of f approaches the graph of the line $y = x - 1$. This line is called an **oblique,** or **slant, asymptote** for the graph of f. A graphing calculator graph is shown in Figure 11(a). The line $y = x - 1$ was graphed as well [Fig. 11(b)]. Notice how the graph of $f(x)$ approaches that line as x gets large in both directions. The graph of f is sketched in Figure 11(c).

Figure 11

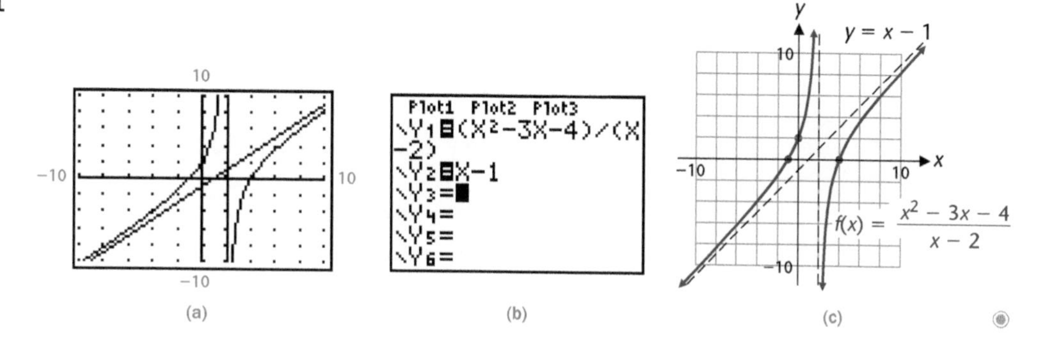

MATCHED PROBLEM 6

Graph, including any slant asymptotes, $f(x) = \dfrac{x^2 + 5}{x + 1}$.

It turns out that rational functions have slant asymptotes exactly when the numerator has degree one more than the denominator.

› THEOREM 4 Oblique Asymptotes and Rational Functions

If $f(x) = p(x)/q(x)$, where $p(x)$ and $q(x)$ are polynomials and the degree of $p(x)$ is 1 more than the degree of $q(x)$, then performing long division enables us to write $f(x)$ in the form

$$f(x) = mx + b + \frac{r(x)}{q(x)}$$

where the degree of $r(x)$ is less than the degree of $q(x)$. The line

$$y = mx + b$$

is an oblique (slant) asymptote for the graph of f.

At the beginning of this section we made the assumption that for a rational function $f(x) = p(x)/q(x)$, the polynomials $p(x)$ and $q(x)$ have no common real zero. Now we will look at a rational function where the numerator and denominator have common zeros. Suppose that $p(x)$ and $q(x)$ have one or more real zeros in common. Then, by the factor theorem, $p(x)$ and $q(x)$ have one or more linear factors in common. We proceed to cancel any common linear factors in

$$f(x) = \frac{p(x)}{q(x)}$$

until we obtain a rational function

$$f_r(x) = \frac{p_r(x)}{q_r(x)}$$

in which $p_r(x)$ and $q_r(x)$ have no common real zero. We analyze and graph $f_r(x)$, then insert "holes" as required in the graph of f_r to obtain the graph of f. Example 7 illustrates the details.

EXAMPLE 7 Graphing Arbitrary Rational Functions

Graph $f(x) = \dfrac{2x^5 - 4x^4 - 6x^3}{x^5 - 3x^4 - 3x^3 + 7x^2 + 6x}$.

SOLUTION

The real zeros of

$$p(x) = 2x^5 - 4x^4 - 6x^3$$

(obtained by graphing or factoring) are -1, 0, and 3.

The real zeros of

$$q(x) = x^5 - 3x^4 - 3x^3 + 7x^2 + 6x$$

are $-1, 0, 2$, and 3. The common zeros are $-1, 0$, and 3. Factoring and cancelling common linear factors gives

$$f(x) = \frac{2x^3(x+1)(x-3)}{x(x+1)^2(x-2)(x-3)} \quad \text{and} \quad f_r(x) = \frac{2x^2}{(x+1)(x-2)}$$

We analyze $f_r(x)$ as usual:

x intercept: $x = 0$
y intercept: $y = f_r(0) = 0$
Vertical asymptotes: $x = -1, x = 2$
Domain: $x \neq -1, 2$
Points of discontinuity: $x = -1, x = 2$
Horizontal asymptote: $y = 2$

The graph of f is identical to the graph of f_r except possibly at the common real zeros -1, 0, and 3. We consider each common zero separately.

$x = -1$: Both f and f_r are undefined (no difference in their graphs).
$x = 0$: f is undefined but $f_r(0) = 0$, so the graph of f has a hole at (0, 0).
$x = 3$: f is undefined but $f_r(3) = 4.5$, so the graph of f has a hole at (3, 4.5).

Therefore, $f(x)$ has the following analysis:

x intercepts: none
y intercepts: none
Domain: $(-\infty, -1) \cup (-1, 0) \cup (0, 2) \cup (2, 3) \cup (3, \infty)$
Points of discontinuity: $x = -1, x = 0, x = 2, x = 3$
Vertical asymptotes: $x = -1, x = 2$
Horizontal asymptotes: $y = 2$
Holes: (0, 0), (3, 4.5)

Figure 12 shows the graphs of f and f_r.

› **Figure 12**

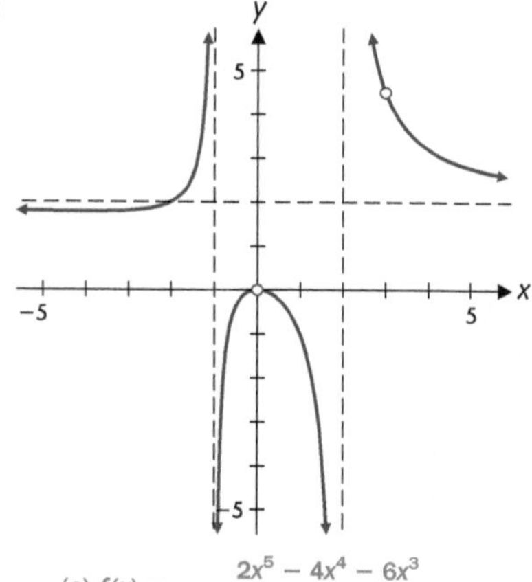

(a) $f(x) = \dfrac{2x^5 - 4x^4 - 6x^3}{x^5 - 3x^4 - 3x^3 + 7x^2 + 6x}$

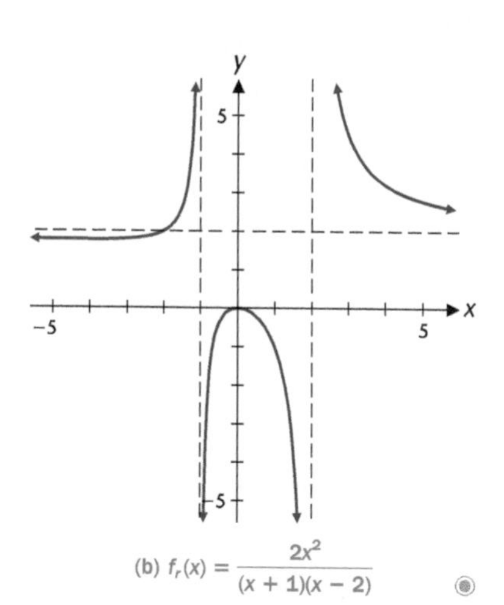

(b) $f_r(x) = \dfrac{2x^2}{(x+1)(x-2)}$

MATCHED PROBLEM 7

Graph $f(x) = \dfrac{x^3 - x}{x^4 - x^2}$.

Solving Rational Inequalities

One of the things we can learn from studying the graphs of rational functions can be applied to solving inequalities. A rational function $f(x) = p(x)/q(x)$ can change sign at a real zero of $p(x)$ (where f has an x intercept) or at a real zero of $q(x)$ (where f is discontinuous), but nowhere else (because f is continuous except where it is not defined). Rational inequalities can therefore be solved in pretty much the same way as polynomial inequalities. The only real difference is that the intervals to be tested are bounded by both the zeros of the numerator and the zeros of denominator.

EXAMPLE 8 Solving Rational Inequalities

Solve $\dfrac{x^3 + 4x^2}{x^2 - 4} < 0$.

SOLUTION

Algebraic Solution

Let

$$f(x) = \frac{x^3 + 4x^2}{x^2 - 4}$$

Find the zeros of the numerator

$$x^3 + 4x^2 = x^2(x + 4);$$

the zeros are 0 and -4. Next, find the zeros of the denominator

$$x^2 - 4 = (x + 2)(x - 2);$$

the zeros are -2 and 2. These four zeros partition the x axis into the five intervals shown in the table. A test number is chosen from each interval as indicated to determine whether $f(x)$ is positive or negative.

Interval	Test number	Result
$(-\infty, -4)$	-5	$-25/21$; negative
$(-4, -2)$	-3	$9/5$; positive
$(-2, 0)$	-1	-1; negative
$(0, 2)$	1	$-5/3$; negative
$(2, \infty)$	3	$63/5$; positive

We conclude that the solution set of the inequality is

$$(-\infty, -4) \cup (-2, 0) \cup (0, 2)$$

Graphical Solution

Let

$$f(x) = \frac{x^3 - 4x^2}{x^2 - 4}.$$

The graph of $f(x)$ (Fig. 13) shows zeros at $x = -4$ and 0, and vertical asymptotes at $x = 2$ and $x = -2$. These are all of the x values where f can change sign, and they partition the x axis into five intervals.

By inspecting the graph of f, we see that f is below the x axis on the intervals $(-\infty, -4)$, $(-2, 0)$, and $(0, 2)$.

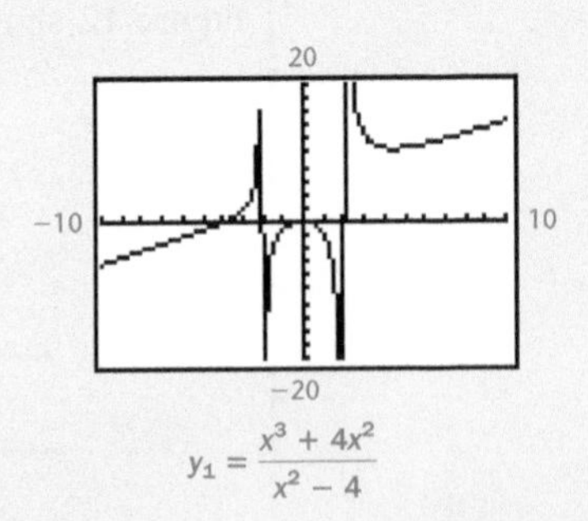

Figure 13

Note that $f(0) = 0$, so $x = 0$ is not a solution to the inequality. We conclude that the solution set is

$$(-\infty, -4) \cup (-2, 0) \cup (0, 2)$$

MATCHED PROBLEM 8

Solve $\dfrac{x^2 - 1}{x^2 - 9} \ge 0$.

EXAMPLE 9 Solving Rational Inequalities

Solve $1 \ge \dfrac{9x - 9}{x^2 + x - 3}$ to three decimal places.

SOLUTION

Our method of solving depends on the inequality being a statement about a function being positive or negative, so we first convert the inequality to an equivalent inequality in which one side is 0:

$$1 \ge \frac{9x - 9}{x^2 + x - 3} \qquad \text{Subtract } \frac{9x-9}{x^2+x-3} \text{ from both sides.}$$

$$1 - \frac{9x - 9}{x^2 + x - 3} \ge 0 \qquad \text{Find a common denominator.}$$

$$\frac{x^2 + x - 3}{x^2 + x - 3} - \frac{9x - 9}{x^2 + x - 3} \ge 0 \qquad \text{Simplify.}$$

$$\frac{x^2 - 8x + 6}{x^2 + x - 3} \ge 0$$

We can use either a graph or the quadratic formula to find the zeros of the numerator and denominator.

The zeros of $x^2 - 8x + 6$, to three decimal places, are 0.838 and 7.162 (details omitted). The zeros of $x^2 + x - 3$ are -2.303 and 1.303. These four zeros partition the x axis into five intervals:

$$(-\infty, -2.303), (-2.303, 0.838), (0.838, 1.303), (1.303, 7.162), \text{ and } (7.162, \infty)$$

We graph

$$f(x) = \frac{x^2 - 8x + 6}{x^2 + x - 3}$$

(Fig. 14) and observe that the graph of f is above the x axis on the intervals $(-\infty, -2.303)$, $(0.838, 1.303)$, and $(7.162, \infty)$. The solution set of the inequality is thus

$$(-\infty, -2.303) \cup [0.838, 1.303) \cup [7.162, \infty)$$

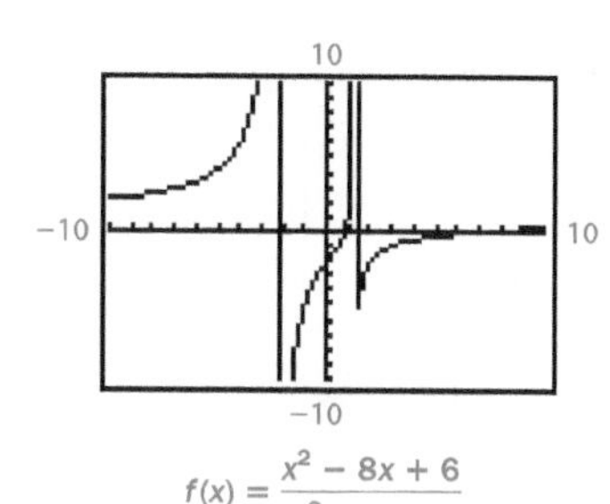

$f(x) = \dfrac{x^2 - 8x + 6}{x^2 + x - 3}$

› **Figure 14**

Note that the endpoints that are zeros of f, namely 0.838 and 7.162, make the inequality true, and are included in the solution set of the inequality. But the endpoints at which f is undefined (-2.303 and 1.303) make the inequality false, and are excluded.

MATCHED PROBLEM 9

Solve $\frac{x^3 + 3x^2 + 5x - 6}{x^2 - 5x - 1} \geq -1$ to three decimal places.

››› CAUTION ›››

When a rational inequality includes equality ($\geq$ or $\leq$), you should include the zeros of the numerator in the solution set, but never the zeros of the denominator.

ANSWERS TO MATCHED PROBLEMS

1. Domain: $(-\infty, -3) \cup (-3, 1) \cup (1, \infty)$; x intercepts: $x = -2$, $x = 2$
2. (A) Properties 3 and 4 are not satisfied. (B) Property 1 is not satisfied.
   (C) Properties 1 and 3 are not satisfied.
3. (A) Vertical asymptotes: $x = -3, x = 1$; horizontal asymptote: $y = 3$
   (B) Vertical asymptotes: $x = -1, x = 0, x = 1$; horizontal asymptote: $y = 0$
   (C) No asymptotes
4. 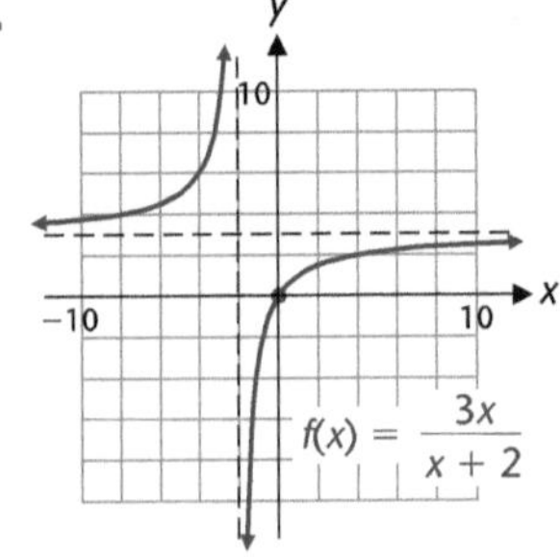

5. 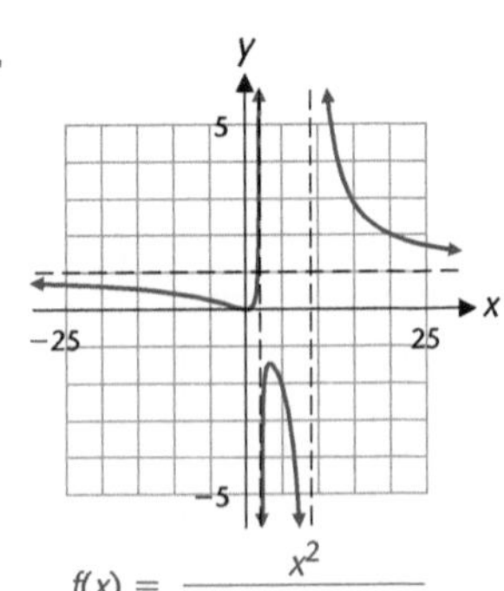

$f(x) = \frac{x^2}{x^2 - 11x + 18}$

6.

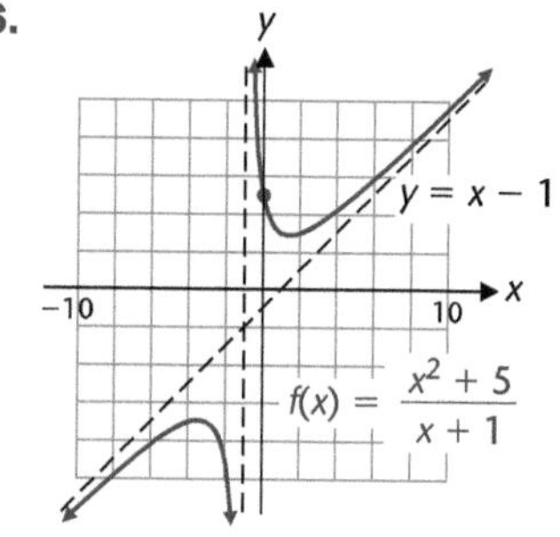

7.

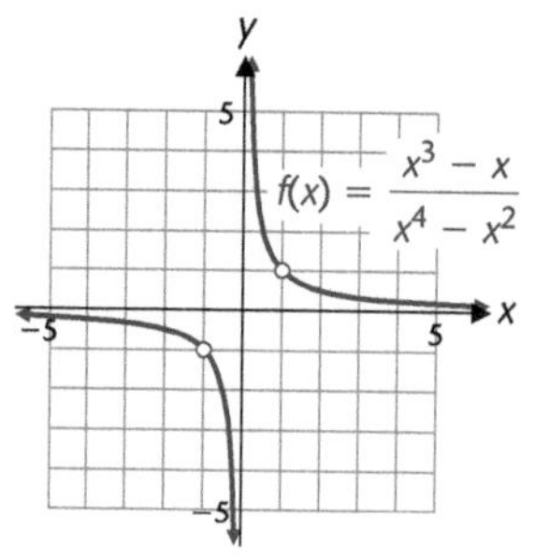

8. $(-\infty, -3) \cup [-1, 1] \cup (3, \infty)$

9. $[-3.391, -1.773] \cup (-0.193, 1.164] \cup (5.193, \infty)$

3-5 Exercises

1. What is a rational function?

2. Describe in your own words how to find the vertical asymptotes of a rational function.

3. Describe in your own words how to find the horizontal asymptotes of a rational function.

4. Is there a limit on the number of vertical asymptotes that the graph of a rational function can have?

5. Is it accurate to say that the graph of a function can never intersect an asymptote? Explain.

6. Is it accurate to say that the solution of a rational inequality with inequality sign $\le$ or $\ge$ should always contain the endpoints of the intervals in the solution? Why or why not?

In Problems 7–10, match each graph with one of the following functions:

$$f(x) = \frac{2x - 4}{x + 2} \qquad g(x) = \frac{2x + 4}{2 - x}$$

$$h(x) = \frac{2x + 4}{x - 2} \qquad k(x) = \frac{4 - 2x}{x + 2}$$

7.

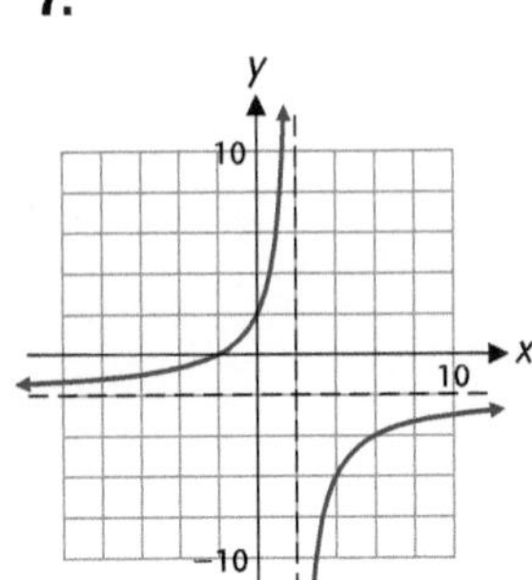

8.

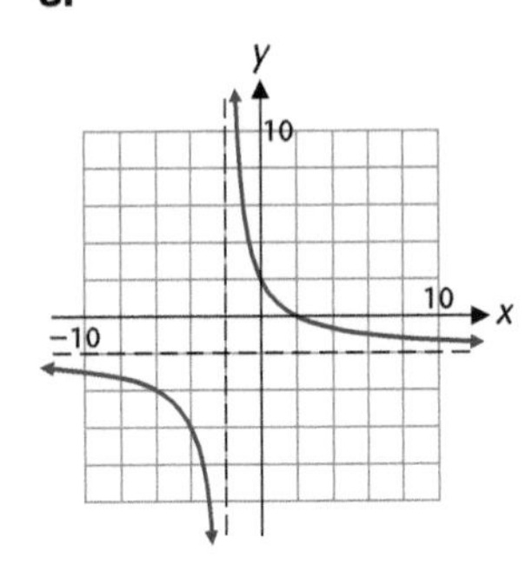

9.

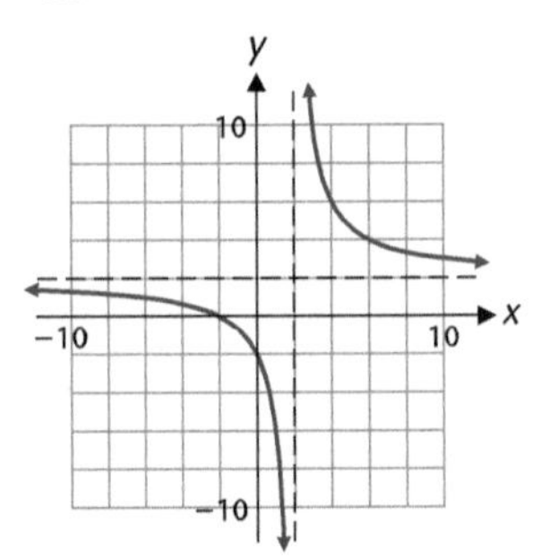

10.

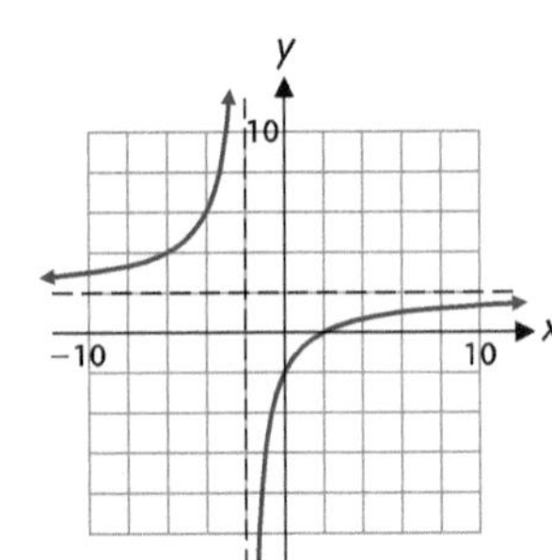

11. Let $f(x) = \dfrac{2x - 4}{x + 2}$. Complete each statement:

(A) As $x \to -2^-$, $f(x) \to ?$
(B) As $x \to -2^+$, $f(x) \to ?$
(C) As $x \to -\infty$, $f(x) \to ?$
(D) As $x \to \infty$, $f(x) \to ?$

12. Let $g(x) = \dfrac{2x + 4}{2 - x}$. Complete each statement:

(A) As $x \to 2^-$, $g(x) \to ?$
(B) As $x \to 2^+$, $g(x) \to ?$
(C) As $x \to -\infty$, $g(x) \to ?$
(D) As $x \to \infty$, $g(x) \to ?$

13. Let $h(x) = \dfrac{2x + 4}{x - 2}$. Complete each statement:

(A) As $x \to 2^-$, $h(x) \to ?$
(B) As $x \to 2^+$, $h(x) \to ?$
(C) As $x \to -\infty$, $h(x) \to ?$
(D) As $x \to \infty$, $h(x) \to ?$

14. Let $k(x) = \dfrac{4 - 2x}{x + 2}$. Complete each statement:

(A) As $x \to 2^-$, $k(x) \to ?$
(B) As $x \to 2^+$, $k(x) \to ?$
(C) As $x \to -\infty$, $k(x) \to ?$
(D) As $x \to \infty$, $k(x) \to ?$

In Problems 15–24, find the domain and x intercepts.

15. $f(x) = \dfrac{2x - 4}{x + 1}$ **16.** $g(x) = \dfrac{3x + 6}{x - 1}$

17. $h(x) = \dfrac{x^2 - 1}{x^2 - 16}$ **18.** $k(x) = \dfrac{x^2 - 36}{x^2 - 25}$

19. $r(x) = \dfrac{x^2 - x - 6}{x^2 - x - 12}$ **20.** $s(x) = \dfrac{x^2 + x - 12}{x^2 + x - 6}$

21. $F(x) = \dfrac{x}{x^2 + 4}$ **22.** $G(x) = \dfrac{x^2}{x^2 + 16}$

23. $u(x) = \dfrac{4 - x^2}{x}$ **24.** $v(x) = \dfrac{2 - 3x + x^2}{x^3}$

In Problems 25–34, find all vertical and horizontal asymptotes.

25. $f(x) = \dfrac{2x}{x - 4}$ **26.** $h(x) = \dfrac{3x}{x + 5}$

27. $s(x) = \dfrac{2x^2 + 3x}{3x^2 - 48}$ **28.** $r(x) = \dfrac{5x^2 - 7x}{2x^2 - 50}$

29. $p(x) = \dfrac{2x}{x^4 + 1}$ **30.** $q(x) = \dfrac{5x^4}{2x^2 + 3x - 2}$

31. $t(x) = \dfrac{6x^4}{3x^2 - 2x - 5}$ **32.** $g(x) = \dfrac{3x}{x^4 + 2x^2 + 1}$

33. $C(x) = \dfrac{4x^2 + 4x - 24}{x^2 - 2x}$ **34.** $D(x) = \dfrac{x^2 + 8x + 7}{8x^2 + 8x}$

In Problems 35–38, explain why each graph is not the graph of a rational function.

35. **36.**

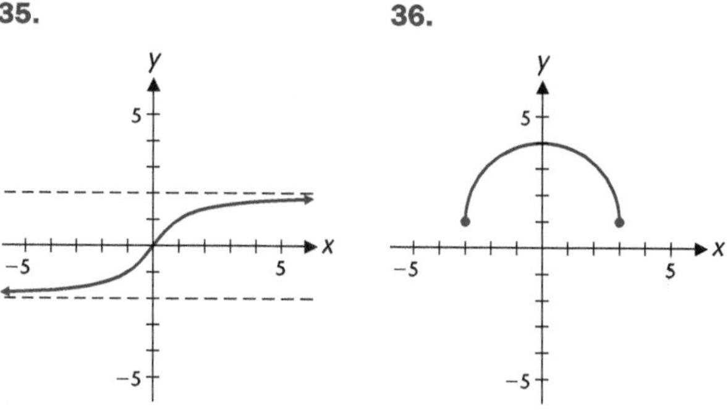

37. **38.**

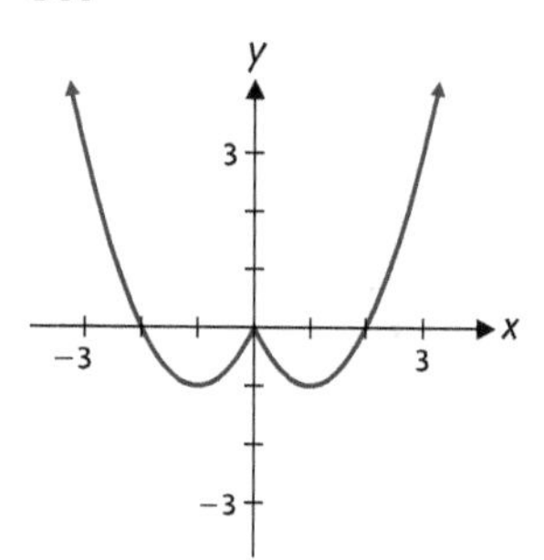

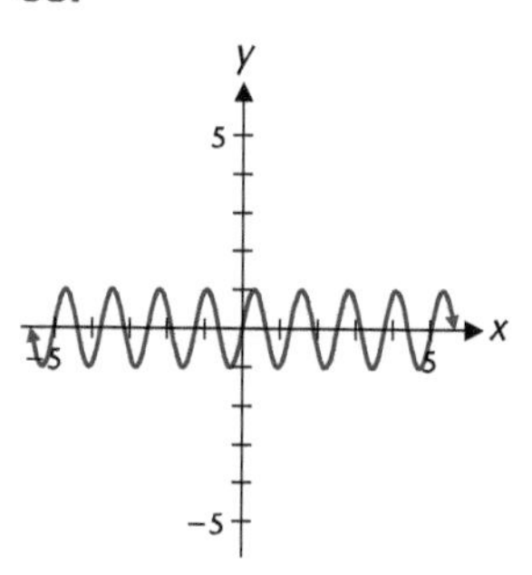

In Problems 39–42, explain how the graph of f differs from the graph of g.

39. $f(x) = \dfrac{x^2 + 2x}{x}$; $g(x) = x + 2$

40. $f(x) = \dfrac{x + 5}{x^2 - 25}$; $g(x) = \dfrac{1}{x - 5}$

41. $f(x) = \dfrac{x + 2}{x^2 + 10x + 16}$; $g(x) = \dfrac{1}{x + 8}$

42. $f(x) = \dfrac{x^2 - x - 12}{x - 4}$; $g(x) = x + 3$

In Problems 43–64, use the graphing strategy outlined in the text to sketch the graph of each function.

43. $f(x) = \dfrac{1}{x - 4}$ **44.** $g(x) = \dfrac{1}{x + 3}$

45. $f(x) = \dfrac{x}{x + 1}$ **46.** $f(x) = \dfrac{3x}{x - 3}$

47. $h(x) = \dfrac{x}{2x - 2}$ **48.** $p(x) = \dfrac{3x}{4x + 4}$

49. $f(x) = \dfrac{2x - 4}{x + 3}$ **50.** $f(x) = \dfrac{3x + 3}{2 - x}$

51. $g(x) = \dfrac{1 - x^2}{x^2}$ **52.** $f(x) = \dfrac{x^2 + 1}{x^2}$

53. $f(x) = \dfrac{9}{x^2 - 9}$ **54.** $g(x) = \dfrac{6}{x^2 - x - 6}$

55. $f(x) = \dfrac{x}{x^2 - 1}$ **56.** $p(x) = \dfrac{x}{1 - x^2}$

57. $g(x) = \dfrac{2}{x^2 + 1}$ **58.** $f(x) = \dfrac{x}{x^2 + 1}$

59. $f(x) = \dfrac{12x^2}{(3x + 5)^2}$ **60.** $f(x) = \dfrac{7x^2}{(2x - 3)^2}$

61. $f(x) = \dfrac{x^2 - 1}{x^2 + 7x + 10}$ **62.** $f(x) = \dfrac{x^2 + 6x + 8}{x^2 - x - 2}$

63. $f(x) = \frac{x^2 - 3x - 10}{x - 5}$

64. $f(x) = \frac{x + 2}{x^2 + 9x + 14}$

In Problems 65–68, give an example of a rational function that satisfies the given conditions.

65. Real zeros: $-2, -1, 1, 2$; vertical asymptotes: none; horizontal asymptote: $y = 3$

66. Real zeros: none; vertical asymptote: $x = 4$; horizontal asymptote: $y = -2$

67. Real zeros: none; vertical asymptote: $x = 10$; slant asymptote: $y = 2x + 5$

68. Real zeros: $1, 2, 3$; vertical asymptotes: none; slant asymptote: $y = 2 - x$

In Problems 69–76, solve each rational inequality.

69. $\frac{x}{x - 2} \le 0$

70. $\frac{2x - 1}{x + 3} > 0$

71. $\frac{x^2 - 16}{5x - 2} > 0$

72. $\frac{x - 4}{x^2 - 9} \le 0$

73. $\frac{x^2 + 4x - 20}{3x} \ge 4$

74. $\frac{3x - 7}{x^2 + 6x} < 2$

75. $\frac{5x}{x^2 - 1} < \frac{9}{x}$

76. $\frac{1}{x^2 + 8x + 12} \ge \frac{1}{x}$

In Problems 77–86, solve each rational inequality to three decimal places.

77. $\frac{x^2 + 7x + 3}{x + 2} > 0$

78. $\frac{x^3 + 4}{x^2 + x - 3} \le 0$

79. $\frac{5}{x^2} - \frac{1}{x + 3} < 0$

80. $\frac{3x}{x + 4} - \frac{x + 1}{x^2} \ge 0$

81. $\frac{9}{x} - \frac{5}{x^2} \le 1$

82. $\frac{x + 4}{x^2 + 1} > 2$

83. $\frac{3x + 2}{x - 5} > 10$

84. $\frac{x}{x^2 + 5x - 6} \le 0.5$

85. $\frac{4}{x + 1} \ge \frac{7}{x}$

86. $\frac{1}{x^2 - 1} < \frac{x^2}{x^4 + 1}$

In Problems 87–92, find all vertical, horizontal, and slant asymptotes.

87. $f(x) = \frac{2x^2}{x - 1}$

88. $g(x) = \frac{3x^2}{x + 2}$

89. $p(x) = \frac{x^3}{x^2 + 1}$

90. $q(x) = \frac{x^5}{x^3 - 8}$

91. $r(x) = \frac{2x^2 - 3x + 5}{x}$

92. $s(x) = \frac{-3x^2 + 5x + 9}{x}$

In Problems 93–96, investigate the behavior of each function as $x \to \infty$ and as $x \to -\infty$, and find any horizontal asymptotes (note that these functions are not rational).

93. $f(x) = \frac{5x}{\sqrt{x^2 + 1}}$

94. $f(x) = \frac{2x}{\sqrt{x^2 - 1}}$

95. $f(x) = \frac{4\sqrt{x^2 - 4}}{x}$

96. $f(x) = \frac{3\sqrt{x^2 + 1}}{x - 1}$

In Problems 97–102, use the graphing strategy outlined in the text to sketch the graph of each function. Write the equations of all vertical, horizontal, and slant asymptotes.

97. $f(x) = \frac{x^2 + 1}{x}$

98. $g(x) = \frac{x^2 - 1}{x}$

99. $k(x) = \frac{x^2 - 4x + 3}{2x - 4}$

100. $h(x) = \frac{x^2 + x - 2}{2x - 4}$

101. $F(x) = \frac{8 - x^3}{4x^2}$

102. $G(x) = \frac{x^4 + 1}{x^3}$

In calculus, it is often necessary to consider rational functions in which the numerator and denominator have a common factor such as the functions given in Problems 103–106. For each function, state the domain. Write the equations of all vertical and horizontal asymptotes, and sketch the graph.

103. $f(x) = \frac{x^2 - 4}{x - 2}$

104. $g(x) = \frac{x^2 - 1}{x + 1}$

105. $r(x) = \frac{x + 2}{x^2 - 4}$

106. $s(x) = \frac{x - 1}{x^2 - 1}$

APPLICATIONS

107. EMPLOYEE TRAINING A company producing electronic components used in television sets has established that on average, a new employee can assemble $N(t)$ components per day after t days of on-the-job training, as given by

$$N(t) = \frac{50t}{t + 4} \qquad t \ge 0$$

Sketch the graph of N, including any vertical or horizontal asymptotes. What does N approach as $t \to \infty$? Explain the significance of this number.

108. PHYSIOLOGY In a study on the speed of muscle contraction in frogs under various loads, researchers W. O. Fems and J. Marsh found that the speed of contraction decreases with increasing loads. More precisely, they found that the relationship between speed of contraction S (in centimeters per second) and load w (in grams) is given approximately by

$$S(w) = \frac{26 + 0.06w}{w} \qquad w \geq 5$$

Sketch the graph of S, including any vertical or horizontal asymptotes. What does S approach as $w \to \infty$? Explain the significance of this number.

109. RETENTION An experiment on retention is conducted in a psychology class. Each student in the class is given 1 day to memorize the same list of 40 special characters. The lists are turned in at the end of the day, and for each succeeding day for 20 days each student is asked to turn in a list of as many of the symbols as can be recalled. Averages are taken, and it is found that a good approximation of the average number of symbols, $N(t)$, retained after t days is given by

$$N(t) = \frac{5t + 30}{t} \qquad t \geq 1$$

Sketch the graph of N, including any vertical or horizontal asymptotes. What does N approach as $t \to \infty$? Explain the significance of this number.

110. LEARNING THEORY In 1917, L. L. Thurstone, a pioneer in quantitative learning theory, proposed the function

$$f(x) = \frac{a(x + c)}{(x + c) + b}$$

to describe the number of successful acts per unit time that a person could accomplish after x practice sessions. Suppose that for a particular person enrolling in a typing class,

$$f(x) = \frac{50(x + 1)}{x + 5} \qquad x \geq 0$$

where $f(x)$ is the number of words per minute the person is able to type after x weeks of lessons. Sketch the graph of f, including any vertical or horizontal asymptotes. What does f approach as $x \to \infty$? Explain the significance of this number.

Problems 111–114 are calculus related.

111. REPLACEMENT TIME A desktop office copier has an initial price of \$2,500. A maintenance/service contract costs \$200 for the first year and increases \$50 per year thereafter. It can be shown that the total cost of the copier after n years is given by

$$C(n) = 2{,}500 + 175n + 25n^2$$

The average cost per year for n years is $\overline{C}(n) = C(n)/n$.
(A) Find the rational function $\overline{C}$.
(B) When is the average cost per year a minimum? (This is frequently referred to as the *replacement time* for this piece of equipment.)
(C) Sketch the graph of C, including any asymptotes.

112. AVERAGE COST The total cost of producing x units of a certain product is given by

$$C(x) = \tfrac{1}{5}x^2 + 2x + 2{,}000$$

The average cost per unit for producing x units is $\overline{C}(x) = C(x)/x$.
(A) Find the rational function $\overline{C}$.
(B) At what production level will the average cost per unit be minimal?
(C) Sketch the graph of $\overline{C}$, including any asymptotes.

113. CONSTRUCTION A rectangular dog pen is to be made to enclose an area of 225 square feet.
(A) If x represents the width of the pen, express the total length L of the fencing material required for the pen in terms of x.
(B) Considering the physical limitations, what is the domain of the function L?
(C) Find the dimensions of the pen that will require the least amount of fencing material.
(D) Graph the function L, including any asymptotes.

114. CONSTRUCTION Rework Problem 113 with the added assumption that the pen is to be divided into two sections, as shown in the figure. (Approximate dimensions to three decimal places.)

3-6 Variation and Modeling

Very few things in our world happen without consequence. In most cases, things that change affect something else. If the number of hours you work at a part-time job goes up, the amount of money you earn goes up along with it. If the number of days you miss a certain class goes up, your grade will go down. Each of these is an example of *variation,* which is an important mathematical way to express a connection between two or more quantities. In this section, we will study different types of variation, and see how to use them to model real-life situations.

› Modeling with Direct Variation

As just mentioned, if the number of hours you work goes up, your pay will go up as well. If the speed you drive goes down, the distance you cover in a certain amount of time will go down as well. These are examples of *direct variation*. We can often describe relationships like this with a simple equation.

› DEFINITION 1 Direct Variation

Let x and y be variables. The statement **y is directly proportional to x** (or **y varies directly as x**) means

$$y = kx$$

for some nonzero constant k, called the **constant of proportionality** (or **constant of variation**).

Informally, when two quantities vary directly and the constant of proportionality is positive, if one increases, the other does as well.

In the first example above, if h represents hours worked and d is the number of dollars earned, we can write $d = kh$; the amount earned is directly proportional to the number of hours worked, and the constant of proportionality k is the hourly wage. In the second example, if r is speed and d is distance, we can write $d = kr$; in this case, the constant of proportionality is the amount of time passed.

Notice that any equation of direct variation $y = kx$, $k \neq 0$, gives a linear model with nonzero slope that passes through the origin (Fig. 1).

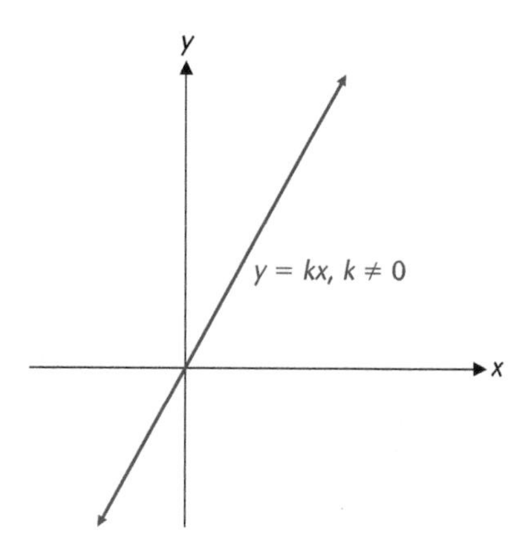

› **Figure 1** Direct variation.

EXAMPLE 1 Direct Variation

The force F exerted by a spring is directly proportional to the distance x that it is stretched. (This is known as Hooke's law.) Find the constant of proportionality and the equation of variation if $F = 12$ pounds when $x = \frac{1}{3}$ foot.

SOLUTION

Since F and x are directly proportional, the equation of variation has the form $F = kx$. To find the constant of proportionality, substitute $F = 12$ and $x = \frac{1}{3}$ and solve for k.

$$F = kx \qquad \text{Let } F = 12 \text{ and } x = \tfrac{1}{3}.$$
$$12 = k(\tfrac{1}{3}) \qquad \text{Multiply both sides by 3.}$$
$$k = 36$$

Therefore, the constant of proportionality is $k = 36$ and the equation of variation is

$$F = 36x$$

MATCHED PROBLEM 1

Find the constant of proportionality and the equation of variation if p is directly proportional to v, and $p = 200$ when $v = 8$.

››› EXPLORE-DISCUSS 1

All real numbers x are in the domain of the linear function $y = kx$, $k \neq 0$. Often in practice, however, $y = kx$ will not provide a good model for all values of x.

(A) Discuss factors that would make the spring model of Example 1 unreasonable for certain values of x.

(B) Explain why both positive and negative values of x could be allowed in the spring model of Example 1. What would be the physical interpretation of a negative force? [*Hint:* Consider a distance the spring is *compressed* to be negative.]

Sometimes a quantity varies directly not with another quantity, but with a certain power of that quantity, as in Example 2.

EXAMPLE 2 Direct Variation

The distance d covered by a falling object is directly proportional to the square of the length of time t since it began falling. If a coin dropped from a suspension bridge falls 144 feet in 3 seconds, find the equation of variation, and use it to find how far the coin would fall in 5 seconds.

SOLUTION

We were given that d varies directly with t^2, so the equation has the form

$$d = kt^2$$

Substitute $d = 144$ and $t = 3$ to find the constant of proportionality:

$$144 = k(3)^2$$
$$144 = 9k$$
$$k = \frac{144}{9} = 16$$

The equation of variation is

$$d = 16t^2$$

and a graph of this relation is shown in Figure 2. (Note that the distance d increases as the coin falls.)

After 5 seconds, the coin will have fallen

$$d = 16(5)^2 = 400 \text{ feet}$$

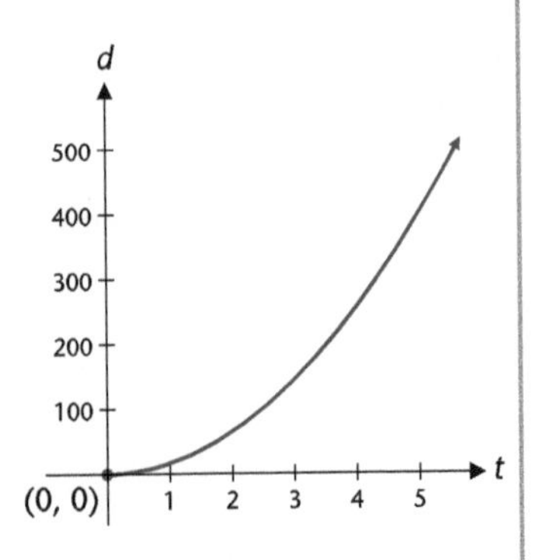

› Figure 2

MATCHED PROBLEM 2

For an object falling toward the surface of the moon, the distance fallen d is directly proportional to the square of the length of time t since it began falling. An object falling toward the moon falls 41.6 feet in 4 seconds. Find the equation of variation, and the distance it will fall in 7 seconds.

Modeling with Inverse Variation

At the beginning of the section, we pointed out that as the number of class periods you miss goes up, your grade is likely to go down. When two quantities are related so that an increase in one goes along with a decrease in the other, we say that they are *inversely proportional.* In mathematical terms, this will correspond to the quantities being related by a constant multiple of the rational function $y = \frac{1}{x}$.

To understand that this makes sense, think about that equation. If x gets larger, it would make the fraction $\frac{1}{x}$ smaller, so that an increase in x corresponds to a decrease in y. Likewise, if x gets smaller, $\frac{1}{x}$ gets bigger, so a decrease in x corresponds to an increase in y.

DEFINITION 2 Inverse Variation

Let x and y be variables. The statement **y is inversely proportional to x** (or **y varies inversely as x**) means

$$y = \frac{k}{x}$$

for some nonzero constant k, called the **constant of proportionality** (or **constant of variation**).

Informally, when two quantities are inversely proportional and the constant of proportionality is positive, if one increases, the other decreases.

If you plan a trip of 100 miles, the faster you go, the less time it will take. Therefore, the rate r and time t it takes to travel a distance of 100 miles are inversely proportional (recall that distance equals rate times time, $d = rt$). The equation of variation is

$$t = \frac{100}{r}$$

and the constant of proportionality is 100.

The equation of inverse variation, $y = k/x$, determines a rational function having the y axis as a vertical asymptote and the x axis as a horizontal asymptote (Fig. 3). In most applications, the constant k of proportionality will be positive, and only the portion of the graph in Quadrant I will be relevant. Note that if x is very large, then y is close to 0; if x is close to 0, then y is very large.

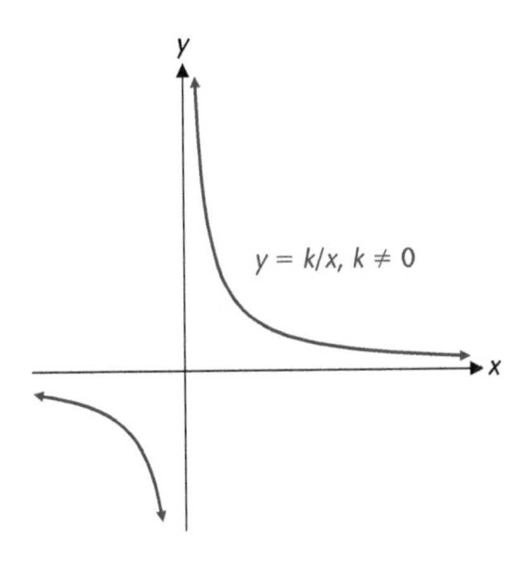

› **Figure 3** Inverse variation.

EXAMPLE 3 Inverse Variation

The note played by each pipe in a pipe organ is determined by the frequency of vibration of air in the pipe. The fundamental frequency f of vibration of air in an organ pipe is inversely proportional to the length L of the pipe. (This is why the low-frequency notes come from the very long pipes.)

(A) Find the constant of proportionality and the equation of variation if the fundamental frequency of an 8-foot pipe is 64 vibrations per second.

(B) Find the fundamental frequency of a 1.6-foot pipe.

SOLUTIONS

(A) Since the two quantities are inversely proportional, we know that the equation has the form $f = k/L$. To find the constant of proportionality, substitute $L = 8$ and $f = 64$ and solve for k.

$$f = \frac{k}{L} \qquad \text{Let } f = 64 \text{ and } L = 8.$$

$$64 = \frac{k}{8} \qquad \text{Multiply both sides by 8.}$$

$$k = 512$$

The constant of proportionality is $k = 512$ and the equation of variation is

$$f = \frac{512}{L}$$

(B) If $L = 1.6$, then $f = \frac{512}{1.6} = 320$ vibrations per second.

MATCHED PROBLEM 3

Find the constant of proportionality and the equation of variation if P is inversely proportional to V, and $P = 56$ when $V = 3.5$.

Modeling with Joint and Combined Variation

In some cases, the size of one quantity is related to two other quantities. For example, the area of a rectangle is determined by both its length and width. This is an example of *joint variation.*

DEFINITION 3 Joint Variation

Let x, y, and w be variables. The statement **w is jointly proportional to x and y** (or **w varies jointly as x and y**) means

$$w = kxy$$

for some nonzero constant k, called the **constant of proportionality** (or **constant of variation**).

The area of a rectangle is jointly proportional to its length and width with constant of proportionality 1; the equation of variation is $A = LW$.

The concept of joint variation can be extended to apply to more than three variables. For example, the volume of a box is jointly proportional to its length, width, and height: $V = LWH$ (again with constant of proportionality 1). Similarly, the concepts of direct and inverse variation can be extended. For example, the area of a circle is directly proportional to the square of its radius; the constant of proportionality is π and the equation of variation is $A = \pi r^2$.

The three basic types of variation also can be combined. For example, Newton's law of gravitation, "The force of attraction F between two objects is jointly proportional to their masses m_1 and m_2 and inversely proportional to the square of the distance d between them," has the equation

$$F = k\frac{m_1 m_2}{d^2}$$

EXAMPLE 4 Joint Variation

The volume V of a right circular cone is jointly proportional to the square of its radius r and its height h. Find the constant of proportionality and the equation of variation if a cone of height 8 inches and radius 3 inches has a volume of 24π (about 75.4) cubic inches.

SOLUTION

Since V is jointly proportional to the square of r and h, the equation of variation has the form $V = kr^2h$. To find the constant of proportionality k, substitute $V = 24\pi$, $r = 3$, and $h = 8$.

$$V = kr^2h \quad \text{Let } V = 24\pi,\ r = 3, \text{ and } h = 8.$$
$$24\pi = k(3)^2 8 \quad \text{Simplify.}$$
$$24\pi = 72k \quad \text{Divide both sides by 72.}$$
$$k = \frac{\pi}{3}$$

The constant of proportionality is $k = \frac{\pi}{3}$ and the equation of variation is

$$V = \frac{\pi}{3}r^2h$$

MATCHED PROBLEM 4

The volume V of a box with a square base is jointly proportional to the square of a side x of the base and the height h. Find the constant of proportionality and the equation of variation if a box with volume 45 cubic inches has base 3 inches by 3 inches and a height of 5 inches.

EXAMPLE 5

Combined Variation

The note played by a string on a guitar is determined by the frequency at which the string vibrates. The frequency f of a vibrating string is directly proportional to the square root of the tension T and inversely proportional to the length L.

(A) If the tension of a guitar string is increased, how does the frequency change? What if the length is increased?

(B) What is the effect on the frequency if the length is doubled and the tension is quadrupled?

SOLUTIONS

(A) The frequency is directly proportional to the square root of the tension. If the tension increases, so does its square root, and consequently the frequency increases as well. On the other hand, the frequency is inversely proportional to length, so if the length is increased, the frequency will decrease.

(B) Since f is directly proportional to $\sqrt{T}$ and inversely proportional to L, the equation of variation has the form

$$f = k\frac{\sqrt{T}}{L}$$

Let f_1, T_1, and L_1 denote the initial frequency, tension, and length, respectively. Then doubling the length makes the new length L_2 satisfy $L_2 = 2L_1$. Likewise, quadrupling the tension makes the new tension T_2 satisfy $T_2 = 4T_1$. Substituting f_2, T_2, and L_2 in the equation of variation, we get

$$f_2 = k\frac{\sqrt{T_2}}{L_2}$$

To compare this to the original frequency, substitute $4T_1$ and $2L_1$ in for T_2 and L_2, respectively.

$$f_2 = k\frac{\sqrt{T_2}}{L_2} \quad \text{Let } L_2 = 2L_1 \text{, and } T_2 = 4T_1.$$

$$= k\frac{\sqrt{4T_1}}{2L_1} \quad \text{Simplify the radical.}$$

$$= k\frac{2\sqrt{T_1}}{2L_1} \quad \text{Cancel and use the equation of variation.}$$

$$= f_1$$

We conclude that there is no effect on the frequency—the pitch remains the same.

MATCHED PROBLEM 5

Refer to Example 5. What is the effect on the frequency if the tension is quadrupled and the length is cut in half?

››› EXPLORE-DISCUSS 2

Refer to the equation of variation of Example 5. Explain why the frequency f, for fixed T, is a rational function of L, but f is *not*, for fixed L, a rational function of T.

ANSWERS TO MATCHED PROBLEMS

1. $k = 25$; $p = 25v$ **2.** $d = 2.6t^2$; 127.4 feet **3.** $k = 196$; $P = \frac{196}{V}$
4. $k = 1$; $V = x^2h$ **5.** The frequency is increased by a factor of 4.

3-6 Exercises

1. Give an example of two quantities that are directly proportional.

2. Give an example of two quantities that are inversely proportional.

3. If x varies directly as y, and y increases, what happens to x? How do you know?

4. If x varies inversely as y, and y increases, what happens to x? How do you know?

5. Explain why the distance traveled in a certain amount of time and the average speed are directly proportional.

6. Explain why the temperature setting of an oven and the amount of time it takes to heat an item to 170 degrees are inversely proportional.

In Problems 7–22, translate each statement into an equation using k as the constant of proportionality.

7. F is inversely proportional to x.

8. y is directly proportional to the square of x.

9. R is jointly proportional to S and T.

10. u is inversely proportional to v.

11. L is directly proportional to the cube of m.

12. W is jointly proportional to X, Y, and Z.

13. A varies jointly as the square of c and d.

14. q varies inversely as t.

15. P varies directly as x.

16. f varies directly as the square of b.

17. h varies inversely as the square root of s.

18. C varies jointly as the square of x and the cube of y.

19. R varies directly as m and inversely as the square of d.

20. T varies jointly as p and q and inversely as w.

21. D is jointly proportional to x and the square of y and inversely proportional to z.

22. S is directly proportional to the square root of u and inversely proportional to v.

23. Refer to Problem 7. If F increases, what happens to x?

24. Refer to Problem 10. If u increases, what happens to v?

25. Refer to Problem 11. If m increases, what happens to L?

26. Refer to Problem 8. If x increases, what happens to y?

27. u varies directly as the square root of v. If $u = 3$ when $v = 4$, find u when $v = 10$.

28. y varies directly as the cube of x. If $y = 48$ when $x = 4$, find y when $x = 8$.

29. L is inversely proportional to the square of M. If $L = 9$ when $M = 9$, find L when $M = 6$.

30. I is directly proportional to the cube root of y. If $I = 5$ when $y = 64$, find I when $y = 8$.

31. Q varies jointly as m and the square of n, and inversely as P. If $Q = 2$ when $m = 3$, $n = 6$, and $P = 12$, find Q when $m = 4$, $n = 18$, and $P = 2$.

32. w varies jointly as x, y, and z. If $w = 36$ when $x = 2$, $y = 8$, and $z = 12$, find w when $x = 1$, $y = 2$, and $z = 4$.

In problems 33–36, the graph of an equation of variation is shown. In each case, describe the type of variation as direct, inverse, or joint.

33.

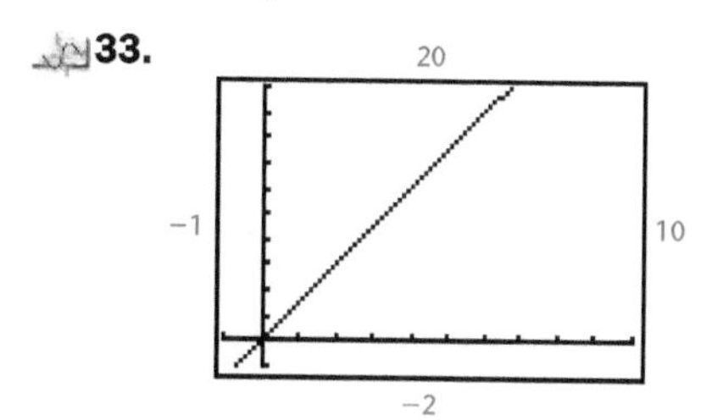

34.

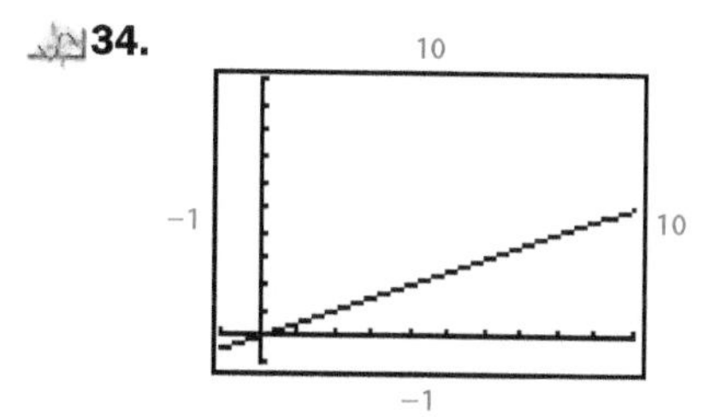

35.

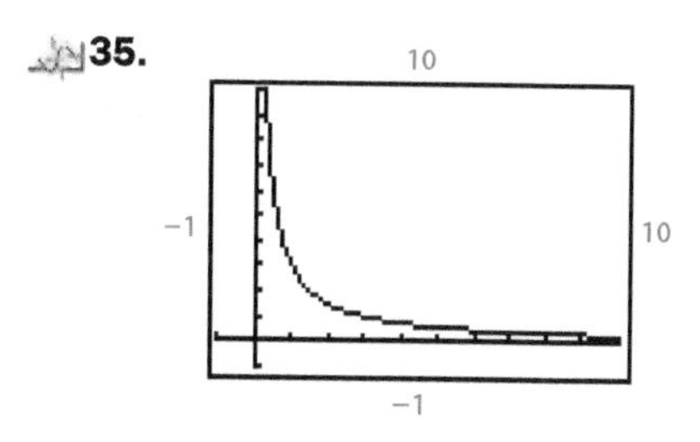

36.

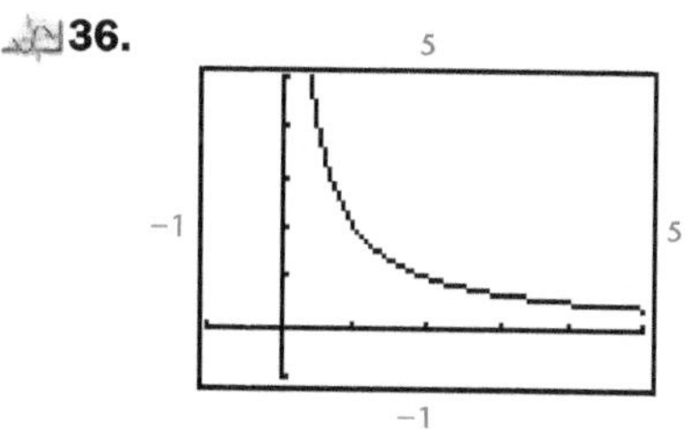

In Problems 37–42, translate each statement into an equation using k as the constant of variation.

37. The biologist René Réaumur suggested in 1735 that the length of time t that it takes fruit to ripen is inversely proportional to the sum T of the average daily temperatures during the growing season.

38. The erosive force P of a swiftly flowing stream is directly proportional to the sixth power of the velocity v of the water.

39. The maximum safe load L for a horizontal beam varies jointly as its width w and the square of its height h, and inversely as its length x.

40. The number N of long-distance phone calls between two cities varies jointly as the populations P_1 and P_2 of the two cities, and inversely as the distance d between the two cities.

41. The f-stop numbers N on a camera, known as focal ratios, are directly proportional to the focal length F of the lens and inversely proportional to the diameter d of the effective lens opening.

42. The time t required for an elevator to lift a weight is jointly proportional to the weight w and the distance d through which it is lifted, and inversely proportional to the power P of the motor.

43. Suppose that f varies directly as x. Show that the ratio x_1/x_2 of two values of x is equal to f_1/f_2, the ratio of the corresponding values of f.

44. Suppose that f varies inversely as x. Show that the ratio x_1/x_2 of two values of x is equal to f_2/f_1, the reciprocal of the ratio of the corresponding values of f.

APPLICATIONS

45. PHYSICS The weight w of an object on or above the surface of the Earth varies inversely as the square of the distance d between the object and the center of Earth. If a girl weighs 100 pounds on the surface of Earth, how much would she weigh (to the nearest pound) 400 miles above Earth's surface? (Assume the radius of Earth is 4,000 miles.)

46. PHYSICS A child was struck by a car in a crosswalk. The driver of the car had slammed on his brakes and left skid marks 160 feet long. He told the police he had been driving at 30 miles per hour. The police know that the length of skid marks L (when brakes are applied) varies directly as the square of the speed of the car v, and that at 30 miles per hour (under ideal conditions) skid marks would be 40 feet long. How fast was the driver actually going before he applied his brakes?

47. ELECTRICITY Ohm's law states that the current I in a wire varies directly as the electromotive forces E and inversely as the resistance R. If $I = 22$ amperes when $E = 110$ volts and $R = 5$ ohms, find I if $E = 220$ volts and $R = 11$ ohms.

48. ANTHROPOLOGY Anthropologists, in their study of race and human genetic groupings, often use an index called the *cephalic index*. The cephalic index C varies directly as the width w of the head and inversely as the length l of the head (both when viewed from the top). If an Indian in Baja California (Mexico) has measurements of $C = 75$, $w = 6$ inches, and $l = 8$ inches, what is C for an Indian in northern California with $w = 8.1$ inches and $l = 9$ inches?

49. PHYSICS If the horsepower P required to drive a speedboat through water is directly proportional to the cube of the speed v of the boat, what change in horsepower is required to double the speed of the boat?

50. ILLUMINATION The intensity of illumination E on a surface is inversely proportional to the square of its distance d from a light source. What is the effect on the total illumination on a book if the distance between the light source and the book is doubled?

51. MUSIC The frequency of vibration f of a musical string is directly proportional to the square root of the tension T and inversely proportional to the length L of the string. If the tension of the string is increased by a factor of 4 and the length of the string is doubled, what is the effect on the frequency?

52. PHYSICS In an automobile accident, the destructive force F of a car is (approximately) jointly proportional to the weight w of the car and the square of the speed v of the car. (This is why accidents at high speeds are generally so serious.) What would be the effect on the destructive forces of a car if its weight were doubled and its speed were doubled?

53. SPACE SCIENCE The length of time t a satellite takes to complete a circular orbit of Earth varies directly as the radius r of the orbit and inversely as the orbital velocity v of the satellite. If $t = 1.42$ hours when $r = 4{,}050$ miles and $v = 18{,}000$ miles per hour (Sputnik I), find t to two decimal places for $r = 4{,}300$ miles and $v = 18{,}500$ miles per hour.

54. GENETICS The number N of gene mutations resulting from x-ray exposure varies directly as the size of the x-ray dose r. What is the effect on N if r is quadrupled?

55. BIOLOGY In biology there is an approximate rule, called the *bioclimatic rule* for temperate climates, which states that the difference d in time for fruit to ripen (or insects to appear) varies directly as the change in altitude h. If $d = 4$ days when $h = 500$ feet, find d when $h = 2{,}500$ feet.

56. PHYSICS Over a fixed distance d, speed r varies inversely as time t. Police use this relationship to set up speed traps. If in a given speed trap $r = 30$ mph when $t = 6$ seconds, what would be the speed of a car if $t = 4$ seconds?

57. PHYSICS The length L of skid marks of a car's tires (when the brakes are applied) is directly proportional to the square of the speed v of the car. How is the length of skid marks affected by doubling the speed?

58. PHOTOGRAPHY In taking pictures using flashbulbs, the lens opening (f-stop number) N is inversely proportional to the distance d from the object being photographed. What adjustment should you make on the f-stop number if the distance between the camera and the object is doubled?

59. ENGINEERING The total pressure P of the wind on a wall is jointly proportional to the area of the wall A and the square of the velocity of the wind v. If $P = 120$ pounds when $A = 100$ square feet and $v = 20$ miles per hour, find P if $A = 200$ square feet and $v = 30$ miles per hour.

60. ENGINEERING The thrust T of a given type of propeller is jointly proportional to the fourth power of its diameter d and the square of the number of revolutions per minute n it is turning. What happens to the thrust if the diameter is doubled and the number of revolutions per minute is cut in half?

61. PSYCHOLOGY In early psychological studies on sensory perception (hearing, seeing, feeling, and so on), the question was asked: "Given a certain level of stimulation S, what is the minimum amount of added stimulation ΔS that can be detected?" A German physiologist, E. H. Weber (1795–1878) formulated, after many experiments, the famous law that now bears his name: "The amount of change ΔS that will be just noticed varies directly as the magnitude S of the stimulus."
(A) Write the law as an equation of variation.
(B) If a person lifting weights can just notice a difference of 1 ounce at the 50-ounce level, what will be the least difference she will be able to notice at the 500-ounce level?
(C) Determine the just noticeable difference in illumination a person is able to perceive at 480 candlepower if he is just able to perceive a difference of 1 candlepower at the 60-candlepower level.

62. PSYCHOLOGY Psychologists in their study of intelligence often use an index called IQ. IQ varies directly as mental age MA and inversely as chronological age CA (up to the age of 15). If a 12-year-old boy with a mental age of 14.4 has an IQ of 120, what will be the IQ of an 11-year-old girl with a mental age of 15.4?

63. GEOMETRY The volume of a sphere varies directly as the cube of its radius r. What happens to the volume if the radius is doubled?

64. GEOMETRY The surface area S of a sphere varies directly as the square of its radius r. What happens to the area if the radius is cut in half?

65. MUSIC The frequency of vibration of air in an open organ pipe is inversely proportional to the length of the pipe. If the air column in an open 32-foot pipe vibrates 16 times per second (low C), then how fast would the air vibrate in a 16-foot pipe?

66. MUSIC The frequency of pitch f of a musical string is directly proportional to the square root of the tension T and inversely proportional to the length l and the diameter d. Write the equation of variation using k as the constant of variation. (It is interesting to note that if pitch depended on only length, then pianos would have to have strings varying from 3 inches to 38 feet.)

CHAPTER 3 Review

3-1 Polynomial Functions and Models

A function that can be written in the form $P(x) = a_nx^n + a_{n-1}x^{n-1} + \cdots + a_1x + a_0$, $a_n \neq 0$, is a **polynomial function of degree *n*.** In this chapter, when not specified otherwise, the coefficients $a_n, a_{n-1}, \ldots, a_1, a_0$ are complex numbers and the domain of P is the set of complex numbers. A number r is said to be a **zero** (or **root**) of a function $P(x)$ if $P(r) = 0$. The zeros of $P(x)$ are thus the solutions of the equation $P(x) = 0$. The real zeros of $P(x)$ are just the x intercepts of the graph of $P(x)$. A point on a continuous graph that separates an increasing portion from a decreasing portion, or vice versa, is called a **turning point.** If $P(x)$ is a polynomial of degree $n > 0$ with real coefficients, then the graph of $P(x)$:

1. Is continuous for all real numbers
2. Has no sharp corners
3. Has at most n real zeros
4. Has at most $n - 1$ turning points
5. Increases or decreases without bound as $x \to \infty$ and as $x \to -\infty$

The left and right behavior of such a polynomial $P(x)$ is determined by its highest degree or **leading term:** As $x \to \pm\infty$, both a_nx^n and $P(x)$ approach $\pm\infty$, with the sign depending on whether n is even or odd and the sign of a_n.

Many graphing calculators can find polynomial regression models to fit data sets; cubic (third-degree) and quartic (fourth-degree) models are often useful to model data with behavior too complicated to be modeled well with a linear or quadratic model.

3-2 Polynomial Division

For any polynomial $P(x)$ of degree n, we have the following important results:

Division Algorithm

For any other polynomial $D(x) \neq 0$, there are unique polynomials $Q(x)$ (the **quotient**) and $R(x)$ (the **remainder**) so that

$$P(x) = D(x)\,Q(x) + R(x)$$

and the degree of $R(x)$ is less than the degree of $D(x)$. $P(x)$ is called the **dividend,** $D(x)$ the **divisor.**

Remainder Theorem

$P(r) = R$, where R is the numeric remainder when P is divided by $x - r$.

Factor Theorem

$x - r$ is a factor of $P(x)$ if and only if the remainder is zero when P is divided by $x - r$.

Zeros Theorem

$P(x)$ has at most n zeros (recall that n is the degree of P).

Polynomials can be divided using a long-division process that is very similar to long division of numbers. **Synthetic division** is an efficient method for dividing polynomials by linear terms of the form $x - r$. Remember that synthetic division only works when the divisor is of the form $x - r$.

3-3 Real Zeros and Polynomial Inequalities

The following theorems are useful in locating and approximating all real zeros of a polynomial $P(x)$ of degree $n > 0$ with real coefficients, $a_n > 0$:

Upper and Lower Bound Theorem

1. Upper bound: A number $r > 0$ is an upper bound for the real zeros of $P(x)$ if, when $P(x)$ is divided by $x - r$ using synthetic division, all numbers in the quotient row, including the remainder, are nonnegative.
2. Lower bound: A number $r < 0$ is a lower bound for the real zeros of $P(x)$ if, when $P(x)$ is divided by $x - r$ using synthetic division, all numbers in the quotient row, including the remainder, alternate in sign.

Location Theorem

Suppose that a function f is continuous on an interval I that contains numbers a and b. If $f(a)$ and $f(b)$ have opposite signs, then the graph of f has at least one x intercept between a and b.

The **bisection method** uses the location theorem to find smaller and smaller intervals containing an x intercept. It can be used to approximate the real zeros of a polynomial.

When real zeros occur at turning points, the bisection method and the ZERO command on a graphing calculator may not be able to locate the zero. In this case, the MAXIMUM or MINIMUM commands should be used.

Polynomial inequalities can be solved using a method similar to the one used to solve quadratic inequalities in Section 2-7. They can also be solved by finding zeros and then examining the graph of an appropriate polynomial with real coefficients.

3-4 Complex Zeros and Rational Zeros of Polynomials

If $P(x)$ is a polynomial of degree $n > 0$, we have the following important theorems:

Fundamental Theorem of Algebra

$P(x)$ has at least one complex zero that may or may not be real.

***n* Linear Factors Theorem**

$P(x)$ can be factored as a product of n linear factors.

If $P(x)$ is factored as a product of linear factors, the number of linear factors that have zero r is said to be the **multiplicity** of r.

Imaginary Zeros Theorem

Imaginary zeros of polynomials with real coefficients, if they exist, occur in conjugate pairs.

Linear and Quadratic Factors Theorem

If $P(x)$ has real coefficients, then $P(x)$ can be factored as a product of linear factors (with real coefficients) and quadratic factors (with real coefficients and imaginary zeros).

Real Zeros and Polynomials of Odd Degree

If $P(x)$ has odd degree and real coefficients, then the graph of P has at least one x intercept.

Zeros of Even or Odd Multiplicity

Let $P(x)$ have real coefficients:

1. If r is a real zero of $P(x)$ of even multiplicity, then $P(x)$ has a turning point at r and does not change sign at r.
2. If r is a real zero of $P(x)$ of odd multiplicity, then $P(x)$ does not have a turning point at r and changes sign at r.

Rational Zero Theorem

If the rational number b/c, in lowest terms, is a zero of the polynomial

$$P(x) = a_nx^n + a_{n-1}x^{n-1} + \cdots + a_1x + a_0 \qquad a_n \neq 0$$

with integer coefficients, then b must be an integer factor of a_0 and c must be an integer factor of a_n.

If $P(x) = (x - r)Q(x)$, then $Q(x)$ is called a **reduced polynomial** for $P(x)$.

3-5 Rational Functions and Inequalities

A function f is a **rational function** if it can be written in the form

$$f(x) = \frac{p(x)}{q(x)}$$

where $p(x)$ and $q(x)$ are polynomials of degrees m and n, respectively (we assume $p(x)$ and $q(x)$ have no common factor).

The graph of a rational function $f(x)$:

1. Is continuous with the exception of at most n real numbers
2. Has no sharp corners
3. Has at most m real zeros
4. Has at most $m + n - 1$ turning points
5. Has the same left and right behavior as the quotient of the leading terms of $p(x)$ and $q(x)$

The vertical line $x = a$ is a **vertical asymptote** for the graph of $f(x)$ if $f(x) \to \infty$ or $f(x) \to -\infty$ as $x \to a^+$ or as $x \to a^-$. If a is a zero of the denominator, then the line $x = a$ is a vertical asymptote of the graph of f provided that the numerator and denominator have no common factors. The horizontal line $y = b$ is a **horizontal asymptote** for the graph of $f(x)$ if $f(x) \to b$ as $x \to -\infty$ or as $x \to \infty$.

$$\text{Let } f(x) = \frac{a_m x^m + \cdots + a_1 x + a_0}{b_n x^n + \cdots + b_1 x + b_0}, a_m \neq 0, b_n \neq 0.$$

1. If $m < n$, the line $y = 0$ (the x axis) is a horizontal asymptote.
2. If $m = n$, the line $y = a_m/b_n$ is a horizontal asymptote.
3. If $m > n$, there is no horizontal asymptote.

The line $y = mx + b$ is an **oblique,** or **slant, asymptote** if the graph of f approaches the graph of that line as $x \to \pm\infty$. Slant asymptotes occur when the degree of the numerator is one more than the degree of the denominator, and can be found by long division.

Analyzing and Sketching the Graph of a Rational Function: $f(x) = p(x)/q(x)$

Step 1. *Intercepts.* Find the real solutions of the equation $p(x) = 0$ and use these solutions to plot any x intercepts of the graph of f. Evaluate $f(0)$, if it exists, and plot the y intercept.

Step 2. *Vertical Asymptotes.* Find the real solutions of the equation $q(x) = 0$ and use these solutions to determine the domain of f, the points of discontinuity, and the vertical asymptotes. Sketch any vertical asymptotes as dashed lines.

Step 3. *Horizontal Asymptotes.* Determine whether there is a horizontal asymptote and if so, sketch it as a dashed line.

Step 4. *Complete the Sketch.* Using a graphing calculator graph as an aid and the information determined in steps 1–3, sketch the graph.

Rational inequalities can be solved using a method similar to that for polynomial inequalities. The main difference is that the zeros of the denominator represent potential changes in sign, as well as the zeros of the function.

3-6 Variation and Modeling

Let x and y be variables. The statement:

1. **y is directly proportional to x** (or **y varies directly as x**) means

$$y = kx$$

for some nonzero constant k.

2. **y is inversely proportional to x** (or **y varies inversely as x**) means

$$y = \frac{k}{x}$$

for some nonzero constant k.

3. **w is jointly proportional to x and y** (or **w varies jointly as x and y**) means

$$w = kxy$$

for some nonzero constant k.

In each case the nonzero constant k is called the **constant of proportionality** (or **constant of variation**).

The three basic types of variation also can be combined. For example, Newton's law of gravitation, "The force of attraction F between two objects is jointly proportional to their masses m_1 and m_2 and inversely proportional to the square of the distance d between them" has the equation

$$F = k\frac{m_1 m_2}{d^2}$$

CHAPTER 3 Review Exercises

Work through all the problems in this chapter review, and check answers in the back of the book. Answers to all review problems are there, and following each answer is a number in italics indicating the section in which that type of problem is discussed. Where weaknesses show up, review appropriate sections in the text.

1. Determine whether the function is a polynomial. If it is, state the degree.

(A) $f(x) = 3x^{1/2} - 7x^3 + \dfrac{5}{x}$

(B) $g(x) = -4x^3 + 5x + 11$

2. List the real zeros and turning points, and state the left and right behavior, of the polynomial function that has the indicated graph.

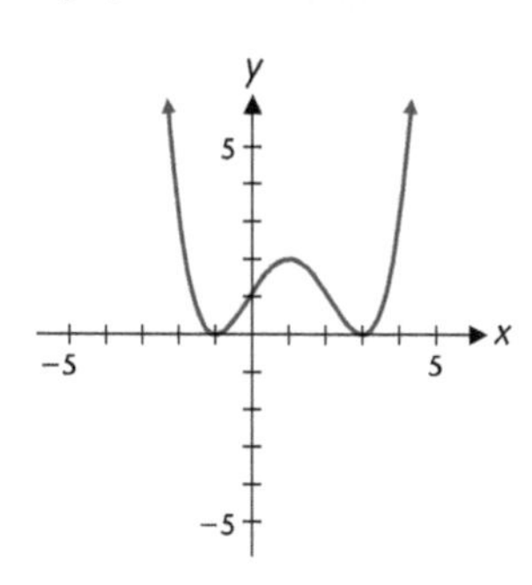

3. Use synthetic division to divide $P(x) = 2x^3 + 3x^2 - 1$ by $D(x) = x + 2$, and write the answer in the form $P(x) = D(x)Q(x) + R$.

4. If $P(x) = x^5 - 4x^4 + 9x^2 - 8$, find $P(3)$ using the remainder theorem and synthetic division.

5. What are the zeros of $P(x) = 3(x - 2)(x + 4)(x + 1)$?

6. Sketch the graph of a polynomial with zeros $x = 5, -3$, and 2, odd degree, and positive leading coefficient.

7. Find a polynomial of least degree that has zeros $x = 5, -3$, and 2. Write your answer in both factored form and standard form.

8. If $P(x) = x^2 - 2x + 2$ and $P(1 + i) = 0$, find another zero of $P(x)$.

9. Let $P(x)$ be the polynomial whose graph is shown in the figure at the top of the next column.

(A) Assuming that $P(x)$ has integer zeros and leading coefficient 1, find the lowest-degree equation that could produce this graph.

(B) Describe the left and right behavior of $P(x)$.

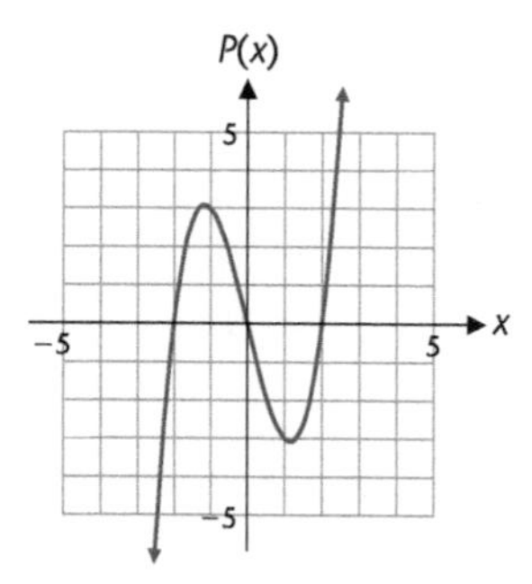

10. According to the upper and lower bound theorem, which of the following are upper or lower bounds of the zeros of $P(x) = x^3 - 4x^2 + 2$?

$$-2, -1, 3, 4$$

11. How do you know that $P(x) = 2x^3 - 3x^2 + x - 5$ has at least one real zero between 1 and 2?

12. Write the possible rational zeros for

$$P(x) = x^3 - 4x^2 + x + 6.$$

13. Find all rational zeros for $P(x) = x^3 - 4x^2 + x + 6$.

14. Find the domain and x intercept(s) for:

(A) $f(x) = \dfrac{2x - 3}{x + 4}$ (B) $g(x) = \dfrac{3x}{x^2 - x - 6}$

15. Find the horizontal and vertical asymptotes for the functions in Problem 14.

In Problems 16–21, translate each statement into an equation using k as the constant of proportionality.

16. F is directly proportional to the square root of x.

17. G is jointly proportional to x and the square of y.

18. H is inversely proportional to the cube of z.

19. R varies jointly as the square of x and the square of y.

20. S varies inversely as the square of u.

21. T varies directly as v and inversely as w.

22. The amount of light captured by a lens is directly proportional to the surface area of the lens. If a lens is exchanged for a similar one with a larger surface area, how will the amount of light captured change?

23. It has been suggested that the cleanliness of a home is inversely proportional to the number of children that live there. If this is true, what would be the effect on cleanliness if another child is added to a home?

24. Explain why the graph is not the graph of a polynomial function.

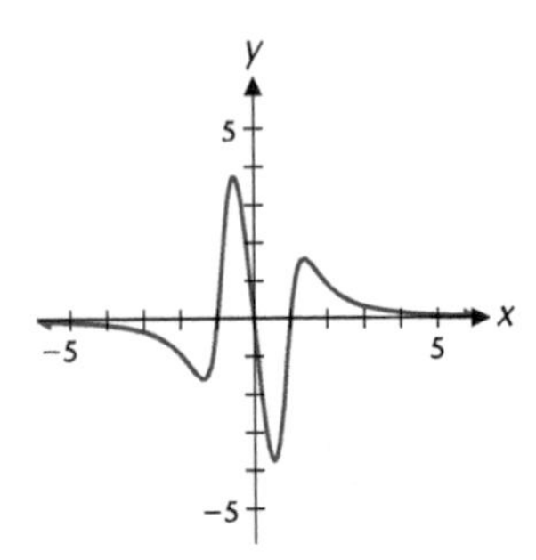

25. Let $P(x) = x^3 - 3x^2 - 3x + 4$.

(A) Graph $P(x)$ and describe the graph verbally, including the number of x intercepts, the number of turning points, and the left and right behavior.

(B) Approximate the largest x intercept to two decimal places.

26. If $P(x) = 8x^4 - 14x^3 - 13x^2 - 4x + 7$, find $Q(x)$ and R such that $P(x) = (x - \frac{1}{4})Q(x) + R$. What is $P(\frac{1}{4})$?

27. Divide, using long division:
$(x^4 - 7x^3 - 5x + 1) \div (x^2 + 2x)$

28. If $P(x) = 4x^3 - 8x^2 - 3x - 3$, find $P(-\frac{1}{2})$ using the remainder theorem and synthetic division.

29. Use the quadratic formula and the factor theorem to factor $P(x) = x^2 - 2x - 1$.

30. Is $x + 1$ a factor of $P(x) = 9x^{26} - 11x^{17} + 8x^{11} - 5x^4 - 7$? Explain, without dividing or using synthetic division.

31. Given that $x = 2$ is a zero of $P(x) = 2x^3 - 9x^2 + 3x + 14$, find all other zeros.

32. Determine all rational zeros of $P(x) = 2x^3 - 3x^2 - 18x - 8$.

33. Factor the polynomial in Problem 32 into linear factors.

34. Find all rational zeros of $P(x) = x^3 - 3x^2 + 5$.

35. Find all zeros (rational, irrational, and imaginary) exactly for $P(x) = 2x^4 - x^3 + 2x - 1$.

36. Factor the polynomial in Problem 35 into linear factors.

37. If $P(x) = (x - 1)^2(x + 1)^3(x^2 - 1)(x^2 + 1)$, what is its degree? Write the zeros of $P(x)$, indicating the multiplicity of each if greater than 1.

38. Factor $P(x) = x^4 + 5x^2 - 36$ in two ways:

(A) As a product of linear factors (with real coefficients) and quadratic factors (with real coefficients and imaginary zeros)

(B) As a product of linear factors with complex coefficients

39. Let $P(x) = x^5 - 10x^4 + 30x^3 - 20x^2 - 15x - 2$.

(A) Approximate the zeros of $P(x)$ to two decimal places and state the multiplicity of each zero.

(B) Can any of these zeros be approximated with the bisection method? The MAXIMUM command? The MINIMUM command? Explain.

40. Let $P(x) = x^4 - 2x^3 - 30x^2 - 25$.

(A) Use the upper and lower bound theorem to find the smallest positive and largest negative integers that are upper and lower bounds, respectively, for the real zeros of $P(x)$.

(B) If $(k, k + 1)$, k an integer, is the interval containing the largest real zero of $P(x)$, determine how many additional intervals are required in the bisection method to approximate this zero to one decimal place.

(C) Approximate the real zeros of $P(x)$ to two decimal places.

41. Let $f(x) = \dfrac{x - 1}{2x + 2}$.

(A) Find the domain and the intercepts for f.

(B) Find the vertical and horizontal asymptotes for f.

(C) Sketch a graph of f. Draw vertical and horizontal asymptotes with dashed lines.

42. Solve the polynomial inequality exactly: $3x^3 \geq 4x^2 + 15x$

43. Solve each polynomial inequality to three decimal places:

(A) $x^3 - 5x + 4 < 0$ (B) $x^3 - 5x + 4 < 2$

44. Explain why the graph is not the graph of a rational function.

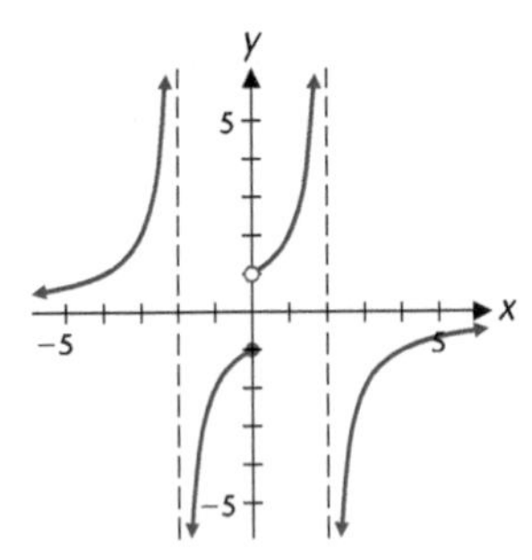

45. B varies inversely as the square root of c. If $B = 5$ when $c = 4$, find B when $c = 25$.

46. D is jointly proportional to x and y. If $D = 10$ when $x = 3$ and $y = 2$, find D when $x = 9$ and $y = 8$.

47. Use synthetic division to divide $P(x) = x^3 + 3x + 2$ by $[x - (1 + i)]$, and write the answer in the form $P(x) = D(x)Q(x) + R$.

48. Find a polynomial of lowest degree with leading coefficient 1 that has zeros $-\frac{1}{2}$ (multiplicity 2), -3, and 1 (multiplicity 3). (Leave the answer in factored form.) What is the degree of the polynomial?

49. Repeat Problem 48 for a polynomial $P(x)$ with zeros $-5, 2 - 3i$, and $2 + 3i$.

50. Find all zeros (rational, irrational, and imaginary) exactly for $P(x) = 2x^5 - 5x^4 - 8x^3 + 21x^2 - 4$.

51. Factor the polynomial in Problem 50 into linear factors.

52. Let $P(x) = x^4 + 16x^3 + 47x^2 - 137x + 73$. Approximate (to two decimal places) the x intercepts and the local extrema.

53. What is the minimal degree of a polynomial $P(x)$, given that $P(-1) = -4$, $P(0) = 2$, $P(1) = -5$, and $P(2) = 3$? Justify your conclusion.

54. If $P(x)$ is a cubic polynomial with integer coefficients and if $1 + 2i$ is a zero of $P(x)$, can $P(x)$ have an irrational zero? Explain.

55. The solutions to the equation $x^3 - 27 = 0$ are the cube roots of 27.

(A) How many cube roots of 27 are there?

(B) 3 is obviously a cube root of 27; find all others.

56. Let $P(x) = x^4 + 2x^3 - 500x^2 - 4{,}000$.

(A) Use the upper and lower bound theorem to find the smallest positive integer multiple of 10 and the largest negative integer multiple of 10 that are upper and lower bounds, respectively, for the real zeros of $P(x)$.

(B) Approximate the real zeros of $P(x)$ to two decimal places.

57. Graph

$$f(x) = \frac{x^2 + 2x + 3}{x + 1}$$

Indicate any vertical, horizontal, or oblique asymptotes with dashed lines.

58. Use a graphing calculator to find any horizontal asymptotes for

$$f(x) = \frac{2x}{\sqrt{x^2 + 3x + 4}}$$

59. Solve each rational inequality to three decimal places:

(A) $\dfrac{x^2 - 3}{x^3 - 3x + 1} \le 0$ (B) $\dfrac{x^2 - 3}{x^3 - 3x + 1} > \dfrac{5}{x^2}$

60. If $P(x) = x^3 - x^2 - 5x + 4$, determine the number of real zeros of $P(x)$ and explain why $P(x)$ has no rational zeros.

61. Give an example of a rational function $f(x)$ that satisfies the following conditions: the real zeros of f are -3, 0, and 2; the vertical asymptotes of f are the lines $x = -1$ and $x = 4$; and the line $y = 5$ is a horizontal asymptote.

APPLICATIONS

62. PROFIT An enterprising college student earns extra money by setting up a small coffee stand in the student union. She wants to figure out how many hours per week she should work the stand, so she tries a variety of hours and keeps track of profit, then uses regression analysis to model her results. She finds that the function $P(x) = -0.167x^3 + 2.50x^2 + 31.7x - 100$ $(0 \le x \le 20)$ describes her weekly profit in dollars, where x is hours per week the stand is open.

(A) How many hours should she work to break even?

(B) How many hours should she work to ensure that her weekly profit is at least $325?

63. PHYSICS The centripetal force F of a body moving in a circular path at constant speed is inversely proportional to the radius r of the path. What happens to F if r is doubled?

64. PHYSICS The Maxwell–Boltzmann equation says that the average velocity v of a molecule varies directly as the square root of the absolute temperature T and inversely as the square root of its molecular weight w. Write the equation of variation using k as the constant of variation.

65. WORK The amount A of work completed varies jointly as the number of workers W used and the time t they spend. If 10 workers can finish a job in 8 days, how long will it take 4 workers to do the same job?

66. SIMPLE INTEREST The simple interest I earned in a given time is jointly proportional to the principal p and the interest rate r. If $100 at 4% interest earns $8, how much will $150 at 3% interest earn in the same period?

In Problems 67–70, express the solutions as the roots of a polynomial equation of the form $P(x) = 0$. Find rational solutions exactly and irrational solutions to three decimal places.

67. ARCHITECTURE An entryway is formed by placing a rectangular door inside an arch in the shape of the parabola with graph $y = 16 - x^2$, x and y in feet (see the figure). If the area of the door is 48 square feet, find the dimensions of the door.

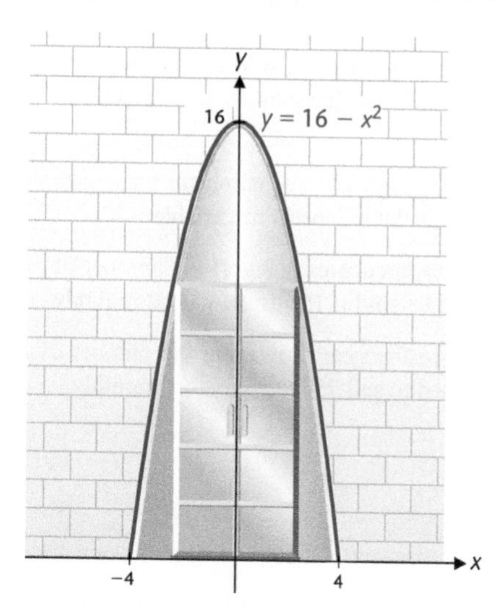

68. CONSTRUCTION A grain silo is formed by attaching a hemisphere to the top of a right circular cylinder (see the figure). If the cylinder is 18 feet high and the volume of the silo is 486π cubic feet, find the common radius of the cylinder and the hemisphere.

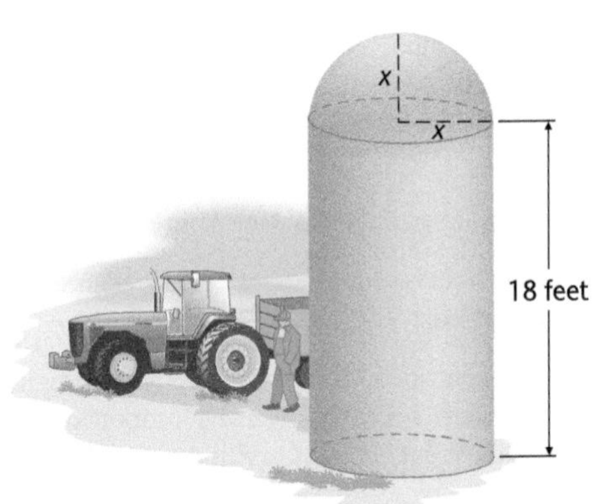

69. MANUFACTURING A box is to be made out of a piece of cardboard that measures 15 by 20 inches. Squares, x inches on a side, will be cut from each corner, and then the ends and sides will be folded up (see the figure). Find the value of x that would result in a box with a volume of 300 cubic inches.

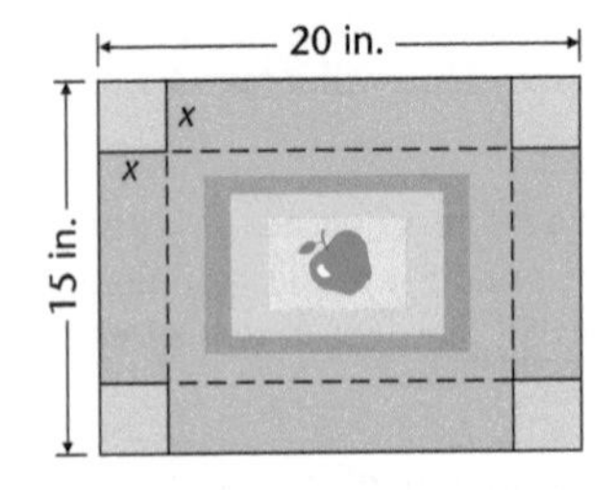

70. GEOMETRY Find all points on the graph of $y = x^2$ that are three units from the point (1, 4).

MODELING AND DATA ANALYSIS

71. ADVERTISING A chain of appliance stores uses television ads to promote the sale of refrigerators. Analyzing past records produced the data in Table 1, where x is the number of ads placed monthly and y is the number of refrigerators sold that month.

(A) Find a cubic regression equation for these data using the number of ads as the independent variable.

(B) Estimate (to the nearest integer) the number of refrigerators that would be sold if 15 ads are placed monthly.

(C) Estimate (to the nearest integer) the number of ads that should be placed to sell 750 refrigerators monthly.

Table 1

Number of Ads x	Number of Refrigerators y
10	270
20	430
25	525
30	630
45	890
48	915

72. WOMEN IN THE WORKFORCE It is reasonable to conjecture from the data given in Table 2 that many Japanese women tend to leave the workforce to marry and have children, but then reenter the workforce when the children are grown.

(A) Explain why you might expect cubic regression to provide a better fit to the data than linear or quadratic regression.

(B) Find a cubic regression model for these data using age as the independent variable.

(C) Use the regression equation to estimate (to the nearest year) the ages at which 65% of the women are in the workforce.

Table 2 Women in the Workforce in Japan (1997)

Age	Percentage of Women Employed
22	73
27	65
32	56
37	63
42	71
47	72
52	68
57	59
62	42

CHAPTER 3

››› GROUP ACTIVITY Interpolating Polynomials

Given two points in the plane, we can use the point–slope form of the equation of a line to find a polynomial whose graph passes through these two points. How can we proceed if we are given more than two points? For example, how can we find the equation of a polynomial $P(x)$ whose graph passes through the points listed in Table 1 and graphed in Figure 1?

Table 1

x	1	2	3	4
$P(x)$	1	3	−3	1

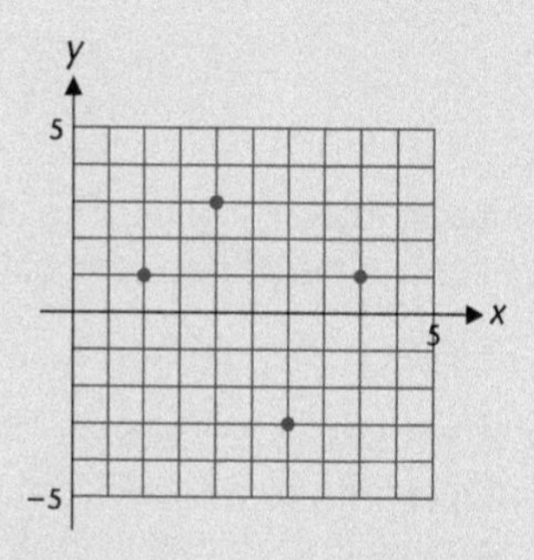

› **Figure 1**

The key to solving this problem is to write the unknown polynomial $P(x)$ in the following special form:

$$P(x) = a_0 + a_1(x - 1) + a_2(x - 1)(x - 2) + a_3(x - 1)(x - 2)(x - 3) \qquad (1)$$

Because the graph of $P(x)$ is to pass through each point in Table 1, we can substitute each value of x in equation (1) to determine the coefficients a_0, a_1, a_2, and a_3. First we evaluate equation (1) at $x = 1$ to determine a_0:

$$1 = P(1)$$
$$= a_0 \qquad \text{All other terms in equation (1) are 0 when } x = 1.$$

Using this value for a_0 in equation (1) and evaluating at $x = 2$, we have

$$3 = P(2) = 1 + a_1(1) \qquad \text{All other terms are 0.}$$
$$2 = a_1$$

Continuing in this manner, we have

$$-3 = P(3) = 1 + 2(2) + a_2(2)(1)$$
$$-8 = 2a_2$$
$$-4 = a_2$$
$$1 = P(4) = 1 + 2(3) - 4(3)(2) + a_3(3)(2)(1)$$
$$18 = 6a_3$$
$$3 = a_3$$

We have now evaluated all the coefficients in equation (1) and can write

$$P(x) = 1 + 2(x - 1) - 4(x - 1)(x - 2) + 3(x - 1)(x - 2)(x - 3) \quad (2)$$

If we expand the products in equation (2) and collect like terms, we can express $P(x)$ in the more conventional form (verify this):

$$P(x) = 3x^3 - 22x^2 + 47x - 27$$

(A) To check these calculations, evaluate $P(x)$ at $x = 1, 2, 3$, and 4 and compare the results with Table 1. Then add the graph of $P(x)$ to Figure 1.
(B) Write a verbal description of the special form of $P(x)$ in equation (1).

In general, given a set of $n + 1$ points:

x	x_0	x_1	$\cdots$	x_n
y	y_0	y_1	$\cdots$	y_n

the **interpolating polynomial** for these points is the polynomial $P(x)$ of degree less than or equal to n that satisfies $P(x_k) = y_k$ for $k = 0, 1, \ldots, n$. The **general form** of the interpolating polynomial is

$$P(x) = a_0 + a_1(x - x_0) + a_2(x - x_0)(x - x_1) + \cdots + a_n(x - x_0)(x - x_1) \cdot \cdots \cdot (x - x_{n-1})$$

(C) Summarize the procedure for using the points in the table to find the coefficients in the general form.
(D) Give an example to show that the interpolating polynomial can have degree strictly less than n.
(E) Could there be two different polynomials of degree less than or equal to n whose graph passes through the given $n + 1$ points? Justify your answer.
(F) Find the interpolating polynomial for each of Tables 2 and 3. Check your answers by evaluating the polynomial, and illustrate by graphing the points in the table and the polynomial in the same viewing window.

Table 2

x	−1	0	1	2
y	5	3	3	11

Table 3

x	−2	−1	0	1	2
y	−3	0	5	0	−3

(G) The student in Problem 62 of this chapter's Review Exercises recorded the data relating hours worked and weekly profit shown in Table 4.

Table 4 Weekly Profit from a Coffee Stand Open x Hours

x (hours)	0	5	10	15
P($)	−100	100	300	375

Find the interpolating polynomial for this data, then use a graphing calculator to find the cubic regression polynomial. Are they the same? Do they agree with the polynomial in Problem 62?

Exponential and Logarithmic Functions

Exponential and Logarithmic Functions

MOST of the functions we have worked with so far have been polynomial or rational functions, with a few others involving roots. Functions that can be expressed in terms of addition, subtraction, multiplication, division, and roots of variables and constants are called *algebraic functions.* In Chapter 4 we will learn about *exponential and logarithmic functions.* These functions are not algebraic; they belong to the class of *transcendental functions.* Exponential and logarithmic functions are used to model a surprisingly wide variety of real-world phenomena: growth of populations of people, animals, and bacteria; radioactive decay; epidemics; and magnitudes of sounds and earthquakes. These and many other applications will be studied in this chapter.

CHAPTER 4

OUTLINE

4-1 Exponential Functions

Many of the functions we've studied so far have included exponents. But in every case, the exponent was a constant, and the base was often a variable. In this section, we will reverse those roles. In an *exponential function,* the variable appears in an exponent. As we'll see, this has a significant effect on the properties and graphs of these functions. A review of the basic properties of exponents in Appendix A, Section A-2, would be very helpful before moving on.

(a)

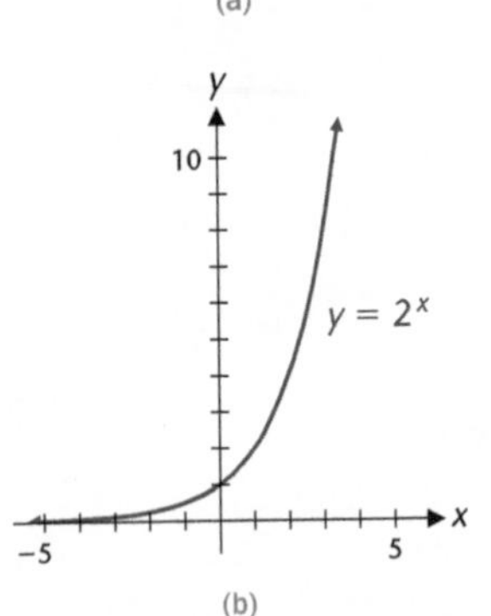

› Figure 1

› Defining Exponential Functions

Let's start by noting that the functions f and g given by

$$f(x) = 2^x \qquad \text{and} \qquad g(x) = x^2$$

are not the same function. Whether a variable appears as an exponent with a constant base or as a base with a constant exponent makes a big difference. The function g is a quadratic function, which we have already discussed. The function f is an *exponential function.*

The graphs of f and g are shown in Figure 1. As expected, they are very different.

We know how to define the values of 2^x for many types of inputs. For positive integers, it's simply repeated multiplication:

$$2^2 = 2 \cdot 2 = 4; \quad 2^3 = 2 \cdot 2 \cdot 2 = 8; \quad 2^4 = 2 \cdot 2 \cdot 2 \cdot 2 = 16$$

For negative integers, we use properties of negative exponents:

$$2^{-1} = \frac{1}{2}; \quad 2^{-2} = \frac{1}{2^2} = \frac{1}{4}; \quad 2^{-3} = \frac{1}{2^3} = \frac{1}{8}$$

For rational numbers, a calculator comes in handy:

$$2^{\frac{1}{2}} = \sqrt{2} \approx 1.4; \quad 2^{\frac{3}{2}} = \sqrt{2^3} \approx 2.8; \quad 2^{\frac{9}{4}} = \sqrt[4]{2^9} \approx 4.8$$

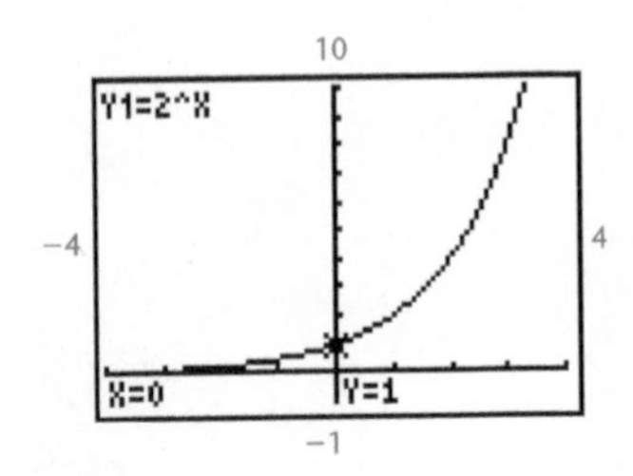

› Figure 2

A graphing calculator can be used to obtain the graph in Figure 1(b) [see Fig. 2].

The only catch is that we don't know how to define 2^x for *all* real numbers. For example, what does

$$2^{\sqrt{2}}$$

mean? Your calculator can give you a decimal approximation, but where does it come from? That question is not easy to answer at this point. In fact, a precise definition of $2^{\sqrt{2}}$ must wait for more advanced courses. For now, we will simply state that for any positive real number b, the expression b^x is defined for all real values of x, and the output is a real number as well. This enables us to draw the continuous graph for $f(x) = 2^x$ in Figure 1. In Problems 85 and 86 in Exercises 4-1, we will explore a method for defining b^x for irrational x values like $\sqrt{2}$.

> **DEFINITION 1 Exponential Function**
>
> The equation
>
> $$f(x) = b^x \qquad b > 0, b \neq 1$$
>
> defines an **exponential function** for each different constant b, called the **base.** The independent variable x may assume any real value.

The domain of f is the set of all real numbers, and it can be shown that the range of f is the set of all positive real numbers. We require the base b to be positive to avoid imaginary numbers such as $(-2)^{1/2}$. Problems 57 and 58 in Exercises 4-1 explore why $b = 0$ and $b = 1$ are excluded.

Analyzing Graphs of Exponential Functions

EXPLORE-DISCUSS 1

Compare the graphs of $f(x) = 3^x$ and $g(x) = 2^x$ by graphing both functions in the same viewing window. Find all points of intersection of the graphs. For which values of x is the graph of f above the graph of g? Below the graph of g? Are the graphs of f and g close together as $x \to \infty$? As $x \to -\infty$? Discuss.

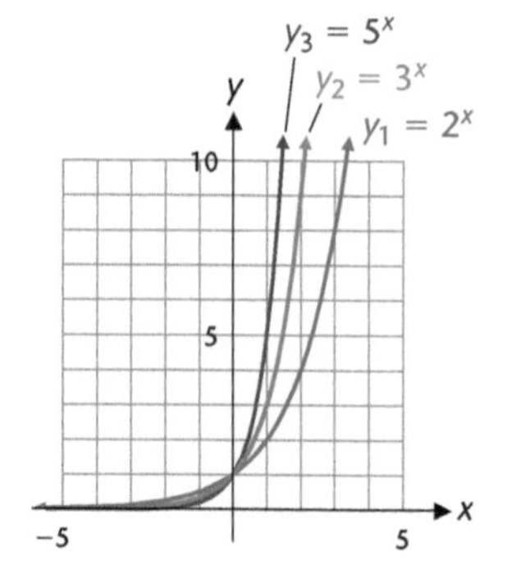

Figure 3 $y = b^x$ for $b = 2, 3, 5$.

The graphs of $y = b^x$ for $b = 2, 3$, and 5 are shown in Figure 3. Note that all three have the same basic shape, and pass through the point (0, 1). Also, the x axis is a horizontal asymptote for each graph, but only as $x \to -\infty$. The main difference between the graphs is their steepness.

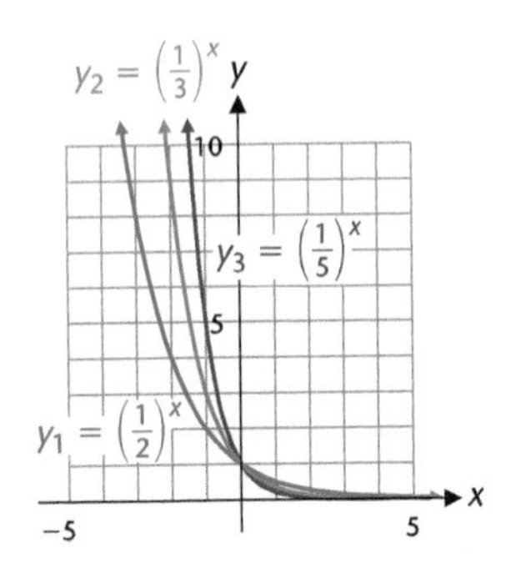

› **Figure 4** $y = b^x$ for $b = \frac{1}{2}, \frac{1}{3}, \frac{1}{5}$.

Next, let's look at the graphs of $y = b^x$ for $b = \frac{1}{2}, \frac{1}{3}$, and $\frac{1}{5}$ (Fig. 4). Again, all three have the same basic shape, pass through (0, 1), and have a horizontal asymptote $y = 0$, but we can see that for $b < 1$, the asymptote is only as $x \to \infty$. In general, for bases less than 1, the graph is a reflection through the y axis of the graphs for bases greater than 1.

The graphs in Figures 3 and 4 suggest that the graphs of exponential functions have the properties listed in Theorem 1, which we state without proof.

› THEOREM 1 Properties of Graphs of Exponential Functions

Let $f(x) = b^x$ be an exponential function, $b > 0, b \neq 1$. Then the graph of $f(x)$:

1. Is continuous for all real numbers
2. Has no sharp corners
3. Passes through the point (0, 1)
4. Lies above the x axis, which is a horizontal asymptote either as $x \to \infty$ or $x \to -\infty$, but not both
5. Increases as x increases if $b > 1$; decreases as x increases if $0 < b < 1$
6. Intersects any horizontal line at most once (that is, f is one-to-one)

These properties indicate that the graphs of exponential functions are distinct from the graphs we have already studied. (Actually, Property 4 is enough to ensure that graphs of exponential functions are different from graphs of polynomials and rational functions.) Property 6 is important because it guarantees that exponential functions have inverses. Those inverses, called *logarithmic functions,* are the subject of Section 4-3.

To begin a study of graphing exponentials, it's helpful to sketch a graph or two by hand after plotting points.

EXAMPLE 1 Drawing the Graph of an Exponential Function

Sketch the graph of each function after plotting at least seven points. Then confirm your result with a graphing calculator.

(A) $f(x) = \left(\frac{3}{2}\right)^x$ (B) $g(x) = \left(\frac{2}{3}\right)^x$

SOLUTIONS

Make a table of values for f and g.

x	$\left(\frac{3}{2}\right)^x$	$\left(\frac{2}{3}\right)^x$
-3	$\left(\frac{3}{2}\right)^{-3} = \left(\frac{2}{3}\right)^3 = \frac{8}{27}$	$\left(\frac{2}{3}\right)^{-3} = \left(\frac{3}{2}\right)^3 = \frac{27}{8}$
-2	$\left(\frac{3}{2}\right)^{-2} = \left(\frac{2}{3}\right)^2 = \frac{4}{9}$	$\left(\frac{2}{3}\right)^{-2} = \left(\frac{3}{2}\right)^2 = \frac{9}{4}$
-1	$\left(\frac{3}{2}\right)^{-1} = \left(\frac{2}{3}\right)^1 = \frac{2}{3}$	$\left(\frac{2}{3}\right)^{-1} = \left(\frac{3}{2}\right)^1 = \frac{3}{2}$
0	$\left(\frac{3}{2}\right)^0 = 1$	$\left(\frac{2}{3}\right)^0 = 1$
1	$\left(\frac{3}{2}\right)^1 = \frac{3}{2}$	$\left(\frac{2}{3}\right)^1 = \frac{2}{3}$
2	$\left(\frac{3}{2}\right)^2 = \frac{9}{4}$	$\left(\frac{2}{3}\right)^2 = \frac{4}{9}$
3	$\left(\frac{3}{2}\right)^3 = \frac{27}{8}$	$\left(\frac{2}{3}\right)^3 = \frac{8}{27}$

The hand sketches are shown in Figures 5 and 6, along with the corresponding graphing calculator graph.

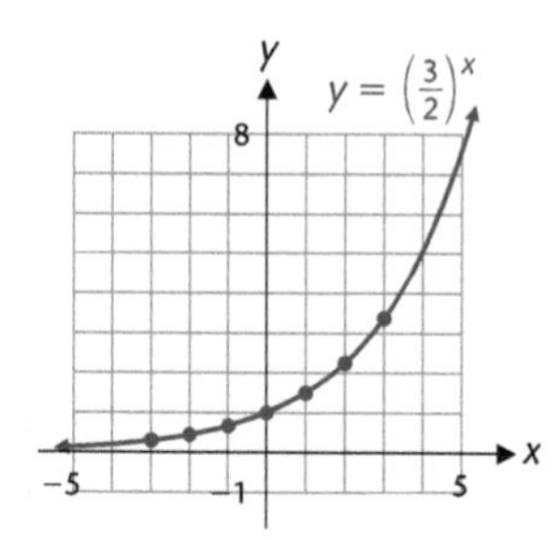

(a)

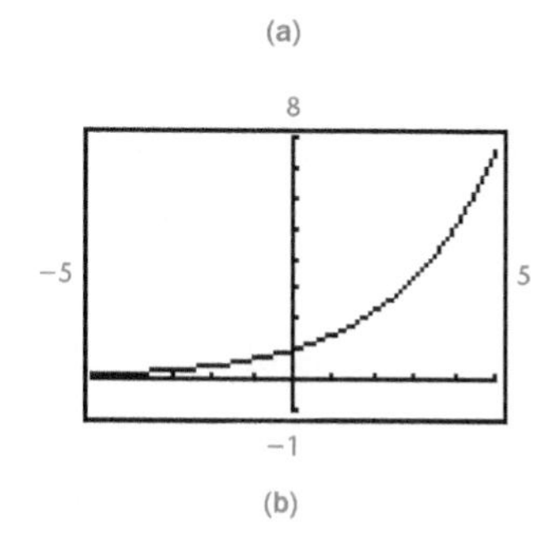

(b)

› **Figure 5**

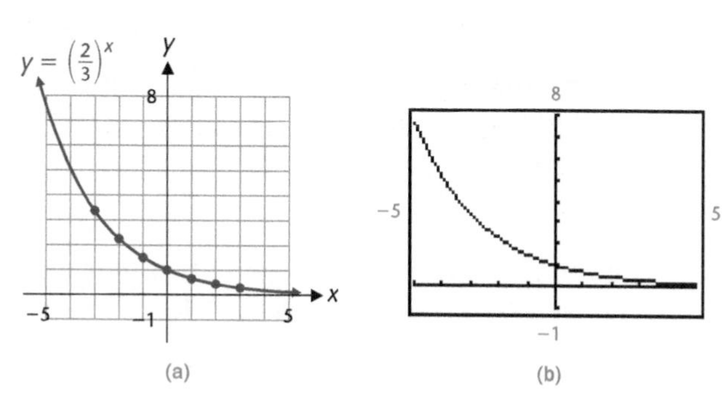

(a)

(b)

› **Figure 6**

Notice that the outputs for $x < 0$ in Figure 5 and for $x > 0$ in Figure 6 get so small that it's hard to distinguish the graph from the x axis. Property 4 in Theorem 1 indicates that the graph of an exponential function is always above the x axis, and approaches height zero as $x \to \infty$ or $x \to -\infty$. (Zooming in on the graph, as in Figure 7, illustrates the behavior a bit better.)

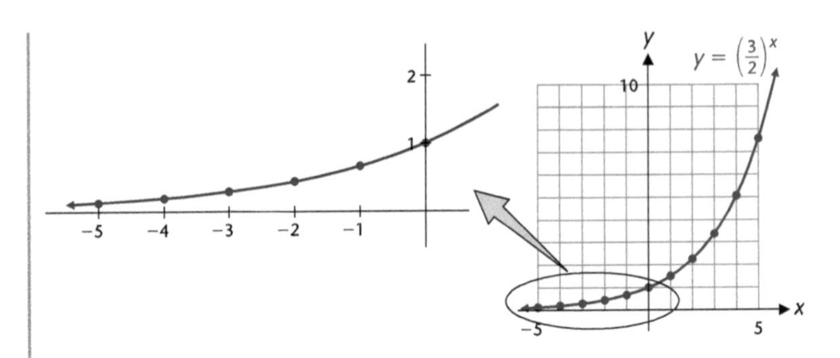

› Figure 7

MATCHED PROBLEM 1

Sketch the graph of each function after plotting at least seven points. Then confirm your result with a graphing calculator.

(A) $f(x) = \left(\frac{3}{4}\right)^x$ (B) $g(x) = \left(\frac{4}{3}\right)^x$

››› EXPLORE-DISCUSS 2

Examine the graphs of $f(x) = (\frac{3}{2})^x$ and $g(x) = (\frac{2}{3})^x$ from Example 1.

(A) What is the relationship between the graphs?

(B) Rewrite $(\frac{2}{3})^x$ as an exponential with base $\frac{3}{2}$. How does this confirm your answer to part A?

We can also use our knowledge of transformations to draw graphs of more complicated functions involving exponentials.

EXAMPLE 2 Drawing the Graph of an Exponential Function

Use transformations of $y = 2^x$ to graph $f(x) = 2^{x-2} + 4$.

SOLUTION

We start with a graph of $y = 2^x$ [Fig. 8(a)], then shift 2 units right and 4 units up [Fig. 8(b)]. A graphing calculator confirms our result [Fig. 8(c)]. Note that in this case, $y = 4$ is a horizontal asymptote.

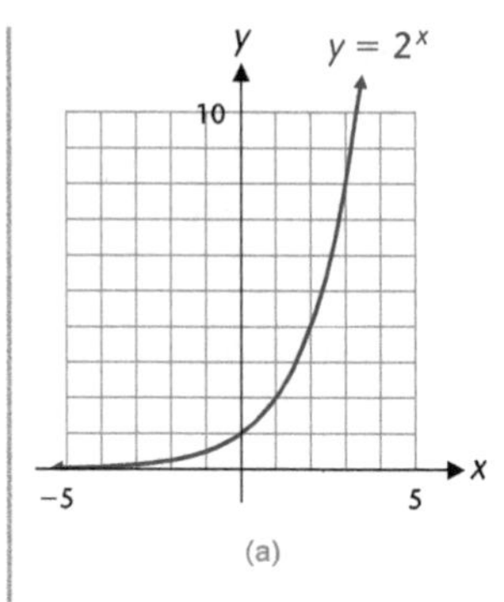

(a)

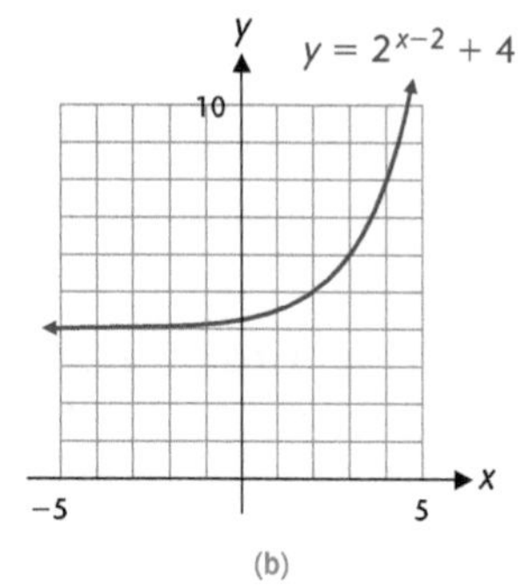

(b)

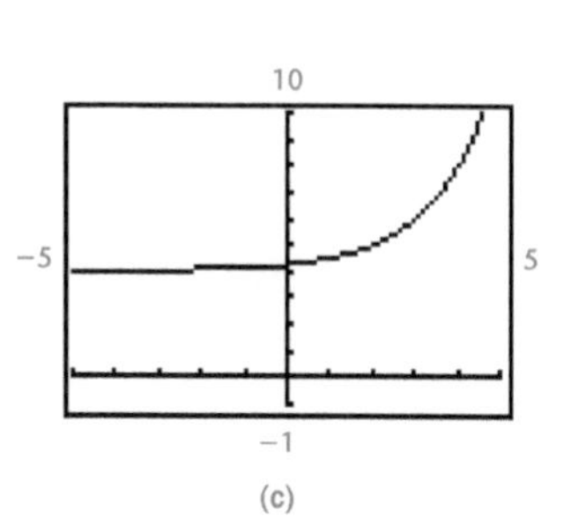

(c)

› **Figure 8**

MATCHED PROBLEM 2

Use transformations of $y = (\frac{1}{2})^x$ to graph $f(x) = (\frac{1}{2})^{x+1} - 3$.

› Additional Properties of Exponential Functions

The properties of exponents you should be familiar with (see Appendix A, Section A-2) are often stated in terms of exponents that are rational numbers. But we're considering irrational exponents as well in defining exponential functions. Fortunately, these properties still apply. We will summarize the key properties we need in this chapter, and add two other useful properties.

› EXPONENTIAL FUNCTION PROPERTIES

For a and b positive, $a \neq 1, b \neq 1$, and for any real numbers x and y:

1. Exponent laws:

$$a^x a^y = a^{x+y} \qquad (a^x)^y = a^{xy} \qquad (ab)^x = a^x b^x$$

$$\left(\frac{a}{b}\right)^x = \frac{a^x}{b^x} \qquad \frac{a^x}{a^y} = a^{x-y} \qquad \frac{2^{5x}}{2^{7x}} \boxed{= 2^{5x-7x}}^* = 2^{-2x}$$

2. $a^x = a^y$ if and only if $x = y$. If $6^x = 6^3$, then $x = 3$.
3. For $x \neq 0$, $a^x = b^x$ if and only if $a = b$. If $a^4 = 3^4$, then $a = 3$.

*The dashed "think boxes" are used to enclose steps that may be performed mentally.

Property 2 is another way to express the fact that the exponential function $f(x) = a^x$ is one-to-one (see Property 6 of Theorem 1). Because all exponential functions pass through the point (0, 1) (see Property 3 of Theorem 1), property 3 indicates that the graphs of exponential functions with different bases do not intersect at any other points.

EXAMPLE 3 Using Exponential Function Properties

Find all solutions to $2^{10x-1} = 2^{5-2x}$.

SOLUTIONS

Algebraic Solution
According to Property 2, $2^{10x-1} = 2^{5-2x}$ implies that

$$10x - 1 = 5 - 2x$$
$$12x = 6$$
$$x = \frac{6}{12} = \frac{1}{2}$$

Check: $2^{10(1/2)-1} = 2^4$; $\quad 2^{5-2(1/2)} = 2^4$

Graphical Solution
Graph $y_1 = 2^{10x-1}$ and $y_2 = 2^{5-2x}$, then use the INTERSECT command to obtain $x = 0.5$ (Fig. 9).

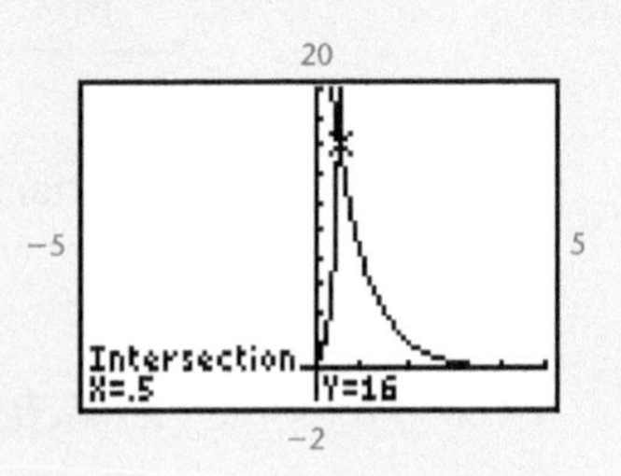

› Figure 9

MATCHED PROBLEM 3

Find all solutions to $3^{3+y} = 3^{4y-9}$.

EXAMPLE 4 Using Exponential Function Properties

Find all solutions to $4^{x-3} = 8$.

SOLUTIONS

Algebraic Solution
Notice that the two bases, 4 and 8, can both be written as a power of 2. This will enable us to use Property 2 to equate exponents.

$4^{x-3} = 8$	Express 4 and 8 as powers of 2.
$(2^2)^{x-3} = 2^3$	$(a^x)^y = a^{xy}$
$2^{2x-6} = 2^3$	Property 2
$2x - 6 = 3$	Add 6 to both sides.
$2x = 9$	Divide both sides by 2.
$x = \frac{9}{2}$	

CHECK

$$4^{(9/2)-3} = 4^{3/2} = (\sqrt{4})^3 = 2^3 \overset{\checkmark}{=} 8$$

Graphical Solution
Graph $y_1 = 4^{x-3}$ and $y_2 = 8$. Use the INTERSECT command to obtain $x = 4.5$ (Fig. 10).

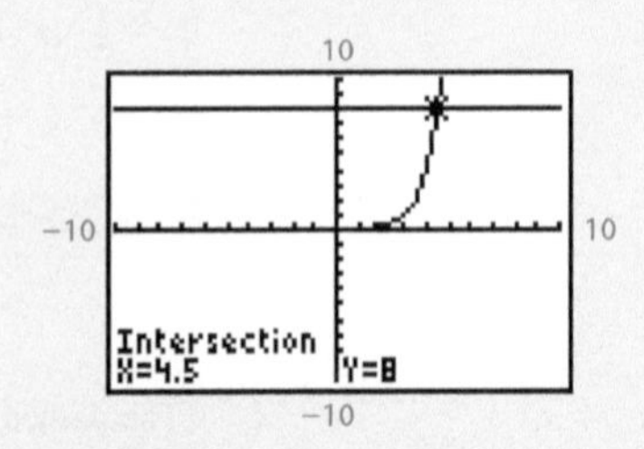

› Figure 10

MATCHED PROBLEM 4

Solve $27^{x+1} = 9$ for x.

The Exponential Function with Base e

Surprisingly, among the exponential functions it is not the function $g(x) = 2^x$ with base 2 or the function $h(x) = 10^x$ with base 10 that is used most frequently in mathematics. Instead, the most commonly used base is a number that you may not be familiar with.

EXPLORE-DISCUSS 3

(A) Calculate the values of $[1 + (1/x)]^x$ for $x = 1, 2, 3, 4,$ and 5. Are the values increasing or decreasing as x gets larger?

(B) Graph $y = [1 + (1/x)]^x$ and discuss the behavior of the graph as x increases without bound.

Table 1

x	$\left(1 + \frac{1}{x}\right)^x$
1	2
10	2.593 74 ...
100	2.704 81 ...
1,000	2.716 92 ...
10,000	2.718 14 ...
100,000	2.718 27 ...
1,000,000	2.718 28 ...

By calculating the value of $[1 + (1/x)]^x$ for larger and larger values of x (Table 1), it looks like $[1 + (1/x)]^x$ approaches a number close to 2.7183. In a calculus course, we can show that as x increases without bound, the value of $[1 + (1/x)]^x$ approaches an irrational number that we call e. Just as irrational numbers such as π and $\sqrt{2}$ have unending, nonrepeating decimal representations, e also has an unending, nonrepeating decimal representation. To 12 decimal places,

$$e = 2.718\ 281\ 828\ 459$$

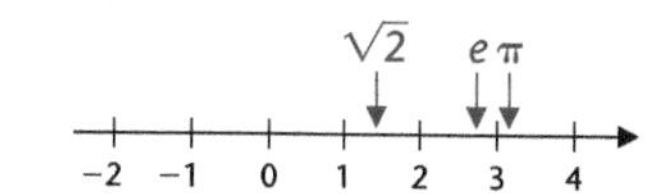

Don't let the symbol "e" intimidate you! It's just a number.

Exactly who discovered e is still being debated. It is named after the great Swiss mathematician Leonhard Euler (1707–1783), who computed e to 23 decimal places using $[1 + (1/x)]^x$.

The constant e turns out to be an ideal base for an exponential function because in calculus and higher mathematics many operations take on their simplest form using this base. This is why you will see e used extensively in expressions and formulas that model real-world phenomena.

DEFINITION 2 Exponential Function with Base e

For x a real number, the equation

$$f(x) = e^x$$

defines the **exponential function with base *e*.**

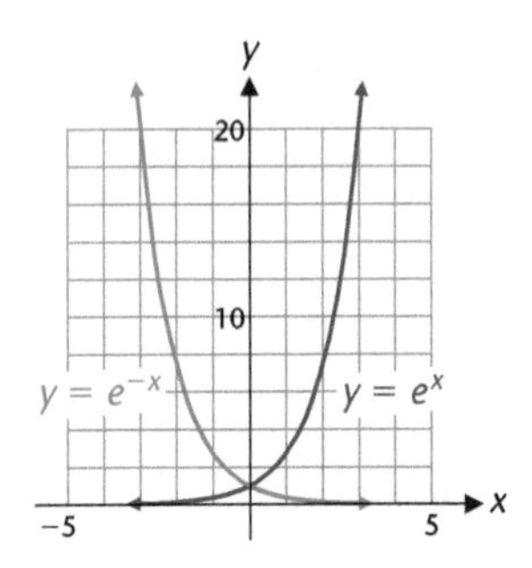

› **Figure 11** Exponential functions.

The exponential function with base e is used so frequently that it is often referred to as *the* exponential function. The graphs of $y = e^x$ and $y = e^{-x}$ are shown in Figure 11.

››› EXPLORE-DISCUSS 4

(A) Graph $y_1 = e^x, y_2 = e^{0.5x}$, and $y_3 = e^{2x}$ in the same viewing window. How do these graphs compare with the graph of $y = b^x$ for $b > 1$?

(B) Graph $y_1 = e^{-x}, y_2 = e^{-0.5x}$, and $y_3 = e^{-2x}$ in the same viewing window. How do these graphs compare with the graph of $y = b^x$ for $0 < b < 1$?

(C) Use the properties of exponential functions to show that all of these functions can be written in the form $y = b^x$.

EXAMPLE 5 Analyzing an Exponential Graph

Describe the graph of $f(x) = 4 - e^{x/2}$, including x and y intercepts, increasing and decreasing properties, and horizontal asymptotes. Round any approximate values to two decimal places.

SOLUTION

A graphing calculator graph of f is shown in Figure 12(a).

y intercept: $f(0) = 4 - e^0 = 4 - 1 = 3$

x intercept: $x \approx 2.77$

Graph is decreasing for all x.

Horizontal asymptote: We can write the exponential function $e^{x/2}$ as $(e^{1/2})^x$, and $e^{1/2} \approx 1.65 > 1$, so our earlier study of exponential graphs indicates that $e^{x/2} \to 0$ as $x \to -\infty$. But then, $4 - e^{x/2} \to 4$ as $x \to -\infty$, and $y = 4$ is a horizontal asymptote for the graph of f. The table in Figure 12(b) supports this conclusion.

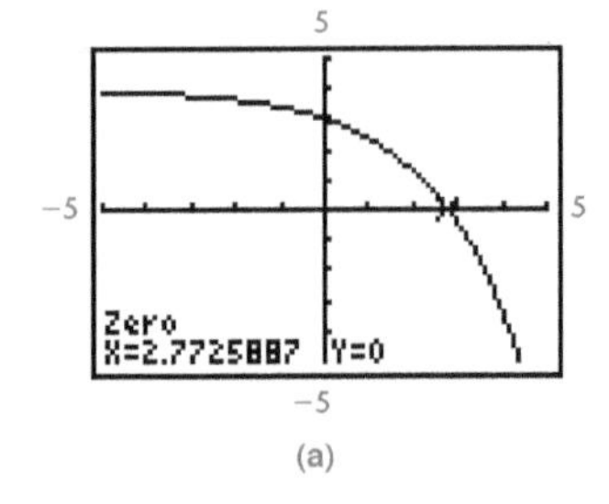

(a)

X	Y1
-5	3.9179
-10	3.9933
-15	3.9994

Y1 = 4−e^(X/2)

(b)

› **Figure 12** $f(x) = 4 - e^{x/2}$.

MATCHED PROBLEM 5

Describe the graph of $f(x) = 2e^{x/2} - 5$, including x and y intercepts, increasing and decreasing properties, and horizontal asymptotes. Round any approximate values to two decimal places.

We will study a wide variety of applications of exponential functions in the next section. For now, it's a good start to examine how exponential functions apply very naturally to the world of finance, something relevant to almost everyone.

Calculating Compound Interest

The fee paid to use someone else's money is called **interest.** It is usually computed as a percentage, called the **interest rate,** of the original amount (or **principal**) over a given period of time. At the end of the payment period, the interest paid is usually added to the principal amount, so the interest in the next period is earned on both the original amount, as well as the interest previously earned. Interest paid on interest previously earned and reinvested in this manner is called **compound interest.**

Suppose you deposit $1,000 in a bank that pays 8% interest compounded semi-annually. How much will be in your account at the end of 2 years? "Compounded semiannually" means that the interest is paid to your account at the end of each 6-month period, and the interest will in turn earn more interest. To calculate the **interest rate per period,** we take the annual rate r, 8% (or 0.08), and divide by the number m of compounding periods per year, in this case 2. If A_1 represents the amount of money in the account after one compounding period (six months), then

Principal + 4% of principal

$$A_1 = \$1{,}000 + \$1{,}000\left(\frac{0.08}{2}\right) \qquad \text{Factor out \$1,000.}$$
$$= \$1{,}000(1 + 0.04)$$

We will next use A_2, A_3, and A_4 to represent the amounts at the end of the second, third, and fourth periods. (Note that the amount we're looking for is A_4.) A_2 is calculated by multiplying the amount at the beginning of the second compounding period (A_1) by 1.04.

$$A_2 = A_1(1 + 0.04) \qquad \text{Substitute our expression for } A_1.$$
$$= [\$1{,}000(1 + 0.04)](1 + 0.04) \qquad \text{Multiply.}$$
$$= \$1{,}000(1 + 0.04)^2 \qquad P\left(1 + \frac{r}{m}\right)^2$$
$$A_3 = A_2(1 + 0.04) \qquad \text{Substitute our expression for } A_2.$$
$$= [\$1{,}000(1 + 0.04)^2](1 + 0.04) \qquad \text{Multiply.}$$
$$= \$1{,}000(1 + 0.04)^3 \qquad P\left(1 + \frac{r}{m}\right)^3$$
$$A_4 = A_3(1 + 0.04) \qquad \text{Substitute our expression for } A_3.$$
$$= [\$1{,}000(1 + 0.04)^3](1 + 0.04) \qquad \text{Multiply.}$$
$$= \$1{,}000(1 + 0.04)^4 \qquad P\left(1 + \frac{r}{m}\right)^4$$
$$= \$1{,}169.86$$

What do you think the savings and loan will owe you at the end of 6 years (12 compounding periods)? If you guessed

$$A = \$1{,}000(1 + 0.04)^{12}$$

you have observed a pattern that is generalized in the following compound interest formula:

COMPOUND INTEREST

If a **principal** P is invested at an annual **rate** r compounded m times a year, then the **amount** A in the account at the end of n compounding periods is given by

$$A = P\left(1 + \frac{r}{m}\right)^n$$

Note that the annual rate r must be expressed in decimal form, and that $n = mt$, where t is years.

EXAMPLE 6 Compound Interest

If you deposit \$5,000 in an account paying 9% compounded daily, how much will you have in the account in 5 years? Compute the answer to the nearest cent.

SOLUTIONS

Interest compounded daily will be compounded 365 times per year.*

Algebraic Solution

We use the compound interest formula with $P = 5{,}000$, $r = 0.09$, $m = 365$, and $n = 5(365) = 1{,}825$:

$$\begin{aligned} A &= P\left(1 + \frac{r}{m}\right)^n \\ &= 5{,}000\left(1 + \frac{0.09}{365}\right)^{1825} \\ &= \$7{,}841.13 \end{aligned}$$

Graphical Solution

Graphing

$$A = 5{,}000\left(1 + \frac{0.09}{365}\right)^x$$

and using the VALUE command (Fig. 13) shows that $A = \$7{,}841.13$.

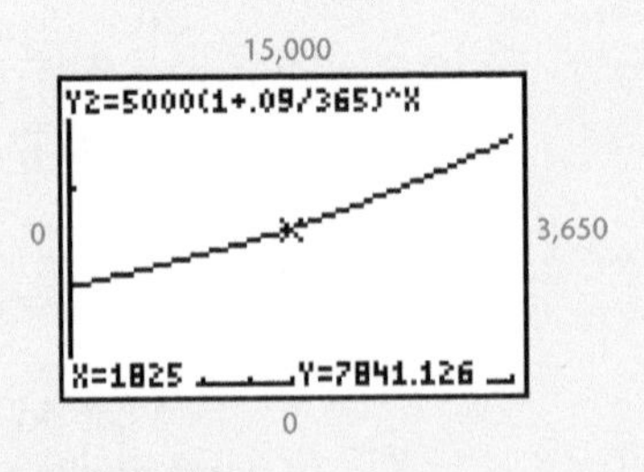

› Figure 13

MATCHED PROBLEM 6

If \$1,000 is invested in an account paying 10% compounded monthly, how much will be in the account at the end of 10 years? Compute the answer to the nearest cent.

*In all problems involving interest compounded daily, we assume a 365-day year.

>>> CAUTION >>>

When using the compound interest formula, don't forget to write the interest rate in decimal form.

EXAMPLE 7 Comparing Investments

If \$1,000 is deposited into an account earning 10% compounded monthly and, at the same time, \$2,000 is deposited into an account earning 4% compounded monthly, will the first account ever be worth more than the second? If so, when?

SOLUTION

Let y_1 and y_2 represent the amounts in the first and second accounts, respectively, then

$$y_1 = 1{,}000(1 + 0.10/12)^x$$
$$y_2 = 2{,}000(1 + 0.04/12)^x$$

where x is the number of compounding periods (months). Using the INTERSECT command to analyze the graphs of y_1 and y_2 [Fig. 14(a)], we see that the graphs intersect at $x \approx 139.438$ months. Because compound interest is paid at the end of each compounding period, we should compare the amount in the accounts after 139 months and after 140 months [Fig. 14(b)]. The table shows that the first account is worth more than the second for $x \geq 140$ months, or 11 years and 8 months.

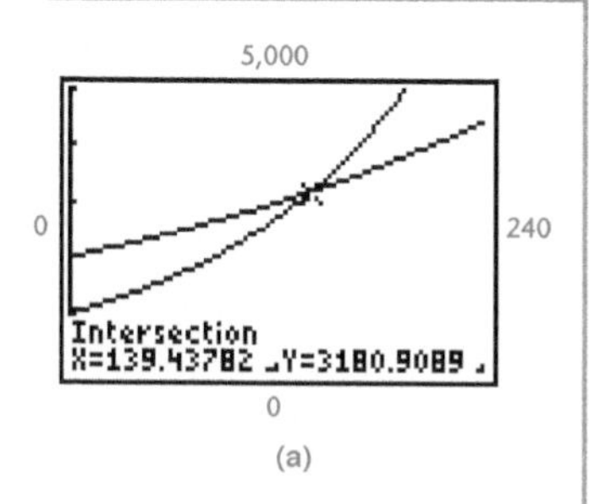

(a)

X	Y1	Y2
139	3169.4	3176.3
140	3195.8	3186.9
X=		

(b)

› Figure 14

MATCHED PROBLEM 7

If \$4,000 is deposited into an account earning 10% compounded quarterly and, at the same time, \$5,000 is deposited into an account earning 6% compounded quarterly, when will the first account be worth more than the second?

› Calculating Interest Compounded Continuously

If \$1,000 is deposited in an account that earns compound interest at an annual rate of 8% for 2 years, how will the amount A change if the number of compounding periods is increased? If m is the number of compounding periods per year, then

$$A = 1{,}000\left(1 + \frac{0.08}{m}\right)^{2m}$$

The amount A is computed for several values of m in Table 2. Notice that the largest gain appears in going from annually to semiannually. Then, the gains slow down as m increases. In fact, it appears that A might be approaching something close to \$1,173.50 as m gets larger and larger.

Table 2 Effect of Compounding Frequency

Compounding frequency	m	$A = 100\left(1 + \frac{0.08}{m}\right)^{2m}$
Annually	1	\$1,166.400
Semiannually	2	1,169.859
Quarterly	4	1,171.659
Weekly	52	1,173.367
Daily	365	1,173.490
Hourly	8,760	1,173.501

We now return to the general problem to see if we can determine what happens to $A = P[1 + (r/m)]^{mt}$ as m increases without bound. A little algebraic manipulation of the compound interest formula will lead to an answer and a significant result in the mathematics of finance:

$$A = P\left(1 + \frac{r}{m}\right)^{mt} \qquad \text{Replace } \frac{r}{m} \text{ with } \frac{1}{m/r}\text{, and } mt \text{ with } \frac{m}{r}\cdot rt.$$

$$= P\left(1 + \frac{1}{m/r}\right)^{(m/r)rt} \qquad \text{Replace } \frac{m}{r} \text{ with variable } x.$$

$$= P\left[\left(1 + \frac{1}{x}\right)^{x}\right]^{rt}$$

Does the expression within the square brackets look familiar? Recall from the first part of this section that

$$\left(1 + \frac{1}{x}\right)^{x} \rightarrow e \quad \text{as} \quad x \rightarrow \infty$$

Because the interest rate r is fixed, $x = m/r \rightarrow \infty$ as $m \rightarrow \infty$. So $(1 + \frac{1}{x})^{x} \rightarrow e$, and

$$P\left(1 + \frac{r}{m}\right)^{mt} = P\left[\left(1 + \frac{1}{x}\right)^{x}\right]^{rt} \rightarrow Pe^{rt} \quad \text{as} \quad m \rightarrow \infty$$

This is known as the **continuous compound interest formula,** a very important and widely used formula in business, banking, and economics.

CONTINUOUS COMPOUND INTEREST FORMULA

If a principal P is invested at an annual rate r compounded continuously, then the amount A in the account at the end of t years is given by

$$A = Pe^{rt}$$

The annual rate r must be expressed as a decimal.

EXAMPLE 8 Interest Compounded Continuously

If \$1,000 is invested at an annual rate of 8% compounded continuously, what amount, to the nearest cent, will be in the account after 2 years?

SOLUTIONS

Algebraic Solution

Use the continuous compound interest formula to find A when $P = \$1,000$, $r = 0.08$, and $t = 2$:

$$\begin{aligned} A &= Pe^{rt} \\ &= \$1,000e^{(0.08)(2)} \\ &= \$1,173.51 \end{aligned}$$

8% is equivalent to $r = 0.08$.

Compare this result with the values calculated in Table 2.

Graphical Solution

Graphing

$$A = 1,000e^{0.08x}$$

and using the VALUE command (Fig. 15) shows

$$A = \$1,173.51.$$

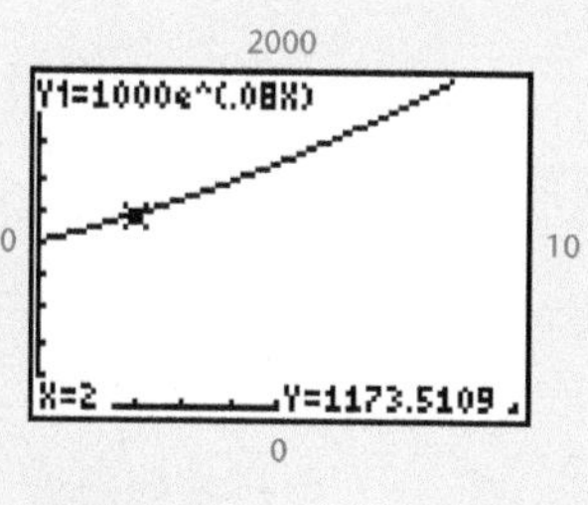

› Figure 15

MATCHED PROBLEM 8

What amount will an account have after 5 years if \$1,000 is invested at an annual rate of 12% compounded annually? Quarterly? Continuously? Compute answers to the nearest cent.

ANSWERS TO MATCHED PROBLEMS

1. (A)

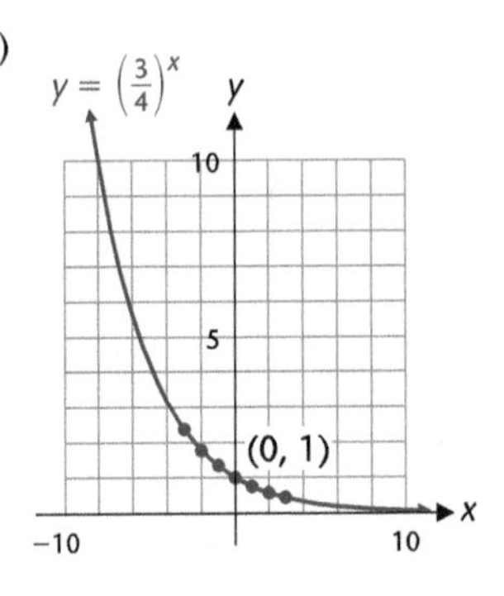

(B)

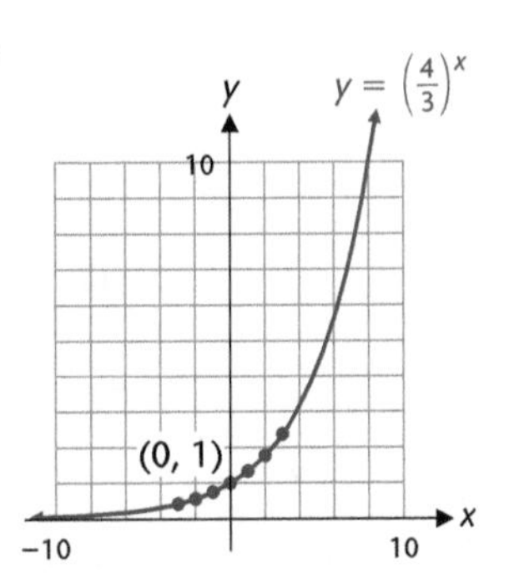

2.

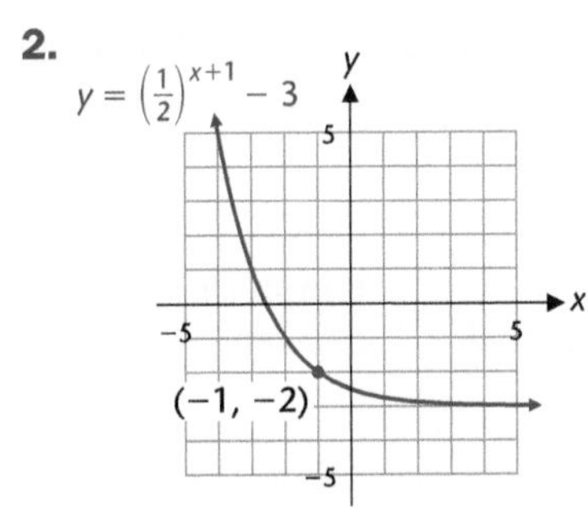

3. $y = 4$ **4.** $x = -\frac{1}{3}$ **5.** y intercept: -3; x intercept: 1.83; increasing for all x; horizontal asymptote: $y = -5$ **6.** \$2,707.04 **7.** After 23 quarters **8.** Annually: \$1,762.34; quarterly: \$1,806.11; continuously: \$1,822.12

4-1 Exercises

1. What is an exponential function?

2. What is the significance of the symbol e in the study of exponential functions?

3. For a function $f(x) = b^x$, explain how you can tell if the graph increases or decreases without looking at the graph.

4. Explain why $f(x) = (1/4)^x$ and $g(x) = 4^{-x}$ are really the same function. Can you use this fact to add to your answer for Question 3?

5. How do we know that the equation $e^x = 0$ has no solution?

6. Define the following terms related to compound interest: principal, interest rate, compounding period.

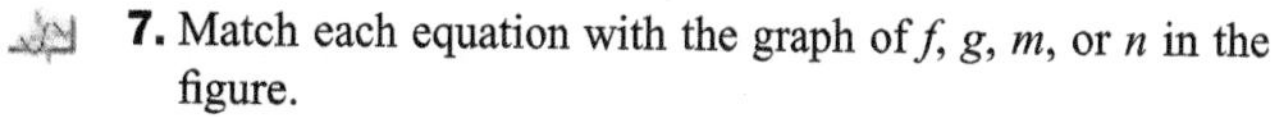

7. Match each equation with the graph of f, g, m, or n in the figure.
(A) $y = (0.2)^x$ (B) $y = 2^x$
(C) $y = (\frac{1}{3})^x$ (D) $y = 4^x$

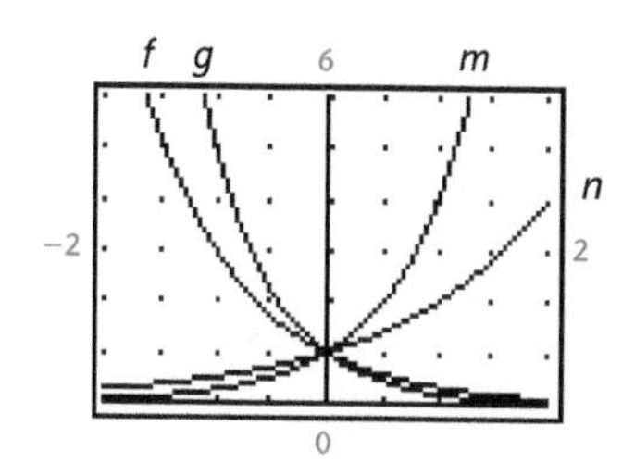

8. Match each equation with the graph of f, g, m, or n in the figure.

(A) $y = e^{-1.2x}$ (B) $y = e^{0.7x}$
(C) $y = e^{-0.4x}$ (D) $y = e^{1.3x}$

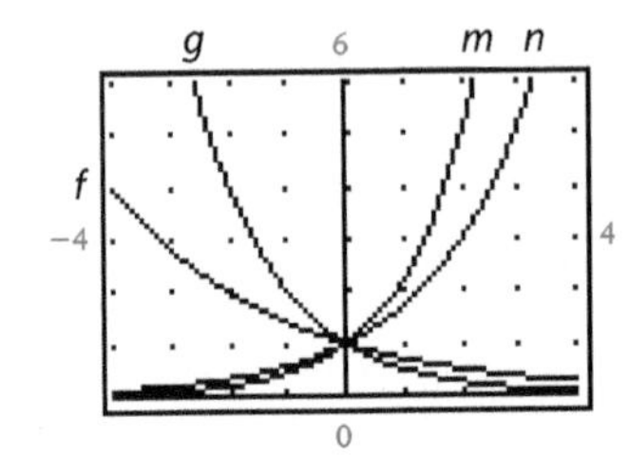

In Problems 9–16, compute answers to four significant digits.

9. $5^{\sqrt{3}}$ **10.** $3^{-\sqrt{2}}$

11. $e^2 + e^{-2}$ **12.** $e - e^{-1}$

13. $\sqrt{e}$ **14.** $e^{\sqrt{2}}$

15. $\frac{2^{\pi} + 2^{-\pi}}{2}$ **16.** $\frac{3^{\pi} - 3^{-\pi}}{2}$

In Problems 17–20, sketch the graph of each function after plotting at least six points. Then confirm your result with a graphing calculator.

17. $y = 3^x$ **18.** $y = 5^x$

19. $y = (\frac{1}{3})^x = 3^{-x}$ **20.** $y = (\frac{1}{5})^x = 5^{-x}$

In Problems 21–28, use properties of exponents to simplify.

21. $10^{3x-1}10^{4-x}$ **22.** $(4^{3x})^{2y}$ **23.** $\frac{3^x}{3^{1-x}}$

24. $\frac{5^{x-3}}{5^{x-4}}$ **25.** $\left(\frac{4^x}{5^y}\right)^{3z}$ **26.** $(2^x3^y)^z$

27. $\frac{e^{5x}}{e^{2x+1}}$ **28.** $\frac{e^{4-3x}}{e^{2-5x}}$

29. (A) Explain what is wrong with the following reasoning about the expression $[1 + (1/x)]^x$: As x gets large, $1 + (1/x)$ approaches 1 because $1/x$ approaches 0, and 1 raised to any power is 1, so $[1 + 1/x]^x$ approaches 1.
(B) Which number does $[1 + (1/x)]^x$ approach as x approaches ∞?

30. (A) Explain what is wrong with the following reasoning about the expression $[1 + (1/x)]^x$: If $b > 1$, then the exponential function b^x approaches ∞ as x approaches ∞, and $1 + (1/x)$ is greater than 1, so $[1 + (1/x)]^x$ approaches infinity as $x \to \infty$.
(B) Which number does $[1 + (1/x)]^x$ approach as x approaches ∞?

In Problems 31–38, graph each function using transformations of an appropriate function of the form $y = b^x$.

31. $f(x) = 2^{x-3} - 1$ **32.** $g(x) = 3^{x+1} + 2$

33. $g(x) = \left(\frac{1}{3}\right)^{x+5} - 10$ **34.** $f(x) = \left(\frac{1}{2}\right)^{x-10} + 5$

35. $g(x) = e^x + 2$ **36.** $g(x) = e^x - 1$

37. $g(x) = 2e^{-(x+2)}$ **38.** $g(x) = 0.5e^{-(x-1)}$

In Problems 39–52, find all solutions to the equation.

39. $5^{3x} = 5^{4x-2}$ **40.** $10^{2-3x} = 10^{5x-6}$

41. $7^{x^2} = 7^{2x+3}$ **42.** $4^{5x-x^2} = 4^{-6}$

43. $(1 - x)^5 = (2x - 1)^5$ **44.** $5^3 = (x + 2)^3$

45. $9^{x^2} = 3^{3x-1}$ **46.** $4^{x^2} = 2^{x+3}$

47. $4^{x^2} = 8^x$ **48.** $9^{x^2} = 27^{x+3}$

49. $2xe^{-x} = 0$ **50.** $(x - 3)e^x = 0$

51. $x^2e^x - 5xe^x = 0$ **52.** $3xe^{-x} + x^2e^{-x} = 0$

53. Find all real numbers a such that $a^2 = a^{-2}$. Explain why this does not violate the second exponential function property in the box on page 387.

54. Find real numbers a and b such that $a \neq b$ but $a^4 = b^4$. Explain why this does not violate the third exponential function property in the box on page 387.

55. Examine the graph of $y = 1^x$ on a graphing calculator and explain why 1 cannot be the base for an exponential function.

56. Examine the graph of $y = 0^x$ on a graphing calculator and explain why 0 cannot be the base for an exponential function. [*Hint:* Turn the axes off before graphing.]

57. Evaluate $y = 1^x$ for $x = -3, -2, -1, 0, 1, 2$, and 3. Why is $b = 1$ excluded when defining the exponential function $y = b^x$?

58. Evaluate $y = 0^x$ for $x = -3, -2, -1, 0, 1, 2$, and 3. Why is $b = 0$ excluded when defining the exponential function $y = b^x$?

59. Explain why the graph of an exponential function cannot be the graph of a polynomial function.

60. Explain why the graph of an exponential function cannot be the graph of a rational function.

In Problems 61–64, simplify.

61. $\frac{-2x^3e^{-2x} - 3x^2e^{-2x}}{x^6}$ **62.** $\frac{5x^4e^{5x} - 4x^3e^{5x}}{x^8}$

63. $(e^x + e^{-x})^2 + (e^x - e^{-x})^2$

64. $e^x(e^{-x} + 1) - e^{-x}(e^x + 1)$

In Problems 65–76, use a graphing calculator to find local extrema, y intercepts, and x intercepts. Investigate the behavior as $x \to \infty$ and as $x \to -\infty$ and identify any horizontal asymptotes. Round any approximate values to two decimal places.

65. $f(x) = 2 + e^{x-2}$

66. $g(x) = -3 + e^{1+x}$

67. $m(x) = e^{|x|}$

68. $n(x) = e^{-|x|}$

69. $s(x) = e^{-x^2}$

70. $r(x) = e^{x^2}$

71. $F(x) = \dfrac{200}{1 + 3e^{-x}}$

72. $G(x) = \dfrac{100}{1 + e^{-x}}$

73. $m(x) = 2x(3^{-x}) + 2$

74. $h(x) = 3x(2^{-x}) - 1$

75. $f(x) = \dfrac{2^x + 2^{-x}}{2}$

76. $g(x) = \dfrac{3^x + 3^{-x}}{2}$

77. Use a graphing calculator to investigate the behavior of $f(x) = (1 + x)^{1/x}$ as x approaches 0.

78. Use a graphing calculator to investigate the behavior of $f(x) = (1 + x)^{1/x}$ as x approaches ∞.

It is common practice in many applications of mathematics to approximate nonpolynomial functions with appropriately selected polynomials. For example, the polynomials in Problems 79–82, called ***Taylor polynomials,*** *can be used to approximate the exponential function $f(x) = e^x$. To illustrate this approximation graphically, in each problem graph $f(x) = e^x$ and the indicated polynomial in the same viewing window, $-4 \le x \le 4$ and $-5 \le y \le 50$.*

79. $P_1(x) = 1 + x + \frac{1}{2}x^2$

80. $P_2(x) = 1 + x + \frac{1}{2}x^2 + \frac{1}{6}x^3$

81. $P_3(x) = 1 + x + \frac{1}{2}x^2 + \frac{1}{6}x^3 + \frac{1}{24}x^4$

82. $P_4(x) = 1 + x + \frac{1}{2}x^2 + \frac{1}{6}x^3 + \frac{1}{24}x^4 + \frac{1}{120}x^5$

83. Investigate the behavior of the functions $f_1(x) = x/e^x$, $f_2(x) = x^2/e^x$, and $f_3(x) = x^3/e^x$ as $x \to \infty$ and as $x \to -\infty$, and find any horizontal asymptotes. Generalize to functions of the form $f_n(x) = x^n/e^x$, where n is any positive integer.

84. Investigate the behavior of the functions $g_1(x) = xe^x$, $g_2(x) = x^2e^x$, and $g_3(x) = x^3e^x$ as $x \to \infty$ and as $x \to -\infty$, and find any horizontal asymptotes. Generalize to functions of the form $g_n(x) = x^ne^x$, where n is any positive integer.

85. The irrational number $\sqrt{2}$ is approximated by 1.414214 to six decimal places. Each of $x = 1.4$, 1.41, 1.414, 1.4142, 1.41421, and 1.414214 is a rational number, so we know how to define 2^x for each. Compute the value of 2^x for each of these x values, and use your results to estimate the value of $2^{\sqrt{2}}$. Then compute $2^{\sqrt{2}}$ using your calculator to check your estimate.

86. The irrational number $\sqrt{3}$ is approximated by 1.732051 to six decimal places. Each of $x = 1.7$, 1.73, 1.732, 1.7321, 1.73205, and 1.732051 is a rational number, so we know how to define 3^x for each. Compute the value of 3^x for each of these x values, and use your results to estimate the value of $3^{\sqrt{3}}$. Then compute $3^{\sqrt{3}}$ using your calculator to check your estimate.

APPLICATIONS*

87. FINANCE Suppose \$4,000 is invested at 11% compounded weekly. How much money will be in the account in
(A) $\frac{1}{2}$ year? (B) 10 years?
Compute answers to the nearest cent.

88. FINANCE Suppose \$2,500 is invested at 7% compounded quarterly. How much money will be in the account in
(A) $\frac{3}{4}$ year? (B) 15 years?
Compute answers to the nearest cent.

89. MONEY GROWTH If you invest \$5,250 in an account paying 11.38% compounded continuously, how much money will be in the account at the end of
(A) 6.25 years? (B) 17 years?

90. MONEY GROWTH If you invest \$7,500 in an account paying 8.35% compounded continuously, how much money will be in the account at the end of
(A) 5.5 years? (B) 12 years?

91. FINANCE If \$3,000 is deposited into an account earning 8% compounded daily and, at the same time, \$5,000 is deposited into an account earning 5% compounded daily, will the first account ever be worth more than the second? If so, when?

92. FINANCE If \$4,000 is deposited into an account earning 9% compounded weekly and, at the same time, \$6,000 is deposited into an account earning 7% compounded weekly, will the first account ever be worth more than the second? If so, when?

93. FINANCE Will an investment of \$10,000 at 8.9% compounded daily ever be worth more at the end of a quarter than an investment of \$10,000 at 9% compounded quarterly? Explain.

94. FINANCE A sum of \$5,000 is invested at 13% compounded semiannually. Suppose that a second investment of \$5,000 is made at interest rate r compounded daily. For which values of r, to the nearest tenth of a percent, is the second investment better than the first? Discuss.

95. PRESENT VALUE A promissory note will pay \$30,000 at maturity 10 years from now. How much should you be willing to pay for the note now if the note gains value at a rate of 9% compounded continuously?

*Round monetary amounts to the nearest cent unless specified otherwise. In all problems involving interest that is compounded daily, assume a 365-day year.

96. PRESENT VALUE A promissory note will pay $50,000 at maturity $5\frac{1}{2}$ years from now. How much should you be willing to pay for the note now if the note gains value at a rate of 10% compounded continuously?

97. MONEY GROWTH *Barron's,* a national business and financial weekly, published the following "Top Savings Deposit Yields" for $2\frac{1}{2}$-year certificate of deposit accounts:

Gill Savings	8.30% (CC)
Richardson Savings and Loan	8.40% (CQ)
USA Savings	8.25% (CD)

where CC represents compounded continuously, CQ compounded quarterly, and CD compounded daily. Compute the value of $1,000 invested in each account at the end of $2\frac{1}{2}$ years.

98. MONEY GROWTH Refer to Problem 97. In another issue of *Barron's,* 1-year certificate of deposit accounts included:

Alamo Savings	8.25% (CQ)
Lamar Savings	8.05% (CC)

Compute the value of $10,000 invested in each account at the end of 1 year.

99. FINANCE A couple just had a new child. How much should they invest now at 8.25% compounded daily to have $100,000 for the child's education 17 years from now? Compute the answer to the nearest dollar.

100. FINANCE A person wishes to have $15,000 cash for a new car 5 years from now. How much should be placed in an account now if the account pays 9.75% compounded weekly? Compute the answer to the nearest dollar.

4-2 Exponential Models

One of the best reasons for studying exponential functions is the fact that many things that occur naturally in our world can be modeled accurately by these functions. In this section, we will study a wide variety of applications, including growth of populations of people, animals, and bacteria; radioactive decay; spread of epidemics; propagation of rumors; light intensity; atmospheric pressure; and electric circuits. The regression techniques we used in Chapter 2 to construct linear and quadratic models will be extended to construct exponential models.

Modeling Exponential Growth

What sort of function is likely to describe the growth of a population? We will consider this question in Explore-Discuss 1.

››› EXPLORE-DISCUSS 1

A certain species of fruit fly reproduces quickly, with a new generation appearing in about a week.

(A) Suppose that a population starts with 200 flies, and we assume that the population increases by 50 flies each week. Calculate the number of flies after 1, 2, 3, 4, and 5 weeks.

(B) Now suppose that the population increases by 25% of the current population each week. Calculate the number of flies after 1, 2, 3, 4, and 5 weeks.

(C) Which scenario do you think is more realistic? Why?

The population model described in part B of Explore-Discuss 1 is the more realistic one. As a population grows, there are more individuals to reproduce, so the rate of increase grows as well. This sounds an awful lot like compound interest: The percentage added to the population is in effect calculated on both the original amount and the number of new individuals. It should come as no surprise, then, that populations of organisms, from bacteria all the way to human beings, tend to grow exponentially.

One convenient and easily understood measure of growth rate is the **doubling time**—that is, the time it takes for a population to double. Over short periods the **doubling time growth model** is often used to model population growth:

$$A = A_0 2^{t/d}$$

where A = Population at time t
A_0 = Population at time $t = 0$
d = Doubling time

Note that when the amount of time passed is equal to the doubling time ($t = d$),

$$A = A_0 2^{t/d} = A_0 2$$

and the population is double the original, as it should be. We will use this model to solve a population growth problem in Example 1.

EXAMPLE 1 Population Growth

Mexico has a population of around 100 million people, and it is estimated that the population will double in 21 years. If population growth continues at the same rate, what will be the population:

(A) 15 years from now? (B) 30 years from now?

Calculate answers to three significant digits.

SOLUTIONS

Algebraic Solutions

We use the doubling time growth model with $A_0 = 100$ and $d = 21$:

$$A = A_0 2^{t/d} \qquad \text{Let } A_0 = 100,\ d = 21$$

$$A = 100(2^{t/21}) \qquad \text{Figure 1}$$

(A) Find A when $t = 15$ years:

$$A = 100(2^{15/21})$$
$$\approx 164 \text{ million people}$$

(B) Find A when $t = 30$ years:

$$A = 100(2^{30/21})$$
$$\approx 269 \text{ million people}$$

› **Figure 1** $A = 100(2^{t/21})$.

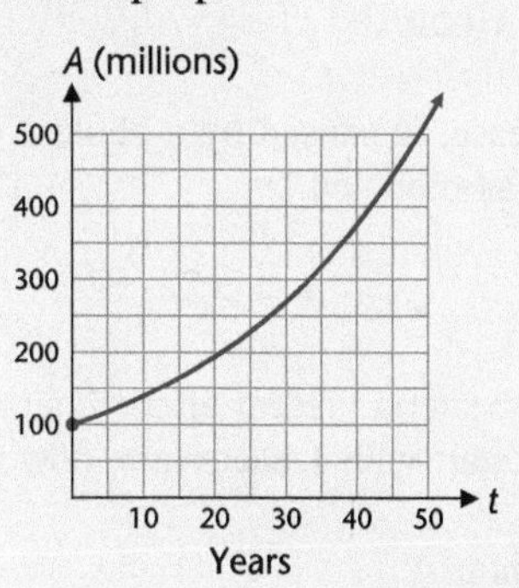

Graphical Solutions

We graph

$$A = 100(2^{x/21})$$

and construct a table of values (Fig. 2).

(A) When $x = 15$ years, $A \approx 164$ million people.

(B) When $x = 30$ years, $A \approx 269$ million people.

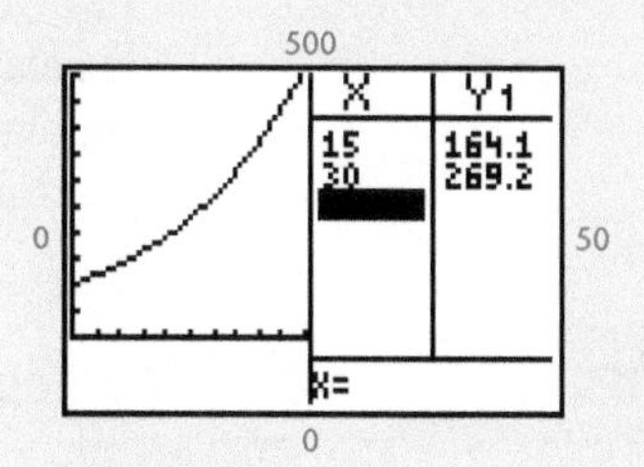

› **Figure 2**

MATCHED PROBLEM 1

The bacterium *Escherichia coli* (*E. coli*) is found naturally in the intestines of many mammals. In a particular laboratory experiment, the doubling time for *E. coli* is found to be 25 minutes. If the experiment starts with a population of 1,000 *E. coli* and there is no change in the doubling time, how many bacteria will be present:

(A) In 10 minutes? (B) In 5 hours?

Write answers to three significant digits.

››› EXPLORE-DISCUSS 2

The doubling time growth model would *not* be expected to give accurate results over long periods. According to the doubling time growth model of Example 1, what was the population of Mexico 500 years ago at the height of Aztec civilization? What will the population of Mexico be 200 years from now? Explain why these results are unrealistic. Discuss factors that affect human populations that are not taken into account by the doubling time growth model.

The doubling time model is not the only one used to model populations. An alternative model based on the continuous compound interest formula will be used in Example 2. In this case, the formula is written as

$$A = A_0e^{kt}$$

where A = Population at time t
A_0 = Population at time $t = 0$
k = Relative growth rate

The **relative growth rate** is written as a percentage in decimal form. For example, if a population is growing so that at any time the population is increasing at 3% of the current population per year, the relative growth rate k would be 0.03.

EXAMPLE 2 Medicine—Bacteria Growth

Cholera, an intestinal disease, is caused by a cholera bacterium that multiplies exponentially by cell division as modeled by

$$A = A_0e^{1.386t}$$

where A is the number of bacteria present after t hours and A_0 is the number of bacteria present at $t = 0$. If we start with 1 bacterium, how many bacteria will be present in

(A) 5 hours? (B) 12 hours?

Compute the answers to three significant digits.

SOLUTIONS

Algebraic Solutions

(A) Use $A_0 = 1$ and $t = 5$:

$$\begin{aligned} A &= A_0e^{1.386t} \\ &= e^{1.386(5)} \\ &= 1{,}020 \end{aligned}$$

(B) Use $A_0 = 1$ and $t = 12$:

$$\begin{aligned} A &= A_0e^{1.386t} \\ &= e^{1.386(12)} \\ &= 16{,}700{,}000 \end{aligned}$$

Graphical Solutions

We graph

$$A = e^{1.386x}$$

and construct a table of values (Fig. 3).

(A) When $x = 5$ hours, $A \approx 1{,}020$ bacteria.

(B) When $x = 12$ hours, $A \approx 16{,}700{,}000$ bacteria.

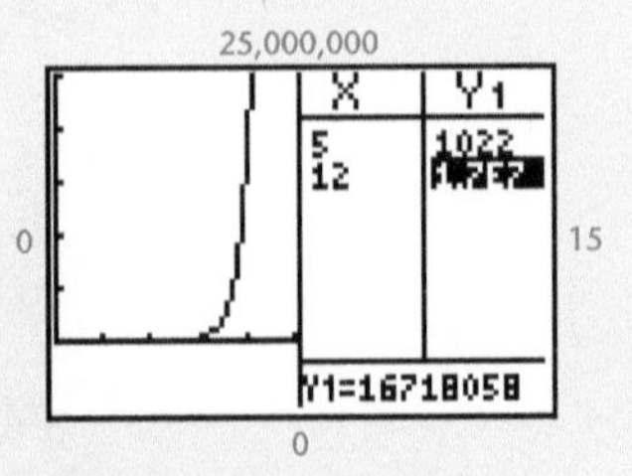

› Figure 3

MATCHED PROBLEM 2

Repeat Example 2 if $A = A_0e^{0.783t}$ and all other information remains the same.

Modeling Negative Exponential Growth

Exponential functions can also be used to model radioactive decay, which is sometimes referred to as **negative growth.** Radioactive materials are used extensively in medical diagnosis and therapy, as power sources in satellites, and as power sources in many countries. If we start with an amount A_0 of a particular radioactive substance, the amount declines exponentially over time. The rate of decay varies depending on the particular radioactive substance. A convenient and easily understood measure of the rate of decay is the **half-life** of the material—that is, the time it takes for half of a particular material to decay. We can use the following **half-life decay model:**

$$A = A_0(\tfrac{1}{2})^{t/h}$$
$$= A_0 2^{-t/h}$$

where A = Amount at time t

A_0 = Amount at time $t = 0$

h = Half-life

Note that when the amount of time passed is equal to the half-life ($t = h$),

$$A = A_0 2^{-h/h} = A_0 2^{-1} = A_0 \cdot \tfrac{1}{2}$$

and the amount of radioactive material is half the original amount, as it should be.

EXAMPLE 3 Radioactive Decay

The radioactive isotope gallium 67 (^{67}Ga), used in the diagnosis of malignant tumors, has a biological half-life of 46.5 hours. If we start with 100 milligrams of the isotope, how many milligrams will be left after

(A) 24 hours? (B) 1 week?

Compute answers to three significant digits.

SOLUTIONS

Algebraic Solutions

We use the half-life decay model with $A_0 = 100$ and $h = 46.5$:

$$A = A_0(\tfrac{1}{2})^{t/h} = A_0 2^{-t/h} \qquad A_0 = 100,\ h = 46.5$$

$$A = 100(2^{-t/46.5}) \qquad \text{See Figure 4.}$$

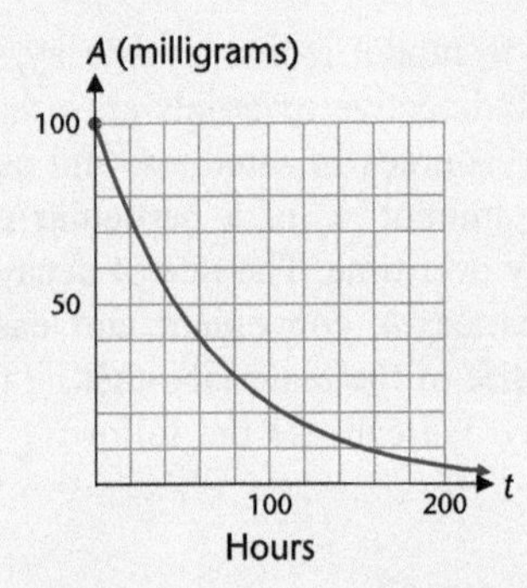

› **Figure 4** $A = 100(2^{-t/46.5})$.

(A) Find A when $t = 24$ hours:

$$A = 100(2^{-24/46.5})$$
$$= 69.9 \text{ milligrams}$$

(B) Find A when $t = 168$ hours (1 week = 168 hours):

$$A = 100(2^{-168/46.5})$$
$$= 8.17 \text{ milligrams}$$

Graphical Solutions

We graph

$$A = 100(2^{-x/46.5})$$

and construct a table of values (Fig. 5).

(A) When $x = 24$ hours, $A \approx 69.9$ milligrams.

(B) When $x = 168$ hours (1 week), $A \approx 8.17$ milligrams.

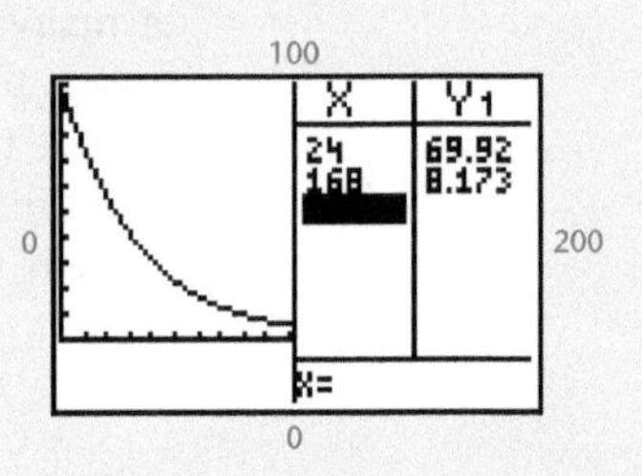

› **Figure 5**

MATCHED PROBLEM 3

Radioactive gold 198 (^{198}Au), used in imaging the structure of the liver, has a half-life of 2.67 days. If we start with 50 milligrams of the isotope, how many milligrams will be left after:

(A) $\frac{1}{2}$ day? (B) 1 week?

Compute answers to three significant digits.

>>> CAUTION >>>

When using exponential models, be aware of the units of time. In Example 3 the half-life was given in hours, so when time was provided in weeks, we had to first convert that into hours before using the half-life formula.

In Example 2, we saw that a base e exponential function can be used as an alternative to the doubling time model. Not surprisingly, the same can be said for the half-life model. In this case, the formula will be

$$A = A_0 e^{-kt}$$

where A = the amount of radioactive material at time t
A_0 = the amount at time $t = 0$
k = a positive constant specific to the type of material

Carbon-14 Dating

Our atmosphere is constantly being bombarded with cosmic rays. These rays produce neutrons, which in turn react with nitrogen to produce radioactive carbon-14. Radioactive carbon-14 enters all living tissues through carbon dioxide, which is first absorbed by plants. As long as a plant or animal is alive, carbon-14 is maintained in the living organism at a constant level. Once the organism dies, however, carbon-14 decays according to the equation

$$A = A_0 e^{-0.000124t} \qquad \textbf{Carbon-14 decay equation}$$

where A is the amount of carbon-14 present after t years and A_0 is the amount present at time $t = 0$. This can be used to calculate the approximate age of fossils.

EXAMPLE 4 Carbon-14 Dating

If 1,000 milligrams of carbon-14 are present in the tissue of a recently deceased animal, how many milligrams will be present in

(A) 10,000 years? (B) 50,000 years?

Compute answers to three significant digits.

SOLUTIONS

Algebraic Solutions

Substituting $A_0 = 1{,}000$ in the decay equation, we have

$$A = 1{,}000e^{-0.000124t} \quad \text{Figure 6}$$

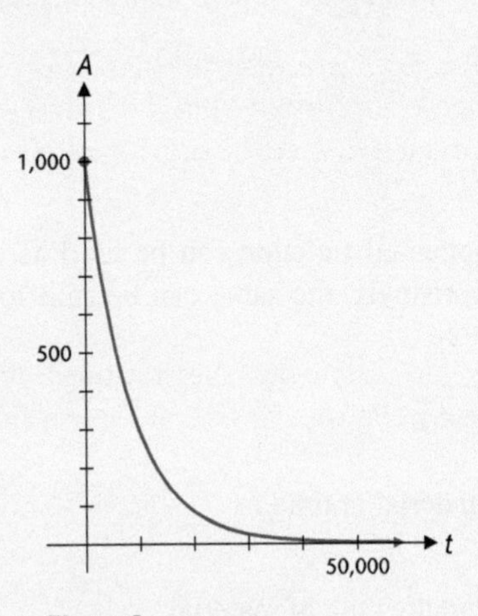

› Figure 6

(A) Find A when $t = 10{,}000$:

$$A = 1{,}000e^{-0.000124(10{,}000)}$$
$$= 289 \text{ milligrams}$$

(B) Find A when $t = 50{,}000$:

$$A = 1{,}000e^{-0.000124(50{,}000)}$$
$$= 2.03 \text{ milligrams}$$

Graphical Solutions

We graph

$$A = 1{,}000e^{-0.000124x}$$

and construct a table of values (Fig. 7).

(A) When $x = 10{,}000$ years, $A \approx 289$ milligrams.

(B) When $x = 50{,}000$ years, $A \approx 2.03$ milligrams.

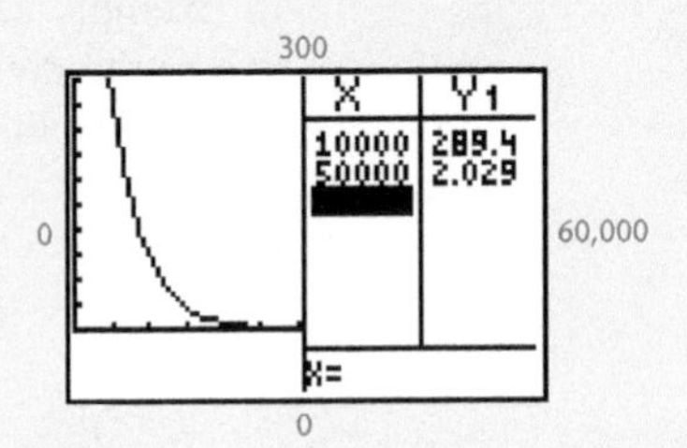

› Figure 7

We will use the carbon-14 decay equation in Exercise 4-5, where we will be interested in solving for t after being given information about A and A_0.

MATCHED PROBLEM 4

Referring to Example 4, how many milligrams of carbon-14 would have to be present at the beginning to have 10 milligrams present after 20,000 years? Approximate the answer to four significant digits.

Modeling Limited Growth

One of the problems with using exponential functions to model things like population is that the growth is completely unlimited in the long term. But in real life, there is often some reasonable maximum value, like the largest population that space and resources allow. We can use modified versions of exponential functions to model such phenomena more realistically.

One such type of function is called a *learning curve* since it can be used to model the performance improvement of a person learning a new task. **Learning curves** are functions of the form $A = c(1 - e^{-kt})$, where c and k are positive constants.

EXAMPLE 5 Learning Curve

People assigned to assemble circuit boards for a computer manufacturing company undergo on-the-job training. From past experience, it was found that the learning curve for the average employee is given by

$$A = 40(1 - e^{-0.12t})$$

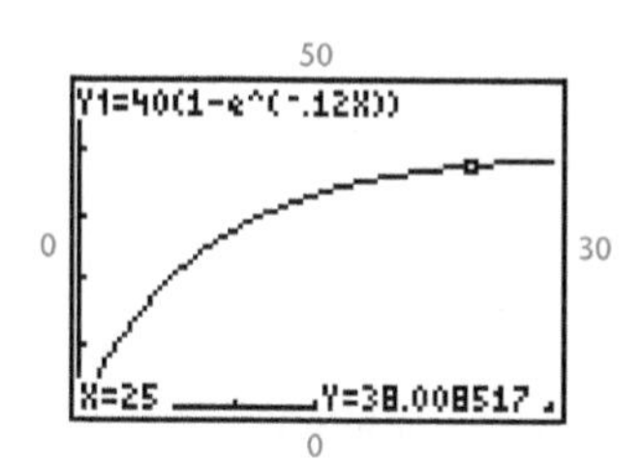

› **Figure 8** Limited growth.

where A is the number of boards assembled per day after t days of training (Fig. 8).

(A) How many boards can an average employee produce after 3 days of training? After 5 days of training? Round answers to the nearest integer.

(B) How many days of training will it take until an average employee can assemble 25 boards a day? Round answers to the nearest integer.

(C) Does A approach a limiting value as t increases without bound? Explain.

SOLUTIONS

(A) When $t = 3$,

$$A = 40(1 - e^{-0.12(3)}) = 12 \quad \text{Rounded to nearest integer}$$

so the average employee can produce 12 boards after 3 days of training. Similarly, when $t = 5$,

$$A = 40(1 - e^{-0.12(5)}) = 18 \quad \text{Rounded to nearest integer}$$

so the average employee can produce 18 boards after 5 days of training.

(B) Solve the equation $40(1 - e^{-0.12t}) = 25$ for t by graphing

$$y_1 = 40(1 - e^{-0.12t}) \quad \text{and} \quad y_2 = 25$$

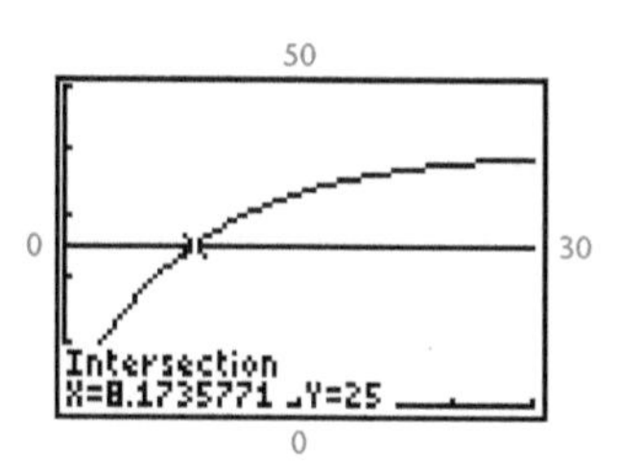

› **Figure 9**
$y_1 = 40(1 - e^{-0.12t})$, $y_2 = 25$.

and using the INTERSECT command (Fig. 9). It will take about 8 days of training.

(C) Because $e^{-0.12t}$ approaches 0 as t increases without bound,

$$A = 40(1 - e^{-0.12t}) \rightarrow 40(1 - 0) = 40$$

So the limiting value of A is 40 boards per day. (This can be supported by the graph.)

MATCHED PROBLEM 5

A company is trying to expose as many people as possible to a new product through television advertising in a large metropolitan area with 2 million potential viewers. A model for the number of people A, in millions, who are aware of the product after t days of advertising was found to be

$$A = 2(1 - e^{-0.037t})$$

(A) How many viewers are aware of the product after 2 days? After 10 days? Express answers as integers, rounded to three significant digits.

(B) How many days will it take until half of the potential viewers will become aware of the product? Round answer to the nearest integer.

(C) Does A approach a limiting value as t increases without bound? Explain.

Another limited-growth model is useful for phenomena such as the spread of an epidemic or the propagation of a rumor. It is called the *logistic equation,* and is given by

$$A = \frac{M}{(1 + ce^{-kt})}$$

where M, c, and k are positive constants. Logistic growth, illustrated in Example 6, also approaches a limiting value as t increases without bound.

EXAMPLE 6 Logistic Growth in an Epidemic

A certain community consists of 1,000 people. One individual who has just returned from another community has a particularly contagious strain of influenza. Assume the community has not had influenza shots and all are susceptible. The spread of the disease in the community is predicted to be given by the logistic curve

$$A(t) = \frac{1{,}000}{1 + 999e^{-0.3t}}$$

where A is the number of people who have contracted influenza after t days.

(A) How many people have contracted influenza after 10 days? After 20 days?

(B) How many days will it take until half the community has contracted influenza? Round answer to the nearest integer.

(C) Does A approach a limiting value as t increases without bound? Explain.

SOLUTIONS

(A) Enter $y_1 = 1{,}000/(1 + 999e^{-0.3t})$ into a graphing calculator. The table in Figure 10(a) shows that $A(10) \approx 20$ individuals and $A(20) \approx 288$ individuals.

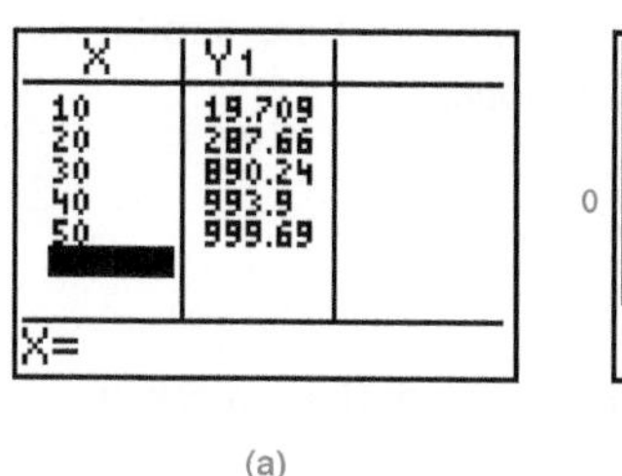

X	Y1
10	19.709
20	287.66
30	890.24
40	993.9
50	999.69

X=

(a)

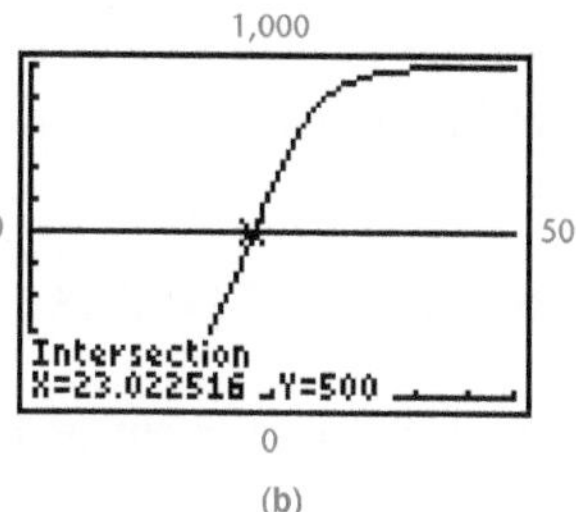

(b)

› **Figure 10** Logistic growth.

(B) Figure 10(b) shows that the graph of $A(t)$ intersects the line $y = 500$ after approximately 23 days.

(C) The values in Figure 10(a) and the graph in Figure 10(b) both indicate that A approaches 1,000 as t increases without bound. We can confirm this algebraically by noting that because $999e^{-0.3t} \to 0$ as t increases without bound,

$$A(t) = \frac{1{,}000}{1 + 999e^{-0.3t}} \to \frac{1{,}000}{1 + 0} = 1{,}000$$

Thus, the upper limit on the growth of A is 1,000, the total number of people in the community.

MATCHED PROBLEM 6

A group of 400 parents, relatives, and friends are waiting anxiously at Kennedy Airport for a charter flight returning students after a year in Europe. It is stormy and the plane is late. A particular parent thought he had heard that the plane's radio had gone out and related this news to some friends, who in turn passed it on to others. The propagation of this rumor is predicted to be given by

$$A(t) = \frac{400}{1 + 399e^{-0.4t}}$$

where A is the number of people who have heard the rumor after t minutes.

(A) How many people have heard the rumor after 10 minutes? After 20 minutes?

(B) How many minutes will it take until half the group has heard the rumor? Round answer to the nearest integer.

(C) Does A approach a limiting value as t increases without bound? Explain.

Data Analysis and Regression

Many graphing calculators with regression commands have options for exponential regression. We can use exponential regression to fit a function of the form $y = ab^x$ to a set of data points, and logistic regression to fit a function of the form

$$y = \frac{c}{1 + ae^{-bx}}$$

to a set of data points. The techniques are similar to those introduced in Chapter 2 for linear and quadratic functions.

EXAMPLE 7 Infectious Diseases

Table 1 Reported Cases of Infectious Diseases

Year	Mumps	Rubella
1970	104,953	56,552
1980	8,576	3,904
1990	5,292	1,125
1995	906	128
2000	323	152

The U.S. Department of Health and Human Services published the data in Table 1.

(A) Let x represent time in years with $x = 0$ representing 1970, and let y represent the corresponding number of reported cases of mumps. Use regression analysis on a graphing calculator to find an exponential function of the form $y = ab^x$ that models the data. (Round the constants a and b to three significant digits.)

(B) Use the exponential regression function to predict the number of reported cases of mumps in 2010.

SOLUTIONS

(A) Figure 11 shows the details of constructing the model on a graphing calculator.

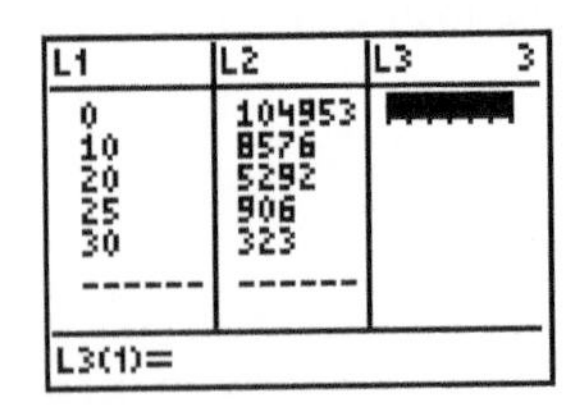

(a) Data

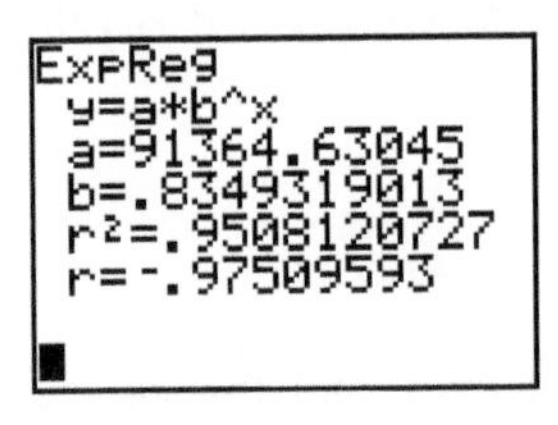

(b) Regression equation

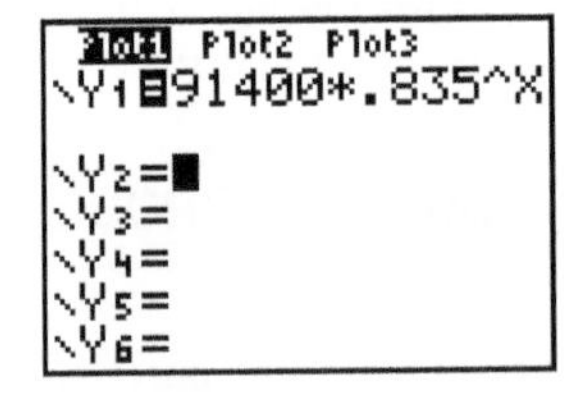

(c) Regression equation entered in equation editor

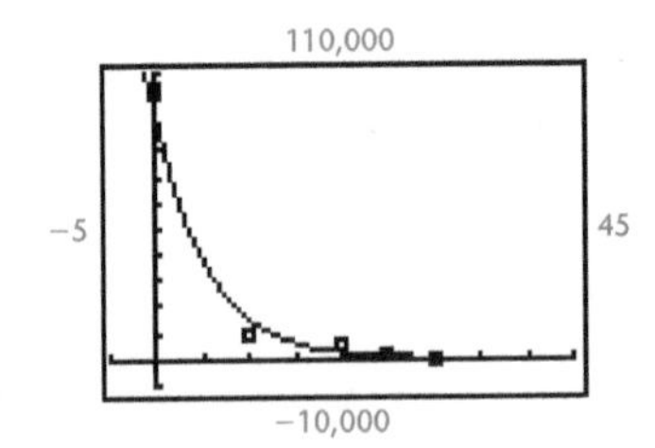

(d) Graph of data and regression equation

Figure 11

(B) Evaluating $y_1 = 91{,}400(0.835)^x$ at $x = 40$ gives a prediction of 67 cases of mumps in 2010.

MATCHED PROBLEM 7

Repeat Example 7 for reported cases of rubella.

EXAMPLE 8 AIDS Cases and Deaths

Table 2 Acquired Immunodeficiency Syndrome (AIDS) Cases and Deaths in the United States

Year	Cases Diagnosed to Date	Known Deaths to Date
1988	107,755	62,468
1991	261,259	159,294
1994	493,713	296,507
1997	672,970	406,179
2000	774,467	447,648
2005	956,665	550,394

The U.S. Department of Health and Human Services published the data in Table 2.

(A) Let x represent time in years with $x = 0$ representing 1988, and let y represent the corresponding number of AIDS cases diagnosed to date. Use regression analysis on a graphing utility to find a logistic function of the form

$$y = \frac{c}{1 + ae^{-bx}}$$

that models the data. (Round the constants a, b, and c to three significant digits.)

(B) Use the logistic regression function to predict the number of cases of AIDS diagnosed by 2015.

SOLUTIONS

(A) Figure 12 shows the details of constructing the model on a graphing calculator.

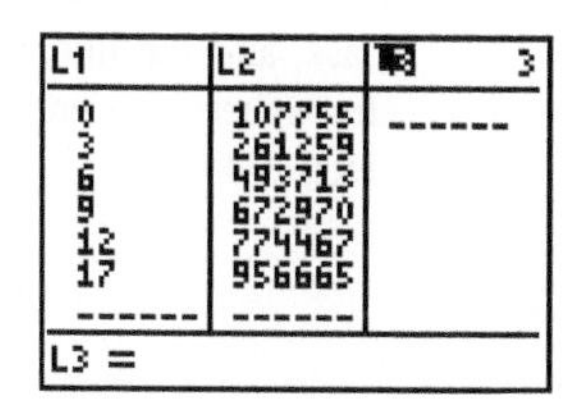

(a) Data

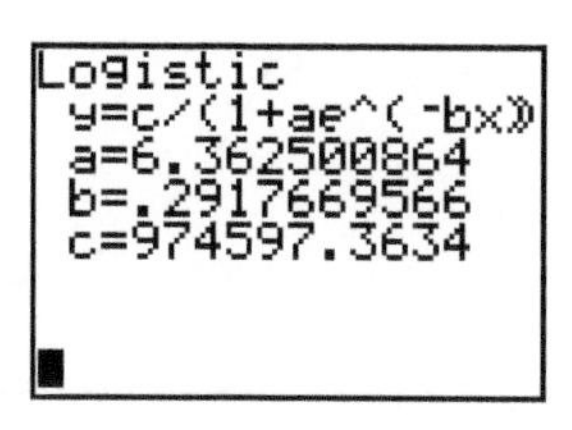

(b) Regression equation

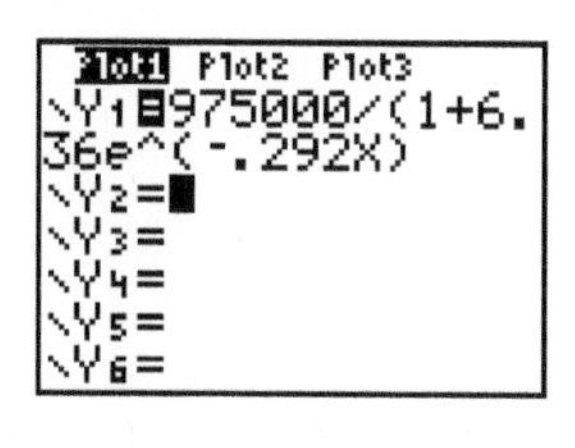

(c) Regression equation entered in equation editor

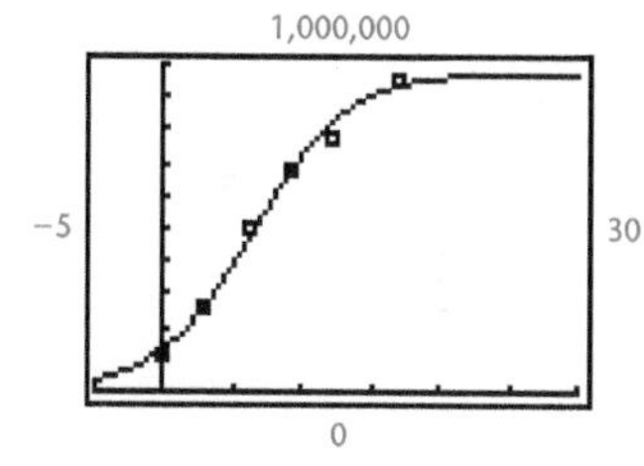

(d) Graph of data and regression equation

› **Figure 12**

(B) Evaluating

$$y_1 = \frac{975{,}000}{1 + 6.36e^{-0.292x}}$$

at $x = 27$ gives a prediction of approximately 973,000 cases of AIDS diagnosed by 2015.

MATCHED PROBLEM 8

Repeat Example 8 for known deaths from AIDS to date.

› A Comparison of Exponential Growth Phenomena

The equations and graphs given in Table 3 compare several widely used growth models. These are divided basically into two groups: unlimited growth and limited growth. Following each equation and graph is a short, incomplete list of areas in which the models are used. We have only touched on a subject that has been extensively developed and that you are likely to study in greater depth in the future.

Table 3 Exponential Growth and Decay

Description	Equation	Graph	Short List of Uses
Unlimited growth	$A = A_0e^{kt}$ $k > 0$	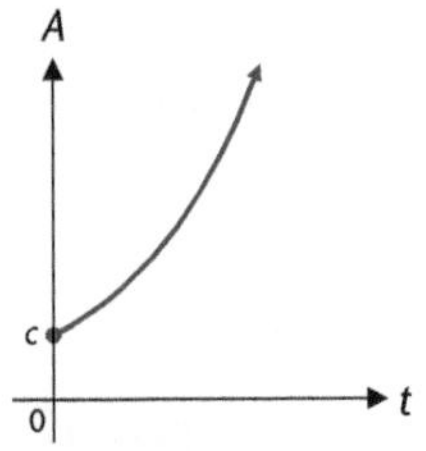	Short-term population growth (people, bacteria, etc.); growth of money at continuous compound interest
Exponential decay	$A = A_0e^{-kt}$ $k > 0$	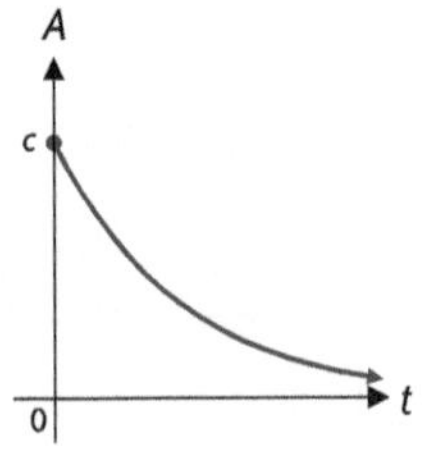	Radioactive decay; light absorption in water, glass, and the like; atmospheric pressure; electric circuits
Limited growth	$A = c(1 - e^{-kt})$ $c, k > 0$	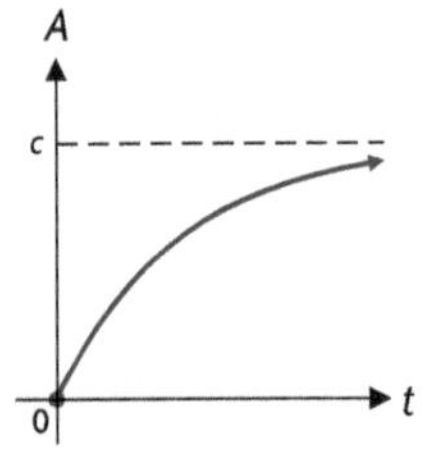	Learning skills; sales fads; company growth; electric circuits
Logistic growth	$A = \dfrac{M}{1 + ce^{-kt}}$ $c, k, M > 0$	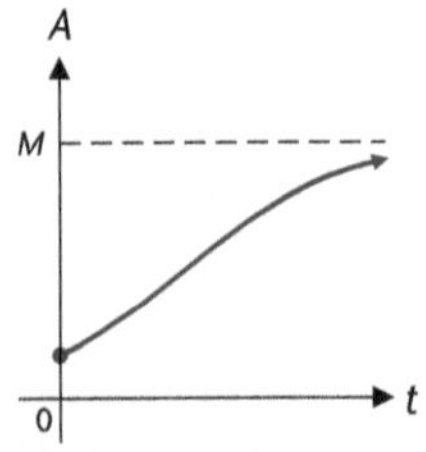	Long-term population growth; epidemics; sales of new products; spread of rumors; company growth

ANSWERS TO MATCHED PROBLEMS

1. (A) 1,320 bacteria (B) 4,100,000 bacteria
2. (A) 50 bacteria (B) 12,000 bacteria **3.** (A) 43.9 milligrams (B) 8.12 milligrams
4. 119.4 milligrams **5.** (A) 143,000 viewers; 619,000 viewers (B) 19 days
(C) A approaches an upper limit of 2 million, the number of potential viewers
6. (A) 48 individuals; 353 individuals (B) 15 minutes (C) A approaches an upper limit of 400, the number of people in the entire group.
7. (A) $y = 44{,}500(0.815)^x$ (B) 12 cases
8. (A) $y = \dfrac{549{,}000}{1 + 6.14e^{-0.311x}}$ (B) 548,000 known deaths

4-2 Exercises

1. Define the terms "doubling time" and "half-life" in your own words.

2. One of the models below represents positive growth, and the other represents negative growth. Classify each, and explain how you decided on your answer. (Assume that $k > 0$.)

$$A = A_0e^{-kt} \qquad A = A_0e^{kt}$$

3. Explain the difference between exponential growth and limited growth.

4. Explain why a limited growth model would be more accurate than regular exponential growth in modeling the long-term population of birds on an island in Lake Erie.

In Problems 5–8, write an exponential equation describing the given population at any time t.

5. Initial population 200; doubling time 5 months

6. Initial population 5,000; doubling time 3 years

7. Initial population 2,000; continuous growth at 2% per year

8. Initial population 500; continuous growth at 3% per week

In Problems 9–12, write an exponential equation describing the amount of radioactive material present at any time t.

9. Initial amount 100 grams; half-life 6 hours

10. Initial amount 5 pounds; half-life 1,300 years

11. Initial amount 4 kilograms; continuous decay at 12.4% per year

12. Initial amount 50 milligrams; continuous decay at 0.03% per year

APPLICATIONS

13. GAMING A person bets on red and black on a roulette wheel using a *Martingale strategy*. That is, a $2 bet is placed on red, and the bet is doubled each time until a win occurs. The process is then repeated. If black occurs n times in a row, then $L = 2^n$ dollars is lost on the nth bet. Graph this function for $1 \le n \le 10$. Although the function is defined only for positive integers, points on this type of graph are usually joined with a smooth curve as a visual aid.

14. BACTERIAL GROWTH If bacteria in a certain culture double every $\frac{1}{2}$ hour, write an equation that gives the number of bacteria N in the culture after t hours, assuming the culture has 100 bacteria at the start. Graph the equation for $0 \le t \le 5$.

15. POPULATION GROWTH Because of its short life span and frequent breeding, the fruit fly *Drosophila* is used in some genetic studies. Raymond Pearl of Johns Hopkins University, for example, studied 300 successive generations of descendants of a single pair of *Drosophila* flies. In a laboratory situation with ample food supply and space, the doubling time for a particular population is 2.4 days. If we start with 5 male and 5 female flies, how many flies should we expect to have in
(A) 1 week? (B) 2 weeks?

16. POPULATION GROWTH If Kenya has a population of about 34,000,000 people and a doubling time of 27 years and if the growth continues at the same rate, find the population in
(A) 10 years (B) 30 years
Compute answers to two significant digits.

17. COMPUTER DESIGN In 1965, Gordon Moore, founder of Intel, predicted that the number of transistors that could be

placed on a computer chip would double every 2 years. This has come to be known as *Moore's law.* In 1970, 2,200 transistors could be placed on a chip. Use Moore's law to predict the number of transistors in
(A) 1990 (B) 2005

18. HISTORY OF TECHNOLOGY The earliest mechanical clocks appeared around 1350 in Europe, and would gain or lose an average of 30 minutes per day. After that, accuracy roughly doubled every 30 years. Find the predicted accuracy of clocks in
(A) 1700 (B) 2000

19. INSECTICIDES The use of the insecticide DDT is no longer allowed in many countries because of its long-term adverse effects. If a farmer uses 25 pounds of active DDT, assuming its half-life is 12 years, how much will still be active after
(A) 5 years? (B) 20 years?
Compute answers to two significant digits.

20. RADIOACTIVE TRACERS The radioactive isotope technetium-99m (^{99m}Tc) is used in imaging the brain. The isotope has a half-life of 6 hours. If 12 milligrams are used, how much will be present after
(A) 3 hours? (B) 24 hours?
Compute answers to three significant digits.

21. POPULATION GROWTH If the world population is about 6.5 billion people now and if the population grows continuously at a relative growth rate of 1.14%, what will the population be in 10 years? Compute the answer to two significant digits.

22. POPULATION GROWTH If the population of Mexico is around 106 million people now and if the population grows continuously at a relative growth rate of 1.17%, what will the population be in 8 years? Compute the answer to three significant digits.

23. POPULATION GROWTH In 2005 the population of Russia was 143 million and the population of Nigeria was 129 million. If the populations of Russia and Nigeria grow continuously at relative growth rates of -0.37% and 2.56%, respectively, in what year will Nigeria have a greater population than Russia?

24. POPULATION GROWTH In 2005 the population of Germany was 82 million and the population of Egypt was 78 million. If the populations of Germany and Egypt grow continuously at relative growth rates of 0% and 1.78%, respectively, in what year will Egypt have a greater population than Germany?

25. SPACE SCIENCE Radioactive isotopes, as well as solar cells, are used to supply power to space vehicles. The isotopes gradually lose power because of radioactive decay. On a particular space vehicle the nuclear energy source has a power output of P watts after t days of use as given by

$$P = 75e^{-0.0035t}$$

Graph this function for $0 \le t \le 100$.

26. EARTH SCIENCE The atmospheric pressure P, in pounds per square inch, decreases exponentially with altitude h, in miles above sea level, as given by

$$P = 14.7e^{-0.21h}$$

Graph this function for $0 \le h \le 10$.

27. MARINE BIOLOGY Marine life is dependent upon the microscopic plant life that exists in the *photic zone,* a zone that goes to a depth where about 1% of the surface light still remains. Light intensity I relative to depth d, in feet, for one of the clearest bodies of water in the world, the Sargasso Sea in the West Indies, can be approximated by

$$I = I_0e^{-0.00942d}$$

where I_0 is the intensity of light at the surface. To the nearest percent, what percentage of the surface light will reach a depth of
(A) 50 feet? (B) 100 feet?

28. MARINE BIOLOGY Refer to Problem 27. In some waters with a great deal of sediment, the photic zone may go down only 15 to 20 feet. In some murky harbors, the intensity of light d feet below the surface is given approximately by

$$I = I_0e^{-0.23d}$$

What percentage of the surface light will reach a depth of
(A) 10 feet? (B) 20 feet?

29. AIDS EPIDEMIC The World Health Organization estimated that 39.4 million people worldwide were living with HIV in 2004. Assuming that number continues to increase at a relative growth rate of 3.2% compounded continuously, estimate the number of people living with HIV in
(A) 2010 (B) 2015

30. AIDS EPIDEMIC The World Health Organization estimated that there were 3.1 million deaths worldwide from HIV/AIDS during the year 2004. Assuming that number continues to increase at a relative growth rate of 4.3% compounded continuously, estimate the number of deaths from HIV/AIDS during the year
(A) 2008 (B) 2012

31. NEWTON'S LAW OF COOLING This law states that the rate at which an object cools is proportional to the difference in temperature between the object and its surrounding medium. The temperature T of the object t hours later is given by

$$T = T_m + (T_0 - T_m)e^{-kt}$$

where T_m is the temperature of the surrounding medium and T_0 is the temperature of the object at $t = 0$. Suppose a bottle of wine at a room temperature of 72°F is placed in the refrigerator to cool before a dinner party. If the temperature in the refrigerator is kept at 40°F and $k = 0.4$, find the temperature of the wine, to the nearest degree, after 3 hours. (In Exercises 4-5 we will find out how to determine k.)

32. NEWTON'S LAW OF COOLING Refer to Problem 31. What is the temperature, to the nearest degree, of the wine after 5 hours in the refrigerator?

33. PHOTOGRAPHY An electronic flash unit for a camera is activated when a capacitor is discharged through a filament of wire. After the flash is triggered, and the capacitor is discharged, the circuit (see the figure) is connected and the battery pack generates a current to recharge the capacitor. The time it takes for the capacitor to recharge is called the *recycle time*. For a particular flash unit using a 12-volt battery pack, the charge q, in coulombs, on the capacitor t seconds after recharging has started is given by

$$q = 0.0009(1 - e^{-0.2t})$$

Find the value that q approaches as t increases without bound and interpret.

34. MEDICINE An electronic heart pacemaker uses the same type of circuit as the flash unit in Problem 33, but it is designed so that the capacitor discharges 72 times a minute. For a particular pacemaker, the charge on the capacitor t seconds after it starts recharging is given by

$$q = 0.000\,008(1 - e^{-2t})$$

Find the value that q approaches as t increases without bound and interpret.

35. WILDLIFE MANAGEMENT A herd of 20 white-tailed deer is introduced to a coastal island where there had been no deer before. Their population is predicted to increase according to the logistic curve

$$A = \frac{100}{1 + 4e^{-0.14t}}$$

where A is the number of deer expected in the herd after t years.
(A) How many deer will be present after 2 years? After 6 years? Round answers to the nearest integer.
(B) How many years will it take for the herd to grow to 50 deer? Round answer to the nearest integer.
(C) Does A approach *a* limiting value as t increases without bound? Explain.

36. TRAINING A trainee is hired by a computer manufacturing company to learn to test a particular model of a personal computer after it comes off the assembly line. The learning curve for an average trainee is given by

$$A = \frac{200}{4 + 21e^{-0.1t}}$$

where A is the number of computers an average trainee can test per day after t days of training.
(A) How many computers can an average trainee be expected to test after 3 days of training? After 6 days? Round answers to the nearest integer.
(B) How many days will it take until an average trainee can test 30 computers per day? Round answer to the nearest integer.
(C) Does A approach a limiting value as t increases without bound? Explain.

Problems 37–40 require a graphing calculator or a computer that can calculate exponential and logistic regression models for a given data set.

37. DEPRECIATION Table 4 gives the market value of a minivan (in dollars) x years after its purchase. Find an exponential regression model of the form $y = ab^x$ for this data set. Round to four significant digits. Estimate the purchase price of the van. Estimate the value of the van 10 years after its purchase. Round answers to the nearest dollar.

Table 4

x	Value ($)
1	12,575
2	9,455
3	8,115
4	6,845
5	5,225
6	4,485

Source: Kelley Blue Book

38. DEPRECIATION Table 5 gives the market value of a luxury sedan (in dollars) x years after its purchase. Find an exponential regression model of the form $y = ab^x$ for this data set. Estimate the purchase price of the sedan. Estimate the value of the sedan 10 years after its purchase. Round answers to the nearest dollar.

Table 5

x	Value ($)
1	23,125
2	19,050
3	15,625
4	11,875
5	9,450
6	7,125

Source: Kelley Blue Book

39. NUCLEAR POWER Table 6 gives data on nuclear power generation by region for the years 1980–1999.

Table 6 Nuclear Power Generation

	(Billion kilowatt-hours)	
Year	North America	Central and South America
1980	287.0	2.2
1985	440.8	8.4
1990	649.0	9.0
1995	774.4	9.5
1998	750.2	10.3
1999	807.5	10.5

Source: U.S. Energy Information Administration

(A) Let x represent time in years with $x = 0$ representing 1980. Find a logistic regression model

$$y = \frac{c}{1 + ae^{-bx}}$$

for the generation of nuclear power in North America. (Round the constants a, b, and c to three significant digits.)
(B) Use the logistic regression model to predict the generation of nuclear power in North America in 2010.

40. NUCLEAR POWER Refer to Table 6.
(A) Let x represent time in years with $x = 0$ representing 1980. Find a logistic regression model

$$y = \frac{c}{1 + ae^{-bx}}$$

for the generation of nuclear power in Central and South America. (Round the constants a, b, and c to three significant digits.)
(B) Use the logistic regression model to predict the generation of nuclear power in Central and South America in 2010.

4-3 Logarithmic Functions

- Defining Logarithmic Functions
- Converting Between Logarithmic Form and Exponential Form
- Properties of Logarithmic Functions
- Common and Natural Logarithms
- The Change-of-Base Formula

Solving an equation like $3^x = 9$ is easy: We know that $3^2 = 9$, so $x = 2$ is the solution. But what about an equation like $3^x = 20$? There probably is an exponent x between 2 and 3 for which 3^x is 20, but its exact value is not at all clear.

Compare this situation to an equation like $x^2 = 9$. This is easy to solve because we know that 3^2 and $(-3)^2$ are both 9. But what about $x^2 = 20$? To solve this equation, we needed to introduce a new function to be the opposite of the squaring function. This, of course, is the function $f(x) = \sqrt{x}$.

In this section, we will do something very similar with exponential functions. In the first section of this chapter, we learned that exponential functions are one-to-one, so we can define their inverses. These are known as the *logarithmic functions.*

Defining Logarithmic Functions

The exponential function $f(x) = b^x$ for $b > 0$, $b \neq 1$, is a one-to-one function, and therefore has an inverse. Its inverse, denoted $f^{-1}(x) = \log_b x$ (read "log to the base b of x") is called the *logarithmic function with base b.* Just like exponentials, there are different logarithmic functions for each positive base other than 1. A point (x, y)

is on the graph of $f^{-1} = \log_b x$ if and only if the point (y, x) is on the graph of $f = b^x$. In other words,

$$y = \log_b x \text{ if and only if } x = b^y$$

In a specific example,

$$y = \log_2 x \text{ if and only if } x = 2^y \text{, and}$$

$\log_2 x$ is the power to which 2 must be raised to obtain x: $2^{\log_2 x} = 2^y = x$.

We can use this fact to learn some things about the logarithmic functions from our knowledge of exponential functions. For example, the graph of $f^{-1}(x) = \log_b x$ is the graph of $f(x) = b^x$ reflected through the line $y = x$. Also, the domain of $f^{-1}(x) = \log_b x$ is the range of $f(x) = b^x$, and vice versa.

In Example 1, we will use information about $f(x) = 2^x$ to graph its inverse, $f^{-1}(x) = \log_2 x$.

EXAMPLE 1 Graphing a Logarithmic Function

Make a table of values for $f(x) = 2^x$ and reverse the ordered pairs to obtain a table of values for $f^{-1}(x) = \log_2 x$. Then use both tables to graph $f(x)$ and $f^{-1}(x)$ on the same set of axes.

SOLUTION

We chose to evaluate f for integer values from −3 to 3. The tables are shown here, along with the graph (Fig. 1). Note the important comments about domain and range below the graph.

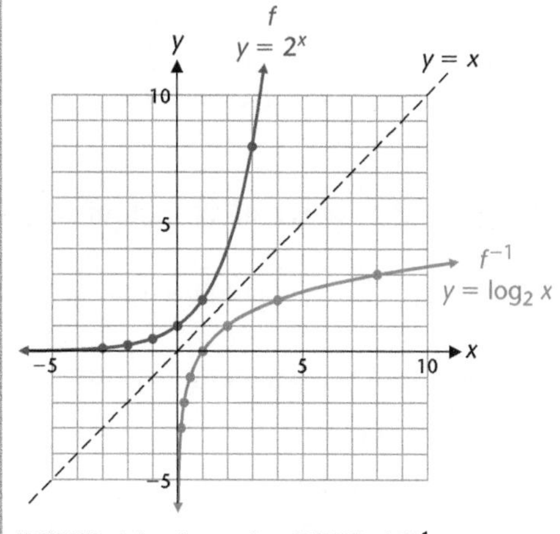

DOMAIN of $f = (-\infty, \infty)$ = RANGE of f^{-1}
RANGE of $f = (0, \infty)$ = DOMAIN of f^{-1}

› **Figure 1** Logarithmic function with base 2.

f: x	$y = 2^x$	f^{-1}: x	$y = \log_2 x$
−3	$\frac{1}{8}$	$\frac{1}{8}$	−3
−2	$\frac{1}{4}$	$\frac{1}{4}$	−2
−1	$\frac{1}{2}$	$\frac{1}{2}$	−1
0	1	1	0
1	2	2	1
2	4	4	2
3	8	8	3

Ordered pairs reversed

MATCHED PROBLEM 1

Repeat Example 1 for $f(x) = (\frac{1}{2})^x$ and $f^{-1}(x) = \log_{1/2} x$.

> **DEFINITION 1 Logarithmic Function**
>
> For $b > 0, b \neq 1$, the inverse of $f(x) = b^x$, denoted $f^{-1}(x) = \log_b x$, is the **logarithmic function** with base b.
>
> | Logarithmic form | | Exponential form |
> |---|---|---|
> | $y = \log_b x$ | is equivalent to | $x = b^y$ |
>
> The log to the base b of x is the exponent to which b must be raised to obtain x. For example,
>
> | | | |
> |---|---|---|
> | $y = \log_{10} x$ | is equivalent to | $x = 10^y$ |
> | $y = \log_e x$ | is equivalent to | $x = e^y$ |
>
> *Remember:* A logarithm is an exponent.

It is very important to remember that the equations $y = \log_b x$ and $x = b^y$ define the same function, and as such can be used interchangeably.

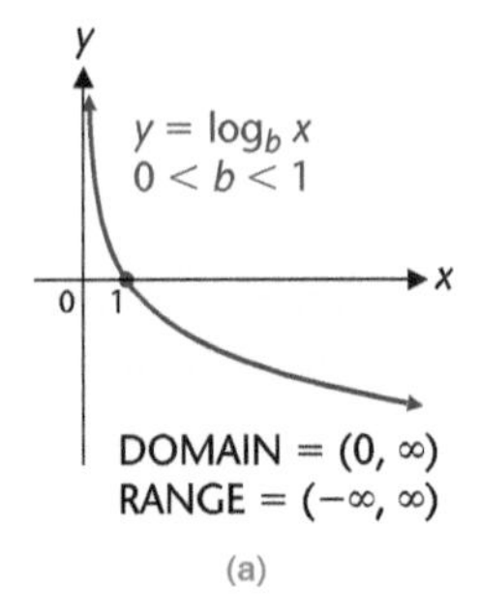

(a)

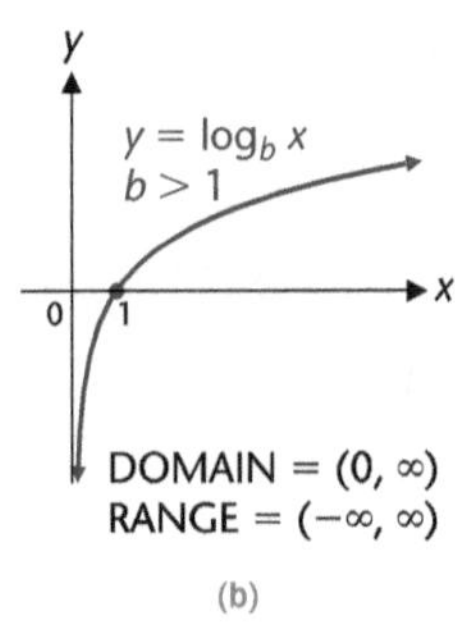

(b)

› **Figure 2** Typical logarithmic graphs.

Because the domain of an exponential function includes all real numbers and its range is the set of positive real numbers, the domain of a logarithmic function is the set of all positive real numbers and its range is the set of all real numbers. Thus, $\log_{10} 3$ is defined, but $\log_{10} 0$ and $\log_{10}(-5)$ are not defined.

In short, the function $y = \log_b x$ for any b is only defined for positive x values. Typical logarithmic curves are shown in Figure 2. Notice that in each case, the y axis is a vertical asymptote for the graph.

The graphs in Example 1 and Figure 2 suggest that logarithmic graphs share some common properties. Several of these properties are listed in Theorem 1. It might be helpful in understanding them to review Theorem 1 in Section 4-1. Each of these properties is a consequence of a corresponding property of exponential graphs.

> **THEOREM 1 Properties of Graphs of Logarithmic Functions**
>
> Let $f(x) = \log_b x$ be a logarithmic function, $b > 0, b \neq 1$. Then the graph of $f(x)$:
>
> 1. Is continuous on its domain $(0, \infty)$
> 2. Has no sharp corners
> 3. Passes through the point $(1, 0)$
> 4. Lies to the right of the y axis, which is a vertical asymptote
> 5. Is increasing as x increases if $b > 1$; is decreasing as x increases if $0 < b < 1$
> 6. Intersects any horizontal line exactly once, so is one-to-one

››› EXPLORE-DISCUSS 1

For the exponential function $f(x) = (\frac{2}{3})^x$, graph f and $y = x$ on the same coordinate system. Then sketch the graph of f^{-1}. Use the DRAW INVERSE command on a graphing calculator to check your work. Discuss the domains and ranges of f and its inverse. By what other name is f^{-1} known?

› Converting Between Logarithmic Form and Exponential Form

We now look into the matter of converting logarithmic forms to equivalent exponential forms, and vice versa. Throughout the remainder of the chapter, it will be useful to sometimes convert a logarithmic expression into the equivalent exponential form. At other times, it will be useful to do the reverse.

EXAMPLE 2 Logarithmic–Exponential Conversions

Change each logarithmic form to an equivalent exponential form.

(A) $\log_2 8 = 3$ (B) $\log_{25} 5 = \frac{1}{2}$ (C) $\log_2 (\frac{1}{4}) = -2$

SOLUTIONS

(A) $\log_2 8 = 3$ is equivalent to $8 = 2^3$.
(B) $\log_{25} 5 = \frac{1}{2}$ is equivalent to $5 = 25^{1/2}$.
(C) $\log_2 (\frac{1}{4}) = -2$ is equivalent to $\frac{1}{4} = 2^{-2}$.

Note that in each case, the base of the logarithm matches the base of the corresponding exponent.

MATCHED PROBLEM 2

Change each logarithmic form to an equivalent exponential form.

(A) $\log_3 27 = 3$ (B) $\log_{36} 6 = \frac{1}{2}$ (C) $\log_3 (\frac{1}{9}) = -2$

EXAMPLE 3

Logarithmic-Exponential Conversions

Change each exponential form to an equivalent logarithmic form.

(A) $49 = 7^2$ (B) $3 = \sqrt{9}$ (C) $\frac{1}{5} = 5^{-1}$

SOLUTIONS

(A) $49 = 7^2$ is equivalent to $\log_7 49 = 2$.
(B) $3 = \sqrt{9}$ is equivalent to $\log_9 3 = \frac{1}{2}$.
(C) $\frac{1}{5} = 5^{-1}$ is equivalent to $\log_5 (\frac{1}{5}) = -1$.

Again, the bases match.

MATCHED PROBLEM 3

Change each exponential form to an equivalent logarithmic form.

(A) $64 = 4^3$ (B) $2 = \sqrt[3]{8}$ (C) $\frac{1}{16} = 4^{-2}$

To gain a little deeper understanding of logarithmic functions and their relationship to the exponential functions, we will consider a few problems where we want to find x, b, or y in $y = \log_b x$, given the other two values. All values were chosen so that the problems can be solved without a calculator. In each case, converting to the equivalent exponential form is useful.

EXAMPLE 4

Solutions of the Equation $y = \log_b x$

Find x, b, or y as indicated.

(A) Find y: $y = \log_4 8$. (B) Find x: $\log_3 x = -2$. (C) Find b: $\log_b 81 = 4$.

SOLUTIONS

(A) Write $y = \log_4 8$ in equivalent exponential form.

$$8 = 4^y \quad \text{Write each number to the same base 2.}$$
$$2^3 = 2^{2y} \quad \text{Recall that } b^m = b^n \text{ if and only if } m = n.$$
$$2y = 3$$
$$y = \frac{3}{2}$$

We conclude that $\frac{3}{2} = \log_4 8$.

(B) Write $\log_3 x = -2$ in equivalent exponential form.

$$x = 3^{-2}$$
$$= \frac{1}{3^2} = \frac{1}{9}$$

We conclude that $\log_3 (\frac{1}{9}) = -2$.

(C) Write $\log_b 81 = 4$ in equivalent exponential form:

$81 = b^4$ Write 81 as a fourth power.

$3^4 = b^4$ b could be 3 or -3, but the base of a logarithm must be positive.

$b = 3$

We conclude that $\log_3 81 = 4$.

MATCHED PROBLEM 4

Find x, b, or y as indicated.

(A) Find y: $y = \log_9 27$. (B) Find x: $\log_2 x = -3$. (C) Find b: $\log_b 100 = 2$.

Properties of Logarithmic Functions

Some of the properties of exponential functions that we studied in Section 4-1 can be used to develop corresponding properties of logarithmic functions. Several of these important properties of logarithmic functions are listed in Theorem 1. We will justify them individually.

THEOREM 2 Properties of Logarithmic Functions

If b, M, and N are positive real numbers, $b \neq 1$, and p and x are real numbers, then

1. $\log_b 1 = 0$
2. $\log_b b = 1$
3. $\log_b b^x = x$
4. $b^{\log_b x} = x, x > 0$
5. $\log_b M = \log_b N$ if and only if $M = N$
6. $\log_b MN = \log_b M + \log_b N$
7. $\log_b \frac{M}{N} = \log_b M - \log_b N$
8. $\log_b M^p = p \log_b M$

>>> CAUTION >>>

1. In Properties 3 and 4, it's essential that the base of the exponential and the base of the logarithm are the same.
2. Properties 6 and 7 are often misinterpreted, so you should examine them carefully.

$$\frac{\log_b M}{\log_b N} \neq \log_b M - \log_b N$$

$\log_b M - \log_b N = \log_b \frac{M}{N}$; $\frac{\log_b M}{\log_b N}$ cannot be simplified.

$$\log_b (M + N) \neq \log_b M + \log_b N$$

$\log_b M + \log_b N = \log_b MN$; $\log_b (M + N)$ cannot be simplified.

Now we will justify properties in Theorem 2.

1. $\log_b 1 = 0$ because $b^0 = 1$
2. $\log_b b = 1$ because $b^1 = b$
3. and 4. These are simply another way to state that $f(x) = b^x$ and $f^{-1}(x) = \log_b x$ are inverse functions. Property 3 can be written as $f^{-1}(f(x)) = x$ for all x in the domain of f. Property 4 can be written as $f(f^{-1}(x)) = x$ for all x in the domain of f^{-1}. This matches our characterization of inverse functions in Theorem 5, Section 1-6. Collectively, these properties say that if you apply an exponential function and a logarithmic function with the same base consecutively (in either order) you end up with the same value you started with.
5. This follows from the fact that logarithmic functions are one-to-one.

Properties 6, 7, and 8 are used often in manipulating logarithmic expressions. We will justify them in Problems 111 and 112 in Exercises 4-3, and Problem 68 in the Chapter 4 Review Exercises.

EXAMPLE 5 Using Logarithmic Properties

Simplify, using the properties in Theorem 2.

(A) $\log_e 1$ (B) $\log_{10} 10$ (C) $\log_e e^{2x+1}$
(D) $\log_{10} 0.01$ (E) $10^{\log_{10} 7}$ (F) $e^{\log_e x^2}$

SOLUTIONS

(A) $\log_e 1 = 0$ Property 1
(B) $\log_{10} 10 = 1$ Property 2
(C) $\log_e e^{2x+1} = 2x + 1$ Property 3
(D) $\log_{10} 0.01 = \log_{10} 10^{-2} = -2$ Property 3
(E) $10^{\log_{10} 7} = 7$ Property 4
(F) $e^{\log_e x^2} = x^2$ Property 4

MATCHED PROBLEM 5

Simplify, using the properties in Theorem 2.

(A) $\log_{10} 10^{-5}$ (B) $\log_5 25$ (C) $\log_{10} 1$
(D) $\log_e e^{m+n}$ (E) $10^{\log_{10} 4}$ (F) $e^{\log_e (x^4+1)}$

Common and Natural Logarithms

To work with logarithms effectively, we will need to be able to calculate (or at least approximate) the logarithms of any positive number to a variety of bases. Historically, tables were used for this purpose, but now calculators are used because they are faster and can find far more values than any table can possibly include.

Of all possible bases, there are two that are used most often. **Common logarithms** are logarithms with base 10. **Natural logarithms** are logarithms with base e. Most calculators have a function key labeled "log" and a function key labeled "ln." The former represents the common logarithmic function and the latter the natural logarithmic function. In fact, "log" and "ln" are both used in most math books, and whenever you see either used in this book without a base indicated, they should be interpreted as follows:

LOGARITHMIC FUNCTIONS

$y = \log x = \log_{10} x$ Common logarithmic function

$y = \ln x = \log_e x$ Natural logarithmic function

EXPLORE-DISCUSS 2

(A) Sketch the graph of $y = 10^x$, $y = \log x$, and $y = x$ in the same coordinate system and state the domain and range of the common logarithmic function.

(B) Sketch the graph of $y = e^x$, $y = \ln x$, and $y = x$ in the same coordinate system and state the domain and range of the natural logarithmic function.

EXAMPLE 6 Calculator Evaluation of Logarithms

Use a calculator to evaluate each to six decimal places.

(A) log 3,184 (B) ln 0.000 349 (C) log (−3.24)

SOLUTIONS

(A) log 3,184 = 3.502 973 (B) ln 0.000 349 = −7.960 439
(C) log (−3.24) = Error

Why is an error indicated in part C? Because −3.24 is not in the domain of the log function. [*Note:* Calculators display error messages in various ways. Some calculators use a more advanced definition of logarithmic functions that involves complex numbers. They will display an ordered pair, representing a complex number, as the value of log (−3.24), rather than an error message. You should interpret such a display as indicating that the number entered is not in the domain of the logarithmic function as we have defined it.]

MATCHED PROBLEM 6

Use a calculator to evaluate each to six decimal places.

(A) log 0.013 529 (B) ln 28.693 28 (C) ln (−0.438)

When working with common and natural logarithms, we will follow the common practice of using the equal sign "=" where it might be technically correct to use the approximately equal sign "≈." No harm is done as long as we keep in mind that in a statement such as log 3.184 = 0.503, the number on the right is only assumed accurate to three decimal places and is not exact.

››› EXPLORE-DISCUSS 3

Graphs of the functions $f(x) = \log x$ and $g(x) = \ln x$ are shown in the graphing calculator display of Figure 3. Which graph belongs to which function? It appears from the display that one of the functions may be a constant multiple of the other. Is that true? Find and discuss the evidence for your answer.

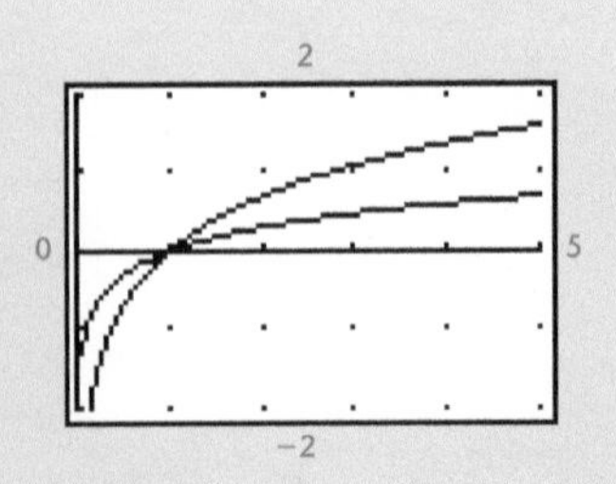

› Figure 3

EXAMPLE 7

Calculator Evaluation of Logarithms

Use a calculator to evaluate each expression to three decimal places.

(A) $\dfrac{\log 2}{\log 1.1}$ (B) $\log \dfrac{2}{1.1}$ (C) $\log 2 - \log 1.1$

SOLUTIONS

(A) $\dfrac{\log 2}{\log 1.1} = 7.273$ Enter as (log 2) ÷ (log 1.1).

(B) $\log \dfrac{2}{1.1} = 0.260$ Enter as log (2 ÷ 1.1).

(C) $\log 2 - \log 1.1 = 0.260$. Note that $\dfrac{\log 2}{\log 1.1} \neq \log 2 - \log 1.1$, but

$\log \dfrac{2}{1.1} = \log 2 - \log 1.1$ (see Theorem 2).

MATCHED PROBLEM 7

Use a calculator to evaluate each to three decimal places.

(A) $\dfrac{\ln 3}{\ln 1.08}$ (B) $\ln \dfrac{3}{1.08}$ (C) $\ln 3 - \ln 1.08$

We now turn to the second problem: Given the logarithm of a number, find the number. To solve this problem, we make direct use of the logarithmic–exponential relationships, and change logarithmic expressions into exponential form.

LOGARITHMIC–EXPONENTIAL RELATIONSHIPS

$\log x = y$ is equivalent to $x = 10^y$

$\ln x = y$ is equivalent to $x = e^y$

EXAMPLE 8

Solving $\log_b x = y$ for x

Find x to three significant digits, given the indicated logarithms.

(A) $\log x = -9.315$ (B) $\ln x = 2.386$

SOLUTIONS

(A) $\log x = -9.315$ Change to exponential form (Definition 1).

$x = 10^{-9.315}$

$= 4.84 \times 10^{-10}$

Notice that the answer is displayed in scientific notation in the calculator.

(B) $\ln x = 2.386$ Change to exponential form (Definition 1).

$$x = e^{2.386}$$
$$= 10.9$$

MATCHED PROBLEM 8

Find x to four significant digits, given the indicated logarithms.

(A) $\ln x = -5.062$ (B) $\log x = 12.0821$

››› EXPLORE-DISCUSS 4

Example 8 was solved algebraically using logarithmic–exponential relationships. Use the INTERSECT command on a graphing calculator to solve this problem graphically. Discuss the relative merits of the two approaches.

› The Change-of-Base Formula

How would you find the logarithm of a positive number to a base other than 10 or e? For example, how would you find $\log_3 5.2$? In Example 9 we evaluate this logarithm using several properties of logarithms. Then we develop a change-of-base formula to find such logarithms more easily.

EXAMPLE 9 **Evaluating a Base 3 Logarithm**

Evaluate $\log_3 5.2$ to four decimal places.

SOLUTION

Let $y = \log_3 5.2$ and proceed as follows:

$$\log_3 5.2 = y$$ Change to exponential form.

$$5.2 = 3^y$$ Apply the natural log (or common log) to each side.

$$\ln 5.2 = \ln 3^y$$ Use $\log_b M^p = p \log_b M$.

$$\ln 5.2 = y \ln 3$$ Solve for y.

$$y = \frac{\ln 5.2}{\ln 3}$$

Replace y with $\log_3 5.2$ from the first step, and use a calculator to evaluate the right side:

$$\log_3 5.2 = \frac{\ln 5.2}{\ln 3} = 1.5007$$

MATCHED PROBLEM 9

Evaluate $\log_{0.5} 0.0372$ to four decimal places.

If we repeat the process we used in Example 9 on a generic logarithm, something interesting happens. The goal is to evaluate $\log_b N$, where b is any acceptable base, and N is any positive real number. As in Example 9, let $y = \log_b N$.

$$\begin{aligned} \log_b N &= y && \text{Write in exponential form.} \\ N &= b^y && \text{Apply natural log to each side.} \\ \ln N &= \ln b^y && \text{Use } \ln b^y = y \ln b \text{ (Property 8, Theorem 2).} \\ \ln N &= y \ln b && \text{Solve for } y. \\ y &= \frac{\ln N}{\ln b} \end{aligned}$$

This provides a formula for evaluating a logarithm to any base by using natural log:

$$\log_b N = \frac{\ln N}{\ln b}$$

We could also have used log base 10 rather than natural log, and developed an alternative formula:

$$\log_b N = \frac{\log N}{\log b}$$

In fact, the same approach would enable us to rewrite $\log_b N$ in terms of a logarithm with any base we choose!

THE CHANGE-OF-BASE FORMULA

For any $b > 0$, $b \neq 1$, and any positive real number N,

$$\log_b N = \frac{\log_a N}{\log_a b}$$

where a is any positive number other than 1.

»» EXPLORE-DISCUSS 5

If b is any positive real number different from 1, the change-of-base formula implies that the function $y = \log_b x$ is a constant multiple of the natural logarithmic function; that is, $\log_b x = k \ln x$ for some k.

(A) Graph the functions $y = \ln x, y = 2 \ln x, y = 0.5 \ln x$, and $y = -3 \ln x$.

(B) Write each function of part A in the form $y = \log_b x$ by finding the base b to two decimal places.

(C) Is every exponential function $y = b^x$ a constant multiple of $y = e^x$? Explain.

ANSWERS TO MATCHED PROBLEMS

1.

f		f^{-1}	
x	$y = \left(\frac{1}{2}\right)^x$	x	$y = \log_{1/2} x$
-3	8	8	-3
-2	4	4	-2
-1	2	2	-1
0	1	1	0
1	$\frac{1}{2}$	$\frac{1}{2}$	1
2	$\frac{1}{4}$	$\frac{1}{4}$	2
3	$\frac{1}{8}$	$\frac{1}{8}$	3

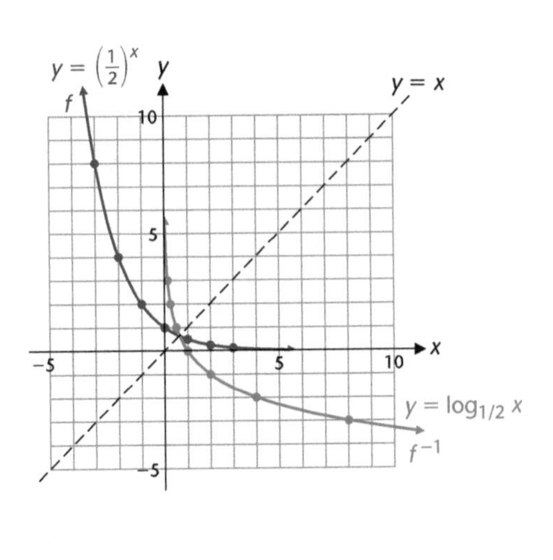

2. (A) $27 = 3^3$ (B) $6 = 36^{1/2}$ (C) $\frac{1}{9} = 3^{-2}$
3. (A) $\log_4 64 = 3$ (B) $\log_8 2 = \frac{1}{3}$ (C) $\log_4 (\frac{1}{16}) = -2$
4. (A) $y = \frac{3}{2}$ (B) $x = \frac{1}{8}$ (C) $b = 10$
5. (A) -5 (B) 2 (C) 0 (D) $m + n$ (E) 4 (F) $x^4 + 1$
6. (A) $-1.868\,734$ (B) $3.356\,663$ (C) Not possible
7. (A) 14.275 (B) 1.022 (C) 1.022
8. (A) $x = 0.006\,333$ (B) $x = 1.208 \times 10^{12}$ **9.** 4.7486

4-3 Exercises

1. Describe the relationship between logarithmic functions and exponential functions in your own words.

2. Explain why there are infinitely many different logarithmic functions.

3. Why are logarithmic functions undefined for zero and negative inputs?

4. Why is $\log_b 1 = 0$ for any base?

5. Explain how to calculate $\log_5 3$ on a calculator that only has log buttons for base 10 and base e.

6. Using the word "inverse," explain why $\log_b b^x = x$ for any x and any acceptable base b.

Rewrite Problems 7–12 in equivalent exponential form.

7. $\log_3 81 = 4$ **8.** $\log_5 125 = 3$

9. $\log_{10} 0.001 = -3$ **10.** $\log_{10} 1{,}000 = 3$

11. $\log_6 \frac{1}{36} = -2$ **12.** $\log_2 \frac{1}{64} = -6$

Rewrite Problems 13–18 in equivalent logarithmic form.

13. $8 = 4^{3/2}$ **14.** $9 = 27^{2/3}$

15. $\frac{1}{2} = 32^{-1/5}$ **16.** $\frac{1}{8} = 2^{-3}$

17. $(\frac{2}{3})^3 = \frac{8}{27}$ **18.** $(\frac{5}{2})^{-2} = 0.16$

In Problems 19–22, make a table of values similar to the one in Example 1, then use it to graph both functions by hand.

19. $f(x) = 3^x$ $f^{-1}(x) = \log_3 x$

20. $f(x) = (\frac{1}{3})^x$ $f^{-1}(x) = \log_{1/3} x$

21. $f(x) = (\frac{2}{3})^x$ $f^{-1}(x) = \log_{2/3} x$

22. $f(x) = 10^x$ $f^{-1}(x) = \log x$

In Problems 23–38, simplify each expression using Theorem 2.

23. $\log_{16} 1$ **24.** $\log_{25} 1$ **25.** $\log_{0.5} 0.5$

26. $\log_7 7$ **27.** $\log_e e^4$ **28.** $\log_{10} 10^5$

29. $\log_{10} 0.01$ **30.** $\log_{10} 100$ **31.** $\log_3 27$

32. $\log_4 256$ **33.** $\log_{1/2} 2$ **34.** $\log_{1/5} (\frac{1}{25})$

35. $e^{\log_e 5}$ **36.** $e^{\log_e 10}$ **37.** $\log_5 \sqrt[3]{5}$

38. $\log_2 \sqrt{8}$

In Problems 39–46, evaluate to four decimal places.

39. $\log 49{,}236$ **40.** $\log 691{,}450$

41. $\ln 54.081$ **42.** $\ln 19.722$

43. $\log_7 13$ **44.** $\log_9 78$

45. $\log_5 120.24$ **46.** $\log_{17} 304.66$

In Problems 47–54, evaluate x to four significant digits.

47. $\log x = 5.3027$ **48.** $\log x = 1.9168$

49. $\log x = -3.1773$ **50.** $\log x = -2.0411$

51. $\ln x = 3.8655$ **52.** $\ln x = 5.0884$

53. $\ln x = -0.3916$ **54.** $\ln x = -4.1083$

Find x, y, or b, as indicated in Problems 55–72.

55. $\log_2 x = 2$ **56.** $\log_3 x = 3$

57. $\log_4 16 = y$ **58.** $\log_8 64 = y$

59. $\log_b 16 = 2$ **60.** $\log_b 10^{-3} = -3$

61. $\log_b 1 = 0$ **62.** $\log_b b = 1$

63. $\log_4 x = \frac{1}{2}$ **64.** $\log_8 x = \frac{1}{3}$

65. $\log_{1/3} 9 = y$ **66.** $\log_{49} (\frac{1}{7}) = y$

67. $\log_b 1{,}000 = \frac{3}{2}$ **68.** $\log_b 4 = \frac{2}{3}$

69. $\log_8 x = -\frac{4}{3}$ **70.** $\log_{25} x = -\frac{3}{2}$

71. $\log_{16} 8 = y$ **72.** $\log_9 27 = y$

In Problems 73–78, evaluate to three decimal places.

73. $\dfrac{\log 2}{\log 1.15}$ **74.** $\dfrac{\log 2}{\log 1.12}$

75. $\dfrac{\ln 3}{\ln 1.15}$ **76.** $\dfrac{\ln 4}{\ln 1.2}$

77. $\dfrac{\ln 150}{2 \ln 3}$ **78.** $\dfrac{\log 200}{3 \log 2}$

In Problems 79–82, rewrite the expression in terms of log x and log y.

79. $\log\left(\dfrac{x}{y}\right)$ **80.** $\log (xy)$

81. $\log (x^4y^3)$ **82.** $\log\left(\dfrac{x^2}{\sqrt{y}}\right)$

In Problems 83–86, rewrite the expression as a single log.

83. $\ln x - \ln y$ **84.** $\log_3 x + \log_3 y$

85. $2 \ln x + 5 \ln y - \ln z$ **86.** $\log a - 2 \log b + 3 \log c$

In Problems 87–90, given that $\log x = -2$ and $\log y = 3$, find:

87. $\log (xy)$ **88.** $\log\left(\frac{x}{y}\right)$ **89.** $\log\left(\frac{\sqrt{x}}{y^3}\right)$ **90.** $\log (x^5y^3)$

In Problems 91–98, use transformations to explain how the graph of g is related to the graph of the given logarithmic function f. Determine whether g is increasing or decreasing, find its domain and asymptote, and sketch the graph of g.

91. $g(x) = 3 + \log_2 x; f(x) = \log_2 x$

92. $g(x) = -4 + \log_3 x; f(x) = \log_3 x$

93. $g(x) = \log_{1/3} (x - 2); f(x) = \log_{1/3} x$

94. $g(x) = \log_{1/2} (x + 3); f(x) = \log_{1/2} x$

95. $g(x) = -1 - \log x; f(x) = \log x$

96. $g(x) = 2 - \log x; f(x) = \log x$

97. $g(x) = 5 - 3 \ln x; f(x) = \ln x$

98. $g(x) = -3 - 2 \ln x; f(x) = \ln x$

In Problems 99–102, find f^{-1}.

99. $f(x) = \log_5 x$ **100.** $f(x) = \log_{1/3} x$

101. $f(x) = 4 \log_3 (x + 3)$ **102.** $f(x) = 2 \log_2 (x - 5)$

103. Let $f(x) = \log_3 (2 - x)$.
(A) Find f^{-1}. (B) Graph f^{-1}.
(C) Reflect the graph of f^{-1} in the line $y = x$ to obtain the graph of f.

104. Let $f(x) = \log_2 (-3 - x)$.
(A) Find f^{-1}. (B) Graph f^{-1}.
(C) Reflect the graph of f^{-1} in the line $y = x$ to obtain the graph of f.

105. What is wrong with the following "proof" that 3 is less than 2?

$$1 < 3 \quad \text{Divide both sides by 27.}$$
$$\tfrac{1}{27} < \tfrac{3}{27}$$
$$\tfrac{1}{27} < \tfrac{1}{9}$$
$$(\tfrac{1}{3})^3 < (\tfrac{1}{3})^2$$
$$\log (\tfrac{1}{3})^3 < \log (\tfrac{1}{3})^2$$
$$3 \log \tfrac{1}{3} < 2 \log \tfrac{1}{3} \quad \text{Divide both sides by } \log \tfrac{1}{3}.$$
$$3 < 2$$

106. What is wrong with the following "proof" that 1 is greater than 2?

$$3 > 2 \quad \text{Multiply both sides by } \log \tfrac{1}{2}.$$
$$3 \log \tfrac{1}{2} > 2 \log \tfrac{1}{2}$$
$$\log (\tfrac{1}{2})^3 > \log (\tfrac{1}{2})^2$$
$$(\tfrac{1}{2})^3 > (\tfrac{1}{2})^2$$
$$\tfrac{1}{8} > \tfrac{1}{4} \quad \text{Multiply both sides by 8.}$$
$$1 > 2$$

*The polynomials in Problems 107–110, called **Taylor polynomials,** can be used to approximate the function $g(x) = \ln(1 + x)$. To illustrate this approximation graphically, in each problem, graph $g(x) = \ln(1 + x)$ and the indicated polynomial in the same viewing window, $-1 \le x \le 3$ and $-2 \le y \le 2$.*

107. $P_1(x) = x - \frac{1}{2}x^2$ **108.** $P_2(x) = x - \frac{1}{2}x^2 + \frac{1}{3}x^3$

109. $P_3(x) = x - \frac{1}{2}x^2 + \frac{1}{3}x^3 - \frac{1}{4}x^4$

110. $P_4(x) = x - \frac{1}{2}x^2 + \frac{1}{3}x^3 - \frac{1}{4}x^4 + \frac{1}{5}x^5$

111. Prove that for any positive M, N, and b ($b \ne 1$), $\log_b (\frac{M}{N}) = \log_b M - \log_b N$. (*Hint:* Start by writing $u = \log_b M$ and $v = \log_b N$ and changing each to exponential form.)

112. Prove that for any positive integer p and any positive b and M ($b \ne 1$), $\log_b M^p = p \log_b M$. [*Hint:* Write M^p as $M \cdot M \cdot \cdots M$ (p factors).]

4-4 Logarithmic Models

- Logarithmic Scales
- Data Analysis and Regression

Logarithmic functions occur naturally as the inverses of exponential functions. But that's not to say that they are not useful in their own right. Some of these uses are probably familiar to you, but you might not have realized that they involved logarithmic functions.

In this section, we will study logarithmic scales that are used to compare the intensity of sounds, the severity of earthquakes, and the brightness of distant stars. We will also look at using regression to model data with a logarithmic function, and discuss what sort of data is likely to fit such a model.

Logarithmic Scales

SOUND INTENSITY: The human ear is able to hear sound over an incredible range of intensities. The loudest sound a healthy person can hear without damage to the eardrum has an intensity 1 trillion (1,000,000,000,000) times that of the softest sound a person can hear. If we were to use these intensities as a scale for measuring volume, we would be stuck using numbers from zero all the way to the trillions, which seems cumbersome, if not downright silly. In the last section, we saw that logarithmic functions increase very slowly. We can take advantage of this to create a scale for sound intensity that is much more condensed, and therefore more manageable.

The decibel scale for sound intensity is an example of such a scale. The **decibel,** named after the inventor of the telephone, Alexander Graham Bell (1847–1922), is defined as follows:

$$D = 10 \log \frac{I}{I_0} \qquad \text{Decibel scale} \qquad (1)$$

where D is the **decibel level** of the sound, I is the **intensity** of the sound measured in watts per square meter (W/m^2), and I_0 is the intensity of the least audible sound that an average healthy young person can hear. The latter is standardized to be $I_0 = 10^{-12}$ watts per square meter. Table 1 lists some typical sound intensities from familiar sources. In Example 1 and Problems 1 and 2 in Exercises 4-4, we will calculate the decibel levels for these sounds.

Table 1 Typical Sound Intensities

Sound Intensity (W/m^2)	Sound
1.0×10^{-12}	Threshold of hearing
5.2×10^{-10}	Whisper
3.2×10^{-6}	Normal conversation
8.5×10^{-4}	Heavy traffic
3.2×10^{-3}	Jackhammer
1.0×10^{0}	Threshold of pain
8.3×10^{2}	Jet plane with afterburner

EXAMPLE 1 Sound Intensity

(A) Find the number of decibels from a whisper with sound intensity 5.20×10^{-10} watts per square meter, then from heavy traffic at 8.5×10^{-4} watts per square meter. Round your answers to two decimal places.

(B) How many times larger is the sound intensity of heavy traffic compared to a whisper?

SOLUTIONS

(A) We can use the decibel formula (1) with $I_0 = 10^{-12}$. First, we use $I = 5.2 \times 10^{-10}$:

$$D = 10 \log \frac{I}{I_0} \quad \text{Substitute } I = 5.2 \times 10^{-10}, I_0 = 10^{-12}.$$

$$= 10 \log \frac{5.2 \times 10^{-10}}{10^{-12}} \quad \text{Simplify the fraction.}$$

$$= 10 \log 520$$

$$= 27.16 \text{ decibels}$$

Next, for heavy traffic:

$$D = 10 \log \frac{I}{I_0} \quad \text{Substitute } I = 8.5 \times 10^{-4}, I_0 = 10^{-12}.$$

$$= 10 \log \frac{8.5 \times 10^{-4}}{10^{-12}} \quad \text{Simplify the fraction.}$$

$$= 10 \log 850{,}000{,}000$$

$$= 89.29 \text{ decibels}$$

(B) Dividing the larger intensity by the smaller,

$$\frac{8.5 \times 10^{-4}}{5.2 \times 10^{-10}} = 1{,}634{,}615.4$$

we see that the sound intensity of heavy traffic is more than 1.6 million times as great as the intensity of a whisper!

MATCHED PROBLEM 1

Find the number of decibels from a jackhammer with sound intensity 3.2×10^{-3} watts per square meter. Compute the answer to two decimal places.

››› EXPLORE-DISCUSS 1

Suppose that you are asked to draw a graph of the data in Table 1, with sound intensities on the x axis, and the corresponding decibel levels on the y axis.

(A) What would be the coordinates of the point corresponding to a jackhammer (see Matched Problem 1)?

(B) Suppose the axes of this graph are labeled as follows: Each tick mark on the x axis corresponds to the intensity of the least audible sound (10^{-12} watts per square meter), and each tick mark on the y axis corresponds to 1 decibel. If there is $\frac{1}{8}$ inch between all tick marks, how far away from the x axis is the point you found in part A? From the y axis? (Give the first answer in inches and the second in miles!) Discuss your result.

EARTHQUAKE INTENSITY: The energy released by the largest earthquake recorded, measured in joules, is about 100 billion (100,000,000,000) times the energy released by a small earthquake that is barely felt. Over the past 150 years several people from various countries have devised different types of measures of earthquake magnitudes so that their severity could be compared without using tremendously large numbers. In 1935 the California seismologist Charles Richter devised a logarithmic scale that bears his name and is still widely used in the United States. The **magnitude** of an earthquake M on the **Richter scale*** is given as follows:

$$M = \frac{2}{3} \log \frac{E}{E_0} \qquad \text{Richter scale} \qquad (2)$$

where E is the energy released by the earthquake, measured in joules, and E_0 is the energy released by a very small reference earthquake, which has been standardized to be

$$E_0 = 10^{4.40} \text{ joules}$$

The destructive power of earthquakes relative to magnitudes on the Richter scale is indicated in Table 2.

Table 2 The Richter Scale

Magnitude on Richter Scale	Destructive Power
$M < 4.5$	Small
$4.5 < M < 5.5$	Moderate
$5.5 < M < 6.5$	Large
$6.5 < M < 7.5$	Major
$7.5 < M$	Greatest

*Originally, Richter defined the magnitude of an earthquake in terms of logarithms of the maximum seismic wave amplitude, in thousandths of a millimeter, measured on a standard seismograph. Equation (2) gives essentially the same magnitude that Richter obtained for a given earthquake but in terms of logarithms of the energy released by the earthquake.

EXAMPLE 2 Earthquake Intensity

The 1906 San Francisco earthquake released approximately 5.96×10^{16} joules of energy. Another quake struck the Bay Area just before game 3 of the 1989 World Series, releasing 1.12×10^{15} joules of energy.

(A) Find the magnitude of each earthquake on the Richter scale. Round your answers to two decimal places.

(B) How many times more energy did the 1906 earthquake release than the one in 1989?

SOLUTIONS

(A) We can use the magnitude formula (2) with $E_0 = 10^{4.40}$. First, for the 1906 earthquake, we use $E = 5.96 \times 10^{16}$:

$$M = \frac{2}{3}\log\frac{E}{E_0} \qquad \text{Substitute } E = 5.96 \times 10^{16},\ E_0 = 10^{4.40}.$$

$$= \frac{2}{3}\log\frac{5.96 \times 10^{16}}{10^{4.40}}$$

$$= 8.25$$

Next, for the 1989 earthquake:

$$M = \frac{2}{3}\log\frac{E}{E_0} \qquad \text{Substitute } E = 1.12 \times 10^{15},\ E_0 = 10^{4.40}.$$

$$= \frac{2}{3}\log\frac{1.12 \times 10^{15}}{10^{4.40}}$$

$$= 7.1$$

(B) Dividing the larger energy release by the smaller,

$$\frac{5.96 \times 10^{16}}{1.12 \times 10^{15}} = 53.2$$

we see that the 1906 earthquake released 53.2 times as much energy as the 1989 quake.

MATCHED PROBLEM 2

The 1985 earthquake in central Chile released approximately 1.26×10^{16} joules of energy. What was its magnitude on the Richter scale? Compute the answer to two decimal places.

EXAMPLE 3 Earthquake Intensity

If the energy release of one earthquake is 1,000 times that of another, how much larger is the Richter scale reading of the larger than the smaller?

SOLUTION

Let

$$M_1 = \frac{2}{3}\log\frac{E_1}{E_0} \qquad \text{and} \qquad M_2 = \frac{2}{3}\log\frac{E_2}{E_0}$$

be the Richter equations for the smaller and larger earthquakes, respectively. Since the larger earthquake released 1,000 times as much energy, we can write $E_2 = 1{,}000E_1$.

$$\begin{aligned} M_2 &= \frac{2}{3}\log\frac{E_2}{E_0} && \text{Substitute } 1{,}000E_1 \text{ for } E_2. \\ &= \frac{2}{3}\log\frac{1{,}000E_1}{E_0} && \text{Use } \log(MN) = \log M + \log N. \\ &= \frac{2}{3}\left(\log 1{,}000 + \log\frac{E_1}{E_0}\right) && \log 1{,}000 = \log 10^3 = 3 \\ &= \frac{2}{3}\left(3 + \log\frac{E_1}{E_0}\right) && \text{Distribute.} \\ &= \frac{2}{3}(3) + \frac{2}{3}\log\frac{E_1}{E_0} && \frac{2}{3}\log\frac{E_1}{E_0} \text{ is } M_1! \\ &= 2 + M_1 \end{aligned}$$

Thus, an earthquake with 1,000 times the energy of another has a Richter scale reading of 2 more than the other.

MATCHED PROBLEM 3

If the energy release of one earthquake is 10,000 times that of another, how much larger is the Richter scale reading of the larger than the smaller?

ROCKET FLIGHT: The theory of rocket flight uses advanced mathematics and physics to show that the **velocity** v of a rocket at burnout (depletion of fuel supply) is given by

$$v = c\ln\frac{W_t}{W_b} \qquad \textbf{Rocket equation} \qquad (3)$$

where c is the exhaust velocity of the rocket engine, W_t is the takeoff weight (fuel, structure, and payload), and W_b is the burnout weight (structure and payload).

Because of the Earth's atmospheric resistance, a launch vehicle velocity of at least 9.0 kilometers per second is required to achieve the minimum altitude needed for a stable orbit. Formula (3) indicates that to increase velocity v, either the weight ratio W_t/W_b must be increased or the exhaust velocity c must be increased. The weight ratio can be increased by the use of solid fuels, and the exhaust velocity can be increased by improving the fuels, solid or liquid.

EXAMPLE 4 Rocket Flight Theory

A typical single-stage, solid-fuel rocket may have a weight ratio $W_t/W_b = 18.7$ and an exhaust velocity $c = 2.38$ kilometers per second. Would this rocket reach a launch velocity of 9.0 kilometers per second?

SOLUTION

We can use the rocket equation (3) with $c = 2.38$ and $W_t/W_b = 18.7$:

$$\begin{aligned} v &= c \ln \frac{W_t}{W_b} \\ &= 2.38 \ln 18.7 \\ &= 6.97 \text{ kilometers per second} \end{aligned}$$

The velocity of the launch vehicle is far short of the 9.0 kilometers per second required to achieve orbit. This is why multiple-stage launchers are used—the deadweight from a preceding stage can be jettisoned into the ocean when the next stage takes over.

MATCHED PROBLEM 4

A launch vehicle using liquid fuel, such as a mixture of liquid hydrogen and liquid oxygen, can produce an exhaust velocity of $c = 4.7$ kilometers per second. However, the weight ratio W_t/W_b must be low—around 5.5 for some vehicles—because of the increased structural weight to accommodate the liquid fuel. How much more or less than the 9.0 kilometers per second required to reach orbit will be achieved by this vehicle?

› Data Analysis and Regression

Based on the logarithmic graphs we studied in the last section, when a quantity increases relatively rapidly at first, but then levels off and increases very slowly, it might be a good candidate to be modeled by a logarithmic function. Most graphing calculators with regression commands can fit functions of the form $y = a + b \ln x$ to a set of data points using the same techniques we used earlier for other types of regression.

EXAMPLE 5 Home Ownership Rates

Table 3 Home Ownership Rates

Year	Home Ownership Rate (%)
1940	43.6
1950	55.0
1960	61.9
1970	62.9
1980	64.4
1990	64.2
2000	67.4

The U.S. Census Bureau published the data in Table 3 on home ownership rates.

(A) Let x represent time in years with $x = 0$ representing 1900, and let y represent the corresponding home ownership rate. Use regression analysis on a graphing calculator to find a logarithmic function of the form $y = a + b \ln x$ that models the data. (Round the constants a and b to three significant digits.)

(B) Use your logarithmic function to predict the home ownership rate in 2010.

SOLUTIONS

(A) Figure 1 shows the details of constructing the model on a graphing calculator.

(B) The year 2010 corresponds to $x = 110$. Evaluating $y_1 = -36.7 + 23.0 \ln x$ at $x = 110$ predicts a home ownership rate of 71.4% in 2010.

(a) Data

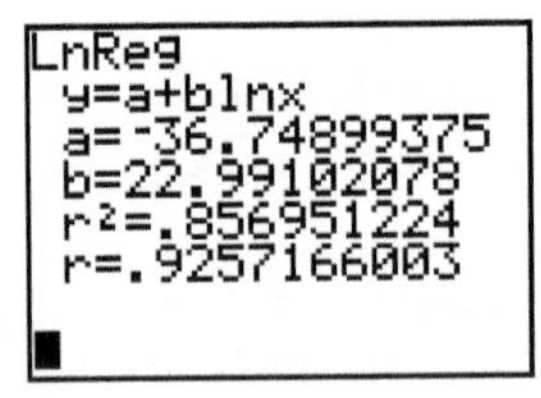

(b) Regression equation

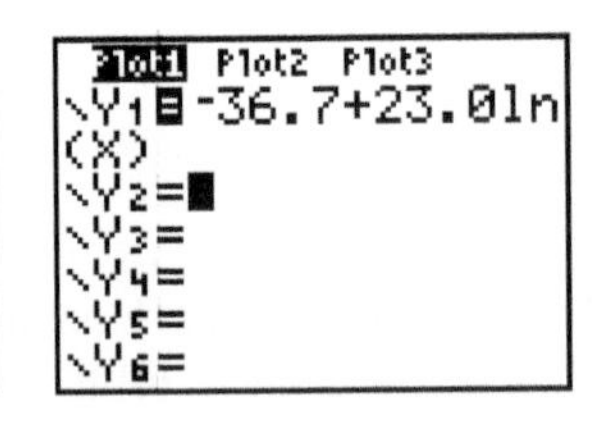

(c) Regression equation entered in equation editor

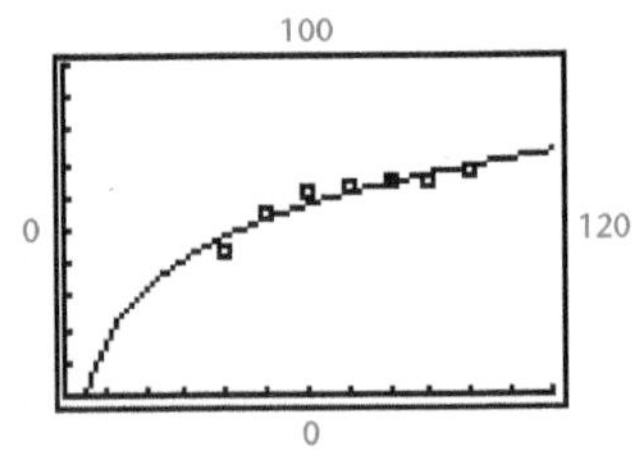

(d) Graph of data and regression equation

› **Figure 1**

MATCHED PROBLEM 5

Refer to Example 5. The home ownership rate in 1995 was 64.7%.

(A) Find a logarithmic regression equation for the expanded data set.

(B) Predict the home ownership rate in 2010.

ANSWERS TO MATCHED PROBLEMS

1. 95.05 decibels **2.** 7.80 **3.** 2.67 **4.** 1 kilometer per second less

5. (A) $-31.5 + 21.7 \ln x$ (B) 70.5%

4-4 Exercises

1. Describe the decibel scale in your own words.

2. Describe the Richter scale in your own words.

3. Explain why logarithms are a good choice for describing sound intensity and earthquake magnitude.

4. Think of a real-life quantity that is likely to be modeled well by a logarithmic function, and explain your reasoning.

APPLICATIONS

5. SOUND What is the decibel level of
(A) The threshold of hearing, 1.0×10^{-12} watts per square meter?
(B) The threshold of pain, 1.0 watt per square meter?
Compute answers to two significant digits.

6. SOUND What is the decibel level of
(A) A normal conversation, 3.2×10^{-6} watts per square meter?
(B) A jet plane with an afterburner, 8.3×10^{2} watts per square meter?
Compute answers to two significant digits.

7. SOUND If the intensity of a sound from one source is 1,000 times that of another, how much more is the decibel level of the louder sound than the quieter one?

8. SOUND If the intensity of a sound from one source is 10,000 times that of another, how much more is the decibel level of the louder sound than the quieter one?

9. EARTHQUAKES One of the strongest recorded earthquakes to date was in Colombia in 1906, with an energy release of 1.99×10^{17} joules. What was its magnitude on the Richter scale? Compute the answer to one decimal place.

10. EARTHQUAKES Anchorage, Alaska, had a major earthquake in 1964 that released 7.08×10^{16} joules of energy. What was its magnitude on the Richter scale? Compute the answer to one decimal place.

11. EARTHQUAKES The 1933 Long Beach, California, earthquake had a Richter scale reading of 6.3, and the 1964 Anchorage, Alaska, earthquake had a Richter scale reading of 8.3. How many times more powerful was the Anchorage earthquake than the Long Beach earthquake?

12. EARTHQUAKES Generally, an earthquake requires a magnitude of over 5.6 on the Richter scale to inflict serious damage. How many times more powerful than this was the great 1906 Colombia earthquake, which registered a magnitude of 8.6 on the Richter scale?

13. EXPLOSIVE ENERGY The atomic bomb dropped on Nagasaki, Japan, on August 9, 1945, released about 1.34×10^{14} joules of energy. What would be the magnitude of an earthquake that released that much energy?

14. EXPLOSIVE ENERGY The largest and most powerful nuclear weapon ever detonated was tested by the Soviet Union on October 30, 1961, on an island in the Arctic Sea. The blast was so powerful there were reports of windows breaking in Finland, over 700 miles away. The detonation released about 2.1×10^{17} joules of energy. What would be the magnitude of an earthquake that released that much energy?

15. ASTRONOMY A moderate-size solar flare observed on the sun on July 9, 1996, released enough energy to power the United States for almost 23,000 years at 2001 consumption levels, 2.38×10^{21} joules. What would be the magnitude of an earthquake that released that much energy?

16. CONSTRUCTION The energy released by a typical construction site explosion is about 7.94×10^{5} joules. What would be the magnitude of an earthquake that released that much energy?

17. SPACE VEHICLES A new solid-fuel rocket has a weight ratio $W_t/W_b = 19.8$ and an exhaust velocity $c = 2.57$ kilometers per second. What is its velocity at burnout? Compute the answer to two decimal places.

18. SPACE VEHICLES A liquid-fuel rocket has a weight ratio $W_t/W_b = 6.2$ and an exhaust velocity $c = 5.2$ kilometers per second. What is its velocity at burnout? Compute the answer to two decimal places.

19. CHEMISTRY The hydrogen ion concentration of a substance is related to its acidity and basicity. Because hydrogen ion concentrations vary over a very wide range, logarithms are used to create a compressed **pH scale,** which is defined as follows:

$$\text{pH} = -\log\,[\text{H}^+]$$

where $[\text{H}^+]$ is the hydrogen ion concentration, in moles per liter. Pure water has a pH of 7, which means it is neutral. Substances with a pH less than 7 are acidic, and those with a pH

greater than 7 are basic. Compute the pH of each substance listed, given the indicated hydrogen ion concentration. Also, indicate whether each substance is acidic or basic. Compute answers to one decimal place.
(A) Seawater, 4.63×10^{-9}
(B) Vinegar, 9.32×10^{-4}

20. CHEMISTRY Refer to Problem 19. Compute the pH of each substance below, given the indicated hydrogen ion concentration. Also, indicate whether it is acidic or basic. Compute answers to one decimal place.
(A) Milk, 2.83×10^{-7}
(B) Garden mulch, 3.78×10^{-6}

21. ECOLOGY Refer to Problem 19. Many lakes in Canada and the United States will no longer sustain some forms of wildlife because of the increase in acidity of the water from acid rain and snow caused by sulfur dioxide emissions from industry. If the pH of a sample of rainwater is 5.2, what is its hydrogen ion concentration in moles per liter? Compute the answer to two significant digits.

22. ECOLOGY Refer to Problem 19. If normal rainwater has a pH of 5.7, what is its hydrogen ion concentration in moles per liter? Compute the answer to two significant digits.

23. ASTRONOMY The brightness of stars is expressed in terms of magnitudes on a numerical scale that increases as the brightness decreases. The magnitude m is given by the formula

$$m = 6 - 2.5 \log \frac{L}{L_0}$$

where L is the light flux of the star and L_0 is the light flux of the dimmest stars visible to the naked eye.
(A) What is the magnitude of the dimmest stars visible to the naked eye?
(B) How many times brighter is a star of magnitude 1 than a star of magnitude 6?

24. ASTRONOMY An optical instrument is required to observe stars beyond the sixth magnitude, the limit of ordinary vision. However, even optical instruments have their limitations. The limiting magnitude L of any optical telescope with lens diameter D, in inches, is given by

$$L = 8.8 + 5.1 \log D$$

(A) Find the limiting magnitude for a homemade 6-inch reflecting telescope.
(B) Find the diameter of a lens that would have a limiting magnitude of 20.6.
Compute answers to three significant digits.

25. AGRICULTURE Table 4 shows the yield (bushels per acre) and the total production (millions of bushels) for corn in the United States for selected years since 1950. Let x represent years since 1900.

Table 4 United States Corn Production

Year	Yield (bushels per acre)	Total Production (million bushels)
1950	37.6	2,782
1960	55.6	3,479
1970	81.4	4,802
1980	97.7	6,867
1990	115.6	7,802
2000	137.0	9,915

Source: U.S. Department of Agriculture

(A) Find a logarithmic regression model ($y = a + b \ln x$) for the yield. Estimate (to one decimal place) the yield in 2003 and in 2010.
(B) The actual yield in 2003 was 142 bushels per acre. How does this compare with the estimated yield in part A? What effect with this additional 2003 information have on the estimate for 2010? Explain.

26. AGRICULTURE Refer to Table 4.
(A) Find a logarithmic regression model ($y = a + b \ln x$) for the total production. Estimate (to the nearest million) the production in 2003 and in 2010.
(B) The actual production in 2003 was 10,114 million bushels. How does this compare with the estimated production in part A? What effect will this 2003 production information have on the estimate for 2010? Explain.

4-5 Exponential and Logarithmic Equations

- Solving Exponential Equations
- Solving Logarithmic Equations

When quantities are modeled by exponential or logarithmic functions, it's not a surprise that solving equations involving expressions of these types is useful in studying those quantities.

Equations involving exponential and logarithmic functions, such as

$$2^{3x-2} = 5 \qquad \text{and} \qquad \log(x + 3) + \log x = 1$$

are called **exponential** and **logarithmic equations,** respectively. The properties of logarithms that we studied in Section 4-3 play a central role in their solution. Of course, a graphing calculator can be used to find approximate solutions for many exponential and logarithmic equations. However, there are situations in which the algebraic solution is necessary. In this section, we will emphasize algebraic solutions, but will still consider graphical solutions in many cases.

Solving Exponential Equations

The distinguishing feature of exponential equations is that the variable appears in an exponent. Before defining logarithms, we didn't have a reliable method for removing variables from an exponent: Now we do. To illustrate the idea, we return to the equation we considered at the beginning of Section 4-3, $3^x = 20$.

EXAMPLE 1 Solving an Exponential Equation

Solve $3^x = 20$. Round your answer to four decimal places.

SOLUTIONS

Algebraic Solution

The key is to apply a logarithmic function to each side, then use one of the properties of logs from Section 4-3.

$3^x = 20$ — Apply common or natural log to both sides.

$\ln 3^x = \ln 20$ — Use $\log_b N^p = p \log_b N$.

$x \ln 3 = \ln 20$ — Solve for x.

$$x = \frac{\ln 20}{\ln 3} \approx 2.7268$$

Notice that the solution is between 2 and 3, as we surmised at the beginning of Section 4-3 (since $3^2 = 9$ and $3^3 = 27$).

Graphical Solution

Graph $y_1 = 3^x$ and $y_2 = 20$ and use the INTERSECT command (Fig. 1).

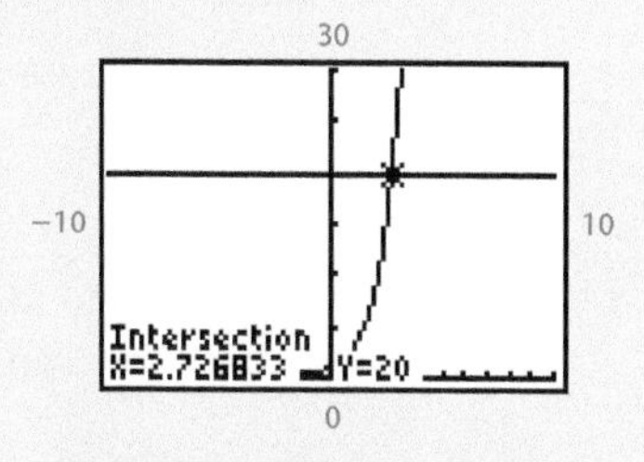

Figure 1 $y_1 = 3^x, y_2 = 20$.

The solution is $x = 2.7268$ to four decimal places.

MATCHED PROBLEM 1

Solve $5^x = 30$. Round your answer to four decimal places.

In Example 1, the choice of natural log to apply to both sides of the equation was unimportant. We could have chosen common log, or really log with any base. We'll usually choose either natural or common log because those are easiest to compute using a calculator.

In Example 2, we will use the technique of Example 1 on a slightly more complicated equation.

EXAMPLE 2 Solving an Exponential Equation

Solve $2^{3x-2} = 5$ for x to four decimal places.

SOLUTIONS

Algebraic Solution

Again, we will use logs to get x out of the exponent.

$2^{3x-2} = 5$ Take the common or natural log of both sides.

$\log 2^{3x-2} = \log 5$ Use $\log_b N^p = p \log_b N$ to get $3x - 2$ out of the exponent position.

$(3x - 2) \log 2 = \log 5$ Solve.

$3x - 2 = \dfrac{\log 5}{\log 2}$ *Remember:* $\dfrac{\log 5}{\log 2} \neq \log 5 - \log 2$.

$3x = 2 + \dfrac{\log 5}{\log 2}$ Multiply both sides by $\frac{1}{3}$.

$x = \dfrac{1}{3}\left(2 + \dfrac{\log 5}{\log 2}\right)$

$= 1.4406$ To four decimal places

Graphical Solution

Graph $y_1 = 2^{3x-2}$ and $y_2 = 5$ and use the INTERSECT command (Fig. 2).

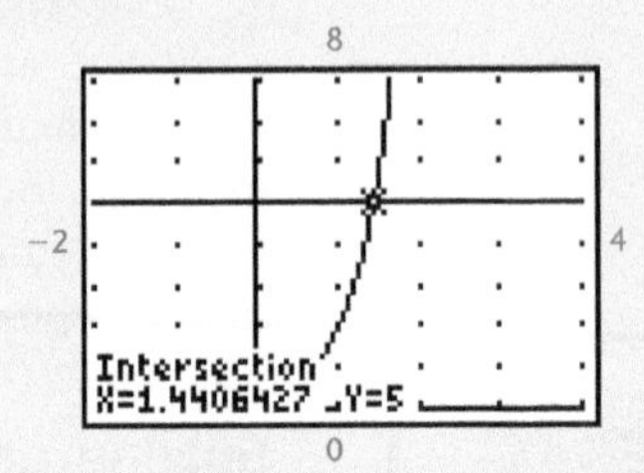

› **Figure 2** $y_1 = 2^{3x-2}, y_2 = 5$.

MATCHED PROBLEM 2

Solve $35^{1-2x} = 7$ for x to four decimal places.

Being able to solve exponential equations comes in handy when working with quantities that can be modeled with exponential functions.

EXAMPLE 3 Compound Interest

A certain amount of money P (principal) is invested at an annual rate r compounded annually. The amount of money A in the account after t years, assuming no withdrawals, is given by

$$A = P\left(1 + \frac{r}{m}\right)^n = P(1 + r)^n \quad m = 1 \text{ for annual compounding}$$

How many years to the nearest year will it take the money to double if it is invested at 6% compounded annually?

SOLUTIONS

Algebraic Solution

We don't know the original amount, so we'll have to just use P to represent it. We can substitute $r = 0.6$ to get

$$A = P(1.06)^n$$

We are asked to find the number of years (n) when the amount (A) equals twice the original amount ($2P$). So we substitute $2P$ for A and solve for n.

$$2P = P(1.06)^n \quad \text{Divide both sides by } P.$$
$$2 = 1.06^n \quad \text{Take the common or natural log of both sides.}$$
$$\log 2 = \log 1.06^n \quad \text{Note how log properties are used to get } n \text{ out of the exponent position.}$$
$$\log 2 = n \log 1.06 \quad \text{Solve for } n.$$
$$n = \frac{\log 2}{\log 1.06}$$
$$= 12 \text{ years} \quad \text{To the nearest year}$$

Graphical Solution

From the first part of the algebraic solution, we need to solve the equation $2 = 1.06^n$.

Graph $y_1 = 1.06^x$ and $y_2 = 2$ and use the INTERSECT command (Fig. 3).

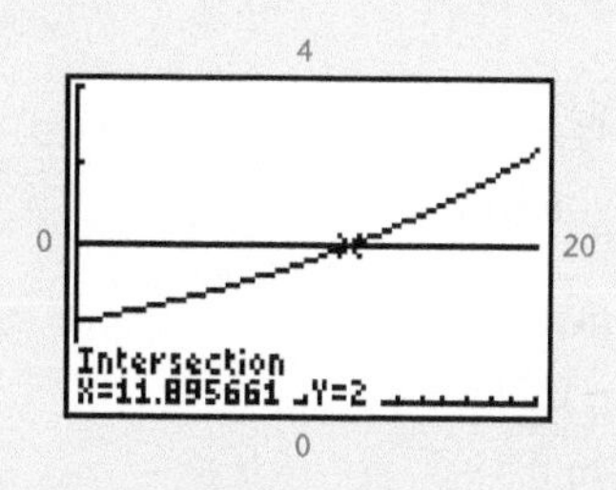

› **Figure 3** $y_1 = 1.06^x, y_2 = 2$.

The solution (rounded to the nearest year) is 12.

MATCHED PROBLEM 3

Repeat Example 3, changing the interest rate to 9% compounded annually.

››› CAUTION ›››

When solving exponential equations, it is crucial to first isolate the exponential expression before applying a log function to each side. [In Example 3, this entailed dividing both sides by P to isolate the exponential expression $(1.06)^n$.]

EXAMPLE 4 Atmospheric Pressure

The atmospheric pressure P, in pounds per square inch, at x miles above sea level is given approximately by

$$P = 14.7e^{-0.21x}$$

At what height will the atmospheric pressure be half the sea-level pressure? Compute the answer to two significant digits.

SOLUTIONS

Algebraic Solution

Since x represents miles above sea level, sea-level pressure is the pressure at $x = 0$:

$$P = 14.7e^{0} = 14.7$$

One-half of sea-level pressure is $14.7/2 = 7.35$. Now our problem is to find x so that $P = 7.35$; that is, we solve $7.35 = 14.7e^{-0.21x}$ for x:

$7.35 = 14.7e^{-0.21x}$ Divide both sides by 14.7 to isolate the exponential expression.

$0.5 = e^{-0.21x}$ Because the base is e, take the natural log of both sides.

$\ln 0.5 = \ln e^{-0.21x}$ Use the property $\ln e^a = a$.

$\ln 0.5 = -0.21x$ Solve for x.

$x = \dfrac{\ln 0.5}{-0.21}$

$= 3.3$ miles To two significant digits.

Graphical Solution

From the first part of the algebraic solution, we need to solve $7.35 = 14.7e^{-0.21x}$.

Graph $y_1 = 14.7e^{-0.21x}$ and $y_2 = 7.35$ and use the INTERSECT command (Fig. 4).

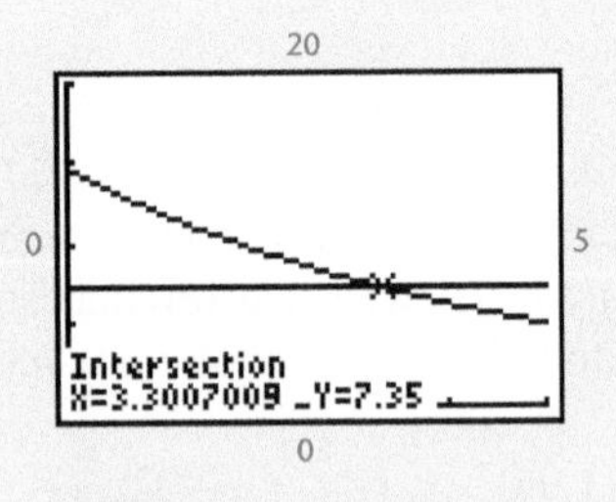

› **Figure 4** $y_1 = 14.7e^{-0.21x}$, $y_2 = 7.35$.

MATCHED PROBLEM 4

Using the formula in Example 4, find the altitude in miles so that the atmospheric pressure will be one-eighth that at sea level. Compute the answer to two significant digits.

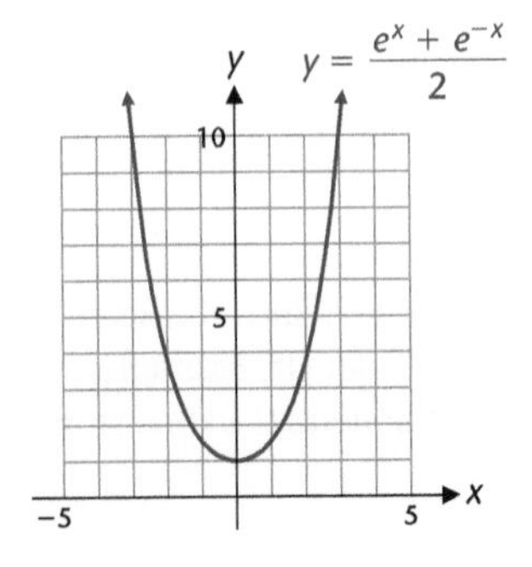

› **Figure 5** Catenary.

Many people assume that a cable hanging between two fixed points (think of utility wires between two poles) are parabolas, but actually they are not. Instead, they follow the shape of the graph in Figure 5, known as a **catenary.** Catenaries are important in engineering and architecture, and are often studied in calculus. The graph of the equation

$$y = \frac{e^x + e^{-x}}{2} \tag{1}$$

is an example of a catenary.

EXAMPLE 5 Solving an Exponential Equation

Given equation (1), find x for $y = 2.5$. Compute the answer to four decimal places.

SOLUTIONS

Algebraic Solution

$$y = \frac{e^x + e^{-x}}{2}$$ Substitute $y = 2.5$.

$$2.5 = \frac{e^x + e^{-x}}{2}$$ Multiply both sides by 2 to clear fractions.

$$5 = e^x + e^{-x}$$ Multiply both sides by e^x to eliminate negative exponents.

$$5e^x = e^{2x} + 1$$ Rearrange so that zero is on one side.

$$e^{2x} - 5e^x + 1 = 0$$ Use the quadratic formula.

Let $u = e^x$, then

$$u^2 - 5u + 1 = 0$$

$$u = \frac{5 \pm \sqrt{25 - 4(1)(1)}}{2}$$

$$= \frac{5 \pm \sqrt{21}}{2}$$ Replace u with e^x and solve for x.

$$e^x = \frac{5 \pm \sqrt{21}}{2}$$ Take the natural log of both sides (both values on the right are positive).

$$\ln e^x = \ln\frac{5 \pm \sqrt{21}}{2}$$ Use $\ln e^x = x$.

$$x = \ln\frac{5 \pm \sqrt{21}}{2}$$

$$= -1.5668, 1.5668$$

Note that the algebraic method produces exact solutions, an important consideration in certain calculus applications (see Problems 69–72 in Exercises 4-5).

Graphical Solution

Graph $y_1 = (e^x + e^{-x})/2$ and $y_2 = 2.5$ and use the INTERSECT command (Fig. 6).

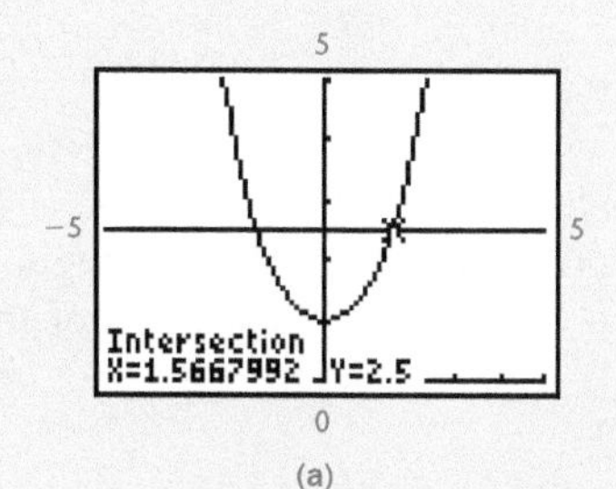

(a)

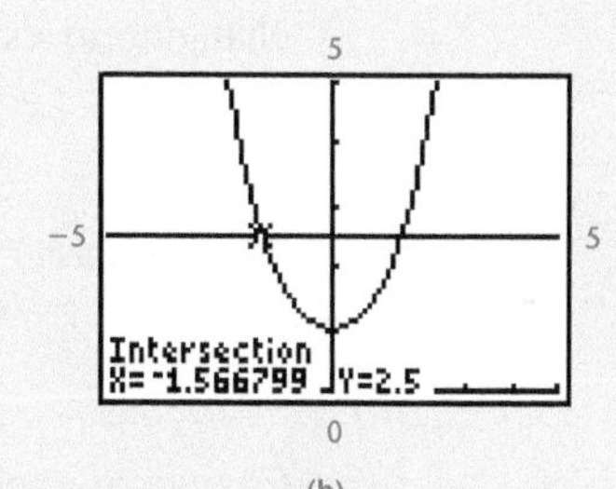

(b)

Figure 6 $y_1 = \frac{e^x + e^{-x}}{2}, y_2 = 2.5.$

The two solutions are $x = -1.5668$ and $x = 1.5668$ to four decimal places.

MATCHED PROBLEM 5

Given $y = (e^x - e^{-x})/2$, find x for $y = 1.5$. Compute the answer to three decimal places.

››› EXPLORE-DISCUSS 1

Let $y = e^{2x} + 3e^{x} + e^{-x}$

(A) Try to find x when $y = 7$ using the method of Example 5. Explain the difficulty that arises.

(B) Use a graphing calculator to find x when $y = 7$.

› Solving Logarithmic Equations

We will begin our study of solving logarithmic equations with a key observation. For equations of the form

$$\log_b x = a$$

changing to exponential form solves the equation, as in Example 6.

EXAMPLE 6

Solve $\log_5 x = 3$.

SOLUTION

Change to exponential form:

$$5^3 = x$$
$$x = 125$$

MATCHED PROBLEM 6

Solve $\log_2 x = -4$.

Obviously, this is a very simple example, but it provides some valuable insight in solving logarithmic equations. If we can reduce an equation to the form $\log_b(\text{expression}) = a$, where "expression" is something involving the variable, then changing to exponential form should result in an equation we already know how to solve.

EXAMPLE 7 Solving a Logarithmic Equation

Solve $\log(x+3) + \log x = 1$, and check.

SOLUTIONS

Algebraic Solution

First use properties of logarithms to express the left side as a single logarithm, then convert to exponential form and solve for x, as in Example 6.

$$\log(x+3) + \log x = 1$$ Combine left side using $\log M + \log N = \log MN$.

$$\log[x(x+3)] = 1$$ Change to equivalent exponential form.

$$x(x+3) = 10^1$$ Write in $ax^2 + bx + c = 0$ form and solve.

$$x^2 + 3x - 10 = 0$$ Factor.

$$(x+5)(x-2) = 0$$

$$x = -5, 2$$

CHECK

$x = -5$: $\log(-5+3) + \log(-5)$ is not defined because the domain of the log function is $(0, \infty)$.

$x = 2$: $\log(2+3) + \log 2 = \log 5 + \log 2 = \log(5 \cdot 2) = \log 10 \overset{\checkmark}{=} 1$

The only solution to the original equation is $x = 2$. Remember, solutions should be checked in the original equation to see whether any should be discarded.

Graphical Solution

Graph $y_1 = \log(x+3) + \log x$ and $y_2 = 1$ and use the INTERSECT command. Figure 7 shows that $x = 2$ is a solution, and also shows that y_1 (the left side of the original equation) is not defined at $x = -5$, the extraneous solution produced by the algebraic method.

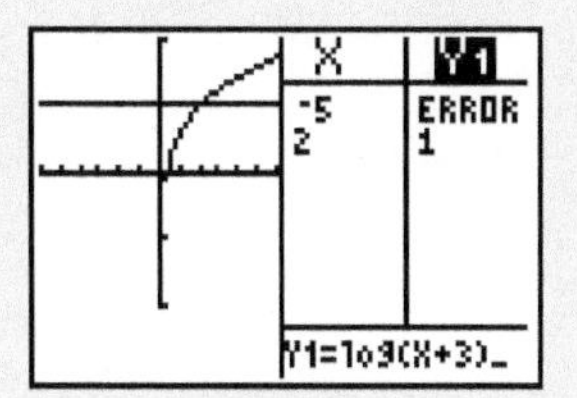

› Figure 7
$y_1 = \log(x+3) + \log x$,
$y_2 = 1$.

MATCHED PROBLEM 7

Solve $\log(x-15) = 2 - \log x$, and check.

››› CAUTION ›››

It's important to check your answer when solving logarithmic equations. Because log functions are undefined for negative inputs, extraneous solutions are common.

EXAMPLE 8 Solving a Logarithmic Equation

Solve $(\ln x)^2 = \ln x^2$.

SOLUTIONS

Algebraic Solution

There are no logarithmic properties for simplifying $(\ln x)^2$. However, we can simplify $\ln x^2$, obtaining an equation involving $\ln x$ and $(\ln x)^2$.

$$(\ln x)^2 = \ln x^2 \quad \text{Use } \log_b N^p = p \log_b N.$$
$$(\ln x)^2 = 2 \ln x \quad \text{Rearrange so that zero is on one side.}$$
$$(\ln x)^2 - 2 \ln x = 0 \quad \text{Factor out } \ln x.$$
$$(\ln x)(\ln x - 2) = 0 \quad \text{Set each factor equal to zero.}$$
$$\ln x = 0 \quad \text{or} \quad \ln x - 2 = 0$$
$$\ln x = 0 \quad \text{or} \quad \ln x = 2 \quad \text{Change to exponential form. Recall that } \ln x = \log_e x.$$
$$e^0 = x \quad \text{or} \quad e^2 = x$$
$$x = 1, e^2$$

Checking that both $x = 1$ and $x = e^2$ are solutions to the original equation is left to you. Don't let us down.

Graphical Solution

Graph $y_1 = (\ln x)^2$ and $y_2 = \ln x^2$ and use the INTERSECT command to obtain the solutions $x = 1$ and $x = 7.3890561$ (Fig. 8). The second solution is not exact; it is an approximation to e^2.

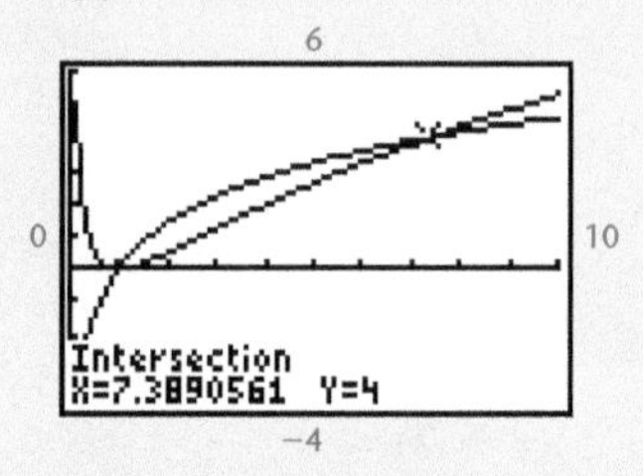

› Figure 8

MATCHED PROBLEM 8

Solve $\log x^2 = (\log x)^2$.

››› CAUTION ›››

Note that

$$(\log_b x)^2 \neq \log_b x^2 \qquad (\log_b x)^2 = (\log_b x)(\log_b x) \quad \log_b x^2 = 2 \log_b x$$

You might find it helpful to keep these straight by writing $\log_b x^2$ as $\log_b (x^2)$.

EXAMPLE 9 Earthquake Intensity

Recall from the last section that the magnitude of an earthquake on the Richter scale is given by

$$M = \frac{2}{3}\log\frac{E}{E_0}$$

Solve for E in terms of the other symbols.

SOLUTION

$$M = \frac{2}{3}\log\frac{E}{E_0} \quad \text{Multiply both sides by } \tfrac{3}{2}.$$

$$\log\frac{E}{E_0} = \frac{3M}{2} \quad \text{Change to exponential form.}$$

$$\frac{E}{E_0} = 10^{3M/2} \quad \text{Multiply both sides by } E_0.$$

$$E = E_0 10^{3M/2}$$

MATCHED PROBLEM 9

Solve the rocket equation from the last section for W_b in terms of the other symbols:

$$v = c\ln\frac{W_t}{W_b}$$

ANSWERS TO MATCHED PROBLEMS

1. 2.1133 **2.** $x = 0.2263$
3. More than double in 9 years, but not quite double in 8 years
4. 9.9 miles **5.** $x = 1.195$ **6.** $x = \frac{1}{16}$
7. $x = 20$ **8.** $x = 1{,}100$ **9.** $W_b = W_t e^{-v/c}$

4-5 Exercises

1. Which property of logarithms do you think is most useful in solving exponential equations? Explain.

2. Which properties of logarithms do you think are most useful in solving equations with more than one logarithm? Explain.

3. If u and v represent expressions with variable x, how can you solve equations of the form $\log_b u = \log_b v$ for x? Explain why this works.

4. Why is it especially important to check answers when solving logarithmic equations?

5. Explain the difference between $(\ln x)^2$ and $\ln x^2$.

6. When solving logarithmic and exponential equations, what is the advantage of solving algebraically, rather than graphically?

Solve Problems 7–22 algebraically and graphically. Round answers to three significant digits.

7. $10^{-x} = 0.0347$ **8.** $10^{x} = 14.3$

9. $10^{3x+1} = 92$ **10.** $10^{5x-2} = 348$

11. $e^{x} = 3.65$ **12.** $e^{-x} = 0.0142$

13. $e^{2x-1} = 405$ **14.** $e^{3x+5} = 23.8$

15. $5^{x} = 18$ **16.** $3^{x} = 4$

17. $2^{-x} = 0.238$ **18.** $3^{-x} = 0.074$

19. $\log_5 (2x - 7) = 2$ **20.** $\log_2 (4 - x) = 4$

21. $\log_3 (x^2 - 8x) = 2$ **22.** $\log_2 (x^2 + 5) = 3$

Solve Problems 23–32 exactly.

23. $\log 5 + \log x = 2$ **24.** $\log x - \log 8 = 1$

25. $\log x + \log (x - 3) = 1$

26. $\log (x - 9) + \log 100x = 3$

27. $\log (x + 1) - \log (x - 1) = 1$

28. $\log (2x + 1) = 1 + \log (x - 2)$

29. $\ln (4x - 3) = \ln (x + 1)$

30. $\log_5 (2 - x) = \log_5 (3x + 8)$

31. $\log_2 (x^2 - 2x) = \log_2 (3x - 6)$

32. $\log_7 (x + 1) = \log_7 (2x^2 - x - 3)$

Solve Problems 33–44 algebraically and graphically. Round answers to three significant digits.

33. $2 = 1.05^{x}$ **34.** $3 = 1.06^{x}$

35. $e^{-1.4x} = 13$ **36.** $e^{0.32x} = 632$

37. $5 + 3^{x} = 10$ **38.** $-3 = (\frac{1}{2})^{x} - 12$

39. $10^{2x+5} - 7 = 13$ **40.** $3 - 4^{7-x} = -16$

41. $123 = 500e^{-0.12x}$ **42.** $438 = 200e^{0.25x}$

43. $e^{-x^2} = 0.23$ **44.** $e^{x^2} = 125$

Solve Problems 45–56 exactly.

45. $\log x - \log 5 = \log 2 - \log (x - 3)$

46. $\log (6x + 5) - \log 3 = \log 2 - \log x$

47. $\ln x = \ln (2x - 1) - \ln (x - 2)$

48. $\ln (x + 1) = \ln (3x + 1) - \ln x$

49. $\log (2x + 1) = 1 - \log (x - 1)$

50. $1 - \log (x - 2) = \log (3x + 1)$

51. $(\ln x)^3 = \ln x^4$ **52.** $(\log x)^3 = \log x^4$

53. $\ln (\ln x) = 1$ **54.** $\log (\log x) = 1$

55. $x^{\log x} = 100x$ **56.** $3^{\log x} = 3x$

In Problems 57–60,
(A) Explain the difficulty in solving the equation exactly.
(B) Determine the number of solutions by graphing the functions on each side of the equation.

57. $e^{x/2} = 5 \ln x$ **58.** $\ln (\ln x) + \ln x = 2$

59. $3^{x} + 2 = 7 + x - e^{-x}$ **60.** $e^{x/4} = 5 \log x + 4 \ln x$

Solve Problems 61–68 for the indicated variable in terms of the remaining symbols. Use the natural log for solving exponential equations.

61. $A = Pe^{rt}$ for r (finance)

62. $A = P\left(1 + \frac{r}{n}\right)^{nt}$ for t (finance)

63. $D = 10 \log \frac{I}{I_0}$ for I (sound)

64. $t = \frac{-1}{k}(\ln A - \ln A_0)$ for A (decay)

65. $M = 6 - 2.5 \log \frac{I}{I_0}$ for I (astronomy)

66. $L = 8.8 + 5.1 \log D$ for D (astronomy)

67. $I = \frac{E}{R}(1 - e^{-Rt/L})$ for t (circuitry)

68. $S = R\frac{(1 + i)^n - 1}{i}$ for n (annuity)

The following combinations of exponential functions define four of six ***hyperbolic functions,*** *an important class of functions in calculus and higher mathematics. Solve Problems 69–72 for x in terms of y. The results are used to define* ***inverse hyperbolic functions,*** *another important class of functions in calculus and higher mathematics.*

69. $y = \frac{e^x + e^{-x}}{2}$

70. $y = \frac{e^x - e^{-x}}{2}$

71. $y = \frac{e^x - e^{-x}}{e^x + e^{-x}}$

72. $y = \frac{e^x + e^{-x}}{e^x - e^{-x}}$

In Problems 73–84, use a graphing calculator to approximate to two decimal places any solutions of the equation in the interval $0 \le x \le 1$. None of these equations can be solved exactly using any step-by-step algebraic process.

73. $2^{-x} - 2x = 0$

74. $3^{-x} - 3x = 0$

75. $x3^x - 1 = 0$

76. $x2^x - 1 = 0$

77. $e^{-x} - x = 0$

78. $xe^{2x} - 1 = 0$

79. $xe^x - 2 = 0$

80. $e^{-x} - 2x = 0$

81. $\ln x + 2x = 0$

82. $\ln x + x^2 = 0$

83. $\ln x + e^x = 0$

84. $\ln x + x = 0$

APPLICATIONS

85. COMPOUND INTEREST How many years, to the nearest year, will it take a sum of money to double if it is invested at 15% compounded annually?

86. COMPOUND INTEREST How many years, to the nearest year, will it take money to quadruple if it is invested at 20% compounded annually?

87. COMPOUND INTEREST At what annual rate compounded continuously will $1,000 have to be invested to grow to $2,500 in 10 years? Compute the answer to three significant digits.

88. COMPOUND INTEREST How many years will it take $5,000 to grow to $8,000 if it is invested at an annual rate of 9% compounded continuously? Compute the answer to three significant digits.

89. IMMIGRATION According to the U.S. Office of Immigration Statistics, there were 10.5 million illegal immigrants in the United States in May 2005, and that number had grown to 11.3 million by May 2007.
(A) Find the relative growth rate if we use the $P = P_0e^{rt}$ model for population growth. Round to three significant digits.
(B) Use your answer from part A to write a function describing the illegal immigrant population in millions in terms of years after May 2005, and use it to predict when the illegal immigrant population should reach 20 million.

90. POPULATION GROWTH According to U.S. Census Bureau estimates, the population of the United States was 227.2 million on July 1, 1980, and 249.5 million on July 1, 1990.
(A) Find the relative growth rate if we use the $P = P_0e^{rt}$ model for population growth. Round to three significant digits.
(B) Use your answer from part A to write a function describing the population of the United States in millions in terms of years after July 1980, and use it to predict when the population should reach 400 million.
(C) Use your function from part B to estimate the population of the United States today, then compare your estimate to the one found at www.census.gov/population/www/popclockus.html.

91. WORLD POPULATION A mathematical model for world population growth over short periods is given by

$$P = P_0e^{rt}$$

where P is the population after t years, P_0 is the population at $t = 0$, and the population is assumed to grow continuously at the annual rate r. How many years, to the nearest year, will it take the world population to double if it grows continuously at an annual rate of 1.14%?

92. WORLD POPULATION Refer to Problem 91. Starting with a world population of 6.5 billion people and assuming that the population grows continuously at an annual rate of 1.14%, how many years, to the nearest year, will it be before there is only 1 square yard of land per person? Earth contains approximately 1.7×10^{14} square yards of land.

93. MEDICAL RESEARCH A medical researcher is testing a radioactive isotope for use in a new imaging process. She finds that an original sample of 5 grams decays to 1 gram in 6 hours. Find the half-life of the sample to three significant digits. [Recall that the half-life model is $A = A_0(\frac{1}{2})^{t/h}$, where A_0 is the original amount and h is the half-life.]

94. CARBON-14 DATING If 90% of a sample of carbon-14 remains after 866 years, what is the half-life of carbon-14? (See Problem 93 for the half-life model.)

As long as a plant or animal remains alive, carbon-14 is maintained in a constant amount in its tissues. Once dead, however, the plant or animal ceases taking in carbon, and carbon-14 diminishes by radioactive decay. The amount remaining can be modeled by the equation $A = A_0e^{-0.000124t}$, where A is the amount after t years, and A_0 is the amount at time $t = 0$. Use this model to solve Problems 95–98.

95. CARBON-14 DATING In 2003, Japanese scientists announced the beginning of an effort to bring the long-extinct woolly mammoth back to life using modern cloning techniques. Their efforts were focused on an especially well-preserved specimen discovered frozen in the Siberian ice. Nearby samples of plant material were found to have 28.9% of the amount of carbon-14 in a living sample. What was the approximate age of these samples?

96. CARBON-14 DATING In 2004, archaeologist Al Goodyear discovered a site in South Carolina that contains evidence of the earliest human settlement in North America. Carbon dating of burned plant material indicated 0.2% of the amount of carbon-14 in a live sample. How old was that sample?

97. CARBON-14 DATING Many scholars believe that the earliest nonnative settlers of North America were Vikings who sailed from Iceland. If a fragment of a wooden tool found and dated in 2004 had 88.3% of the amount of carbon-14 in a living sample, when was this tool made?

98. CARBON-14 DATING In 1998, the Shroud of Turin was examined by researchers, who found that plant fibers in the fabric had 92.1% of the amount of carbon-14 in a living sample. If this is accurate, when was the fabric made?

99. PHOTOGRAPHY An electronic flash unit for a camera is activated when a capacitor is discharged through a filament of wire. After the flash is triggered and the capacitor is discharged, the circuit (see the figure) is connected and the battery pack generates a current to recharge the capacitor. The time it takes for the capacitor to recharge is called the *recycle time.* For a particular flash unit using a 12-volt battery pack, the charge q, in coulombs, on the capacitor t seconds after recharging has started is given by

$$q = 0.0009(1 - e^{-0.2t})$$

How many seconds will it take the capacitor to reach a charge of 0.0007 coulomb? Compute the answer to three significant digits.

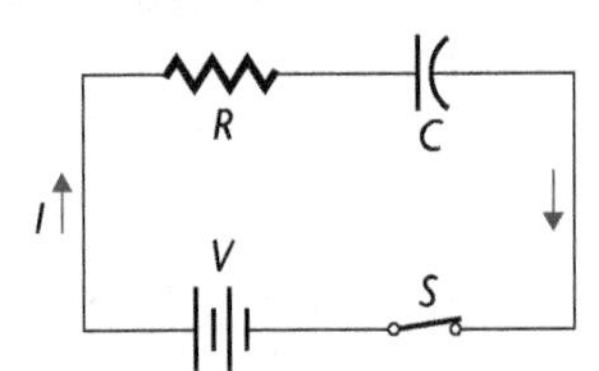

100. ADVERTISING A company is trying to expose as many people as possible to a new product through television advertising in a large metropolitan area with 2 million possible viewers. A model for the number of people N, in millions, who are aware of the product after t days of advertising was found to be

$$N = 2(1 - e^{-0.037t})$$

How many days, to the nearest day, will the advertising campaign have to last so that 80% of the possible viewers will be aware of the product?

101. NEWTON'S LAW OF COOLING This law states that the rate at which an object cools is proportional to the difference in temperature between the object and its surrounding medium. The temperature T of the object t hours later is given by

$$T = T_m + (T_0 - T_m)e^{-kt}$$

where T_m is the temperature of the surrounding medium and T_0 is the temperature of the object at $t = 0$. Suppose a bottle of wine at a room temperature of 72°F is placed in a refrigerator at 40°F to cool before a dinner party. After an hour the temperature of the wine is found to be 61.5°F. Find the constant k, to two decimal places, and the time, to one decimal place, it will take the wine to cool from 72 to 50°F.

102. MARINE BIOLOGY Marine life is dependent upon the microscopic plant life that exists in the *photic zone,* a zone that goes to a depth where about 1% of the surface light still remains. Light intensity is reduced according to the exponential function

$$I = I_0 e^{-kd}$$

where I is the intensity d feet below the surface and I_0 is the intensity at the surface. The constant k is called the *coefficient of extinction.* At Crystal Lake in Wisconsin it was found that half the surface light remained at a depth of 14.3 feet. Find k, and find the depth of the photic zone. Compute answers to three significant digits.

Problems 103–106 are based on the Richter scale equation from Section 4-4, $M = \frac{2}{3} \log \frac{E}{10^{4.40}}$, where M is the magnitude and E is the amount of energy in joules released by the earthquake. Round all calculations to three significant digits.

103. EARTHQUAKES There were 11 earthquakes recorded worldwide in 2005 with magnitude at least 7.0.
(A) How much energy is released by a magnitude 7.0 earthquake?
(B) The total average daily consumption of energy for the entire United States in 2006 was 2.88×10^{14} joules. How many days could the energy released by a magnitude 7.0 earthquake power the United States?

104. EARTHQUAKES On December 26, 2004, a magnitude 9.0 earthquake struck in the Indian Ocean, causing a massive tsunami that resulted in over 230,000 deaths.
(A) How much energy was released by this earthquake?
(B) The total average daily consumption of energy for the entire United States in 2006 was 2.88×10^{14} joules. How many days could the energy released by a magnitude 9.0 earthquake power the United States?

105. EARTHQUAKES There were 10 earthquakes worldwide in 2005 with magnitudes between 7.0 and 7.9. Assume that these earthquakes had an average magnitude of 7.5. How long could the total energy released by these ten earthquakes power the United States, which had a total energy consumption of 1.05×10^{17} joules in 2006?

106. EARTHQUAKES There were 144 earthquakes worldwide in 2005 with magnitudes between 6.0 and 6.9. Assume that these earthquakes had an average magnitude of 6.5. How long could the total energy released by these 144 earthquakes power the United States, which had a total energy consumption of 1.05×10^{17} joules in 2006?

CHAPTER 4 Review

4-1 Exponential Functions

The equation $f(x) = b^x, b > 0, b \neq 1$, defines an **exponential function** with **base *b***. The domain of f is $(-\infty, \infty)$ and the range is $(0, \infty)$. The graph of f is a continuous curve that has no sharp corners; passes through $(0, 1)$; lies above the x axis, which is a horizontal asymptote; increases as x increases if $b > 1$; decreases as x increases if $b < 1$; and intersects any horizontal line at most once. The function f is one-to-one and has an inverse. The following **exponential function properties** are useful in working with these functions.

1. $a^x a^y = a^{x+y}$ $\quad (a^x)^y = a^{xy}$ $\quad (ab)^x = a^x b^x$

   $\left(\frac{a}{b}\right)^x = \frac{a^x}{b^x}$ $\quad \frac{a^x}{a^y} = a^{x-y}$

2. $a^x = a^y$ if and only if $x = y$.

3. For $x \neq 0$, $a^x = b^x$ if and only if $a = b$.

As x approaches ∞, the expression $[1 + (1/x)]^x$ approaches the irrational number $e \approx 2.718\,281\,828\,459$. The function $f(x) = e^x$ is called the **exponential function with base *e*.** The growth of money in an account paying **compound interest** is described by $A = P(1 + r/m)^n$, where P is the **principal,** r is the annual **rate,** m is the number of compounding periods in 1 year, and A is the **amount** in the account after n compounding periods.

If the account pays **interest compounded continuously,** the amount A in the account after t years is given by $A = Pe^{rt}$.

4-2 Exponential Models

Exponential functions are used to model various types of growth:

1. *Population growth* can be modeled by using the **doubling time growth model** $A = A_0 2^{t/d}$, where A is the population at time t, A_0 is the population at time $t = 0$, and d is the **doubling time**—the time it takes for the population to double. Another model of population growth, $A = A_0 e^{kt}$, where A_0 is the population at time zero and k is a positive constant called the **relative growth rate**, uses the exponential function with base e. This model is used for many other types of quantities that exhibit exponential growth as well.

2. *Radioactive decay* can be modeled by using the **half-life decay model** $A = A_0(\frac{1}{2})^{t/h} = A_0 2^{-t/h}$, where A is the amount at time t, A_0 is the amount at time $t = 0$, and h is the **half-life**—the time it takes for half the material to decay. Another model of radioactive decay, $A = A_0 e^{-kt}$, where A_0 is the amount at time zero and k is a positive constant, uses the exponential function with base e. This model can be used for other types of quantities that exhibit negative exponential growth as well.

3. *Limited growth*—the growth of a company or proficiency at learning a skill, for example—can often be modeled by the equation $y = A(1 - e^{-kt})$, where A and k are positive constants.

Logistic growth is another limited growth model that is useful for modeling phenomena like the spread of an epidemic, or sales of a new product. The logistic model is $y = M/(1 + ce^{-kt})$, where c, k, and M are positive constants. A good comparison of these different exponential models can be found in Table 3 at the end of Section 4-2.

Exponential regression can be used to fit a function of the form $y = ab^x$ to a set of data points. Logistic regression can be use to find a function of the form $y = c/(1 + ae^{-bx})$.

4-3 Logarithmic Functions

The **logarithmic function with base *b*** is defined to be the inverse of the exponential function with base b and is denoted by $y = \log_b x$. Thus, $y = \log_b x$ if and only if $x = b^y, b > 0, b \neq 1$. This relationship can be used to convert an expression from logarithmic to exponential form, and vice versa.

The domain of a logarithmic function is $(0, \infty)$ and the range is $(-\infty, \infty)$. The graph of a logarithmic function is a continuous curve that always passes through the point $(1, 0)$ and has the y axis as a vertical asymptote. The following **properties of logarithmic functions** are useful in working with these functions:

1. $\log_b 1 = 0$
2. $\log_b b = 1$
3. $\log_b b^x = x$
4. $b^{\log_b x} = x, x > 0$
5. $\log_b M = \log_b N$ if and only if $M = N$
6. $\log_b MN = \log_b M + \log_b N$
7. $\log_b \frac{M}{N} = \log_b M - \log_b N$
8. $\log_b M^p = p \log_b M$

Logarithms to the base 10 are called **common logarithms** and are denoted by $\log x$. Logarithms to the base e are called **natural**

logarithms and are denoted by $\ln x$. Thus, $\log x = y$ is equivalent to $x = 10^y$, and $\ln x = y$ is equivalent to $x = e^y$.

The **change-of-base formula,** $\log_b N = (\log_a N)/(\log_a b)$, relates logarithms to two different bases and can be used, along with a calculator, to evaluate logarithms to bases other than e or 10.

4-4 Logarithmic Models

Logarithmic functions increase very slowly as the input gets very large, so they can be used to scale down quantities that involve very large numbers, like the intensity of sound waves and the energy released by earthquakes.

The following applications involve logarithmic functions:

1. The **decibel** is defined by $D = 10 \log (I/I_0)$, where D is the **decibel level** of a sound, I is the **intensity** of the sound, and $I_0 = 10^{-12}$ watts per square meter is a standardized sound level.

2. The **magnitude** M of an earthquake on the **Richter scale** is given by $M = \frac{2}{3} \log (E/E_0)$, where E is the energy released by the earthquake and $E_0 = 10^{4.40}$ joules is a standardized energy level.

3. The **velocity** v of a rocket at burnout is given by the **rocket equation** $v = c \ln(W_t/W_b)$, where c is the exhaust velocity, W_t is the takeoff weight, and W_b is the burnout weight.

Logarithmic regression is used to fit a function of the form $y = a + b \ln x$ to a set of data points.

4-5 Exponential and Logarithmic Equations

Exponential equations are equations in which the variable appears in an exponent. If the exponential expression is isolated, applying a logarithmic function to both sides and using the property $\log_b N^p = p \log_b N$ will enable you to remove the variable from the exponent. If the exponential expression is not isolated, we can use previously developed techniques to first solve for the exponential, then solve as above.

Logarithmic equations are equations in which the variable appears inside a logarithmic function. In most cases, the key to solving them is to change the equation to the equivalent exponential expression. For equations with multiple log expressions, properties of logarithms can be used to combine the expressions before solving.

CHAPTER 4 Review Exercises

Work through all the problems in this chapter review and check answers in the back of the book. Answers to all review problems are there, and following each answer is a number in italics indicating the section in which that type of problem is discussed. Where weaknesses show up, review appropriate sections in the text.

1. Match each equation with the graph of f, g, m, or n in the figure.

(A) $y = \log_2 x$ (B) $y = 0.5^x$

(C) $y = \log_{0.5} x$ (D) $y = 2^x$

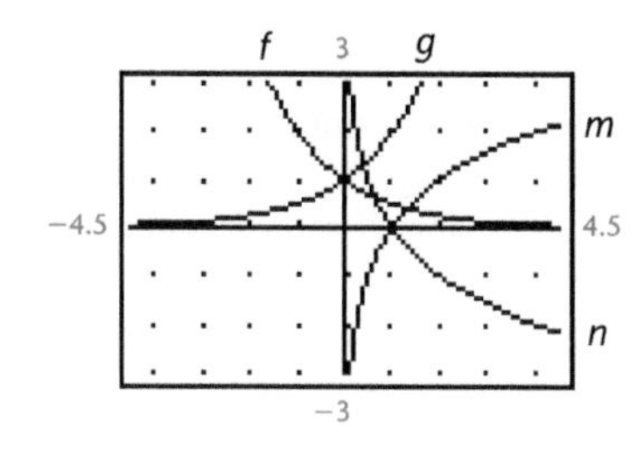

2. Write in logarithmic form using base 10: $m = 10^n$.

3. Write in logarithmic form using base e: $x = e^y$.

Write Problems 4 and 5 in exponential form.

4. $\log x = y$ **5.** $\ln y = x$

6. (A) Plot at least five points, then draw a hand sketch of the graph of $y = (\frac{4}{3})^x$.

(B) Use your result from part A to sketch the graph of $y = \log_{4/3} x$.

In Problems 7 and 8, simplify using properties of exponents.

7. $\dfrac{7^{x+2}}{7^{2-x}}$ **8.** $\left(\dfrac{e^x}{e^{-x}}\right)^x$

Solve Problems 9–11 for x exactly. Do not use a calculator or table.

9. $\log_2 x = 3$ **10.** $\log_x 25 = 2$ **11.** $\log_3 27 = x$

Solve Problems 12–15 for x to three significant digits.

12. $10^x = 17.5$

13. $e^x = 143{,}000$

14. $\ln x = -0.015\ 73$

15. $\log x = 2.013$

Evaluate Problems 16–19 to four significant digits using a calculator.

16. $\ln \pi$

17. $\log(-e)$

18. $\pi^{\ln 2}$

19. $\dfrac{e^{\pi} + e^{-\pi}}{2}$

20. Write as a single log: $\log x + 3 \log y - \frac{1}{2} \log z$

21. Write in terms of $\ln x$ and $\ln y$: $\ln \frac{x^3}{y}$

Solve Problems 22–34 for x exactly. Do not use a calculator or table.

22. $\ln(2x - 1) = \ln(x + 3)$

23. $\log(x^2 - 3) = 2 \log(x - 1)$

24. $e^{x^2-3} = e^{2x}$

25. $4^{x-1} = 2^{1-x}$

26. $4 - 3^x = 2$

27. $5 + \frac{1}{2}e^x = \frac{17}{2}$

28. $2x^2e^{-x} = 18e^{-x}$

29. $\log_{1/4} 16 = x$

30. $\log_x 9 = -2$

31. $\log_{16} x = \frac{3}{2}$

32. $\log_x e^5 = 5$

33. $10^{\log_{10} x} = 33$

34. $\ln x = 0$

Solve Problems 35–44 for x to three significant digits.

35. $x = 2(10^{1.32})$

36. $x = \log_5 23$

37. $\ln x = -3.218$

38. $x = \log(2.156 \times 10^{-7})$

39. $x = \dfrac{\ln 4}{\ln 2.31}$

40. $25 = 5(2^x)$

41. $4{,}000 = 2{,}500(e^{0.12x})$

42. $0.01 = e^{-0.05x}$

43. $5^{2x-3} = 7.08$

44. $\dfrac{e^x - e^{-x}}{2} = 1$

Solve Problems 45–50 for x exactly. Do not use a calculator or table.

45. $\log 3x^2 - \log 9x = 2$

46. $\log x - \log 3 = \log 4 - \log(x + 4)$

47. $\ln(x + 3) - \ln x = 2 \ln 2$

48. $\ln(2x + 1) - \ln(x - 1) = \ln x$

49. $(\log x)^3 = \log x^9$

50. $\ln(\log x) = 1$

In Problems 51 and 52, simplify.

51. $(e^x + 1)(e^{-x} - 1) - e^x(e^{-x} - 1)$

52. $(e^x + e^{-x})(e^x - e^{-x}) - (e^x - e^{-x})^2$

In Problems 53–56, use a graphing calculator to help you draw the graph of each function. Then find the domain and range, intercepts, and asymptotes. Round all approximate values to two decimal places.

53. $y = 2^{x-1}$

54. $f(t) = 10e^{-0.08t}$

55. $y = \ln(x - 1)$

56. $N = \dfrac{100}{1 + 3e^{-t}}$

57. If the graph of $y = e^x$ is reflected through the line $y = x$, the graph of what function is obtained? Discuss the functions that are obtained by reflecting the graph of $y = e^x$ through the x axis and the y axis.

58. Approximate all real zeros of $f(x) = 4 - x^2 + \ln x$ to three decimal places.

59. Find the coordinates of the points of intersection of $f(x) = 10^{x-3}$ and $g(x) = 8 \log x$ to three decimal places.

Solve Problems 60–63 for the indicated variable in terms of the remaining symbols.

60. $D = 10 \log \dfrac{I}{I_0}$ for I (sound intensity)

61. $y = \dfrac{1}{\sqrt{2\pi}} e^{-x^2/2}$ for x (probability)

62. $x = -\dfrac{1}{k} \ln \dfrac{I}{I_0}$ for I (x-ray intensity)

63. $r = P \dfrac{i}{1 - (1 - i)^{-n}}$ for n (finance)

64. (A) Explain why the equation $e^{-x/3} = 4 \ln(x + 1)$ has exactly one solution.

(B) Find the solution of the equation to three decimal places.

65. Write $\ln y = -5t + \ln c$ in an exponential form free of logarithms; then solve for y in terms of the remaining symbols.

66. For $f(x) = \log_2 x$, graph f and f^{-1} on the same coordinate system. What are the domains and ranges for f and f^{-1}?

67. Explain why 1 cannot be used as a logarithmic base.

68. Prove that for any positive M, N, and b ($b \neq 1$), $\log_b MN = \log_b M + \log_b N$. (*Hint:* Start by writing $u = \log_b M$ and $v = \log_b N$ and changing each to exponential form.)

APPLICATIONS

Solve these application problems algebraically or graphically, whichever seems more appropriate.

69. POPULATION GROWTH Many countries have a population growth rate of 3% (or more) per year. At this rate, how many years will it take a population to double? Use the annual compounding growth model $P = P_0(1 + r)^t$. Compute the answer to three significant digits.

70. POPULATION GROWTH Repeat Problem 69 using the continuous compounding growth model $P = P_0e^{rt}$.

71. CARBON 14-DATING How many years will it take for carbon-14 to diminish to 1% of the original amount after the death of a plant or animal? Use the formula $A = A_0e^{-0.000124t}$. Compute the answer to three significant digits.

72. MEDICINE One leukemic cell injected into a healthy mouse will divide into two cells in about $\frac{1}{2}$ day. At the end of the day these two cells will divide into four. This doubling continues until 1 billion cells are formed; then the animal dies with leukemic cells in every part of the body.

(A) Write an equation that will give the number N of leukemic cells at the end of t days.

(B) When, to the nearest day, will the mouse die?

73. MONEY GROWTH Assume $1 had been invested at an annual rate of 3% compounded continuously in the year A.D. 1. What would be the value of the account in the year 2011? Compute the answer to two significant digits.

74. PRESENT VALUE Solving $A = Pe^{rt}$ for P, we obtain $P = Ae^{-rt}$, which is the **present value** of the amount A due in t years if money is invested at a rate r compounded continuously.

(A) Graph $P = 1{,}000(e^{-0.08t})$, $0 \le t \le 30$.

(B) What does it appear that P tends to as t tends to infinity? [*Conclusion:* The longer the time until the amount A is due, the smaller its present value, as we would expect.]

75. EARTHQUAKES The 1971 San Fernando, California, earthquake released 1.99×10^{14} joules of energy. Compute its magnitude on the Richter scale using the formula $M = \frac{2}{3}\log(E/E_0)$, where $E_0 = 10^{4.40}$ joules. Compute the answer to one decimal place.

76. EARTHQUAKES Refer to Problem 75. If the 1906 San Francisco earthquake had a magnitude of 8.3 on the Richter scale, how much energy was released? Compute the answer to three significant digits.

77. SOUND If the intensity of a sound from one source is 100,000 times that of another, how much more is the decibel level of the louder sound than the softer one? Use the formula $D = 10\log(I/I_0)$.

78. MARINE BIOLOGY The intensity of light entering water is reduced according to the exponential function

$$I = I_0e^{-kd}$$

where I is the intensity d feet below the surface, I_0 is the intensity at the surface, and k is the coefficient of extinction. Measurements in the Sargasso Sea in the West Indies have indicated that half the surface light reaches a depth of 73.6 feet. Find k, and find the depth at which 1% of the surface light remains. Compute answers to three significant digits.

79. WILDLIFE MANAGEMENT A lake formed by a newly constructed dam is stocked with 1,000 fish. Their population is expected to increase according to the logistic curve

$$N = \frac{30}{1 + 29e^{-1.35t}}$$

where N is the number of fish, in thousands, expected after t years. The lake will be open to fishing when the number of fish reaches 20,000. How many years, to the nearest year, will this take?

MODELING AND DATA ANALYSIS

80. MEDICARE The annual expenditures for Medicare (in billions of dollars) by the U.S. government for selected years since 1980 are shown in Table 1. Let x represent years since 1980.

(A) Find an exponential regression model of the form $y = ab^x$ for these data. Round to three significant digits. Estimate (to the nearest billion) the total expenditures in 2010 and in 2020.

(B) When (to the nearest year) will the total expenditures reach $900 billion?

Table 1 Medicare Expenditures

Year	Billion $
1980	37
1985	72
1990	111
1995	181
2000	225
2005	342

Source: U.S. Bureau of the Census

81. AGRICULTURE The total U.S. corn consumption (in millions of bushels) is shown in Table 2 for selected years since 1975. Let x represent years since 1900.

(A) Find a logarithmic regression model of the form $y = a + b \ln x$ for these data. Round to four significant digits. Estimate (to the nearest million) the total consumption in 1996 and in 2010.

(B) The actual consumption in 1996 was 1,583 million bushels. How does this compare with the estimated consumption in part A? What effect will this additional 1996 information have on the estimate for 2010? Explain.

Table 2 Corn Consumption

Year	Total Consumption (million bushels)
1975	522
1980	659
1985	1,152
1990	1,373
1995	1,690

Source: U.S. Department of Agriculture

CHAPTER 4

»» GROUP ACTIVITY Comparing Regression Models

We have used polynomial, exponential, and logarithmic regression models to fit curves to data sets. And there are other equations that can be used for curve fitting (the TI-84 graphing calculator has 12 different equations on its STAT-CALC menu). How can we determine which equation provides the best fit for a given set of data? There are two principal ways to select models. The first is to use information about the type of data to help make a choice. For example, we expect the weight of a fish to be related to the cube of its length. And we expect most populations to grow exponentially, at least over the short term. The second method for choosing among equations involves developing a measure of how closely an equation fits a given data set. This is best introduced through an example. Consider the data set in Figure 1, where L1 represents the x coordinates and L2 represents the y coordinates. The graph of this data set is shown in Figure 2. Suppose we arbitrarily choose the equation $y_1 = 0.6x + 1$ to model these data (Fig. 3).

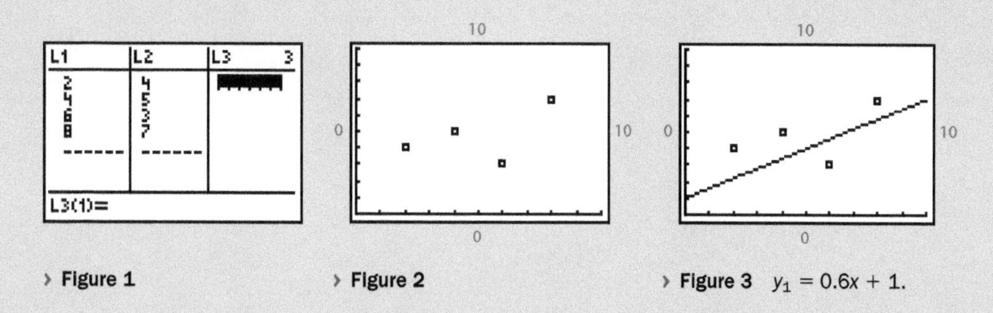

› Figure 1 › Figure 2 › Figure 3 $y_1 = 0.6x + 1$.

To measure how well the graph of y_1 fits these data, we examine the difference between the y coordinates in the data set and the corresponding y coordinates on the graph of y_1 (L3 in Figs. 4 and 5). Each of these differences is called a **residual.** The most commonly accepted measure of the fit provided by a given model is the **sum of the squares of the residuals (SSR).** Computing this quantity is a simple matter on a graphing calculator (Fig. 6).

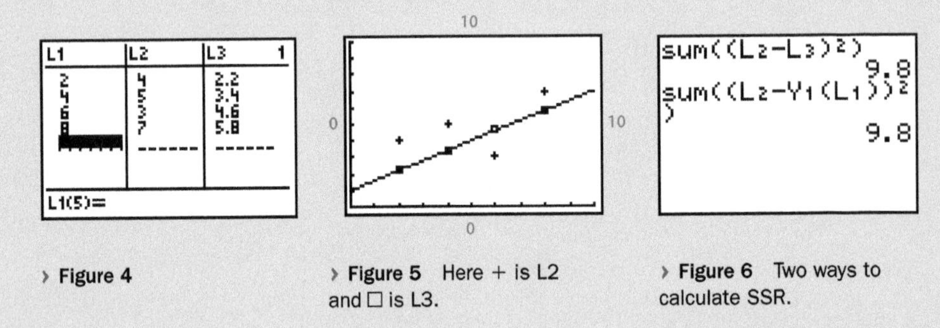

› **Figure 4**

› **Figure 5** Here + is L2 and □ is L3.

› **Figure 6** Two ways to calculate SSR.

(A) Find the linear regression model for the data in Figure 1, compute the SSR for this equation, and compare it with the one we computed for y_1.

It turns out that among all possible linear polynomials, **the linear regression model minimizes the sum of the squares of the residuals.** For this reason, the linear regression model is often called the **least-squares line.** A similar statement can be made for polynomials of any fixed degree. That is, the quadratic regression model minimizes the SSR over all quadratic polynomials, the cubic regression model minimizes the SSR over all cubic polynomials, and so on. The same statement cannot be made for exponential or logarithmic regression models. Nevertheless, the SSR can still be used to compare exponential, logarithmic, and polynomial models.

(B) Find the exponential and logarithmic regression models for the data in Figure 1, compute their SSRs, and compare with the linear model.

(C) National annual advertising expenditures for selected years since 1950 are shown in Table 1 where x is years since 1950 and y is total expenditures in billions of dollars. Which regression model would fit this data best: a quadratic model, a cubic model, or an exponential model? Use the SSRs to support your choice.

Table 1 Annual Advertising Expenditures, 1950–2005

x (years)	0	5	10	15	20	25	30	35	40	45	50	55
y (billion $)	5.7	9.2	12.0	15.3	19.6	27.9	53.6	94.8	128.6	160.9	243.3	271.1

Source: U.S. Bureau of the Census

CHAPTERS 3–4 Cumulative Review

Work through all the problems in this cumulative review and check answers in the back of the book. Answers to all review problems are there, and following each answer is a number in italics indicating the section in which that type of problem is discussed. Where weaknesses show up, review appropriate sections in the text.

1. Let $P(x)$ be the polynomial whose graph is shown in the figure on the next page.

(A) Assuming that $P(x)$ has integer zeros and leading coefficient 1, find the lowest-degree equation that could produce this graph.

(B) Describe the left and right behavior of $P(x)$.

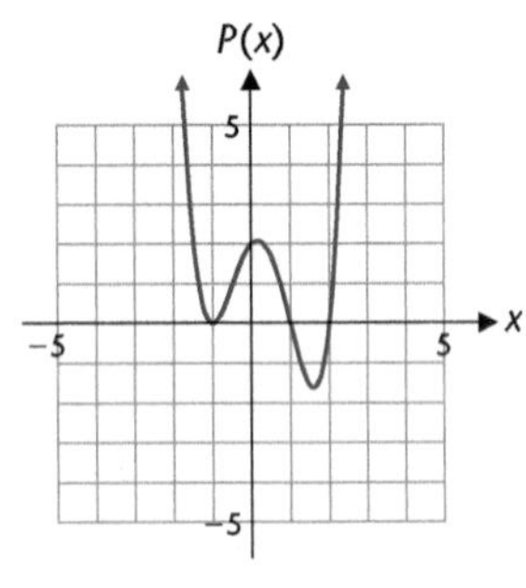

2. Draw the graph of a polynomial with lowest possible degree that has zeros -5, 1, and 6, and has a negative leading coefficient.

3. Match each equation with the graph of f, g, m, or n in the figure.

(A) $y = (\frac{3}{4})^x$ (B) $y = (\frac{4}{3})^x$

(C) $y = (\frac{3}{4})^x + (\frac{4}{3})^x$ (D) $y = (\frac{4}{3})^x - (\frac{3}{4})^x$

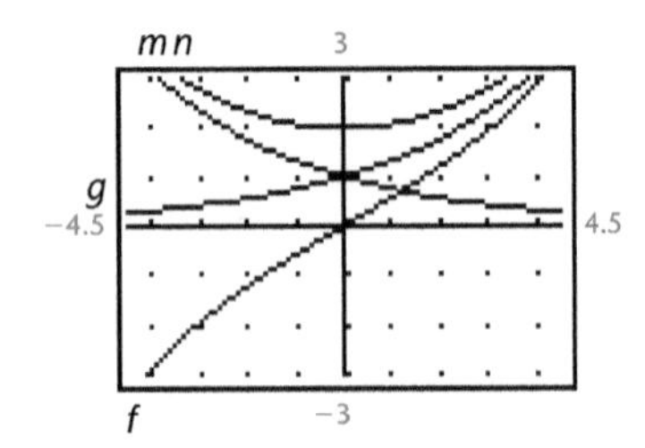

4. For $P(x) = 3x^3 + 5x^2 - 18x - 3$ and $D(x) = x + 3$, use synthetic division to divide $P(x)$ by $D(x)$, and write the answer in the form $P(x) = D(x)Q(x) + R$.

5. Let $P(x) = 2(x + 2)(x - 3)(x - 5)$. What are the zeros of $P(x)$?

6. Let $P(x) = 4x^3 - 5x^2 - 3x - 1$. How do you know that $P(x)$ has at least one real zero between 1 and 2?

7. Let $P(x) = x^3 + x^2 - 10x + 8$. Find all rational zeros for $P(x)$.

8. Solve for x.

(A) $y = 10^x$ (B) $y = \ln x$

9. Simplify using properties of exponents.

(A) $(2e^x)^3$ (B) $\frac{e^{3x}}{e^{-2x}}$

10. Solve for x exactly. Do not use a calculator or a table.

(A) $\log_3 x = 2$ (B) $\log_3 81 = x$ (C) $\log_x 4 = -2$

11. Solve for x to three significant digits.

(A) $10^x = 2.35$ (B) $e^x = 87{,}500$

(C) $\log x = -1.25$ (D) $\ln x = 2.75$

In Problems 12 and 13, translate each statement into an equation using k as the constant of proportionality.

12. E varies directly as p and inversely as the cube of x.

13. F is jointly proportional to q_1 and q_2 and inversely proportional to the square of r.

14. Explain why the graph in the figure is not the graph of a polynomial function.

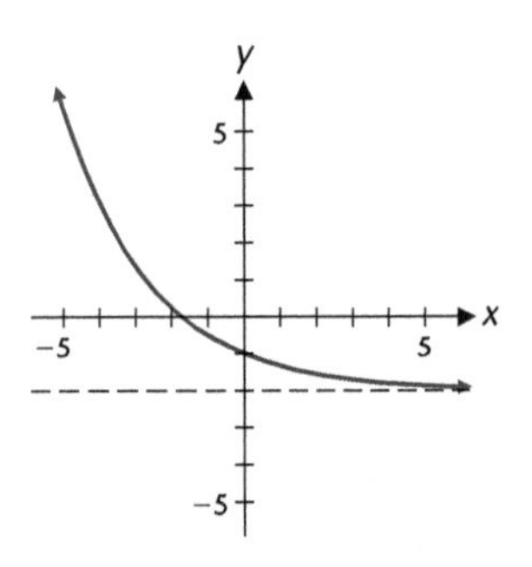

15. Explain why the graph in the figure is not the graph of a rational function.

16. The function f subtracts the square root of the domain element from three times the natural log of the domain element. Write an algebraic definition of f.

17. Write a verbal description of the function

$$f(x) = 100e^{0.5x} - 50.$$

18. Let $f(x) = \frac{2x + 8}{x + 2}$.

(A) Find the domain and the intercepts for f.

(B) Find the vertical and horizontal asymptotes for f.

(C) Sketch the graph of f. Draw vertical and horizontal asymptotes with dashed lines.

19. Find all zeros of $P(x) = (x^3 + 4x)(x + 4)$, and specify those zeros that are x intercepts.

20. Solve $(x^3 + 4x)(x + 4) \le 0$.

21. If $P(x) = 2x^3 - 5x^2 + 3x + 2$, find $P(\frac{1}{2})$ using the remainder theorem and synthetic division.

22. One of the zeros of $P(x) = 3x^3 - 7x^2 - 18x - 8$ is $x = -1$. Find all others.

23. Which of the following is a factor of

$$P(x) = x^{25} - x^{20} + x^{15} + x^{10} - x^5 + 1$$

(A) $x - 1$ (B) $x + 1$

24. Let $P(x) = x^4 - 8x^2 + 3$.

(A) Graph $P(x)$ and describe the graph verbally, including the number of x intercepts, the number of turning points, and the left and right behavior.

(B) Approximate the largest x intercept to two decimal places.

25. Let $P(x) = x^5 - 8x^4 + 17x^3 + 2x^2 - 20x - 8$.

(A) Approximate the zeros of $P(x)$ to two decimal places and state the multiplicity of each zero.

(B) Can any of these zeros be approximated with the bisection method? The MAXIMUM command? The MINIMUM command? Explain.

26. Let $P(x) = x^4 + 2x^3 - 20x^2 - 30$.

(A) Use the upper and lower bound theorem to find the smallest positive and largest negative integers that are upper and lower bounds, respectively, for the real zeros of $P(x)$.

(B) If $(k, k + 1)$, k an integer, is the interval containing the largest real zero of $P(x)$, determine how many additional intervals are required in the bisection method to approximate this zero to one decimal place.

(C) Approximate the real zeros of $P(x)$ to two decimal places.

27. Find all zeros (rational, irrational, and imaginary) exactly for $P(x) = 4x^3 - 20x^2 + 29x - 15$.

28. Find all zeros (rational, irrational, and imaginary) exactly for $P(x) = x^4 + 5x^3 + x^2 - 15x - 12$, and factor $P(x)$ into linear factors.

Solve Problems 29–39 for x exactly. Do not use a calculator or a table.

29. $2^{x^2} = 4^{x+4}$

30. $\frac{13}{2} - 3^x = \frac{1}{2}$

31. $2x^2e^{-x} + xe^{-x} = e^{-x}$

32. $e^{\ln x} = 2.5$

33. $\log_x 10^4 = 4$

34. $\log_9 x = -\frac{3}{2}$

35. $\ln (x + 4) - \ln (x - 4) = 2 \ln 3$

36. $\ln (2x^2 + 2) = 2 \ln (2x - 4)$

37. $\log x + \log (x + 15) = 2$

38. $\log (\ln x) = -1$

39. $4(\ln x)^2 = \ln x^2$

Solve Problems 40–44 for x to three significant digits.

40. $x = \log_3 41$

41. $\ln x = 1.45$

42. $4(2^x) = 20$

43. $10e^{-0.5x} = 1.6$

44. $\dfrac{e^x - e^{-x}}{e^x + e^{-x}} = \dfrac{1}{2}$

In Problems 45–49, use a graphing calculator to draw the graph of each function. The find the domain and range, intercepts, and asymptotes. Round all approximate values to two decimal places.

45. $f(x) = 3^{1-x}$

46. $g(x) = \ln(2 - x)$

47. $A(t) = 100e^{-0.3t}$

48. $h(x) = -2e^{-x} + 3$

49. $N(t) = \dfrac{6}{2 + e^{-0.1t}}$

50. If the graph of $y = \ln x$ is reflected through the line $y = x$, the graph of what function is obtained? Discuss the functions that are obtained by reflecting the graph of $y = \ln x$ in the x axis and in the y axis.

51. (A) Explain why the equation $e^{-x} = \ln x$ has exactly one solution.

(B) Approximate the solution of the equation to two decimal places.

In Problems 52 and 53, factor each polynomial in two ways:
(A) As a product of linear factors (with real coefficients) and quadratic factors (with real coefficients and imaginary zeros)
(B) As a product of linear factors with complex coefficients

52. $P(x) = x^4 + 9x^2 + 18$

53. $P(x) = x^4 - 23x^2 - 50$

54. G is directly proportional to the square of x. If $G = 10$ when $x = 5$, find G when $x = 7$.

55. H varies inversely as the cube of r. If $H = 162$ when $r = 2$, find H when $r = 3$.

56. Graph f and indicate any horizontal, vertical, or slant asymptotes with dashed lines:

$$f(x) = \frac{x^2 + 4x + 8}{x + 2}$$

57. Solve $\dfrac{x^3 - x}{x^3 - 8} \geq 0$.

58. Let $P(x) = x^4 - 28x^3 + 262x^2 - 922x + 1{,}083$. Approximate (to two decimal places) the x intercepts and the local extrema.

59. Find a polynomial of lowest degree with leading coefficient 1 that has zeros -1 (multiplicity 2), 0 (multiplicity 3), and $3 - 5i$. Leave the answer in factored form. What is the degree of the polynomial?

60. If $P(x)$ is a fourth-degree polynomial with integer coefficients and if i is a zero of $P(x)$, can $P(x)$ have any irrational zeros? Explain.

61. Let $P(x) = x^4 + 9x^3 - 500x^2 + 20{,}000$.

(A) Use the upper and lower bound theorem to find the smallest positive integer multiple of 10 and the largest negative integer multiple of 10 that are upper and lower bounds, respectively, for the real zeros of $P(x)$.

(B) Approximate the real zeros of $P(x)$ to two decimal places.

62. Find all zeros (rational, irrational, and imaginary) exactly for

$$P(x) = x^5 - 4x^4 + 3x^3 + 10x^2 - 10x - 12$$

and factor $P(x)$ into linear factors.

63. Find rational roots exactly and irrational roots to two decimal places for

$$P(x) = x^5 + 4x^4 + x^3 - 11x^2 - 8x + 4$$

64. Give an example of a rational function $f(x)$ that satisfies the following conditions: the real zeros of f are 5 and 8; $x = 1$ is the only vertical asymptote; and the line $y = 3$ is a horizontal asymptote.

65. Use natural logarithms to solve for n.

$$A = P\frac{(1 + i)^n - 1}{i}$$

66. Solve $\ln y = 5x + \ln A$ for y. Express the answer in a form that is free of logarithms.

67. Solve for x.

$$y = \frac{e^x - 2e^{-x}}{2}$$

68. Solve (to three decimal places)

$$\frac{4x}{x^2 - 1} < 3$$

APPLICATIONS

69. PROFIT ANALYSIS The daily profit in dollars made by the snack bar at a small college can be modeled by the function

$$P(x) = -4.8x^3 + 47x^2 - 35x - 40 \quad (0 \le x \le 12)$$

where x is the number of hours the snack bar is open per day.

(A) How many hours should the snack bar be open to maximize its profit?

(B) How long will the snack bar need to stay open to make a profit of \$300?

(C) For what range of hours will the snack bar at least break even?

70. EFFICIENCY After learning how to solve a Rubik's Cube puzzle, a student practices for 2 hours each week, trying to decrease her best time to solve the puzzle. Suppose that the function

$$T(w) = 540 - \frac{450w}{w + 2}$$

describes her best time in seconds after w weeks of practice.

(A) What was her best time after one week of practice?

(B) Find the horizontal asymptote of this rational function. What does it tell you about this student's performance?

(C) Explain why the vertical asymptote is not relevant to this problem.

71. SHIPPING A mailing service provides customers with rectangular shipping containers. The length plus the girth of one of these containers is 10 feet (see the figure). If the end of the container is square and the volume is 8 cubic feet, find the dimensions. Find rational solutions exactly and irrational solutions to two decimal places.

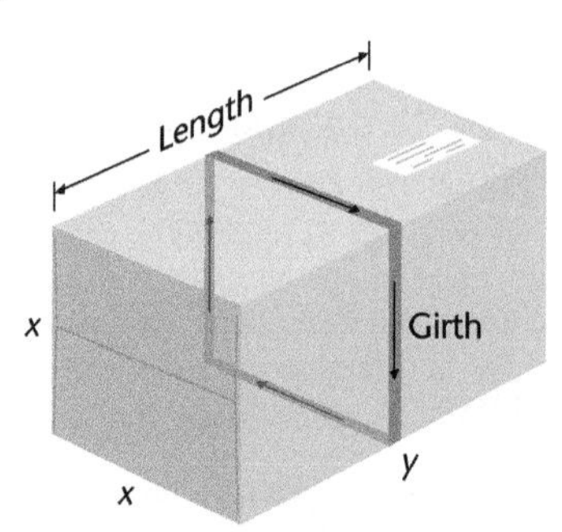

72. GEOMETRY The diagonal of a rectangle is 2 feet longer than one of the sides, and the area of the rectangle is 6 square feet. Find the dimensions of the rectangle. Find rational solutions exactly and irrational solutions to two decimal places.

73. ASTRONOMY The square of the time t required for a planet to make one orbit around the sun varies directly as the cube of its mean (average) distance d from the sun. Write the equation of variation, using k as the constant of variation.

74. PHYSICS Atoms and molecules that make up the air constantly fly about like microscopic missiles. The velocity v of a particle at a fixed temperature varies inversely as the square root of its molecular weight w. If an oxygen molecule in air at room temperature has an average velocity of 0.3 mile/second, what will be the average velocity of a hydrogen molecule, given that the hydrogen molecule is one-sixteenth as heavy as the oxygen molecule?

75. POPULATION GROWTH If the Democratic Republic of the Congo has a population of about 60 million people and a doubling time of 23 years, find the population in

(A) 5 years (B) 30 years

Compute answers to three significant digits.

76. COMPOUND INTEREST How long will it take money invested in an account earning 7% compounded annually to double? Use the annual compounding growth model $P = P_0(1 + r)^t$, and compute the answer to three significant digits.

77. COMPOUND INTEREST Repeat Problem 76 using the continuous compound interest model $P = P_0e^{rt}$.

78. EARTHQUAKES If the 1906 and 1989 San Francisco earthquakes registered 8.3 and 7.1, respectively, on the Richter scale, how many times more powerful was the 1906 earthquake than the 1989 earthquake? Use the formula $M = \frac{2}{3}\log(E/E_0)$, where $E_0 = 10^{4.40}$ joules, and compute the answer to one decimal place.

79. SOUND If the decibel level at a rock concert is 88, find the intensity of the sound at the concert. Use the formula $D = 10\log(I/I_0)$, where $I_0 = 10^{-12}$ watts per square meter, and compute the answer to two significant digits.

MODELING AND DATA ANALYSIS

80. Table 1 shows the life expectancy (in years) at birth for residents of the United States from 1970 to 1995. Let x represent years since 1970. Use the indicated regression model to estimate the life expectancy (to the nearest tenth of a year) for a U.S. resident born in 2010.

(A) Linear regression

(B) Quadratic regression

(C) Cubic regression

(D) Exponential regression

Table 1

Year	Life expectancy
1970	70.8
1975	72.6
1980	73.7
1985	74.7
1990	75.4
1995	75.9
2000	77.0
2005	77.7

Source: U.S. Census Bureau

81. Refer to Problem 80. The Census Bureau projected the life expectancy for a U.S. resident born in 2010 to be 77.9 years. Which of the models in Problem 80 is closest to the Census Bureau projection?